## 2. TIME DIAGRAM

To get an accurate picture of a problem, it is helpful to draw a cash flow or time diagram. This is simply a freehand sketch with a time scale in days, months or years to fit the problem. The date and size of each transaction are put on the diagram. Analysis of a problem is helped if:

**Outflows and dates are put on one side of the time line**

**Inflows and dates are put on the other side**

## 3. EQUATION OF VALUE

A mathematics of finance problem is solved with an equation of value. This is an equality between outflows and inflows of sums of money *after they have been brought to the same point in time*. When a time diagram has been drawn and a focal date chosen, all flows are brought to the focal date, using appropriate time value formulas. Then the following *equation of value* is set up and solved:

**Sum of outflows at the focal date** = **Sum of inflows at the focal date**

There are many business and economic applications of the mathematics of finance. The three basic tools are used in analyzing and solving all types of problems.

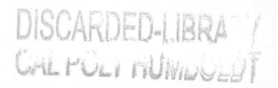

# MATHEMATICS OF FINANCE

**DATE DUE**

HOUGHTON MIFFLIN COMPANY   BOSTON

Atlanta   Dallas   Geneva, Illinois
Hopewell, New Jersey   Palo Alto

# MATHEMATICS OF FINANCE
## FOURTH EDITION

**ROBERT CISSELL**
*Xavier University*
**HELEN CISSELL**

Library of Congress Catalog Card Number: 72-4397

ISBN: 0-395-14023-4

# Preface

The mathematics of finance enables a student to identify mathematics with the world he knows. Most students will in later life buy a car, home, or other items on time, borrow money, and take out life insurance. Many will seek a second income by putting savings in bonds, stocks, or other investments. A knowledge of the mathematics of finance will enable them to borrow or invest more wisely.

To make this revision especially suitable for students of economics, business, and accounting, we have included practical and current material on the mathematics used in modern business transactions. To meet the needs and interests of all students, including those taking liberal arts and general college courses, the book emphasizes financial transactions that are important to individuals and families.

Financial decision making should take into account the time value of money. This is emphasized throughout the book, particularly in the discussion of the important management function of capital budgeting.

Interest, the price paid for credit, plays an important part in the economic progress of nations. Increased governmental emphasis on orderly economic development means new and interesting applications for the mathematics of finance. Material is included on gross national product, the consumer price index, and other economic time series to show how the mathematics of finance is needed for intelligent analysis of the live issues of economics.

Throughout the book, practical problems are used to illustrate the application of the formulas and tables. Many of the problems are based on data taken from actual business transactions. Students are interested in discovering that "easy" credit terms may actually conceal a very high rate which can be determined by the methods given in this book. Students find the mathematics of finance more interesting when they know they will benefit financially from what they are learning.

In a mathematics of finance course, most of the problems are word or thought problems. Analyzing word problems and expressing them in equations is invaluable preparation for applying mathematics to real life problems. Because students have had trouble with word problems in algebra, they expect the mathematics of finance to be a succession of difficult problems. Fortunately, most thought problems are not difficult if the student will do two things: make a time diagram and use an equation of value. Both of these are used in the examples throughout this book.

Algebraic derivations are accompanied or illustrated by numerical examples. This is particularly helpful to students who have a limited knowledge of algebra and find it difficult to follow a derivation that is presented only in general terms.

A modern treatment of the mathematics of finance should include a discussion of corporate stocks which are important in both business financing and in the financial planning of individuals and families. Because the mathematics required in the chapter on stocks is covered earlier in the book, students should find this material usable even if there is no time for formal coverage in class.

Past users of this textbook have indicated that it has a balanced and adequate selection of problems involving discrete interest computations. We have included additional examples of applications and more solved problems. Bank discount is now covered in a separate chapter, which includes descriptions of money market instruments. Here students can see how vast sums are transferred by using slips of paper and the mathematics they are learning.

A chapter on continuous compounding has been added. Students who will use calculus in economics and business decision analysis need to understand the methods and formulas that are based on continuous compounding and continuous money flows. Many students have not had calculus when they take the mathematics of finance, so all calculus-based material is put in this chapter. Most practical business transactions can be handled with periodic compounding, which is used in the rest of the book and which requires only simple algebra.

So that the student can check on his progress, answers are given to many of the problems. Because the answer to a problem in the mathematics of finance usually does not help in determining the method of solution, the answers are given at the end of the problem to save time that would otherwise be spent looking in the back of the book. Solutions to all problems and suggestions about what to include or omit in varying circumstances are given in the teacher's manual.

Tables are an indispensable part of a mathematics of finance textbook. The tables in this text have been selected carefully and are those used in modern business firms. Because these tables are well organized and include all necessary functions, they save valuable time that can be used to work more problems. The mathematical tables are also useful sources of data for other courses and for solving practical business problems. Tables 2, 3, and 4 are reproduced, with permission, from the Financial Compound Interest and Annuity Tables of the Financial Publishing Company, Boston. Tables 5 and 6 are reproduced from publications of the Society of Actuaries with permission of Mr. Walter L. Grace, Secretary of the Society. Table 7 is taken from the *Mathematics of Business, Accounting, and Finance* by Kenneth L. Trefftzs and E. J. Hills, published by Harper & Row. These excellent tables of logarithms are used with the permission of Professor Trefftzs who prepared them. Because most problems require the use of one or more functions from the tables, they have been printed together in a section at the end of the book and are separated from the text by a colored divider for easy reference. Table 8, Reciprocals, was taken from the twelfth edition of the Chemical Rubber Company Standard Mathematical Tables by permission of Robert C. Weast, Editor. Mr. Louis J. Dunham Jr., Director of the Franklin Institute of Boston, supplied the interesting history of the bequest of Benjamin Franklin. The accomplishments made possible by this gift provide impressive evidence of the power of compound interest.

To insure that the book will be in line with present commercial practices and of the greatest practical value to students, the material has been checked by authorities in banking, insurance, investments, and other financial fields. Suggestions from practical financiers and teachers, listed separately on pages ix and x, have helped insure the inclusion of the latest commercial practices in a teachable way.

We wish to express our appreciation to Dr. Frank C. Genovese, Dean of Graduate Programs, Babson College, who read the entire manuscript and made many valuable suggestions for improvements. The General Editor of earlier editions, Dr. Marshall D. Ketchum, Professor of Finance at the University of Chicago, has helped in many ways to make the book a more useful one for financial analysts. Sincere appreciation is due especially to Mr. Odin Nielsen of Laventhol Krekstein Horwath and Horwath, Certified Public Accountants. From his detailed analysis of this and earlier editions have come many ideas which help to make the book a more effective means for teaching the mathematics of finance in line with current business practices.

Robert Cissell
Helen Cissell

Cincinnati, Ohio

# Acknowledgments

We are grateful to the following persons for many valuable suggestions. The businessmen in this list are using mathematics of finance in their work and have helped us prepare a text which is in line with current business practices. The teachers of mathematics have suggested ways to make the material clearer and more interesting. Teachers in related fields, such as accounting and finance, have checked the text to see that it provides the mathematical preparation which students need for their courses.

David R. Andrew, Head, Mathematics Department, University of Southwestern Louisiana.

David Bolivar, Trenton State College.

Thomas J. Bruggeman, Assistant Professor of Mathematics, Xavier University.

David W. Cook, A.S.A., Assistant Actuary, Group Insurance, The Ohio National Life Insurance Company.

Dr. James A. Delaney, Associate Professor of Mathematics, Xavier University.

Wayne E. Dydo, University of Notre Dame.

Rudolph Feige, Lecturer in Mathematics, Xavier University.

Dr. Allen O. Felix, Education Director, New York Stock Exchange, Inc.

Lawrence Fitzgerald, Vice-President, Merrill Lynch, Pierce, Fenner and Smith, Inc.

Miles C. Hartley, Chairman, Department of Mathematics, University of Tampa.

Mrs. A. Z. Hays, Assistant Professor of Mathematics, Abilene Christian College.

Victor E. Henningsen, F.S.A., Senior Vice-President, Insurance, The Northwestern Mutual Life Insurance Company.

Robert Lee Howard, Department of Business Administration, Central State University.

Harry R. Maly, C.P.A., Chairman, Department of Accounting, Xavier University.

Dr. Z. I. Mosesson, F.S.A., Assistant Actuary (retired), The Prudential Insurance Company of America.

Ralph D. Ondersma, Chairman, Economics and Business, The Defiance College.

J. Byron Pennington, Department of Business Administration, Central State University.

Charles F. Pinzka, Associate Professor, University of Cincinnati.

Emmett S. Sams, Professor of Mathematics, Mars Hill College.

E. Wesley Sanders, Mathematics Department, Sam Houston State University.

Jacob W. Schweizer, Assistant Professor of Accounting, Xavier University.

William E. Smith, C.P.A., Associate Professor of Accounting, Xavier University.

James B. Van Flandern, Institutional Account Executive, Merrill Lynch, Pierce, Fenner and Smith, Inc.

Edward F. Wilz, C.P.A., Professor of Financial Management, Xavier University; Vice-President of Finance, Blue Cross of Southwest Ohio.

# Contents

# MATHEMATICS OF FINANCE

# 1

# Simple
# Interest

## 1.1 Money

"He is (or is not) worth his salt" is an expression that goes back to the time when workmen were paid in blocks of salt. Money is anything that is commonly accepted in exchange for goods and services. Wampum, snail shells, beads, slabs of stone, and other objects have served as money. As an economy develops, the money system must be changed to meet new needs. Wampum, which was once used as money by the Indians, will no longer buy food and clothing.

In the United States money usually is defined as the sum of currency in circulation and demand deposits. This is sometimes called the narrow money supply and is designated by the symbol $M_1$.* Currency consists of coins (jingling money) and bills (folding or paper money). Demand deposits (checkbook money) are private checking accounts in commercial banks. Only currency and demand deposits can be used as a medium of exchange. When time deposits at commercial banks are added to the narrow money supply, we get what is called the broad money supply, designated by the symbol $M_2$.

While there is talk of a moneyless society, facts point the other way. In 1960, currency averaged $160 per person. By 1970, the average was $238. As the graph below shows, the money supply has been increased over the years to meet the needs of a growing economy. The graph also shows that checkbook money, with its safety and convenience, amounts to over three-fourths of the money supply.

## Money Supply

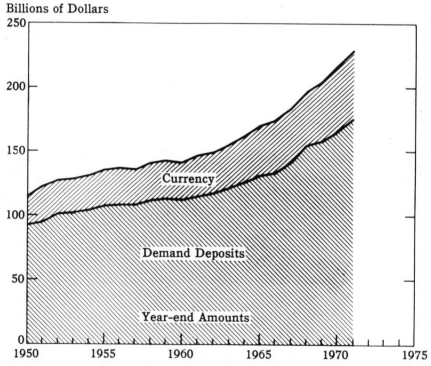

Source: *1972 Economic Report of the President*, Table B-52.

* The Federal Reserve's detailed definition of $M_1$ includes: (1) demand deposits at all commercial banks other than those due to domestic commercial banks and the United States Government, less cash items in the process of collection and Federal Reserve float; (2) foreign demand balances at Federal Reserve Banks; (3) currency outside Treasury, Federal Reserve Banks, and vaults of all commercial banks. *Federal Reserve Bulletin*, November 1971, page 889.

The money supply has a marked effect on a country's economic life and the well-being of its people. If there is not enough money, recession occurs with attendant unemployment and economic hardship for those out of work and their dependents. Too much money means inflation with runaway prices and economic hardship for those whose incomes do not keep up with prices.

In the United States the primary instrumentality for controlling the money supply is the Federal Reserve System which was established by law in 1913. By its control over credit and other means, the Fed provides the country with an elastic money supply—one that should expand and contract according to the needs of the people. The Fed attempts to meet the public's changing needs for money in a way that facilitates sound economic growth, a high and growing level of employment, reasonable price stability, and protection of the dollar in international trade and investment. Since these goals may conflict, there is often disagreement over the proper rate and timing of changes in the money supply. Economists argue with each other. The President of the United States and the Chairman of the Federal Reserve Board may disagree on monetary policy. In Chapter 3 the mathematics of finance is used to analyze changes in the money supply.

## 1.2  Putting Money to Work

Money in your pocket or checking account is always available for making payments, but otherwise it is not doing much for you. With today's high interest rates, surplus cash is an expensive luxury. Smart money managers, from canny housewives to shrewd corporate treasurers, have a common goal: put dormant dollars to work. This can be done by becoming a lender or an owner. Lenders buy debt instruments which pay interest. Owners purchase equities in the hope that the enterprise will be successful and produce profits or capital gains better than the rate of interest they can get on bonds and other debt instruments.

Everyone should know how the ownership of money market instruments is transferred. A **bearer** instrument is payable to the holder. It is cashable by anyone who has possession of the paper. Because of increased thefts of bearer instruments, some institutions require evidence of ownership before buying a bearer security. However, even if a thief does have to sell his haul of bearer paper to a fence at a large discount, the rightful owner still suffers a total loss. Bearer instruments should be protected as carefully as cash.

Other **negotiable** instruments with the expression "pay to the order of" can have title transferred by endorsement and delivery. Negotiable paper should be safeguarded, for replacement can be costly and time consuming.

There are two markets in which financial instruments are sold. New issues are first sold in the **primary market**. Typically a new issue is underwritten by an investment banker who purchases the entire issue and forms a syndicate to help him sell the issue to new owners.

Outstanding issues are sold by existing holders to other investors in the **secondary** or **trading market**. The secondary market consists of organized exchanges located in specific places, such as the New York and American Stock Exchanges, and the over-the-counter market (OTC). An over-the-counter sale is a transaction not handled on an organized exchange. Over-the-counter sales are often made by dealers who communicate with each other by telephone, teletype, or electronically.

Financial paper can be negotiable but not **marketable**. To be marketable, a security must be salable on short notice at a reasonable transaction cost in a well-organized secondary market. Marketable instruments may change hands many times after the original sale on the primary market. A negotiable instrument which is nonmarketable is "illiquid."

## 1.3  Holder in Due Course

A person who receives negotiable paper and who complies with legal require-ments which apply to the transaction becomes a **holder in due course**. He gets the paper free of claims which might have been made against the person who transferred it to him. A person who becomes a holder in due course may have good title to the paper although the person who negotiated the paper to him did not. The holder in due course doctrine promotes the free transferability of commercial paper and other negotiable instruments.

While the holder in due course doctrine has advantages for carrying on business, it can cause problems. Financial organizations can buy retail install-ment contracts from disreputable businesses with no responsibility to the consumer, who then finds himself stuck with shoddy or defective merchandise. Against the holder in due course, the consumer is virtually defenseless. He must pay the current owner of the paper even if the seller of the merchandise refuses to repair or replace a defective item.

When you sign your name to negotiable paper, the instrument may be sold and resold. Ultimately there will be an owner who expects to collect from you. He will probably succeed no matter how unhappy you may be about the original deal. Before your signature goes on anything, satisfy yourself that you are dealing with a reputable organization. Your signature is a valuable possession. It can be worth money to less deserving people if you sign a note which can bind you to make payments to a holder in due course although he has no obligation to satisfy your just complaints about the merchandise.

## 1.4   Investment Goals

Anyone with idle money can find a place for it to earn money among the many and varied debt and equity instruments in today's money markets. But no one investment will do everything. Money managers study the qualities of different debt and equity instruments so that they can choose the best *mix* of securities to achieve their overall objectives. They consider the strong and weak points of productive assets in terms of:

1. Liquidity—ready conversion into money with little or no loss of principal;
2. Safety—protection of principal;
3. Current yield—short-run return from working money;
4. Capital gains—increases in the value of an investment;
5. Marketability—existence of an active secondary market for the asset which makes for quick sales at reasonable transaction costs;
6. Tax advantages—tax-free current income and favorable rates on capital gains.

## 1.5   Our Credit-fueled Economy

Most young couples can buy a home only if they have the use of other people's money. Businesses are dependent on borrowed money for both day-to-day operations and long-term expansion. Government at all levels is a big borrower. The United States, during its nearly two centuries of existence, always has been in debt. The low point was in 1836 when the gross public debt was down to $38,000, less than a cent per person. In 1970 the public debt of the Federal Government was $389 billion or $1894 per person. No doubt the Federal Government, along with many states, cities, and corporations, never will be out of debt. But debt is no cause for worry as long as it is within the needs and resources of the borrower. When a person or an institution borrows money, a debt is created. But at the same time, an asset is also created. The extent to which we use each other's money is indicated by the figures on the following page.

Used wisely, credit can help both borrower and lender. A person with more money than he needs could hide it in a mattress or store it in a checking account. The money would be available at all times for spending, but it would not grow. If, on the other hand, someone else is allowed to use the money, the lender will have the pleasant experience of watching his money grow. The borrower, although he pays for the use of the lender's money, may also gain. He can get something he needs, such as a home, or he can use the money in a business venture which may not only pay the cost of borrowed capital, but also result in a profit for the borrower.

With credit now a way of life and a necessary means for conducting much of the nation's business, it is important that this tool be used wisely. A proper

*What We Owed Each Other*

|  | 1970 | 1969 | INCREASE |
|---|---|---|---|
|  | (BILLIONS) | | |
| Gross U.S. Government debt | $389.2 | $368.2 | 5.7% |
| State and local government debt | 143.3 | 131.4 | 9.1 |
| Corporation debt | 774.1 | 715.5 | 8.2 |
| Nonfarm mortgages | 321.3 | 304.8 | 5.4 |
| Farm mortgages and production loans | 58.7 | 55.5 | 5.8 |
| Consumer credit | 126.8 | 122.5 | 3.5 |

Source: *1972 Economic Report of the President*, Tables B-62 and B-67.

use of credit requires a knowledge of its true price and the ability to determine if a proposed loan is worth the price. Methods developed in this book show how to get the true cost of credit and how to use this cost as a basis for making decisions both in managing personal finances and in operating a business or government agency.

## 1.6   Price of Credit

The price paid for the use of borrowed money is an interest rate. *Time Magazine* calls interest rates "the most important regulator of the pace of business and the prosperity of nations."* Basically, interest is a simple idea. It is rent paid for the use of money. If the true interest rate is 6% per annum, it means that the lender receives as interest or "rent" on his money 6 cents for each dollar which the borrower has for a year. Unfortunately, true interest rates are often difficult to determine. Consumers encounter ingenious methods and easy credit claims that conceal high rates. Businessmen must solve investment problems that involve many variables and require sophisticated methods to get true rates.

There are great variations in interest rates. In any country at any time, there is a whole spectrum of rates. The lowest rates are paid on almost riskless government securities. The Federal Government issues four major types of marketable securities: bills, certificates of indebtedness, notes, and bonds. Treasury bills mature in three months to one year, certificates generally mature in one year, notes in one to seven years, and bonds in more than five years. The lowest commercial rate is the prime rate ($4\frac{1}{2}$ to $5\frac{3}{8}$% in 1972) which banks charge their largest and most creditworthy business borrowers. The prime rate is a key rate with other bank rates scaled up from it. Borrowers with low and moderate incomes may have to pay from 10 to 42% for small loans from legal lenders. Loan sharks illegally charge up to 500% and more for their loans.

* February 3, 1967, page 69.

# Interest Rates

PERCENT PER ANNUM

SHORT-TERM

PRIME BANK RATE

PRIME COMMERCIAL
PAPER

FEDERAL RESERVE
DISCOUNT RATE

3-MONTH TREASURY BILLS
(New Issues)

LONG-TERM

FHA NEW HOME
MORTGAGES

CORPORATE Aaa BONDS

HIGH-GRADE
MUNICIPAL BONDS

U.S. GOVERNMENT BONDS

SOURCES: DEPARTMENT OF HOUSING AND URBAN DEVELOPMENT, TREASURY DEPARTMENT,
BOARD OF GOVERNORS OF THE FEDERAL RESERVE SYSTEM, MOODY'S INVESTORS
SERVICE, AND STANDARD & POOR'S CORPORATION

During periods of easy money—when money is readily available for borrow-ing—rates tend to move down together. During times of tight money—when there is less available for borrowing—interest rates go up. The preceding chart from the *1972 Economic Report of the President* shows recent variations in rates for high quality or low risk debt instruments. In general, short-term loans mature in a year or less and long-term obligations in more than a year.

The availability of credit and its price, in the form of interest rates, not only affects individuals and businesses, but also the overall well-being of the economy. Rates must be low enough to encourage business to borrow and invest these funds in ways that will result in jobs for a growing labor force. But if low rates result in the demand for goods outpacing the supply, a rapidly rising general price level can mean a lower standard of living for many persons. Monetary authorities seek to avoid both inflation and deflation, and they alter the avail-ability of loan funds and interest rates as part of this endeavor.

An additional complication is a country's international balance of payments which may cause monetary authorities to attempt to change interest rates. A choice may have to be made between lowering interest rates to spur the domestic economy, and raising them to prevent a serious balance-of-payments deficit. Because of the international mobility of money, interest rates have an important bearing on the flows of funds among nations. If interest rates are high in one nation, capital tends to flow there as investors seek higher returns. This inter-national flow of capital can affect the price structure and economic growth of the countries involved. A healthy development of the world economy requires that all countries take account of the impact of their levels of interest rates on other nations as well as on their own. It is usually thought that short rates are more important for balance-of-payment matters and long rates for domestic in-vestment decisions.

Whether you will be managing a household budget, a business, or a nation's economy, you will be concerned with the cost of credit. The best way to learn how this cost is determined is to work problems in the mathematics of finance. In this chapter we discuss simple interest, a common way to get the cost of a loan with a maturity of one year or less. Another way to price short-term loans is bank discount described in Chapter 2.

## 1.7   Simple Interest

The sum of money borrowed in an interest transaction is called the **principal**. The number of dollars received by the borrower is the **present value** of the loan. In simple interest loans the principal and present value are equal. The **time** or **term of the loan** is the period during which the borrower has the use of all or part of the borrowed money. **Simple interest** loans have interest computed entirely on the original principal. **Compound interest**, discussed in Chapter 3, is based on a principal which is increased each time interest is earned.

The price of a simple interest loan is expressed as an **interest rate**, a fixed portion of the principal which is to be paid for its use. Simple interest rates are usually stated as a specified percent per unit of time. One percent means one part in a hundred. If the interest rate is 5 percent (5%) per annum, the interest earned in one year will be $\frac{5}{100} = .05$ of the principal. An interest rate of $\frac{1}{2}\%$ per month results in a month's interest of $\frac{5}{1000} = .005$ of the principal.

Simple interest is defined as the product of principal, rate, and time. This leads to the simple interest formula,

$$I = Prt \tag{1}*$$

$I =$ simple interest in dollars
$P =$ principal in dollars
$r =$ interest rate or percent of the principal which is to be paid per unit of time
$t =$ time in units that correspond to the rate

Note that $r$ and $t$ must be consistently stated. That is, if the rate is an annual rate, the time must be stated in years; if the rate is a monthly rate, the time must be stated in months. Before signing a contract, a person should be sure that the time interval associated with an interest rate is stated in writing. In practice, simple interest transactions are often on a yearly or per annum basis. To avoid repetition in this text, rates are annual rates unless the problem states otherwise.

When an interest rate is stated as a percent, it should be converted to a fraction or decimal when used in the simple interest formula. If a simple interest rate of 6% is used in (1), $r$ would be replaced by $\frac{6}{100}$ or .06. Note that a rate in percent can be changed to a decimal by simply moving the decimal point two places to the left and dropping the percent symbol.

Small differences in interest rates are often expressed in terms of **basis points**. One hundred basis points equal one percent. If two securities are quoted at yields of 6.80% and 6.65%, there is a spread of 15 basis points.

## 1.8   Simple Interest Applications

The first experience most people have with simple interest is a **time deposit** in a bank. A time deposit is money held in the bank account of a person or firm for which the bank can require advance notice of withdrawal. There are three types of time deposits: savings accounts, open accounts, and certificates of deposit.

---

* Formulas are numbered consecutively. When used in examples, formulas are identified by number for easy reference in the Index of Formulas in the inside back covers.

**Savings accounts**, sometimes called passbook savings accounts, may be subject to prior notice of withdrawal. However, in practice individuals can usually make withdrawals on request, so these accounts are useful to people who want a return on funds which are still available when needed. Insured savings accounts are a safe place to put money. While the current return is modest, savings accounts provide liquidity, safety, and the flexibility of being able to make deposits and withdrawals at any time. Some institutions now have savings accounts with the desirable feature of interest from the date of deposit to the date of withdrawal.

**Open accounts** usually pay somewhat higher rates than savings accounts because of restrictions on deposits and withdrawals. These accounts differ widely in maturity, denomination, and rates of interest. Special passbook accounts may have a minimum initial deposit such as $500 and minimum additional deposits of some round figure such as $100. Savings certificates have minimum amounts and definite maturity dates. To get funds out earlier may require a written notice of redemption a stated period before the funds can be obtained. If withdrawn before the maturity date, there may be total or partial loss of interest.

An unusual open account is the noninterest-paying Christmas Club. Club members make periodic deposits and have their faithfulness recognized by entries in a special passbook. As the time to make merry draws near, club members get back their deposits without interest. Good money managers save for the holidays in more productive ways. If a Christmas Club appeals to you, look for one that pays interest.

**Certificates of Deposit** are money market instruments for fixed sums, time periods, and interest rates. Nonnegotiable, consumer-type certificates which are sold to individual savers are issued in face values of $500, $1000, $2000, and other round amounts. Interest rates are usually $\frac{1}{4}\%$ or more higher than the rate being paid on savings accounts. There is some loss in liquidity since the borrowing institution does not have to redeem a CD until maturity. In some cases a certificate may be redeemed earlier but with loss of interest. Some investors get both liquidity and higher yield by staggering purchases so that at no point in time is there much of a wait for a CD to mature. There are also negotiable certificates for large investors. These are described in Chapter 2.

**A promissory note** is a written promise to pay money. The person who makes the promise and signs the note is called the maker. A promissory note may be made payable to a named person, to his order, or to bearer.

The expressions used when dealing with notes are defined below. While various forms are used, the note shown is a typical example of the commercial forms in use today.

| EXPRESSION | EXAMPLE |
|---|---|
| *Face value* is the amount loaned or borrowed. This is usually given in figures and in words. | $600.00 |
| *Date* is the date the note is made. | June 1, 1972 |
| *Term* is the time from the date of the note to the maturity or due date. | Sixty days |
| *Rate* is the percent at which interest is to be calculated. (The time period associated with a rate should be stated.) | 5% per annum |
| *Payee* is the person or firm to whom the note is due. | William Rettig |
| *Maker* is the person or firm executing the note, the one who owes the money. | Robert Boster |
| *Maturity date* is the date the note is due. This is calculated from the date and term of the note. | July 31, 1972 |
| *Maturity value* is the face value plus interest, if any. If no interest rate is given in a note, it is noninterest-bearing and the maturity value equals the face value. This does not necessarily mean that the original debt did not bear interest. It merely means that the interest, if any, has been added to the principal and the note has been drawn for the maturity of the debt. | $605.00 |

### A Promissory Note

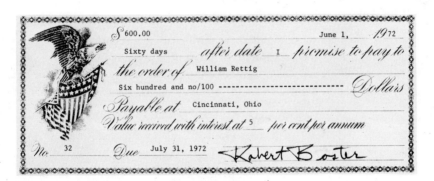

In addition to interest computations, the simple interest formula has many other applications. Savings and loan associations and credit unions use it to determine dividends on share accounts held by their members. The current yield on common and preferred stocks is obtained by substitution in the simple interest formula.

EXAMPLE 1: A bank pays $4\frac{1}{2}\%$ per annum on savings accounts. Interest is credited quarterly on March 31, June 30, September 30, and December 31. Money deposited by the 10th of the month earns interest for the entire month. A person opens an account with a deposit of $250 on January 8. How much interest will be get on March 31?

SOLUTION: Since the rate is an annual rate, the time must be expressed in years. Substituting $P = 250$, $r = .045$, and $t = \frac{3}{12}$ or $\frac{1}{4}$ year in (1),

$$I = 250 \times .045 \times \tfrac{1}{4} = \$2.81$$

EXAMPLE 2: A couple buys a home and gets a loan for $15,000. The annual interest rate is $8\frac{1}{2}\%$. The term of the loan is 25 years and the monthly payment is $120.79. At the end of a month, the husband says, "Dear, I am going down to make the first payment on our new home." Find the interest for the first month and the amount of house purchased with the first payment.

SOLUTION: Substituting $P = 15,000$, $r = .085$, and $t = \frac{1}{12}$ in (1),

$$I = 15,000 \times .085 \times \tfrac{1}{12} = \$106.25$$

While home owning eliminates rent on property, the rent on borrowed money can be substantial. In this case the $120.79 payment buys only $120.79 - 106.25 = \$14.54$ worth of house.

EXAMPLE 3: The interest paid on a loan of $500 for 4 months was $12.50. What was the interest rate?

SOLUTION: When a rate is required, we ordinarily get it correct to the nearest hundredth of $1\%$. We substitute $I = 12.50$, $P = 500$, and $t = \frac{4}{12}$ or $\frac{1}{3}$ in (1). It makes no difference which member of an equation is to the left of the equal sign. Many people find it easier to solve equations when the unknown is on the left, as shown below.

$$500 \times r \times \tfrac{1}{3} = 12.50$$

$$r = \frac{3 \times 12.50}{500} = .075 = 7\tfrac{1}{2}\%$$

EXAMPLE 4: A man gets $63.75 every 6 months from an investment which pays $4\frac{1}{4}\%$ interest. How much money does he have invested?

SOLUTION: Substituting $I = 63.75$, $r = .0425$, and $t = \frac{1}{2}$ in (1),

$$P \times .0425 \times \tfrac{1}{2} = 63.75$$

$$P = \frac{63.75 \times 2}{.0425} = \$3000.00$$

EXAMPLE 5: How long will it take $5000 to earn $50 interest at $6\%$?

SOLUTION: Substituting $I = 50$, $P = 5000$, and $r = .06$ in (1),

$$5000 \times .06 \times t = 50$$

$$t = \frac{50}{5000 \times .06} = \frac{1}{6} \text{ year or 2 months}$$

EXAMPLE 6: General Motors $100 par value $3.75\%$ preferred stock was quoted at 52. At this price, what yield will a buyer receive on his investment?

SOLUTION: In this problem, two rates are involved. The return in dollars is the stated rate times the par value or $.0375 \times 100 = \$3.75$. This amount will be paid to the owner regardless of what he paid for the stock. To find the yield rate received by a buyer who paid $52, substitute in (1),

$$52 \times r \times 1 = 3.75$$

$$r = \frac{3.75}{52} = .072 = 7.2\%$$

Although this is a safe investment, the market price of $52 is lower than the par value of $100 because interest rates are now much higher than when the stock was issued. Fixed return investments are quite sensitive to interest rates.

EXAMPLE 7: A man borrows $2000 from a credit union. Each month he is to pay $100 on the principal. He also pays interest at the rate of $\frac{3}{4}\%$ a month on the unpaid balance at the beginning of the month. Find the total interest.

SOLUTION: Note that the rate is a monthly rate. The first month's interest is

$$I = 2000 \times .0075 \times 1 = \$15.00$$

The total payment for the first month is $115 and the new unpaid balance is $1900. For the second month the interest is

$$I = 1900 \times .0075 \times 1 = \$14.25$$

Since the unpaid balance decreases $100 a month, the interest decreases $.75 each month. After 19 payments the debt is down to $100 and the last interest payment is

$$I = 100 \times .0075 \times 1 = \$.75$$

The interest payments form an arithmetic progression which can be summed using the formula:

$$Sum = \frac{n}{2}(t_1 + t_n)$$

where $n$ is the number of terms and $t_1$ and $t_n$ are the first and last terms. In this problem, they stand for the first and last interest payments. Substituting,

$$Total\ interest = \tfrac{20}{2}(15.00 + .75) = \$157.50$$

## 1.9   Amount

The sum of the principal and the interest is called the **amount**, symbol $S$. This definition leads to the formula,

$$S = P + I$$
$$= P + Prt$$

Factoring, we have

$$S = P(1 + rt) \tag{2}$$

EXAMPLE: A man borrows $350 for 6 months at $8\%$. What amount must he repay?

SOLUTION: Substituting $P = 350$, $r = .08$, and $t = \frac{1}{2}$ in (2),

$$S = 350(1 + .08 \times \tfrac{1}{2}) = 350(1.04) = \$364.00$$

This problem could have been worked by getting the simple interest and adding it to the principal.

$$I = Prt = 350 \times .08 \times \tfrac{1}{2} = \$14.00$$
$$S = P + I = 350.00 + 14.00 = \$364.00$$

Many problems in the mathematics of finance can be solved by more than one method. Students should look for the easiest way, thereby reducing both labor and the risk of numerical errors. It is often desirable to work a problem more than one way as a check.

As the last example shows, the dollar value of a past or future sum of money will vary in accordance with the time and rate. Students who are accustomed to thinking of money only in terms of so much cash, should now get into the habit of taking into account these other variables. A debt of $1000 due in one year with interest at $6\%$ may be considered as an obligation of $1060 due in one year. If a time is not stated, we shall assume that the designated sum is the present or cash value. Thus, if a problem states that the price of a car is $2000, this means the cash price. If a sum is due in the future "without interest" or if a rate is not stated, we shall assume that the given value is the maturity value of the obligation. Thus "$3000 due in 6 months" means that 6 months hence the debtor must pay $3000. In the business world, this obligation would be worth less than $3000 before the end of 6 months.

Students also need to learn that different amounts of money may be *equivalent in value*. At $5\%$ interest, $100 now is equivalent in value to $105 in a year. What this means in practice is that a borrower is willing to repay $105 one year hence if he can get the use of $100 immediately. The lender is willing to lose the use of $100 for a year if he gets $5 interest. The equivalent values of different sums is the basis for the useful equations of value used throughout the mathematics of finance.

Another way of expressing an interest rate is to say that "money is worth so much." This expression is often used in problems to specify the rate which the parties to a transaction have agreed to use in arriving at a settlement. In practical business usage this rate is usually the current rate for that type of transaction in the particular locality.

## 1.10   Rounding

Money answers in mathematics of finance are rounded off to values that can be paid in standard coinage. In this book, unless stated otherwise, answers are rounded to the nearest cent. Calculated values ending in exactly half a cent or more are rounded up.

| CALCULATED VALUE | ROUNDED VALUE |
|---|---|
| $45.789 | $45.79 |
| 45.443 | 45.44 |
| 45.375 | 45.38 |
| 45.4650 | 45.47 |
| 45.6749 | 45.67 |

Note that in the last case .6749 is rounded down to .67. Since we are rounding to the nearest cent, it would be wrong to make the 4 a 5 in one step and round to 45.68 in a second step.

While exceptions to the above rule are noted as we come to them, we mention a couple now to illustrate how commercial practices affect rounding. Mortgage and other installment lenders customarily round up any fraction of a cent. Thus a monthly payment of $85.142 would be rounded up to $85.15. Had the fraction of a cent been dropped, the deficiency which accumulates over a long series of payments would all be made up on the concluding payment, making this payment larger than the others. By rounding up, the reverse is true, and the concluding payment will be somewhat smaller. This probably makes for happier customers. Some lenders even round up to the nearest dime. A monthly payment of $112.125 would be rounded up to $112.20. Again no injustice is done as the overpayment of a few cents each month is offset by the smaller concluding payment.

When data are approximate, rounding should not imply a degree of accuracy that is not possible with the data. Suppose that the market value of a stock has been increasing at about 10% a year. With so many uncertainties involved in the stock market, it would be foolish to predict the price a year from now to the nearest cent. A reasonable procedure would be to round off the answer to the nearest dollar and then qualify this as only a prediction.

Another practical question is how many decimal places to retain when a factor involves an unending decimal. If we want the amount of $4800 at 4% for 1 month, we can substitute in (2),

$$S = 4800(1 + .04 \times \tfrac{1}{12}) = 4800(1.003333\ldots)$$

The second factor must be terminated somewhere. If a calculator is available, as it is in most businesses, a good practice is to carry 8 or more decimal places and then round the answer. This practice does not appeal to students who do not have access to a calculator. Yet a thorough understanding of the mathematics of finance requires carrying many problems to the final dollars and cents answer. Only in this way can a student learn to solve practical problems including the important decision problems that involve a choice among two or more alternatives. When calculations must be made by pencil and paper methods, a good working rule is to round factors to the same number of decimal places as there are digits in the sum of money including the cents. The required arithmetic can then be done by conventional multiplication or by the short-cut method described in the appendix. In $4800.00 there are 6 digits, so we have

$$S = 4800.00(1.003333) = 4815.9984 = \$4816.00$$

Students should look for the easiest way to do problems. This conserves time and reduces the risk of errors. In getting the amount at simple interest, it is usually easier to get the interest using (1) and then add principal and interest to get the amount.

$$I = 4800.00 \times .04 \times \tfrac{1}{12} = \$16.00$$
$$S = 4800.00 + 16.00 = \$4816.00$$

## 1.11  Time Diagrams

All financial decision making must take into account the basic idea that **money has time value**. A hundred dollars today is worth more than a hundred dollars in a year, because a hundred dollars today can be invested to give a hundred dollars plus interest in a year.

An easy and accurate way to keep track of the varying dollar values of sums of money is to use a time diagram which shows the sums and the points in time at which they have particular dollar values. Students find diagrams of great help in the analysis and solution of problems. The simple time diagram below shows how the different dollar values of an obligation are placed at the corresponding points in time.

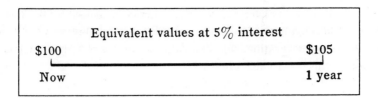

Equivalent values at 5% interest

$100                                            $105

Now                                             1 year

EXAMPLE 1: The current annual dividend rate of a savings and loan association is $4\frac{1}{2}\%$. Dividends are credited to a person's account on June 30 and December 31. Money put in by the 10th of the month earns dividends for the entire month. If money is put in after the 10th, it starts earning dividends the following month. A person opens an account on January 7 with $400. On February 25 he adds $200, and on June 10 he puts $240 in the association. What is the amount in his account on June 30?

SOLUTION: In this problem, as in all practical problems, the solution must be based on the rules governing the transaction. Although savings and loan associations pay dividends rather than interest, calculations are made using the simple interest formula. We allow 6 months dividends on the initial $400 although the actual time is a few days less. The $200 gets 4 months dividends although it is in the association a few days longer. Locating the deposits on a time diagram helps to get the length of time each earns dividends.

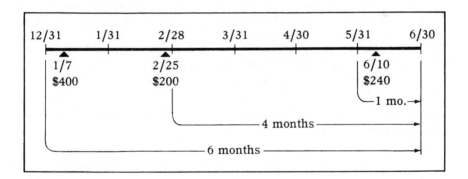

Using (1), the dividend is computed on each sum.

$$400 \times .045 \times \tfrac{1}{2} = \$9.00$$
$$200 \times .045 \times \tfrac{1}{3} = 3.00$$
$$240 \times .045 \times \tfrac{1}{12} = .90$$
$$\text{Total dividends} = \$12.90$$

Summing all deposits and dividends makes the June 30 balance $852.90.

EXAMPLE 2: The normal fee for travelers checks is $1 per $100. A seller of travelers checks advertised an unusual offer during May only—"...just in time for summer vacations you can save as much as $48 (see chart below), because of this remarkable offer":

| AMOUNT OF TRAVELERS CHECKS | USUAL FEE | MAY FEE | YOU SAVE |
|---|---|---|---|
| $300 | $3.00 | $2.00 | $1.00 |
| 500 | 5.00 | 2.00 | 3.00 |
| 1000 | 10.00 | 2.00 | 8.00 |
| 2500 | 25.00 | 2.00 | 23.00 |
| 5000 | 50.00 | 2.00 | 48.00 |

The ad continued, "Many smart people take advantage of our Unusual Offer and buy...Travelers Checks during May...then keep them on hand throughout the year either for their vacation or against the time they may need cash for an emergency. Why not follow this Smart lead?" While this is a smart lead for a person who is leaving soon, it is not so smart for the person whose vacation is several months away.

Instead of buying $1000 worth of travelers checks on May 1 for an October trip, a person put $1002 in a savings and loan association paying 5% converted quarterly on March 31, June 30, September 30, and December 31. On October 1 he withdrew the money and bought $1000 worth of travelers checks. How much did this smart person gain?

SOLUTION: The dividend for May and June equals

$$1002 \times .05 \times \tfrac{2}{12} = \$8.35$$

There is now a balance in the account of $1010.35 which gets dividends on September 30 of

$$1010.35 \times .05 \times \tfrac{3}{12} = 12.63$$
$$\text{Balance on October 1} = 1010.35 + 12.63 = \$1022.98$$
$$\text{Cost of travelers checks} = 1000 + 10.00 = 1010.00$$
$$\text{Savings} \quad \$\ \ 12.98$$

The advertised plan is a smart one for the issuer of travelers checks who has money interest free as long as the checks are outstanding.

EXAMPLE 3: A national magazine is sponsoring a contest in which the first prize is $100 a year for life. Every month the magazine will deposit $100 in a local bank chosen by the winner. To make the contest more appealing, the magazine mails out sample deposit books which show how the account grows if the bank pays 5% per annum with interest credited on March 31, June 30, September 30, and December 31. This means that interest is accumulated and added to the balance every 3 months. *The first three entries* in the promotional bank book are shown below. Compute the interest and balance on 12/31/74, using the 5% rate.

| DATE | DEPOSIT | INTEREST | BALANCE |
|------|---------|----------|---------|
| 10/1/74 | $100.00 | | $100.00 |
| 11/1/74 | $100.00 | | $200.00 |
| 12/1/74 | $100.00 | | $300.00 |

SOLUTION: The first payment earns interest for 3 months, the second for 2 months, and the third for 1 month. Substituting in (1),

$$100.00 \times .05 \times \tfrac{3}{12} = \$1.25$$
$$100.00 \times .05 \times \tfrac{2}{12} = \quad .83$$
$$100.00 \times .05 \times \tfrac{1}{12} = \quad .42$$
$$\text{Total interest} \quad \$2.50$$

Balance on 12/31/74 is $302.50.

When the payments are equal in size, an equivalent way to get simple interest is to assume that one deposit of $100.00 has earned 6 months interest.

$$100.00 \times .05 \times \tfrac{6}{12} = \$2.50$$

*EXERCISE 1a*

1. Find the simple interest on $750 for 2 months at 7% and the amount.
($8.75, $758.75)
2. Find the simple interest on $1225 for 3 months at $3\tfrac{1}{2}$% and the amount.
3. The contest passbook in Example 3, page 18, shows the following entries for the first six months. Compute the interest and balance on 3/31/75.
($6.28, $608.78)

| DATE | DEPOSIT | INTEREST | BALANCE |
|------|---------|----------|---------|
| 10/1/74 | $100.00 | | $100.00 |
| 11/1/74 | $100.00 | | $200.00 |
| 12/1/74 | $100.00 | | $300.00 |
| 12/31/74 | | $2.50 | $302.50 |
| 1/1/75 | $100.00 | | $402.50 |
| 2/1/75 | $100.00 | | $502.50 |
| 3/1/75 | $100.00 | | $602.50 |
| 3/31/75 | | | |

4. Find the balance on June 30, 1975, for the above account.

5. A man borrows $10,000 to buy a home. The interest rate is 6% and the monthly payment is $64.43. How much of the first payment goes to interest and how much to principal?                (Interest $50.00; principal $14.43)

6. A $15,000 home loan is to be repaid with monthly payments of $100. If the interest rate is $6\frac{1}{2}\%$, how much of the first payment goes to interest and how much to principal?

7. A savings and loan association advertises a rate of $4\frac{1}{2}\%$ compounded semiannually. Deposits made by the 10th of the month earn dividends from the 1st of that month. Deposits made after the 10th earn dividends from the 1st of the following month. Dividends are credited on June 30 and December 31. A depositor had $2045 in his account on June 30, 1973. He deposited $1120 on September 7, 1973. How much will he have in his account on December 31, 1973?                ($3227.81)

8. A man has an account in a savings and loan association that pays 5% compounded semiannually. Dividend dates are June 30 and December 31. Money deposited by the 10th of a month earns dividends from the 1st of that month. Deposits after the 10th earn dividends from the first of the following month. This man had a balance of $1600 on December 31, 1972. He deposited $400 on February 8, 1973, and $600 on April 25, 1973. Find the final entry in his passbook after interest is credited on June 30, 1973.

9. A man borrowed $150 for two months and paid $9.00 interest. What was the annual rate?                (36%)

10. A mechanic borrowed $125 from a licensed loan company and at the end of one month paid off the loan with $128.75. What annual rate of interest did he pay?

11. If a person loans $6000 at 5%, how long will it take him to get $75.00 interest?                (3 months)

12. How long will it take $8400 to earn $24.50 interest at 3.5%?

13. How long a time will be required for $625 to earn $25 interest at 4.8%?                (10 months)

14. How long will it take $1800 to earn $63.75 interest at $4\frac{1}{4}\%$?

15. What is the amount if $3.6 million is borrowed for 1 month at $2\frac{7}{8}\%$?                ($3,608,625)

16. What is the amount if $14.4 million is borrowed for 2 months at $3\frac{1}{4}\%$?

17. A man borrows $95. Six months later he repays the loan, principal and interest, with a payment of $100. What interest rate did he pay?   (10.53%)

18. A loan shark made a loan of $50 to be repaid with $55 at the end of one month. What was the annual interest rate?

19. A waitress, who was temporarily pressed for funds, pawned her watch and diamond ring for $55. At the end of 1 month she redeemed them by paying $59.40. What was the annual rate of interest?                (96%)

20. A loan shark was charging $10 interest for a $50 loan for a month. What was the annual interest rate?

21. A teacher borrowed $200 from the credit union to which she belonged. Every month for 8 months she paid $25 on the principal and interest at the rate of 1% a month on the unpaid balance at the beginning of the month. The first interest payment would be 1% of $200, the second interest payment would be 1% of $175, and so on until the loan was repaid. What was the total interest paid on this loan? ($9.00)

22. A person borrowed $800 from a credit union which charges $\frac{3}{4}$% per month on the outstanding balance of a loan. Every month for 8 months he paid $100 on the principal plus interest on the balance at the beginning of the month. Find the total interest.

23. The value of fixed income investments is very sensitive to changes in interest rates. In 1963, when money was relatively easy or cheap, Cincinnati Gas and Electric $100 par value, 4% preferred stock was quoted at 94. Early in 1972, when interest rates were higher, the stock could be purchased for $61. What rates of return or yield rates were received at these prices?

(4.26% at $94; 6.56% at $61)

24. Philadelphia Electric $100 par value, 3.8% preferred stock was quoted at $54\frac{1}{2}$ in the January 31, 1972, issue of *The Wall Street Journal*. What was the yield rate? Find the current yield on this stock. See Chapter 11 for information on how to read stock tables.

25. Three issues of Union Electric preferred stock were quoted as follows in the January 31, 1972, issue of *The Wall Street Journal*.

Un El pf 4.50    $64\frac{1}{4}$
Un El pf 4.00    59
Un El pf 3.50    $52\frac{1}{2}$

What were the yield rates? (7.00%; 6.78%; 6.67%)
Find the current yields on these stocks.

26. Use current data from your local paper to complete the table below for preferred stocks designated by your instructor.

| STOCK AND DIVIDEND | HIGH | LOW | CLOSE | YIELD RATE IN PERCENT BASED ON CLOSING PRICE |
|---|---|---|---|---|
| | | | | |
| | | | | |
| | | | | |

## 1.12 Exact and Ordinary Interest

When the time is in days and the rate is an annual rate, it is necessary to convert the days to a fractional part of a year when substituting in the simple interest formulas. Interest computed using a divisor of 360 is called ordinary interest. When the divisor is 365 or 366, the result is known as exact interest.

For a given rate of interest, a denominator of 360 results in a borrower paying more interest in dollars than would be the case if 365 or 366 were used. On individual loans the difference may not be large. But when many borrowers each pay a little more, the total difference is a substantial sum. This increased revenue makes the 360-day year popular with lenders.

EXAMPLE: Get the ordinary and exact interest on a 60-day loan of $300 if the rate is 8%.

SOLUTION: Substituting $P = 300$ and $r = .08$ in (1), we have

$$\text{Ordinary interest} = 300 \times .08 \times \tfrac{60}{360} = \$4.00$$
$$\text{Exact interest} = 300 \times .08 \times \tfrac{60}{365} = \$3.95$$

Note that ordinary interest is greater than exact interest. Also it is easier to compute when the work must be done without a calculator.

## 1.13 Exact and Approximate Time

There are two ways to compute the number of days between calendar dates. The more common method is the **exact** method which includes all days except the first. A simple way to determine the exact number of days is to use Table 1 in the back of this book, which gives the serial numbers of the days in the year. Another method is to add the number of days in each month during the term of the loan, not counting the first day but counting the last one. The **approximate** method is based on the assumption that all of the full months contain 30 days. To this number is added the exact number of days that remain in the term of the loan.

EXAMPLE: Find the exact and approximate time between March 5 and September 28.

SOLUTION: From Table 1 we find that September 28 is the 271st day in the year and March 5 is the 64th day. Therefore the exact time = 271 − 64 = 207 days. If a table of calendar days is not available, we can set up a table as follows:

|         |     |          |
|---------|-----|----------|
| March   | 26  | (31 − 5) |
| April   | 30  |          |
| May     | 31  |          |
| June    | 30  |          |
| July    | 31  |          |
| August  | 31  |          |
| Sept.   | 28  |          |
| Total   | 207 days |     |

To get the approximate time we count the number of months from March 5 to September 5. This gives us 6 × 30 = 180 days. To this we add the 23 days from September 5 to September 28 to get a total of 203 days.

## 1.14   Commercial Practice

Since we have exact and ordinary interest and exact and approximate time, there are four ways to compute simple interest:

1. Ordinary interest and exact time (Bankers' Rule)
2. Exact interest and exact time
3. Ordinary interest and approximate time
4. Exact interest and approximate time

This brings out the fact that in computing simple interest, as in all problems in the mathematics of finance, both parties to the transaction should understand what method is to be used. In this book, when the time is in days, we use ordinary interest and exact time unless another method is specified. This is known as **Bankers' Rule** and is the common commercial practice.

When an obligation has a stated time to run, it is necessary to determine the due date. If the time is stated in days, the due date is the exact number of days after the loan begins. If the time is stated in months, the due date is the same as the date on which the term of the loan begins unless the date of the loan is larger than the last date of the month in which the loan matures. When this happens, we take as the maturity date the last date of the month. Examples,

| DATE OF LOAN   | TERM OF LOAN | MATURITY DATE          |
|----------------|--------------|------------------------|
| June 15, 1972  | 60 days      | August 14, 1972        |
| June 15, 1972  | 2 months     | August 15, 1972        |
| Dec. 10, 1972  | 4 months     | April 10, 1973         |
| Dec. 10, 1972  | 120 days     | April 9, 1973          |
| Dec. 10, 1971  | 120 days     | April 8, 1972          |
|                |              | (1972 is a leap year)  |

| Dec. 28, 29, 30 or 31, 1972 | 2 months | Feb. 28, 1973 |
| Dec. 29, 30 or 31, 1971 | 2 months | Feb. 29, 1972 |

EXAMPLE 1: On November 15, 1973, a man borrowed $500 at 5%. The debt is repaid on February 20, 1974. Find the simple interest using the four methods.

SOLUTION: We first get the exact and approximate time.

| EXACT TIME | APPROXIMATE TIME |

From Table 1:

November 15 is the 319th day      November 15 to February 15 is three
February 20 is the 51st day         months
In 1973 there are $365 - 319 = 46$ days   Three months $\times$ 30 days = 90 days
In 1974 there are       51 days   February 15 to 20      = 5 days

       Total time   97 days         Total time   95 days

Ordinary interest and exact time
  (Bankers' Rule)            $I = 500 \times .05 \times \frac{97}{360} = \$6.74$
Exact interest and exact time      $I = 500 \times .05 \times \frac{97}{365} = \$6.64$
Ordinary interest and approximate time    $I = 500 \times .05 \times \frac{95}{360} = \$6.60$
Exact interest and approximate time     $I = 500 \times .05 \times \frac{95}{365} = \$6.51$

To encourage prompt payment of bills, many merchants allow discounts for payments in advance of the final due date. Terms of 2/10, $n/30$ mean that if payment is made within 10 days from the date of the invoice, 2% of the amount of the invoice can be deducted. If the bill is paid after 10 days but on or before the 30th day, the net amount of the invoice must be paid. A buyer who takes advantage of cash discounts in effect lends money to the seller and receives as interest the cash discount. Interest rates earned in this way usually are so high that it is good business practice to take advantage of savings through cash discounts.

EXAMPLE 2: A merchant receives an invoice for $2000 with terms 2/10, $n/30$. If he pays on the 10th day, he earns what rate of interest?

SOLUTION: The cash discount is $40 making the principal $1960. Substituting in (1),

$$1960 \times r \times \frac{20}{360} = 40$$

$$r = \frac{40 \times 360}{1960 \times 20} = .367 = 36.7\%$$

Banks sometimes require business borrowers to keep a **compensating balance** on deposit with the bank as one of the conditions for getting a loan. If a borrower gets a $1000 loan with a 20% compensating balance, he will be required to maintain $200 (20% of $1000) in his demand account. If he normally maintains less than $200, part of the loan proceeds must be used to meet the compensating balance requirement. While he pays interest at 8% on the full $1000, he will have the use of less than $1000. The effective rate of interest will be greater than the stated 8%. The difference will depend on the size of the compensating balance, and the balance the borrower would ordinarily keep anyway.

EXAMPLE 3: A borrower gets a $100,000 loan at 8% at a bank which requires the lender to keep a compensating balance of 20%. If all of this balance is a net increase in the demand account balance which the borrower would normally maintain, what is the equivalent rate paid by the borrower?

SOLUTION: On an annual basis he is paying $8000 interest for the use of $80,000. This is equivalent to a rate of 10%.

EXAMPLE 4: If the borrower in Example 3 normally keeps a demand deposit balance of $5000, the required balance would result in what equivalent rate?

SOLUTION: He is still paying $8000 interest on an annual basis. He now takes $15,000 out of the loan to get the required $20,000 compensating balance. In effect he is paying $8000 for the use of $85,000. On an annual basis the rate is $8000/85,000 = .094 = 9.4\%$.

EXAMPLE 5: Builders of homes, apartment houses, and commercial building often get construction loans. Construction loan funds are not supplied at one time but rather are advanced gradually as construction progresses. The loan may be repaid in a lump sum shortly after completion of the project.

The builder of an apartment building obtained an $800,000 construction loan at an annual rate of 9%. The money was advanced as follows.

| | |
|---|---|
| March 1, 1973 | $300,000 |
| June 1, 1973 | 200,000 |
| October 1, 1973 | 200,000 |
| December 1, 1973 | 100,000 |

The building was completed in February of 1974 and the loan repaid on March 1, 1974. Find the amount using ordinary interest and approximate time.

SOLUTION: Interest on each part of the loan is

$$300,000 \times .09 \times 1 \ = \$27,000$$
$$200,000 \times .09 \times \tfrac{9}{12} = \ \ 13,500$$
$$200,000 \times .09 \times \tfrac{5}{12} = \ \ \ \ 7,500$$
$$100,000 \times .09 \times \tfrac{3}{12} = \ \ \ \ 2,250$$

Total interest    $50,250

Amount of loan $= 800,000 + 50,250 = \$850,250$

### EXERCISE 1b

1. Find the ordinary and exact interest on $750 for 100 days at 3%.
   ($6.25, $6.16)
2. Find the ordinary and exact interest on $6080.50 for 60 days at $3\tfrac{1}{4}$%.
3. Find the ordinary and exact interest on $1200 for 45 days at $4\tfrac{1}{2}$%.
   ($6.75, $6.66)
4. If $P = \$9800$ and $r = 2\tfrac{1}{8}$%, get the ordinary and exact interest for a 120-day loan.
5. Use exact time and find the ordinary and exact interest on $300 at 5% from May 5, 1974, to September 12, 1974.            ($5.42, $5.34)
6. Use exact time and find the ordinary and exact interest on $500 from November 30, 1974, to March 15, 1975, using a rate of $7\tfrac{1}{2}$%.
   (Use Bankers' Rule in Problems 7 to 12)
7. What amount must be repaid on November 21, 1973, if $7000 is borrowed at 7% on November 1, 1973?            ($7027.22)
8. A man borrows $7760 on December 15, 1974. He repays the debt on March 3, 1975 with interest at $6\tfrac{1}{2}$%. Find the amount repaid.
9. A debt of $500 is due on June 15, 1973. After that date the borrower is required to pay 5% interest. If the debt is settled on January 10, 1974, what must be repaid?            ($514.51)
10. On May 4, 1973, a man borrows $1850 which he promises to repay in 120 days with interest at 3%. If he does not pay on time his contract requires him to pay 8% on the unpaid amount for the time after the due date. Determine how much he must pay to settle the debt on December 15, 1973.
11. A man borrows $3050 on December 15, 1971, at $3\tfrac{1}{4}$%. What amount must he repay on April 8, 1972? Note that for leap years, the number of the day after February 28 is one more than the number in Table 1. ($3081.66)
12. A man borrows $5000 on November 11, 1971, at $5\tfrac{1}{2}$%. What amount must he repay on March 10, 1972?
13. On December 31 a man has $3000 in his account in a savings and loan association. His money will earn dividends at $4\tfrac{1}{2}$% if it is left on deposit until the next interest date which is June 30. Money withdrawn before

June 30 does not get any interest. On May 1 the man needs $1000. Instead of drawing the money out of his account, he makes a passbook loan using his passbook as security. He plans to repay this loan from his account on June 30 when he gets his interest. If the savings and loan association charges 6% for a passbook loan, this plan will save the man how much money as of June 30? The savings and loan association uses Bankers' Rule in getting interest on passbook loans.                    ($12.50)

14. Get the answer to Problem 13 if the loan is for $1500 and is made on March 31.

15. A merchant receives an invoice for $2000 with terms 2/10, $n/60$. If he pays on the 10th, he will earn what rate of interest?                    (14.7%)

16. An invoice for $5000 has terms 3/10, $n/45$. What rate of interest is earned if payment is made on the 10th?

## 1.15   Present Value at Simple Interest

To get the amount of a principal invested at simple interest, we use the formula, $S = P(1 + rt)$. If the amount is known and we want to get the principal, we solve the formula for $P$.

$$P = \frac{S}{1 + rt} \tag{3}$$

EXAMPLE: If money is worth 5%, what is the present value of $105 due in one year?

SOLUTION: Substituting $S = 105$, $r = .05$, and $t = 1$ in (3),

$$P = \frac{105}{1 + .05 \times 1} = \$100.00$$

This means that $100 invested now at 5% should amount to $105 in a year. Substituting in the amount formula verifies this.

$$S = 100(1 + .05 \times 1) = \$105.00$$

Getting the present value of a sum due in the future is called **discounting**. When the simple interest formula is used to get the present value, the difference between the amount and present value is called **simple discount**. Note that the simple discount on the future amount is the same as the simple interest on the principal or present value.

## 1.16   Use of Reciprocals

Only by working many problems and checking the results, can a person acquire an understanding of the mathematics of finance. To make it possible for students to work a greater diversity of problems, we use data that simplify computations. Division, which is often the most time-consuming arithmetic operation, can sometimes be done more rapidly by multiplying by the reciprocal of the divisor from Table 8 in the back of the book.

EXAMPLE 1: If money is worth 7%, what is the present value of $2000 due in 1 year?

SOLUTION: Substituting $S = 2000$, $r = .07$, and $t = 1$ in (3),

$$P = \frac{2000}{1.07} = 2000 \times \frac{1}{1.07}$$

To get $1/1.07$, we can write $1/1.07 = 100 \times 1/107$

$$= 100 \times .00934\ 5794$$
$$= .934\ 579$$

Practically it is usually easier and most students prefer to locate the decimal point by inspection. In any case, the answer is found by a simple multiplication.

$$P = 2000 \times .934\ 579 = \$1869.16$$

EXAMPLE 2: If money is worth 4%, what is the present value of $5000 due in 2 months?

SOLUTION: Substituting in (3),

$$P = \frac{5000}{1 + .04 \times \frac{1}{6}} = \frac{5000}{1.006667}$$

To divide this out would be a lot of work. However, to use the reciprocal tables, the denominator must have 3 or less significant figures. By multiplying numerator and denominator by 6,

$$P = \frac{30,000}{6.04} = 30,000 \times .165\ 5629 = \$4966.89$$

## 1.17   Use Your Head

All answers should be subjected to a common-sense check. Many mistakes are whoppers, resulting from such common slips as misplaced decimal points and inverted fractions. There is no disgrace in making such mistakes. Not catching them is another matter. The student who is looking for the present value at 4% of $5000 due in 2 months and writes down $49,668.87 should not expect credit because he got everything right except the decimal point. Common sense should tell him to expect an answer less than $5000.

## 1.18   What Is It Worth, Now?

The mathematics of finance can be used to find the best answer to many practical business problems. Typical of the many important questions which we consider in this and later chapters are: Should we pay cash or use credit? Is it better to buy or lease? Will a new machine pay for itself?

A good way to compare different plans is to get all of them on a present value basis. Just as we can compare two items when we know their cash prices, so are we helped to choose between more complicated alternatives when we know what each is worth *now*.

EXAMPLE: A man can buy a piece of property for $5000 cash or $5300 in a year. He has the cash and can invest it at 5%. Which is better and by how much now?

SOLUTION: The propositions as they stand cannot be compared because they are at different points in time. By using (3), we are able to find that at 5% the $5300 due in a year has a present value of

$$P = \frac{5300}{1.05} = \$5047.62$$

This means that the buyer would have to invest $5047.62 now at 5% to have $5300 in a year. (Check: 5047.62 × 1.05 = $5300.00.) By paying cash, the buyer saves $47.62 now.

If he could get another rate of return on his money, there might be a different decision. For example,

| RATE OF RETURN | PRESENT VALUE OF $5300 DUE IN 1 YEAR | BETTER PLAN |
|---|---|---|
| 5% | $5047.62 | Save $47.62 now by paying cash |
| 6% | 5000.00 | Plans are equivalent |
| 7% | 4953.27 | Save $46.73 now by paying $5300 in 1 year |

**EXERCISE 1c**

1. What is the present value of $1500 due in 9 months if money is worth 4%? ($1456.31)

2. At an interest rate of $4\frac{1}{2}$% what is the present value of $4300 due in 3 months?

3. At 6% interest what is the present value of $600 due in 6 months? ($582.52)

4. What is the present value of $600 due in 6 months at: (a) 2%; (b) 3%; (c) 4%?

5. What is the present value of $100 due in 1 year at: (a) 4%; (b) 5%; (c) 6%? [(a) $96.15; (b) $95.24; (c) $94.34]

6. At 5% find the present value of $2000 due in: (a) 3 months; (b) 6 months; (c) 9 months.

7. A man can get a building lot for $3000 cash or $3100 in one year. He has the cash but can invest it at 4%. Which is more advantageous to him and by how much now? (By paying $3100 in a year he saves $19.23 now)

8. If a person can earn $4\frac{1}{2}$% on his money, is it better to pay $1990 cash for an item or to pay $2090 in a year? Give the cash equivalent of the savings resulting from adopting the better plan.

9. A man may discharge an obligation by paying either $200 now or $208 in 6 months. If money is worth 4% to the man, what is the cash equivalent of choosing the better plan? (By paying $200 cash he saves $3.92 now)

10. A man can settle a debt by paying either $1475 now or $1500 in 3 months. If the man can earn 4% on his money, which plan is more advantageous and by how much now?

## 1.19   Present Value of Interest-Bearing Debt

We must first get the maturity value of interest-bearing debts, using the stated interest rate for the term of the loan. Then we get the present value of this maturity value for the time between the day it is discounted and the due date using the rate specified for discounting. Since two rates and two times may be involved in discounting an interest-bearing debt, a time diagram helps to prevent errors.

EXAMPLE: A debtor signs a note for $2000 due in 6 months with interest at 4%. One month after the debt is contracted, the holder of the note sells it to a third party who determines the present value at 6%. How much is received for the note?

SOLUTION: A time diagram is made. The maturity value is obtained, and then discounted for the five months between the discount date and the due date.

A common error in problems of this type is to use the time between the original loan and the discount date for getting the present value. That would be one month in this example. The person who buys the note is not interested in how long it has run, but in how long it still has to run. In this example, the buyer of the note is loaning $1990.24 to the holder of the note. The $2040 he gets five months later is a return of his principal with interest at 6%.

## 1.20   Equations of Value

Sometimes it is desired to replace one or more obligations with one or more payments at different times that will be equivalent in value to the original obligations. For example, a man may owe the same creditor $200 due now and $106 due in a year. He has cash with which he can settle all his obligations. However, he would be foolish to make a cash payment of $306 because part of the debt is not due now. He will want the creditor to make some allowance for the early payment of the $106 due in a year. If simple interest is to be used in arriving at a settlement, the two parties must agree on a rate. Suppose they decide to use 6%. Then we simply get the present value at 6% of $106 due in a year.

$$P = \frac{106}{1 + .06 \times 1} = \$100$$

We can add this to the $200 due now to get a total cash settlement of $300. Note that two sums of money cannot be added *until they have been brought to the same point in time*.

Suppose in the above example that the man did not have the cash and asked his creditor to allow him to settle all the debts in a year. Now he must expect to pay interest on the $200 due now. If the agreed rate is 6%, the $200 would amount to $212 in a year. Because it is at the same point in time as the

$106 the two could be added making the total debt *at that time* $318. The three alternatives we have discussed can be summarized as follows:

$200 now and $106 in a year ⎱ are equivalent in
$300 now ⎰ value if money is
$318 in a year ⎰ worth 6%

We have gone into this point in detail because of its fundamental importance in the mathematics of finance and the difficulty it causes students. ALWAYS bring obligations to the same point using the specified rate before combining them. This common point is called a **focal date** or **comparison date**. When everything has been brought to a focal date, an **equation of value** can be set up and unknown quantities determined. If any obligations are interest bearing, maturity values must be determined before moving them to the focal date.

A very effective way to solve many problems in the mathematics of finance is to make a time diagram, select a focal date, and then use an equation of value in which the original obligations are set equal to the payments after *both* have been brought to the focal date using the specified interest rate. If obligations are put on one side of the time line and payments on the other side, it is easy to tell them apart when setting up the equation of value.

If a student draws a good time diagram, he will often find that the equation of value practically writes itself.

In simple interest problems the answer will vary slightly depending on the location of the focal date. In compound interest problems the location of the focal date does not affect the answer. Students should recognize that the focal date is simply an arbitrary point in time which we must have so that all obligations and payments can be brought to the same time and an equation of value obtained.

There are only two ways to move money—backward and forward. Look at your time diagram. If a sum is to be moved forward, use an amount formula; if backward, a present value formula.

EXAMPLE 1: A man owes $200 due in 6 months and $300 due in 1 year. He and his creditor agree that he can make a cash settlement of both debts using a simple interest rate of 5% and putting the focal date now. Get the size of the cash settlement.

SOLUTION: A time diagram with the original debts on one side of the line and the new obligations on the other side will make it easy to obtain the correct equation.

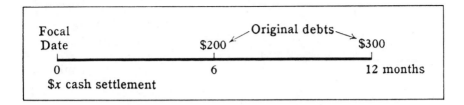

To get the $200 to the focal date we discount it for 6 months. The $300 must be discounted for 1 year. Since the unknown payment is at the focal date it simply equals $x. Now that everything is at the same point in time, we set up the equation of value:

$$x = \frac{200}{1 + .05 \times \frac{1}{2}} + \frac{300}{1 + .05 \times 1} = 195.12 + 285.71 = \$480.83$$

EXAMPLE 2: Solve the above problem using 12 months hence as the focal date.

SOLUTION: The $200 must be accumulated for 6 months, the $300 is at the focal date, and the unknown payment must be accumulated for 1 year. This leads to the equation of value:

$$x(1 + .05 \times 1) = 200(1 + .05 \times \tfrac{1}{2}) + 300$$
$$1.05x = 205 + 300 = 505$$

$$x = \frac{505}{1.05} = \$480.95$$

This example shows that in simple interest problems the answer varies slightly with the location of the focal date so that both parties must agree on both the rate and the focal date.

EXAMPLE 3: A man owes $1000 due in 1 year with interest at 6%. He wants to discharge this obligation with two equal payments in 3 and 9 months respectively. What will be the size of these payments if he and the creditor agree to use an interest rate of 6% and a focal date 1 year hence?

SOLUTION: First get the maturity value of the $1000 debt.

$$S = 1000(1 + .06 \times 1) = \$1060$$

No further use will be made of the original debt of $1000. Now make a time diagram, move everything to the focal date, and set up the equation of value.

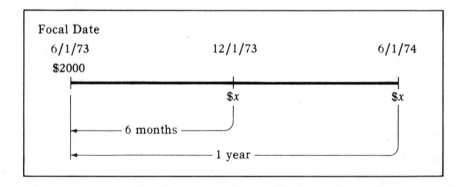

$$x(1 + .06 \times \tfrac{3}{4}) + x(1 + .06 \times \tfrac{1}{4}) = 1060$$
$$1.045x + 1.015x = 1060$$
$$2.06x = 1060$$

$$x = \frac{1060}{2.06} = \$514.56$$

EXAMPLE 4: A person borrows \$2000 at 6% interest on June 1, 1973. He is to repay the debt with 2 equal payments, one on December 1, 1973, and the other on June 1, 1974. Put the focal date on June 1, 1973, and find the size of the payments. Use approximate time and ordinary interest.

SOLUTION: A time diagram shows in what direction and how far each sum is to be moved.

The \$2000 is already at the focal date. The unknown payments are brought back using (3). Setting up an equation of value and using reciprocals to simplify computations, we have

$$\frac{x}{1 + .06 \times \frac{1}{2}} + \frac{x}{1 + .06 \times 1} = 2000$$

$$\frac{x}{1.03} + \frac{x}{1.06} = 2000$$

$$.970874x + .943396x = 2000$$

$$x = \frac{2000}{1.914270} = \$1044.78$$

EXAMPLE 5: Work Example 4 with the focal date on June 1, 1974.

SOLUTION: The equation of value is

$$x(1 + .06 \times \tfrac{1}{2}) + x = 2000(1.06)$$
$$1.03x + x = 2120$$

$$x = \frac{2120}{2.03} = \$1044.33$$

Note that a different focal date resulted in simpler computations and a slightly different answer.

EXAMPLE 6: A man borrows $6000 on September 15, 1972. He agrees to pay $2000 on January 15, 1973, and $2000 on May 15, 1973. If the interest rate is $4\frac{1}{2}\%$, find how much he would have to pay on September 15, 1973, to pay off the debt. Use approximate time and ordinary interest. In this problem the logical place for the focal date is on September 15, 1973, the final settlement date.

SOLUTION: All transactions are put on a time diagram.

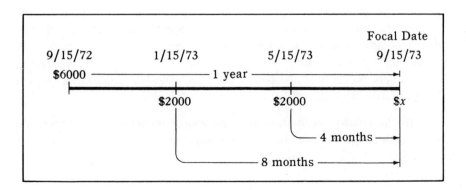

The debt and two payments are carried forward to the focal date using (2). We then write the equation of value

$$x = 6000(1 + .045 \times 1) - 2000(1 + .045 \times \tfrac{2}{3}) - 2000(1 + .045 \times \tfrac{1}{3})$$
$$= 6270 - 2060 - 2030 = \$2180.00$$

## 1.21   Investment Analysis

Equations of value are often used in the valuation of assets. Acquiring an asset usually means an immediate outlay for the acquisition cost of the investment, followed by a stream of earnings and costs over time. The immediate outlay and subsequent earnings and costs are called cash inflows and outflows. These flows sometimes occur almost continuously rather than at stated time intervals. A store, for example, has money coming in every day that the store is open. However, it is simpler and usually more satisfactory in making practical decisions to assume that the flows during a time period are concentrated at the end of the period. Some analysts put outflows at the beginning of the period, and inflows at the end of the period.

Before an investment decision is made, it is important to try to predict whether or not the investment will be profitable. Cash flow analysis is a general and powerful technique for analyzing investment problems. Both the timing and the size of the cash flows must be taken into account when making investment decisions.

There are two ways to use cash flows to analyze investments. One is to discount all cash flows at a given rate. The algebraic sum of the discounted cash flows is called the **net present value** or simply the **present value** of the investment. If the present value is positive at an acceptable yield rate, the investment is an attractive one. What constitutes an acceptable rate depends on the cost of capital. This is discussed under Capital Budgeting in Chapter 8. The other method is to find the rate which makes the inflows and outflows equal as of a certain point in time. This rate is called the **profit rate**, the **marginal efficiency of investment**, or the **internal rate of return**. This rate must usually be found by trial and error.

In this chapter cash flow analysis is applied to problems involving a limited number of flows and simple interest. When there is a stream of many costs and earnings, it is necessary to use compound interest methods described in later chapters. Regardless of whether there are a few or many flows, a good method of solution is to

1. Get the inflows and outflows at their proper points in time. If there are more than a couple of flows, draw a time diagram.
2. Select a focal or comparison date.
3. Write an equation of value.

EXAMPLE 1: A project which requires an investment of $1900 is expected to result in a return of $2000 in 6 months. What would be the net present value of this investment based on an interest rate of: (a) 10%; (b) 12%?

SOLUTION: We must compare an outflow of $1900 now with an inflow of $2000 in 6 months. Note that outflows are negative. Putting the focal date now and using (3) to discount the $2000, we have

$$\text{At } 10\%: \text{Net present value} = -1900 + \frac{2000}{1 + .10 \times \frac{1}{2}}$$

$$= -1900 + 1904.76 = \$4.76$$

$$\text{At } 12\%: \text{Net present value} = -1900 + \frac{2000}{1 + .12 \times \frac{1}{2}}$$

$$= -1900 + 1886.79 = -\$13.21$$

If the investor is satisfied with a 10% return, this would be an attractive investment since it has a positive present value at this rate. The investor who wants 12% would not be satisfied because the negative net present value indicates that the return is less than 12%.

EXAMPLE 2: Find the rate of return on the project in Example 1.

SOLUTION: Since there is only one inflow, this can be handled as a problem in simple interest using (1).

$$1900 \times r \times \tfrac{1}{2} = 100$$

$$r = \frac{2 \times 100}{1900} = .1053 = 10.53\%$$

CHECK: The interest on $1900 at $10.53\% = 1900 \times .1053 \times \frac{1}{2} = \$100.04$. The 4 cent difference is due to rounding.

EXAMPLE 3: A company can put $3600 in an investment that is expected to result in cash inflows of $1000 in 6 months and $3000 in 1 year. Find the internal rate of return.

SOLUTION: A time diagram shows the amount and time of all cash flows.

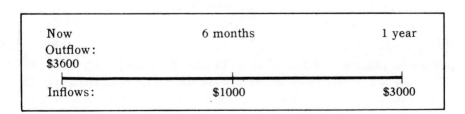

By trial and error we seek a rate which makes the discounted value of the inflows equal to $3600. Although experience with similar problems is of some help, the first trial rate is largely a guess. At 8%,

$$\text{Present value of inflows} = \frac{1000}{1.04} + \frac{3000}{1.08} = 961.54 + 2777.78 = \$3739.32$$

This result indicates that the rate is much higher than 8% so we make a bold jump to 16% in the hope that this will bring us below $3600, giving us a bracket on the true rate. At 16%,

$$\text{Present value of inflows} = \frac{1000}{1.08} + \frac{3000}{1.16} = 925.93 + 2586.21 = \$3512.14$$

Splitting the difference and trying 12%,

$$\text{Present value of inflows} = \frac{1000}{1.06} + \frac{3000}{1.12} = 943.40 + 2678.57 = \$3621.97$$

The rate is now known to be between 12 and 16%. At 14%,

$$\text{Present value of inflows} = \frac{1000}{1.07} + \frac{3000}{1.14} = 934.58 + 2631.58 = \$3566.16$$

We now know that the rate is between 12 and 14%. This trial and error seeking the answer is known as **iteration**. It can be done rapidly using a computer. However, in simple problems the use of a table of reciprocals and good judgment in choosing trial rates can quickly get the problem to a point where interpolation can be used to get an answer that is good enough for making practical decisions.

Interpolation is the way mathematicians read between the lines. Since the mathematics of finance often involves interpolation, it is well to learn a systematic method. Record the closest values on both sides of the unknown and compute differences as shown below.

| | RATE | PRESENT VALUE OF INFLOWS | |
|---|---|---|---|
| | 12% | 3621.97 | |
| 2% $d$ | $r$ | 3600.00 $\quad$ 21.97 | 55.81 |
| | 14% | 3566.16 | |

We now have two columns of data. In one all entries are known; in the other there is an unknown value. We assume that $r$ is the same fraction of the distance from 12 to 14% as 3600 is from 3621.97 to 3566.16. We let $d$ represent the unknown increment in the rate and set up a proportion.

$$\frac{d}{2} = \frac{21.97}{55.81}$$

$$d = \frac{2 \times 21.97}{55.81} = .8$$

$$r = 12.0 + .8 = 12.8\%$$

Students often ask if it matters which way they go. The answer is no. All that matters is going the same way in both columns. Coming up from the bottom in this problem results in

$$\frac{d}{2} = \frac{33.84}{55.81}$$

$$d = \frac{2 \times 33.84}{55.81} = 1.2$$

$$r = 14.0 - 1.2 = 12.8\% \text{ (note subtraction)}$$

An interpolated result is always between the known values. Remembering this may catch an arithmetic error or a wrong sign applied to the incremental change.

The method described here is linear interpolation which assumes a straight line change between values. Although many mathematics of finance functions are curved, linear interpolation usually leads to results that are accurate enough for practical work. If a very high degree of precision is required, more refined methods of interpolation can be found in books on numerical analysis and in the Compound Interest and Annuity Tables published by the Financial Publishing Company.

### EXERCISE 1d

1. A man owes $200 due in 4 months and $800 due in 8 months. What single payment 6 months hence will discharge these obligations if the settlement is based on an interest rate of 4% and the focal date is 6 months hence?
   ($996.03)

2. A man owes $350 due in 3 months and $525 due in 6 months. If money is worth 5%, what single payment in 6 months will settle both obligations? Put the focal date at 6 months.

3. A person owes $200 due in 6 months and $400 due in 1 year. What cash payment will retire both debts if money is worth 5%? Use now as the focal date.
   ($576.07)

4. Debts of $500 and $1500 are due in 3 and 6 months respectively. What

cash settlement will settle these debts if it is based on an interest rate of 6%
and the time of the cash settlement is used for the focal date?

5. A debtor signs a note for $1000 due in 1 year with interest at 6%. Three
months after the debt is contracted, the holder of the note sells it to a third
party who determines its values at 8% simple interest. How much does
the seller of the note receive? ($1000.00)

6. A borrower signs a note for $2500 due in 6 months with interest at 5%.
Two months after the note is signed, the holder of the note sells it to a
buyer who charges 6% simple interest for discounting. How much does the
seller receive?

7. A debtor owes $1000 due in 1 year. He agrees to pay $500 in 3 months.
If money is worth 4%, what payment must he make 15 months hence to
retire the rest of the debt? Put focal date 15 months hence. ($490.00)

8. A man owes $4000. He and his creditor agree that he can pay $2000 now
and the balance in 6 months. Find the payment in 6 months if the settlement is based on an interest rate of 4% and the focal date is 6 months hence.

9. On June 1, 1973, a man incurs a debt for $1500 due in 3 months with
interest at $4\frac{1}{2}$%. On July 1, 1973, he pays $500 on the debt. What balance
will he owe on the original due date if the two parties to the transaction
agree to use $4\frac{1}{2}$% in arriving at a settlement? Use the due date as the focal
date and approximate time and ordinary interest. ($1013.13)

10. On April 1, 1973, a man buys merchandise and agrees to pay $2000 in
2 months. On May 1, 1973, he pays $800 on the debt. What balance will he
owe on the due date if the creditor agrees to use 5% in arriving at a settlement? Use the due date as the focal date and approximate time and ordinary
interest.

11. A company has an investment opportunity that would require spending
$9500 now. It is expected that the investment will be worth $10,000 in 1
year. What is its net present value at: (a) 5%; (b) 6%?
[(a) $23.81; (b) −$66.04]

12. An investment requires a cash outlay of $4200. It is estimated that the
investment will return $5000 in one year. Find the net present value at: (a)
18%; (b) 20%.

13. Find the internal rate of return for Problem 11. (5.3%)

14. Find the internal rate of return for Problem 12.

15. An investment costs $18,500. It is expected to produce cash inflows of
$10,000 in 6 and 12 months. Find the net present value at 10%. ($114.72)

16. An investment requires a cash outlay of $2750. It is expected to produce
a cash inflow of $1000 in 6 months and $2000 in 12 months. Find the net
present value at 8%.

17. Find the internal rate of return for Problem 15. (10.9%)

18. Find the internal rate of return for Problem 16.

## 1.22   Partial Payments

When a person borrows money, it is desirable to have an agreement with his creditor under which he can reduce the interest by making partial payments before the due date. There are two common ways to allow interest credit on short-term transactions: **Merchants' Rule** and **United States Rule**. Under Merchants' Rule the entire debt earns interest to the final settlement date. Each partial payment also earns interest from the time it is made to the final settlement date. The balance due on the final date is simply the difference between the amount of the debt and the sum of the amounts of the partial payments. Note that this is essentially a focal date problem using the given interest rate and putting the focal date at the final settlement date. Merchants' Rule is used frequently with short-term obligations.

Under United States Rule the interest on the outstanding principal is computed each time a partial payment is made. If the payment is greater than the interest, the difference is used to reduce the principal. If the payment is less than the interest, it is held without interest until another partial payment is made. The two payments are then added. If they exceed the interest at that time, the difference is used to reduce the principal. The final settlement is the last outstanding principal carried to the final settlement date.

In the examples below, solutions are given in tabular form instead of the usual equations of value form. The tabular method of solution may be preferred by some for this type of problem.

EXAMPLE 1: A debt of $1000 is due in 1 year with interest at 6%. The debtor pays $300 in 4 months and $200 in 10 months. Find the balance due in 1 year using Merchants' Rule and United States Rule.

SOLUTION BY MERCHANTS' RULE: This is equivalent to putting a focal date at the time of the final settlement. A diagram helps to determine the time each sum is to be moved.

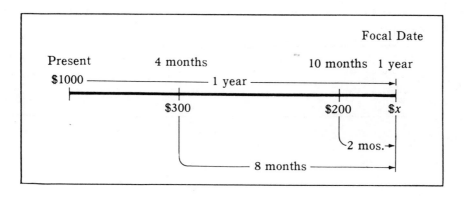

Computations are given below.

### Merchants' Rule

---

| Original debt | | $1000.00 |
| Interest on $1000 for 1 year | | 60.00 |
| | | $1060.00 |
| First payment | $300.00 | |
| Interest on $300 for 8 months | 12.00 | |
| | $312.00 | |
| Second payment | $200.00 | |
| Interest on $200 for 2 months | 2.00 | |
| | $202.00 | |
| Sum of partial payments accumulated to the final settlement date | | 514.00 |
| Balance due on final settlement date | | $ 546.00 |

---

SOLUTION BY UNITED STATES RULE: Instead of having one point to which all sums are brought, the solution is based on what amounts to a floating focal or comparison date. Each time a payment is made, the preceding balance is brought at interest to this point and a new balance is obtained. In this problem, intermediate balances are obtained at 4 and 10 months and a final settlement at 12 months. A diagram helps to get the time from one payment to the next.

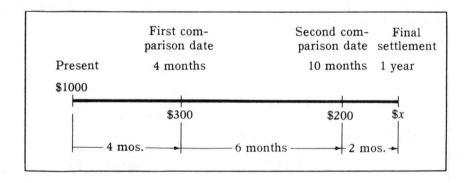

Computations are given on the following page.

### United States Rule

| | |
|---|---|
| Original debt | $1000.00 |
| Interest on $1000 for 4 months | 20.00 |
| Amount due after 4 months | $1020.00 |
| Deduct first payment | 300.00 |
| New balance due | $ 720.00 |
| Interest on $720 for 6 months | 21.60 |
| Amount due after 10 months | $ 741.60 |
| Deduct second payment | 200.00 |
| New balance due | $ 541.60 |
| Interest on $541.60 for 2 months | 5.42 |
| Balance due on final settlement date | $ 547.02 |

Note that the two methods lead to different concluding payments. Again we see why the two parties to a business transaction must agree on the method of calculating interest.

EXAMPLE 2: On June 15, 1971, a man borrows $5000 at 5%. He pays $2000 on July 10, 1971, $50 on November 20, 1971, and $1000 on January 12, 1972. What is the balance due on March 10, 1972, by United States Rule?

SOLUTION: This example shows how to handle a payment that is smaller than the outstanding interest.

### United States Rule

| | |
|---|---|
| Debt on June 15, 1971 | $5000.00 |
| Interest at 5% on $5000 from June 15 to July 10 (25 days) | 17.36 |
| Amount due | $5017.36 |
| Payment of $2000 on July 10, 1971 | 2000.00 |
| Balance as of July 10, 1971 | $3017.36 |
| Interest on $3017.36 from July 10 to November 20, 1971 (133 days), is $55.74. Since this is more than the $50 payment on November 20, this payment is held without interest and no deduction is made. | |
| Interest on $3017.36 from July 10, 1971, to January 12, 1972 (186 days) | 77.95 |
| Amount due | $3095.31 |
| Payments: November 20, 1971     $   50.00 | |
| January 12, 1972     1000.00 | 1050.00 |
| Balance as of January 12, 1972 | $2045.31 |
| Interest on $2045.31 from January 12, 1972, to March 10, 1972 (58 days). Note extra day for leap year | 16.48 |
| Balance due on March 10, 1972 | $2061.79 |

An important application of United States Rule is getting the month-to-month balance on home loans. Home loans usually are repaid with equal monthly payments. The monthly payment depends on the size of the loan, the interest rate, and the number of payments. After the monthly payment is determined using methods given in Chapter 3, simple interest is used to determine how much of each payment goes to interest. The balance of the payment is used to reduce the principal. A long-term loan at a high rate results in very little house being obtained with the early payments.

EXAMPLE 3: A couple gets a $10,000, 25-year, $8\frac{1}{2}\%$ loan. The monthly payment is $80.53. How much of the first two payments go to interest and how much to principal?

SOLUTION: Substituting $P = 10,000$, $r = .085$, and $t = \frac{1}{12}$ in (1),

$$I = 10,000 \times .085 \times \tfrac{1}{12} = \$70.83$$

$$\text{Payment to principal} = 80.53 - 70.83 = \$9.70$$

The picture now gets brighter. The balance owed on the loan is reduced to $10,000.00 - 9.70 = $9990.30.

Back to (1) to find the second month's interest,

$$I = 9990.30 \times .085 \times \tfrac{1}{12} = \$70.76$$

$$\text{Payment to principal} = 80.53 - 70.76 = \$9.77$$

With the second payment the couple gets more house, 7 cents more, as a matter of fact.

The first two payments totaling $161.06 buy $19.47 worth of house while the remaining $141.59 is interest. The happy "home owners" are now renting money instead of an apartment.

### EXERCISE 1e

(When calendar dates are given and all payments are made on the same day of the month, base interest computations on approximate time and ordinary interest. For example, take the time between June 1 and September 1 as 3 months or $\frac{1}{4}$ year, etc. In all other calendar date problems use Bankers' Rule.)
1. A man borrows $5000 at 5%. He pays $2000 in 2 months and $2000 in 4 months. How much would he have to pay in 6 months to cancel the debt by Merchants' Rule? By U.S. Rule?                    ($1075.00, $1075.91)
2. A debt of $7000 is due in 6 months with interest at 4%. Partial payments of $1500 and $2000 are made in 2 and 4 months respectively. What is the balance due on the final settlement date by Merchants' Rule? By U.S. Rule?

3. The Main Hardware Co. was in arrears in their account with the Reliance Supply Corp. to the extent of $1200 on June 1 and were required to pay 8% interest from that date. On July 1 they paid $400 and on August 1 they paid $300. What was the balance due on September 1 by Merchants' Rule? By U.S. Rule? ($516.67, $516.81)

4. An obligation of $650 is due on April 15, after which the borrower must pay interest at $4\frac{1}{2}\%$. If he pays $200 on June 15 and $100 on August 15, how much will he have to pay on October 15 to discharge the obligation if the final settlement is based on Merchants' Rule? On U.S. Rule?

5. A man borrows $3000 at 4% on August 15, 1969. He pays $600 on September 15, 1969; $800 on October 15, 1969; and $600 on December 15, 1969. If he makes a final settlement on February 15, 1970, how much will he have to pay by Merchants' Rule? By U.S. Rule? ($1035.33; $1035.68)

6. A couple purchased a lot on June 1, for $1200 and paid $500 down. They agree to pay interest on the balance at 5%. If they pay $300 on August 15 and $200 on September 30, how much must they pay on November 1 to own the lot by Merchants' Rule? By U.S. Rule?

7. What is the balance due by Merchants' Rule for Example 2 on page 43?
($2060.20)

8. On June 1, 1970, a man borrowed $1000 at 3% for 1 year. If not paid on the due date, the maturity value of the debt was to bear interest at 8% from the due date. The borrower paid $300 on July 15, 1971, $15 on November 20, 1971, and $200 on January 10, 1972. What payment would be required on April 30, 1972, to settle the debt by Merchants' Rule? By U.S. Rule?

9. A couple buys an $18,000 house and pays $3000 down. If they get a $15,000, 20-year, $8\frac{1}{2}\%$ loan, the monthly payment will be $130.18. How much of the first two payments will go to interest and how much to principal?

|  | Payment to Interest | Principal |
|---|---|---|
| First payment | $106.25 | $23.93 |
| Second payment | 106.08 | 24.10 |

10. After shopping for credit, the couple finds a lender who will make the loan at 8% with monthly payments of $125.47. Find the payment to interest and principal for the first two payments.

# 2

## Bank
## Discount

### 2.1 Bank Discount

The charge for many loans is based on the final amount rather than the present value. This charge is called **bank discount** or **discount**. The money which the borrower receives is called **bank proceeds** or **proceeds**. The per cent used in computing the discount is called the **bank discount rate** or **discount rate**.

As an illustration of a bank discount transaction, consider the case of a man who wants to borrow $100 for a year from a lender who uses a discount rate of 6%. The lender will take 6% of $100 from the $100 and give the borrower $94. Thus the computation of bank discount is exactly the same as the computation of simple interest except that it is based on the amount rather than the present value. This leads to the bank discount formula:

$$D = Sdt \tag{4}$$

$D$ = the bank discount in dollars
$S$ = the amount or maturity value
$d$ = the discount rate per unit of time expressed as a decimal
$t$ = the time in units that correspond to the rate

Since the proceeds or present value of the loan is the difference between the amount and the discount, we can say

$$P = S - D$$
$$= S - Sdt$$

Factoring, we have

$$P = S(1 - dt) \tag{5}$$

Solving this expression for $S$ results in a formula which is useful when a borrower wants a certain amount of cash and the problem is to determine the maturity of the loan to be discounted.

$$S = \frac{P}{1 - dt} \tag{6}$$

EXAMPLE 1: A man borrows $600 for 6 months from a lender who uses a discount rate of 8%. What is the discount and how much money does the borrower get?

SOLUTION: Substituting $S = 600$, $d = .08$, and $t = \frac{1}{2}$ in (4), we have

$$D = 600 \times .08 \times \tfrac{1}{2} = \$24.00$$

Since the proceeds are the difference between the maturity value and the discount, the borrower will get $600.00 - 24.00 = \$576.00$.

EXAMPLE 2: A man wants to get $2000 cash with the loan to be repaid in 6 months. If he borrows the money from a bank that charges a 6% discount rate, what size loan should he ask for?

SOLUTION: Substituting $P = 2000$, $d = .06$, and $t = \frac{1}{2}$ in (6),

$$S = \frac{2000}{1 - .06 \times \tfrac{1}{2}} = \frac{2000}{.97} = \$2061.86$$

CHECK: $D = 2061.86 \times .06 \times \tfrac{1}{2} = \$61.86$
Proceeds $= 2061.86 - 61.86 = \$2000.00$

Bank discount is sometimes called interest in advance because it is based on the future amount rather than on the present value. Because it requires only multiplication, bank discount is easier to compute than discount at a simple interest rate which requires division. A given bank discount rate results in a larger money return to a lender than the same simple interest rate. For these reasons, bank discount is commonly used to discount sums of money for periods of time of a year or less.

EXAMPLE 3: Get the present value of $100 due in 1 year at a simple interest rate of 6%. At a bank discount rate of 6%.

SOLUTION: For a simple interest rate of 6% we substitute $S = 100$, $r = .06$, and $t = 1$ in (3):

$$P = \frac{100}{1 + .06 \times 1} = \frac{100}{1.06} = \$94.34$$

For a bank-discount rate of 6% we substitute $S = 100$, $d = .06$, and $t = 1$ in (4):

$$D = 100 \times .06 \times 1 = \$6.00$$

$$\text{Present value or proceeds} = 100 - 6.00 = \$94.00$$

Note that the present value at 6% bank discount is 34 cents less for the same maturity value than if it were based on a 6% interest rate.

## 2.2   Interest Rate Equivalent to a Bank Discount Rate

As the above example shows, the present value at a given discount rate is less than the present value based on the same interest rate. For comparison purposes, it is desirable to be able to determine the interest rate which is equivalent to a given discount rate. **Coupon equivalent** is a common expression for the simple interest rate equivalent to a bank discount rate. The reason is that some securities bear coupons which are clipped and cashed to get the periodic interest payments. The dollar value of each coupon is based on simple interest.

A discount rate and an interest rate are equivalent if the two rates result in the same present value for an amount due in the future. To get the relationship between $r$ and $d$, all we have to do is get the present value of an amount $S$ due in the future by (3) and set it equal to the present value of the same amount $S$ by (5).

$$\frac{S}{1 + rt} = S(1 - dt)$$

Dividing both sides by $S$,

$$\frac{1}{1 + rt} = 1 - dt$$

Inverting both sides,

$$1 + rt = \frac{1}{1 - dt}$$

Subtracting 1 from both sides and simplifying,

$$rt = \frac{1}{1 - dt} - 1 = \frac{1 - 1 + dt}{1 - dt} = \frac{dt}{1 - dt}$$

Dividing both sides by $t$,

$$r = \frac{d}{1 - dt} \qquad (7)$$

In a similar way we find that the discount rate corresponding to a given interest rate is

$$d = \frac{r}{1 + rt} \qquad (8)$$

EXAMPLE 1: A bank discounts a \$200 note due in a year using a bank discount rate of 6%. What interest rate are they getting?

SOLUTION: Substituting $d = .06$ and $t = 1$ in (7),

$$r = \frac{.06}{1 - .06 \times 1} = \frac{.06}{.94} = .0638 \text{ or } 6.38\%$$

EXAMPLE 2: A lender charges a discount rate of $7\frac{1}{2}\%$ for discounting a note for \$600 due in 2 months. What is the equivalent interest rate?

SOLUTION: Substituting $d = .075$ and $t = \frac{1}{6}$ in (7),

$$r = \frac{.075}{1 - .075 \times \frac{1}{6}} = \frac{.075}{.9875} = .0759 = 7.59\%$$

EXAMPLE 3: To earn an interest rate of 6% on a 6 months' loan, a lender should charge what discount rate?

SOLUTION: Substituting $r = .06$ and $t = \frac{1}{2}$ in (8),

$$d = \frac{.06}{1 + .06 \times \frac{1}{2}} = \frac{.06}{1.03} = .0583 = 5.83\%$$

To avoid division we could use the reciprocal of 1.03.

$$d = .06 \times .9709 = .05825 = 5.83\%$$

**EXERCISE 2a**

1. Get the bank discount and the proceeds if $1500 is discounted for 3 months at a discount rate of 6%.                                    ($22.50, $1477.50)

2. Get the bank discount and the proceeds if $4400 is discounted at a discount rate of 8% for 2 months.

3. Get the discount on $3200 for 60 days at $4\frac{1}{2}\%$ discount. What are the proceeds?                                                       ($24.00, $3176.00)

4. Get the discount on $568.30 for 120 days at $6\frac{1}{2}\%$ discount. What are the proceeds?

5. Find the bank discount and the present value of $5000 due in 5 months using a discount rate of 5%.                                      ($104.17, $4895.83)

6. An obligation of $6040 is due in 10 months. What is the present value of this obligation at a bank discount rate of $4\frac{1}{4}\%$?

7. A bank charges 6% for discounting loans. If a man agrees to repay $1200 in 3 months, how much does he receive now?                     ($1182.00)

8. An obligation of $650 is due on August 10. What is its value on April 6 if it is discounted at a discount rate of 6%?

9. Find the bank discount and the proceeds if $450 is discounted for 30 days at 6%.                                                        ($2.25, $447.75)

10. Find the bank discount and the proceeds if $250,000 is discounted for 60 days at 4%.

11. A man wants $5000 for 3 months. What size loan should he get if his bank charges a discount rate of 5%?                              ($5063.29)

12. A man wants $800 for 6 months. What size loan should he ask for if his bank charges a discount rate of $4\frac{1}{2}\%$?

13. George Wilson needs $800 on February 10. He plans to repay the money on June 30. What size loan should he request if his bank's discount rate is 6%?                                                             ($819.11)

14. A borrower needs $4000 on June 1. He expects to repay the loan on July 16. What size loan should he request from a lender whose discount rate is 6%?

15. A bank discounts a sum which is due in 1 year. If the discount rate is 8%, what is the equivalent interest rate?                        (8.70%)

16. If a sum is due in 90 days, what is the interest rate equivalent to a discount rate of 6%?

17. If a sum is due in 6 months, what is the interest rate equivalent to a discount rate of 5%?                                            (5.13%)

18. If a sum is due in 1 month, what is the interest rate equivalent to a discount rate of 5%?

19. A lender wants to get an 8% interest rate on a loan which he is making for 6 months. What discount rate should he use?                  (7.69%)

**20.** To get 7% interest on 120-day loans, what discount rate should be charged?

## 2.3 Promissory Notes

Bank discount is used to determine the value of a promissory note at a stated point in time. The proceeds of a note are found as follows.

1. Get the maturity value of the note. This is the face value if it is noninterest-bearing. If the note is interest-bearing, the maturity value is the face value plus interest at the stated rate for the term of the note, the time from the date of the note to the maturity date.

2. Discount the maturity value using the discount rate from the date the note is discounted to the maturity date.

3. Subtract the discount from the maturity value.

EXAMPLE 1: On July 28, 1974, John A. Blalock discounts the note below at a bank which charges a discount rate of 8%. Find the proceeds.

### A Noninterest-bearing Note

SOLUTION: Table 1 in the back of the book is helpful in getting the discount period.

| DATE | DAY OF YEAR |
|---|---|
| Maturity date, December 15, 1974 | 349 |
| Discount date, July 28, 1974 | 209 |
| Discount period | 140 days |

Substituting $S = 3000$, $d = .08$, and $t = 140/360$ in (4),

$$D = 3000 \times .08 \times 140/360 = \$93.33$$
$$\text{Proceeds} = 3000.00 - 93.33 = \$2906.67$$

EXAMPLE 2: On July 28, 1974, John A. Blalock discounts the note below at a bank which charges a discount rate of 8%. Find the proceeds.

## An Interest-bearing Note

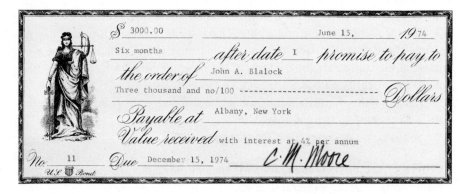

SOLUTION: First get the maturity value, substituting $P = 3000$, $r = .07$, and $t = \frac{1}{2}$ in (1),

$$I = 3000 \times .07 \times \tfrac{1}{2} = \$105.00$$
$$S = 3000.00 + 105.00 = \$3105.00$$

The elapsed time from July 28 to December 15 is 140 days. Substituting $S = 3105.00$, $d = .08$, and $t = 140/360$ in (4),

$$D = 3105.00 \times .08 \times 140/360 = \$96.60$$
$$\text{Proceeds} = 3105.00 - 96.60 = \$3008.40$$

A time diagram can be used to illustrate the step-by-step solution of a note problem. The sketch below shows how a time diagram, if drawn approximately to scale, is a help in checking times in a problem.

After working enough note problems to become familiar with the three steps—maturity value, discount, proceeds—a person may prefer to arrange the work in tabular form as shown below for the above examples.

|  | NONINTEREST-BEARING NOTE | 7% INTEREST-BEARING NOTE |
|---|---|---|
| Face value | $3000.00 | $3000.00 |
| Interest for 6 months |  | 105.00 |
| Maturity value | $3000.00 | $3105.00 |
| 8% discount for 140 days | 93.33 | 96.60 |
| Proceeds | $2906.67 | $3008.40 |

### EXERCISE 2b

(If the time in a note is given in months, the due date is the same date of the month as the date of the note. A three months' note dated March 1 would be due on June 1. If the time is given in days use exact time when getting the maturity date. When getting the discount, use exact time from the discount date to the due date and a 360-day year.)

1. On August 5, 1974, A. E. Spraul discounts the note below at a bank which charges a discount rate of 6%. What are the proceeds? ($753.10)

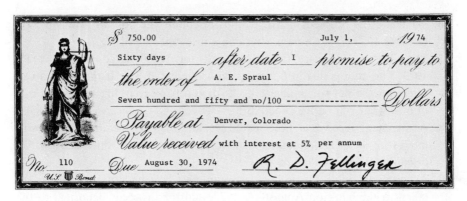

2. What are the proceeds if Mr. Spraul discounts the note in Problem 1 on July 1, 1974, at a bank charging a discount rate of 6%?
3. On February 1, 1973, John P. Foley discounts the note below at a bank which charges a discount rate of 6%. How much does he get? ($7962.67)

4. What are the proceeds if Mr. Foley discounts the note in Problem 3 on February 15, 1973, at a bank charging a discount rate of $5\frac{1}{2}\%$?

5. On December 20, 1974, F. A. Collins discounts the note below at a bank which charges a discount rate of 5%. How much does he receive? ($3033.28)

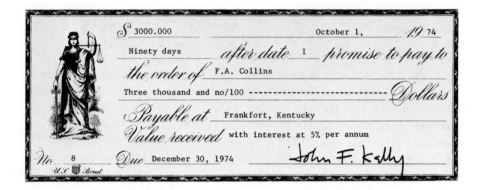

6. What are the proceeds if Mr. Collins discounts the note in Problem 5 on October 15, 1974, at a bank charging a discount rate of 5%?

7. The Gibson Hardware Co. has a note for $1200 dated November 15, 1973. The note is due in 6 months with interest at 5%. If the Gibson Co. discounts the note on January 30, 1974, at a bank charging a discount rate of 6%, what will be the proceeds?                ($1208.47)

8. A merchant receives a note for $1245.40 which is due in 60 days with interest at $4\frac{1}{2}\%$. He discounts it immediately at a bank which charges 5% discount. What are the proceeds?

9. A company holds the following noninterest-bearing notes. They are all taken to the bank on August 14, 1972, and the proceeds deposited to the company's account. Get the total proceeds if the discount rate is 6%.
                                                      ($5777.33)

| DATE OF NOTE | TERM | FACE VALUE |
| --- | --- | --- |
| July 15, 1972 | 90 days | $1000 |
| Aug. 14, 1972 | 45 days | 800 |
| June 25, 1972 | 60 days | 4000 |

10. A company holds the following noninterest-bearing notes. They were taken to the bank on November 5, 1973, and the proceeds deposited to the company's account. Get the total proceeds if the discount rate is 6%.

| DATE OF NOTE | TERM | FACE VALUE |
| --- | --- | --- |
| Sept. 6, 1973 | 90 days | $2000 |
| Oct. 16, 1973 | 60 days | 2500 |
| Oct. 12, 1973 | 30 days | 4800 |

11. A company holds the following interest-bearing notes. They were discounted at 6% on June 1, 1974. Find the total proceeds. ($3013.18)

| DATE OF NOTE | TERM | FACE VALUE | RATE |
|---|---|---|---|
| April 2, 1974 | 90 days | $2000 | 5% |
| June 1, 1974 | 30 days | 1000 | 4% |

12. A company holds the following interest-bearing notes. They were discounted at 6% on July 15, 1973. Find the total proceeds.

| DATE OF NOTE | TERM | FACE VALUE | RATE |
|---|---|---|---|
| May 16, 1973 | 120 days | $4200 | 5% |
| June 10, 1973 | 45 days | 6000 | 4% |

13. A man buys merchandise costing $340. He wants to give a 30-day non-interest-bearing note which, if his creditor discounts it immediately at 4%, will result in proceeds of $340. For what amount should he make the note? ($341.14)

14. The owner of a store needs $500 cash for a business transaction. He arranges to get the money from a bank which charges a discount rate of 6%. If the note is for 90 days, it should have what face value if the proceeds are to be $500?

15. On April 10, a man obtains a loan from his bank to be repaid on June 29. If the bank's discount rate is 5%, what must be the face value of a non-interest-bearing note which will have proceeds of $860? ($869.66)

16. On July 10 a man needs $2350 which he plans to repay on September 18. He gets the loan from a bank which has a bank discount rate of 6%. What will be the face value of the noninterest-bearing note which he signs?

17. On June 1, Fanger and Rampke buy merchandise amounting to $3000. If they pay cash they will get a 2% cash discount. To take advantage of this cash discount, they sign a 60-day noninterest-bearing note at their bank which charges a discount rate of 6%. What should be the face value of this note to give them the exact amount they need to pay cash for the merchandise? ($2969.70)

18. The Economy Appliance store buys merchandise totaling $4560. A 3% discount will be allowed for cash payment. They get the cash by signing a 30-day noninterest-bearing note at a bank which charges a discount rate of 7%. Get the face value of the note.

## 2.4 Promises and Orders

There are two types of negotiable financial paper—promises to pay and orders to pay.

Time deposits, notes, and certificates of deposit are examples of promises to pay. Drafts and bills of exchange (sometimes called acceptances) are examples of orders to pay.

A **draft** is a written order by a first party (drawer) directing a second party (drawee) to make a certain payment to a third party (payee). There are three parties to a draft, but only two persons may be involved. Thus the drawer may make himself the payee.

A common form of draft is the ordinary bank check. When you open a checking account, there is an agreement between you and the bank that the bank will honor your checks (orders for payment) up to the amount you have on deposit. The importance of checks as a means of payment is shown by the fact that 90 percent of financial transactions by volume are handled by check. Since checks are the first contact most students have with negotiable financial paper, suggestions from the American Bankers' Association on how to write and endorse checks are given on the next page. Following them can save you trouble, time, and money.

## 2.5   Money and Capital Markets

Needs of government and business for large sums of money for short periods of time are met by the **money market** which is really a group of markets for a wide variety of short-term credit instruments. Maturities may be as long as one year but often are of 90 days or less and can be arranged for only a few days or even one day.

**Capital market** instruments, such as bonds and mortgages, have a term to maturity of over a year. When long periods of time are involved, the market value of a capital market instrument may vary greatly over the life of the instrument due to changes in interest rates and other causes. However, lender and borrower can count on predictable interest income and costs far into the future. Capital market instruments will be described after compound interest is covered in Chapter 3. A capital market instrument may be considered a money market instrument when it is within a year of its maturity date.

The short terms of money market instruments reduce the risk of loss due to changes in interest rates. There is safety of principal when money market instruments are issued by borrowers in sound financial condition. Money market rates are often below rates on bank loans, so it is advantageous to be able to borrow in the money market. By bringing together lenders with cash surpluses and borrowers with cash deficits, the money market makes possible a more efficient use of money. Lenders with temporarily surplus cash can invest in producing assets until the money is needed for predictable obligations such as tax payments, dividends, and debt repayment. Borrowers who need cash for inventory financing and other short-term requirements can sell money market paper.

## tips on how to write a check

**1** Start with the stub. Fill in check number and amount of check.

Date. Then person to whom the check is written (Payee). The purpose for which the check is written.

Be sure the balance is carried over from the previous stub.

Add latest deposits. Write in amount of this check. Subtract from balance. Carry new balance on to next stub.

**2** Fill in the number of the check, the date, and the person to whom the money is to be paid.

**3** The **Amount of the Check in Numbers:** Write it as close to the dollar sign as possible to prevent anyone from adding other numbers.

**4** Start at the extreme left — again to prevent any additions. Fill in wavy line after the words, all the way over to "dollars." NOTE: Change is written as a fraction. Write carefully—it's your money you're ordering paid out!

**5** These odd-looking numbers are the MICR Numbers (Magnetic Ink Character Recognition). They are the account and bank numbers used for high-speed automatic processing.

**6** This number simplifies the process of exchanging out-of-town checks by indicating the proper route and clearing house through which the check should be sent for sorting and exchanging.

Always use ink — no pencil. This is to prevent anyone from altering the check. Never cross out or erase or change a check after it's written.

If an error is made, tear up the check and start another. Mark "void" on the stub.

Commercial Banks offer two kinds of checking accounts: REGULAR and SPECIAL. In addition to personal checks, banks offer CERTIFIED Checks (Payment guaranteed by the Bank) and CASHIER'S or OFFICIAL CHECKS. (Drawn by a bank on itself.)

## how to endorse a check:

To cash or deposit a check, you must sign your name exactly as it appears on the face of the check. The following are types of endorsements—

**Blank:** Signature alone. When so endorsed, anyone may be able to cash it. Wait until you reach the bank before signing a blank endorsement.

**Restrictive:** The signature appears beneath the words "For deposit only."

**Transfer to a Second Party** (or account): Signature appears beneath "Pay to the order of. . . ."

**Misspelling:** If your name is misspelled, first sign as it actually appears. Then, sign correctly beneath it.

## what happens to a check when it's cashed?

**A** Example: You send your check to a downtown department store.

**B** The department store deposits the check in its bank.

**C** The bank sends your check, along with the others it has received, to a clearing house, where checks are exchanged by banks each day.

**D** From the clearing house, your check is returned to your bank, which deducts the amount of the check from your account.

**E** At the end of the month, your bank returns your check to you, along with the other checks you have written and your bank statement.

In the case of an out-of-town transaction, the check travels on a longer journey, with more stops along the way, but the basic process of clearing the check by having the different banks exchange each other's checks is exactly the same.

While rates on money market instruments tend to fluctuate together, there are times when the return on a particular instrument may get out of line. When alert money managers note abnormal differences between rates, they shift from one instrument to another to improve their position. In time this restores normal rate relations between the various short-term instruments.

A well-managed, short-term portfolio may include several types of securities selected for the amount of risk, rate of return, and degree of liquidity consistent with the objectives of the portfolio manager. Many money market instruments are traded on a discount basis. These instruments do not have a stated rate of return. The investor realizes his return by appreciation of the instrument to its face value at maturity. Some money market instruments are interest-bearing. These instruments have a maturity value equal to the face value plus interest for the term of the loan. The following table gives the general characteristics of common money market instruments.

| MONEY MARKET INSTRUMENT | BASIS | COMMON DENOMINATIONS | COMMON MATURITIES |
|---|---|---|---|
| Treasury bills | Discount | $10,000, $15,000, $100,000, $500,000, $1 million | 91, 182, 273, 365 days |
| Commercial paper | Discount or interest | Multiples of $5000, amounts of $5 million or more | 3 to 270 days |
| Negotiable certificates of deposit | Interest | $100,000, $500,000, $1 million | 1 to 4 or more months |
| Bankers' acceptances | Discount | $25,000 to $1 million | 30 to 180 days |
| Federal funds | Interest | Units of $200,000 and $1 million | 1 day |
| Federal agency issues | Usually interest | Various | Various |

Money market rates vary both over time and among the different instruments. Because of the large sums, a spread of even a few basis points can result in large dollar differences in returns on alternative investments.

## 2.6   Treasury Bills

Treasury bills are the shortest term security issued by the United States Government. Bills are the most liquid of all securities. As the illustration below shows, a bill is a noninterest, bearer instrument. The buyer's return is the difference between the price he pays and the face value he gets from the government when the bill matures. The ownership of vast sums can be transferred with very simple instruments. On the due date, which must be entered on the bill, the bearer of a bill like the following one would receive one million dollars.

The tax anticipation bill is a special form of Treasury bill designed to help the Treasury smooth out its flow of tax receipts while providing companies an attractive investment for funds accumulated for tax payments. Although these bills mature a week after a tax date, they are accepted at par in payment of taxes on the tax date. Like other Treasury bills, tax anticipation bills are sold at a discount in competitive auctions.

Institutions often have idle cash which has been accumulated for payment of obligations of known amounts and due dates, or as a reserve against contingencies. These excess cash reserves can be converted into riskless, earning assets by buying T-bills. The highly organized secondary market for bills insures their easy convertibility into cash should money be needed before the maturity of the bills. The short maturities of T-bills minimize the risk of price fluctuations resulting from market conditions. T-bills form the cornerstone of many short-term portfolios.

Bills are sold at weekly public auctions with competitive bids expressed on the basis of 100 with not more than three decimals. The yield on T-bills is reported on a bank discount basis. To get the bank discount corresponding to a given bid, we substitute $100 = S$, bid price $= P$, and time in days $= t$ in (5) and solve for $d$.

$$P = 100 \left( 1 - \frac{dt}{360} \right)$$

$$\frac{P}{100} = 1 - \frac{dt}{360}$$

$$\frac{dt}{360} = 1 - \frac{P}{100} = \frac{100 - P}{100}$$

$$d = \frac{360}{t} \left( \frac{100 - P}{100} \right)$$

EXAMPLE 1: A bank bids 98.871 for a 91-day $1 million bill. This means the bank is willing to pay $988,710.00 for the bill which will be worth $1,000,000 91 days after its issuance. If the bid is accepted, what yield will the bank get on a bank discount basis?

SOLUTION:

$$d = \frac{360}{91} \left( \frac{100.000 - 98.871}{100} \right) = .04466 = 4.466\%$$

EXAMPLE 2: Find the yield on the bill in Example 1 on a coupon equivalent or simple interest basis.

SOLUTION: The discount rate and time are substituted in (7).

$$r = \frac{.04466}{1 - .04466 \times \frac{91}{360}} = .04517 = 4.517\%$$

The owner of a bill can hold it to maturity and have the Treasury redeem it for face value. If the owner needs cash, he can sell the bill. Yields of outstanding bills normally begin to drop as issues approach maturity. This occurs because there are usually some investors who are willing to accept a lower yield for the privilege of investing in a bill that is close to maturity. A company with several hundred thousand dollars that they will not need for a few days can earn substantial sums by investing in bills. Now the purchase will be made from another owner of bills rather than from the Treasury. Such sales may offer an opportunity for the seller of bills to improve his return for the period he held the bill.

EXAMPLE 3: The investor in Example 1 held the bill for 60 days and sold it for $996,950. Find the interest rate he earned for the period he held the bill, and the discount and interest rate the buyer will earn.

SOLUTION: The cost of the bill was $988,710. The interest earned over the 60 days is 996,950 − 988,710 = $8240. Substituting in (1),

$$8240 = 988,710 \times r \times \tfrac{60}{360}$$

$$r = \frac{360 \times 8240}{60 \times 988,710} = .050 = 5.0\%$$

The buyer of the bill in effect is bidding 99.695 for a bill that has 31 days to maturity.

$$d = \frac{360}{31}\left(\frac{100.000 - 99.695}{100}\right) = .0354 = 3.54\%$$

$$r = \frac{.0354}{1 - .0354 \times \tfrac{31}{360}} = .0355 = 3.55\%$$

This is a transaction where everyone comes out ahead. The buyer of the bill is able to put his money to work for 31 days. When the Treasury redeems the bill, the buyer will get $3050 more than he paid. The seller of the bill has increased his yield rate for the period he held the bill. To improve his yield for the period as a whole, he must now reinvest the funds at a suitable rate. If current rates do not favor a sale and new investment, the owner of a bill can simply hold it to maturity.

Firms are finding that holding cash to the minimum needed to meet current obligations increases the productivity of company funds. Use of sophisticated management techniques allows rapid assembly of information on cash positions and better projections of cash inflows and outflows. Some firms are finding portfolio income attractive because it can be obtained at relatively low expense.

## 2.7   Commercial Paper

Negotiable, short-term promissory notes issued by commercial organizations are called commercial paper. This paper is often issued in face amounts of $100,000, $250,000, $500,000, $1,000,000 and combinations thereof. Lenders may also have commercial paper tailored to their specifications. Maturities vary from a few days to nine months. Commercial paper with a term of 270 days or less is not registered with the Securities and Exchange Commission. There are no interest rate ceilings on commercial paper.

These corporate IOU's enable a corporation with temporarily excess funds to help another company that needs a short-term loan. By issuing commercial paper, a corporate treasurer can bypass banks and escape restrictions on bank credit. The seller (borrower) can get short-term cash at rates lower than he would pay for a bank loan. The buyer (lender) gets a higher return than he would receive on other short-term money market instruments.

Commercial paper is usually unsecured and may be issued in bearer form. The discount or interest is calculated on the face value of the paper and a 360-day year.

The commercial paper shown below, copyright 1972 General Motors Acceptance Corporation, is an example of a short-term discount note. This illustration shows how large sums are transferred with very simple instruments.

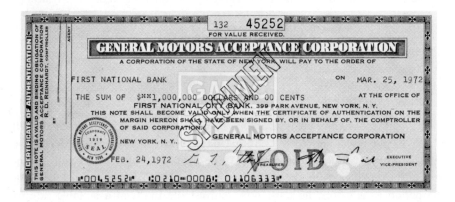

The purchaser of this note knows that he will get $1,000,000 in 30 days. The purchase price will depend on the discount rate. If the discount rate is $4\frac{1}{8}\%$ we get the discount by substituting in (4).

$$\text{Discount} = 1,000,000 \times .04125 \times \tfrac{30}{360} = \$3437.50$$
$$\text{Proceeds} = 1,000,000.00 - 3437.50 = \$996,562.50$$

Commercial paper has had a good reputation for safety. However, a cash shortage or other financial problem can be serious when the time comes for a corporation to sell new paper or borrow elsewhere to make payment on the maturity date of an issue of commercial paper. After large operating losses, the Penn Central in 1970 was unable to pay off outstanding commercial paper and had to declare bankruptcy. While disasters have been rare, buyers should check carefully the credit worthiness of the issuing corporation. Dealer paper is sold through commercial paper dealers. Directly issued paper is sold directly to investors by the borrowing firm. If a corporation can place its own paper, it may make substantial savings on a large loan.

There is a less active secondary market for commercial paper than for many other money market instruments. For this reason, investors in commercial paper may look for a maturity that coincides with their investment needs. Some dealers and finance companies will repurchase outstanding paper if the buyer requests it. There are large dealers who maintain a market in the paper they underwrite and thereby provide liquidity for investors who need money to meet contingencies.

EXAMPLE 1: A company issues a $5 million piece of commercial paper to mature on June 1, 1974. This is purchased by the firm of Merrill Lynch, Pierce, Fenner, and Smith on March 3. What is the purchase price if the discount rate is 7%?

SOLUTION: We find the time to maturity using Table 1.

| DATE | DAY OF THE YEAR |
|---|---|
| June 1 | 152 |
| March 3 | 62 |
| | 90 days |

Substituting in (4),

$$D = 5,000,000 \times .07 \times \tfrac{90}{360} = \$87,500$$
$$\text{Purchase price} = 5,000,000 - 87,500 = \$4,912,500$$

EXAMPLE 2: Merrill Lynch sells the above paper in the secondary market to a buyer on April 5. Find the price if based on a discount rate of 6.95%.

SOLUTION: We get the time to maturity.

| DATE | DAY OF THE YEAR |
|---|---|
| June 1 | 152 |
| April 5 | 95 |
| | 57 days |

$$D = 5,000,000 \times .0695 \times \tfrac{57}{360} = \$55,020.83$$
$$\text{Sale Price} = 5,000,000.00 - 55,020.83 = \$4,944,979.17$$

EXAMPLE 3: What interest rate did Merrill Lynch earn while holding the paper?

SOLUTION: Interest $= 4,944,979.17 - 4,912,500.00 = \$32,479.17$. Time from March 3 to April 5 is 33 days. Substituting in (1),

$$32,479.17 = 4,912,500 \times r \times \tfrac{33}{360}$$

$$r = \frac{360 \times 32,479.17}{4,912,500 \times 33} = .0721 = 7.21\%$$

## 2.8    Certificates of Deposit

A negotiable certificate of deposit is a marketable receipt issued by a bank in exchange for the deposit of money. Certificates may be in registered or bearer form, with the latter more convenient for secondary market trading. The bank agrees to repay the amount deposited plus interest on the maturity date of the certificate. Negotiable CD's are commonly available in amounts of $100,000, $500,000, and $1 million. Certificates are sometimes issued for amounts as low as $25,000 and as high as $10 million or more. Negotiable certificates are issued and traded on a bond yield equivalent or simple interest basis using a 360-day year.

The development of an active secondary market has contributed to the marketability of certificates. In the secondary market, the common trading unit is $1 million. Smaller denomination CD's issued by smaller banks are less actively traded.

EXAMPLE 1: On March 10, 1973, a bank sells a $1 million CD which is to bear interest at 6.25% and mature on December 5, 1973. If the buyer holds the CD to maturity, what will the bank pay him?

SOLUTION: We get the time to maturity.

| DATE | DAY OF THE YEAR |
|------|-----------------|
| December 5 | 339 |
| March 10 | 69 |
|  | 270 days |

Substituting in (1),

$$I = 1,000,000 \times .0625 \times \tfrac{270}{360} = \$46,875.00$$
$$\text{Amount} = 1,000,000.00 + 46,875.00 = \$1,046,875.00$$

EXAMPLE 2: On November 5, 1973, the owner of the certificate in Example 1 sold it to a buyer who wanted a return of 4.8% on a simple interest or bond yield equivalent basis. Find the sale price.

SOLUTION: The new buyer will collect $1,046,875 when the CD matures in 30 days. To find the purchase price, substitute in (3),

$$P = \frac{1,046,875}{1 + .048 \times \tfrac{30}{360}} = \frac{1,046,875}{1.004} = \$1,042,704.18$$

## 2.9  Bankers' Acceptances

An **acceptance** is a form of draft or order to pay. An after-date draft is payable a stated time after the date of the draft. An after-sight draft is payable a stated time after the drawee (the person who will make payment) signs the draft and writes the date of acceptance. After-sight and after-date drafts are known as time drafts and may be sold or discounted.

A **trade acceptance** is a draft drawn by the seller of goods on the purchaser, and accepted by the purchaser. The buyer of the goods designates the bank at which the acceptance is payable and returns it to the seller who may hold it or discount (i.e., sell) it. An acceptance is two-name paper. It is a primary liability of the purchaser (drawee or acceptor), and a secondary liability of the seller (drawer). It should be self-liquidating from the sale of the goods.

A **bankers' acceptance** is a time draft drawn by the seller of merchandise upon the bank of the buyer and accepted by that bank. Now there is an agreement by a bank to pay a specific bill for a customer when the bill comes due. An acceptance which represents the liability of a well-known bank is a more desirable credit instrument than one drawn on an unknown person or firm. After a draft is accepted by a bank, the payee (the party to whom payment is to be made) may discount it in the money market. Subsequent holders in due course may either hold the acceptance or sell it.

Bankers' acceptances are widely used in international trade. Assume that a retailer in the United States wants to buy clothing from an English firm. The American buyer arranges with his bank to accept the seller's draft with the understanding that the buyer will provide the funds by the due date of the acceptance. The American bank issues a letter of credit in favor of the English exporter. This letter states that the American bank will accept time drafts drawn on the American bank provided they are drawn in accordance with details of shipment, terms, and amount given in the letter of credit. The obligation for payment is now shifted from the American importer to his bank and the English exporter can be confident that payment will be made. When shipment is made, the English firm prepares a draft on the American bank and discounts this draft at its bank. The draft is sent by the English bank to the American bank. When the time draft drawn by the English firm is marked "accepted" and signed by an officer of the American bank, it becomes a bankers' acceptance. It is now an irrevocable obligation of the American bank. The English bank will probably discount the acceptance with the American bank which can either hold the paper to maturity and collect the face value or the English bank's United States agent may sell it to a dealer in the acceptance market. Bankers' acceptances have a fine record for safety and they are widely traded in secondary markets. Their safety and liquidity make them a useful instrument for investment of short-term funds. Maturities range from 30 to 180 days but are often 90 days.

EXAMPLE 1: A Cleveland importer wants to import a shipment of shoes from an Italian manufacturer. He has his bank issue a letter of credit in favor of the Italian firm, giving shipment details including the amount for which the firm may draw a time draft on the bank. When shipment is made, the Italian firm prepares a 90-day draft for $10,000 dated July 10, 1974, drawn on the Cleveland bank. On July 10 the exporter discounts the draft at his Italian bank. Find the proceeds if the bank uses a discount rate of 8%.

SOLUTION: Substituting in (4),

$$D = 10,000 \times .08 \times \tfrac{90}{360} = \$200$$
$$\text{Proceeds} = 10,000.00 - 200.00 = \$9800.00$$

EXAMPLE 2: On July 20 the Italian bank discounts the acceptance of the Cleveland bank. Find the proceeds if the Cleveland bank uses a discount rate of $7\tfrac{7}{8}\%$.

SOLUTION: The maturity date of the acceptance, 90 days after July 10, is October 8. We get the time to maturity.

| DATE | DAY OF THE YEAR |
|---|---|
| October 8 | 281 |
| July 20 | 201 |
| | 80 days |

$$D = 10,000 \times .07875 \times \tfrac{80}{360} = \$175.00$$
$$\text{Proceeds} = 10,000.00 - 175.00 = \$9825.00$$

## 2.10   Federal Funds

Banks that are members of the Federal Reserve System are required to keep percentages of their time and demand deposits as reserves. The reserves may be held as nonearning demand deposits with Federal Reserve banks or as vault cash. These deposit balances at Federal Reserve Banks are called Federal funds. Because deposit balances at the Fed do not produce income, banks prefer to keep their reserves near the legally required minimum. One way to do this is to lend excess reserves to borrowing banks who use the loan proceeds to cover their reserve deficiencies. Both lending and borrowing banks may profit by such loans. The lending bank earns interest while the borrowing bank has a convenient way to bring its reserves to the required level.

Most Federal funds transactions are for one day with the cost determined on a simple interest basis using a 365-day year. Among larger banks Federal funds are usually traded in units of $1 million. As interest rates have risen, smaller banks have become more concerned about the cost of holding idle funds. As these banks have entered the Federal funds market, trading in amounts of $200,000 or less has become more common.

EXAMPLE: To correct its reserve position, a bank gets a $5 million loan from another bank which has surplus reserves. Find the cost of the loan if it is for 1 day at 5.75%.

SOLUTION: Substituting in (1),

$$I = 5,000,000 \times .0575 \times \tfrac{1}{365} = \$787.67$$

## 2.11  Federal Agency Issues

The following federally sponsored credit agencies issue their own securities and borrow directly from the public.

| ISSUING AGENCY | TYPES OF SECURITIES |
| --- | --- |
| Federal National Mortgage Association | Debentures and discount notes |
| Federal home loan banks | Bonds and discount notes |
| Federal land banks | Bonds |
| Federal intermediate credit banks | Debentures |
| Banks for cooperatives | Debentures |

A debenture is a debt which is not protected by a lien or mortgage on property.

Money market and capital instruments of federal agencies are issued to finance obligations of the individual agencies. Their financing is carried out separately from the regular debt operations of the Federal Government. The federal agencies help to channel funds from capital surplus to capital deficit areas in the nation. Agency issues are not part of the public debt, are not a legal obligation of the Federal Government, and are not guaranteed by the Federal Government. However, there is probably little difference in risk between federal agency issues and United States Treasury issues. Federal agency issues usually provide a somewhat higher yield than Treasury obligations. The combination of yield, liquidity, and safety make Federal agency issues attractive investments. Terms of agency securities range from 30 days to nearly 20 years.

## 2.12  Summary of Simple Interest and Bank Discount Formulas

Short term credit costs can be based on either the present value of a loan (simple interest) or on the maturity value (bank discount). Formulas for the two methods are summarized below.

| SIMPLE INTEREST | BANK DISCOUNT |
|---|---|
| Cost of credit is based on present value | Cost of credit is based on maturity value |
| (1) $I = Prt$ | (4) $D = Sdt$ |
| (2) $S = P(1 + rt)$ | (5) $P = S(1 - dt)$ |
| (3) $P = \dfrac{S}{1 + rt}$ | (6) $S = \dfrac{P}{1 - dt}$ |
| (7) $r = \dfrac{d}{1 - dt}$ | (8) $d = \dfrac{r}{1 + rt}$ |
| $I$ is simple interest | $D$ is bank discount |
| $P$ is present value or principal | $S$ is maturity value or amount |
| $r$ is interest rate | $P$ is present value or proceeds |
| $S$ is amount or maturity value | $d$ is bank discount rate |
| $d$ is bank discount rate | $t$ is time |
| $t$ is time | $r$ is simple interest rate |

## 2.13   Term Structure of Interest Rates

The relationship between yield and length of time until a loan becomes due is called the **term structure of interest rates**. A curve which shows yield to maturity as a function of time to maturity is called a **yield curve**. As the price of a fixed income security goes down, the yield goes up. Conversely a rising price means a decreasing yield. Yield curves should be drawn only for issues of comparable credit quality that differ in time to maturity. Factors which affect the shape of a yield curve include:

1. Expectations. What borrowers and lenders think will happen to interest rates in the future has an effect on security prices now.

2. Liquidity preferences. Lenders may accept a lower yield on short-term obligations which they can expect to sell with little risk of capital loss.

3. Transaction costs. Costs involved in buying and selling securities may affect the length of time an investor prefers to hold securities.

4. Institutional preferences. Different types of institutions may have different choices of terms to maturity. A bank, which has large amounts of short-term liabilities in the form of passbook accounts and certificates of deposit, will want short-term earning assets that can be sold readily. An insurance company, which has commitments to pay out funds far into the future, can hedge against changes in interest rates by buying long-term bonds which will provide predictable interest income for 20 years or longer.

Curves showing how interest rates vary as a function of term to maturity have a variety of shapes as shown below.

## Yield Curves

**Downward Sloping**

Per Cent

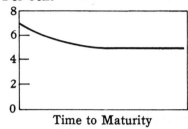

Time to Maturity

Descending yield curves have been observed during tight money periods when rates are high relative to historical experience. Investors expect rates to go down and the market value of fixed income securities to go up.

**Upward Sloping**

Per Cent

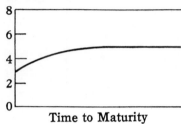

Time to Maturity

Ascending yield curves have been observed when rates are low. Investors expect rates to go up and the market value of securities to go down. When investors favor shorter-term issues to minimize capital losses, the pressure on long-term rates results in higher yields for longer maturities.

**Relatively Flat**

Per Cent

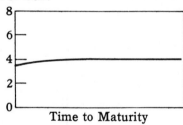

Time to Maturity

Relatively flat curves occur during periods when little change is expected in future rates. Investors accept slightly lower yields for the more liquid short-term securities.

**Humped**

Per Cent

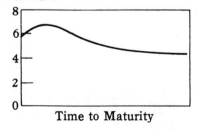

Time to Maturity

Humped curves have appeared when rates are generally high and credit is tight. When investors expect rates to rise and then fall, a humped curve may result.

Since the term structure of interest rates is affected by anticipated price changes, fluctuations in the level of economic activity, and monetary policy, yield curves should be based on yields as of a certain date. The graphs below, prepared by the Federal Reserve Bank of Chicago, show  that large changes in yield curves can occur over a short period of time.

Examples of Yield Curves

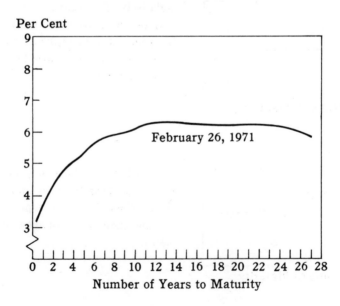

## 2.14   Riding the Yield Curve

Since marketable securities need not be held to maturity, there are times when a profitable investment strategy is to sell some securities and buy others. Riding the yield curve means buying and selling securities to take advantage of yield differentials on securities of varying maturities. While riding the yield curve is not an exact science, it can be a useful technique in the hands of an alert portfolio manager. By selling one marketable issue before maturity and buying another, a portfolio manager may be able to improve the overall yield on invested funds.

Suppose that an investor keeps about a million dollars in Treasury bills. He buys a 6-month bill which will yield 5% on a discount basis. After holding the bill for 4 months, he finds a buyer who is willing to accept a 4% yield on a security that will mature in 2 months. By selling the bill, the first investor will increase his return to more than 5% for the 4 months he has held the bill. Before making a sale, he should check investment opportunities that are now available. If new Treasury bills are still available at a price that will yield 5% or better, the switch could be a profitable one. Repeated purchases at issuance and sales at lower discount rates before maturity is called "riding the yield curve down."

### EXERCISE 2c

1. A bank obtained a $1 million, 182-day Treasury bill at a price of 97.200. Find the yield on a bank discount and simple interest basis.
$$(d = 5.54\%, r = 5.70\%)$$

2. An investor purchased a $500,000, 91-day Treasury bill at a price of 98.100. Find the yield on a bank discount and simple interest basis.

3. The bank in Problem 1 held the bill for 120 days and then sold it in the secondary market for $993,000. Find:
   (a) Interest rate earned by the bank during the period the bill was held.
   (b) Yield new buyer will get on a discount basis if he holds the bill to maturity.
   (c) Yield new buyer will get on an interest basis if he holds the bill to maturity.                          [(a) 6.48%, (b) 4.06%, (c) 4.09%]

4. The investor in Problem 2 held the bill for 81 days and then sold it in the secondary market for $499,400. Find:
   (a) Interest rate earned by the investor during the period he held the bill.
   (b) Yield new buyer will get on a discount basis if he holds the bill to maturity.
   (c) Yield new buyer will get on an interest basis if he holds the bill to maturity.

5. A company issued a $2 million piece of commercial paper to mature on August 1, 1974. The paper is purchased by an investor on June 2, 1974. Find the purchase price if based on a discount rate of 6%.   ($1,980,000)

6. A company issued a $5 million piece of commercial paper on May 31, 1975. The paper is to mature in 45 days. It is purchased on May 31 to yield 5.5% on a bank discount basis. Find the purchase price.

7. The investor in Problem 5 sells the paper on July 12 at a price that will yield the new buyer 5% on a discount basis. Find the purchase price.

($1,994,444.44)

8. On June 30, 1975, the company in Problem 6 sold the paper in the secondary market. Find the sale price if based on a discount rate of 4.5%.

9. On June 5, 1974, a bank sold a $500,000 certificate of deposit which is to mature on August 4, 1974, and bear interest at 6.5%. If the buyer holds the CD to maturity, what will the bank pay him?         ($505,416.67)

10. On December 1, 1974, a bank sold a $100,000 certificate of deposit to mature on March 1, 1975, and bear interest at 5.75%. If the buyer holds the certificate to maturity, what will the bank pay him?

11. On July 20, 1974, the owner of the certificate in Problem 9 sold it in the secondary market to a buyer who wanted a return of 6% on a simple interest or bond yield equivalent basis. Find the sale price.   ($504,156.28)

12. On February 19, 1975, the owner of the certificate in Problem 10 sold it to a buyer who wanted a return of 5% on a simple interest basis. Find the sale price.

13. A Richmond bank arranges for its bank to accept drafts from a German exporter. The exporter ships goods to the Richmond firm and prepares a 60-day draft for $30,000 dated May 1 and drawn on the Richmond bank. On May 1 the exporter discounts the draft at his German bank. Find the proceeds if the discount rate is 7%.         ($29,650.00)

14. The bank of a St. Louis retailer agrees to accept drafts from a Scottish exporter. On September 15 the exporter draws a 90-day draft for $25,000 on the St. Louis bank. Find the proceeds if the exporter discounts the draft at his bank on September 15 and the discount rate is 7.75%.

15. On May 11 the German bank in Problem 13 discounts the acceptance at the Richmond bank. Find the proceeds if the discount rate is $7\frac{1}{8}$%.

($29,703.12)

16. On September 30 the Scottish bank in Problem 14 discounts the acceptance at the St. Louis bank. Find the proceeds if the discount rate is 7.5%.

17. A bank gets a 1-day, $10 million Federal funds loan at 4.80%. Find the interest.         ($1315.07)

18. A bank gets a 1-day, $2 million Federal funds loan at 5.25%. Find the interest.

**19.** If a Federal funds loan is made on Friday, the next clearing date is three days away and interest is charged for three days. A bank borrowed $1 million in Federal funds on Friday. If the rate is 6%, find the interest due on Monday.                                                                ($493.15)

**20.** A Federal funds loan of $5 million was made on Friday. Find the interest for three days at 5.80%.

# 3

# Compound
# Interest

## 3.1  Eighth Wonder of the World

When Baron Rothschild, one of the world's wealthiest bankers, was asked if
he could name the Seven Wonders of the World, he said: "No, but I can tell
you what the Eighth Wonder is. This Eighth Wonder should be utilized by all
of us to accomplish what we want. **It is compound interest**."*

   The following table shows the impressive growth that results when compound
interest is applied to a modest starting sum.

* Loraine L. Blaire, *Your Financial Guide for Living*, Prentice-Hall, Inc., Englewood Cliffs,
N.J., 1963, p. 62.

*Growth of $100 at Compound Interest*

| Time in Years | ANNUAL INTEREST RATE | | | |
|---|---|---|---|---|
| | 4% | 6% | 8% | 10% |
| 10 | $148.02 | $179.08 | $215.89 | $259.37 |
| 20 | 219.11 | 320.71 | 466.10 | 672.75 |
| 30 | 324.34 | 574.35 | 1,006.27 | 1,744.94 |
| 40 | 480.10 | 1,028.57 | 2,172.45 | 4,525.93 |
| 50 | 710.67 | 1,842.02 | 4,690.16 | 11,739.09 |
| 60 | 1,051.96 | 3,298.77 | 10,125.71 | 30,448.16 |
| 70 | 1,557.16 | 5,907.59 | 21,860.64 | 78,974.70 |
| 80 | 2,304.98 | 10,579.60 | 47,195.48 | 204,840.02 |
| 90 | 3,411.93 | 18,946.45 | 101,891.51 | 531,302.26 |
| 100 | 5,050.49 | 33,930.21 | 219,976.13 | 1,378,061.23 |

Applications of compound interest go far beyond keeping track of bank accounts. It is used for business and government planning, gauging the health of the economy, making judgments about the growth of the American economy relative to other national economies and for many other applications. Leonard S. Silk, senior editor of *Business Week*, has stated: "Explaining compound interest—for a bank or a nation—is the central problem of economics."*

The graph below shows the effect of time and rate on the growth of a sum of money at compound interest. With increasing time and higher rates, the curves get progressively steeper. But there are many functions that look about like this on an arithmetic graph. On such a graph it is not possible to tell if a time series is growing according to the compound interest law or some other relationship.

When data following the compound interest law are plotted on a semi-logarithmic or ratio graph, an interesting and important thing happens—the data plot as a straight line. If two time series plot as parallel lines on a ratio graph, they are changing at the same rate. If one curve is steeper than the other, its rate of change is greater.

Rates of change are of great importance in economic analysis and forecasting. When a time series plots as approximately a straight line on a ratio graph, the analyst has valuable information. He can now use the compound interest law as a practical tool for making predictions.

* Leonard S. Silk, *The Research Revolution*, McGraw-Hill Book Co., Inc., New York, 1960, p. 38.

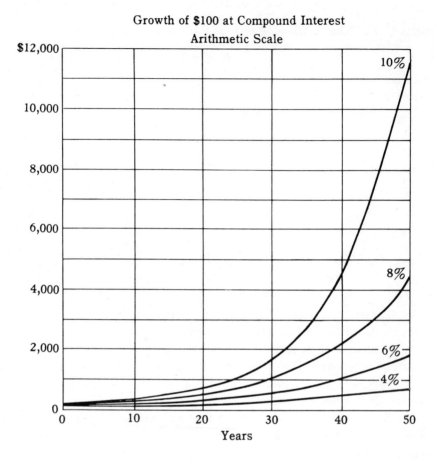

Growth of $100 at Compound Interest
Arithmetic Scale

## 3.2   Benjamin Franklin's 1000 Pounds

An example of the magic of compound interest is a bequest of 1000 pounds which Benjamin Franklin willed to Boston. Dr. Franklin died on April 17, 1790, and the then Town of Boston accepted the donation at a town meeting on June 1, 1790. Franklin's will stipulated that the money was to be loaned at interest to young and needy apprentices. The interest was to augment the principal and at the end of one hundred years, part of the fund was to be expended for public works and the balance was to be compounded for a second hundred years. The administrators of the fund followed Franklin's instructions as closely as possible.

In 1907 the building of the Franklin Institute of Boston was started with $438,742 from the fund. Over 75,000 students have been enrolled in this institute which opened in 1908. The balance of the fund was left to accumulate and amounted to $2,552,267 in 1971. This money is now being used to make loans to medical students. All of this from a bequest which was equivalent to about $4570.

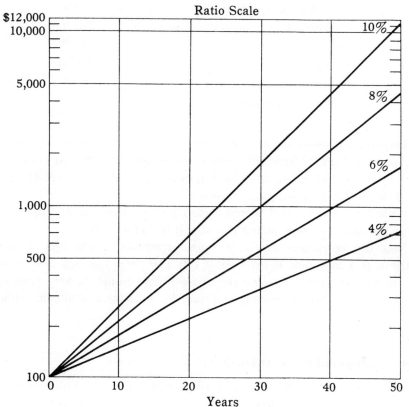

Growth of $100 at Compound Interest

## 3.3 Simple Interest Over and Over

While compound interest is the Eighth Wonder of the World in terms of results, it is basically simple. As the following example shows, compound interest is simple interest applied over and over to a sum which is increased by the simple interest each time it is earned. This ever-increasing principal explains the snowball effect of compound interest.

An investment of $1000 at 4% simple interest earns $40 per year. In three years the simple interest would amount to $120. However, if the interest as it is earned is added to the principal and this new principal draws interest, the investment increases more rapidly than with simple interest. Interest paid on an increasing principal in this way is known as **compound interest**. The following example shows the increase in an investment of $1000 if the interest rate is 4% compounded annually.

| | |
|---|---:|
| Original principal | $1000.00 |
| Interest for first year at 4% | 40.00 |
| Principal at the start of the second year | 1040.00 |
| Interest for second year at 4% | 41.60 |
| Principal at the start of the third year | 1081.60 |
| Interest for third year at 4% | 43.26 |
| Amount at the end of three years | $1124.86 |

Thus, the compound interest earned on the original investment is $124.86 as compared to the $120.00 which would be earned at simple interest in the same length of time. The difference of $4.86 is interest earned on interest. The total, $1124.86, is called the **compound amount**.

From here on compound interest is used in all problems in this book except when the time is a single interest period or a part of a period.

Note that compound interest is simply a repeated application of simple interest. If a long time is involved, say two or three hundred interest payments, the computations using the above system would be very laborious. Fortunately it is easy to develop a formula that gives the final amount without the intermediate computations.

## 3.4   Compound Amount Formula

In the preceding example the interest was computed and added to the principal every year. In many business transactions the interest is computed annually, semiannually, quarterly, monthly, daily, or at some other time interval. The time between successive interest computations is called the **conversion** or **interest period**. This is the basic unit of time in all compound interest problems. The important rate is the **interest rate per conversion period** which is designated by the symbol $i$. The symbol for the total number of conversion periods is $n$.

In most business transactions the practice is to quote an annual interest rate and the frequency of conversion. From this information the rate per period is determined. Thus 6% compounded (or converted) semiannually means that 3% interest will be earned every six months. The quoted annual rate is called the **nominal rate** and is indicated by the symbol $j$. The number of interest conversion periods per year is indicated by the symbol $m$. The equation relating $j$, $i$, and $m$ is $i = j/m$ or $j = im$ ("Jim"). The symbol $j_{(m)}$ means a nominal rate $j$ converted $m$ times a year. When no conversion period is stated in a problem, assume that the interest is compounded annually.

The following table shows a few examples of quoted or nominal rates and the corresponding conversion periods per year and rate per period.

| QUOTED OR NOMINAL RATE | CONVERSION PERIODS PER YEAR | RATE PER PERIOD $i = j/m$ | |
|---|---|---|---|
| $j$ | $m$ | PERCENT | DECIMAL |
| 6% compounded annually | 1 | 6 | .06 |
| 6% compounded semiannually | 2 | 3 | .03 |
| 6% compounded quarterly | 4 | $1\frac{1}{2}$ | .015 |
| 6% compounded monthly | 12 | $\frac{1}{2}$ | .005 |
| 3% compounded quarterly | 4 | $\frac{3}{4}$ | .0075 |
| 5% compounded semiannually | 2 | $2\frac{1}{2}$ | .025 |
| 5% compounded monthly | 12 | $\frac{5}{12}$ | .004167 |

To eliminate the tedious period-by-period computations used in the example at the beginning of this chapter, we invest $P$ dollars for $n$ periods at a rate of $i$ per period and derive a formula for the final amount. A numerical example is used to illustrate the steps. In this example $P = \$1000$, $i = .04$, and $n = 2$. The principal at the end of the first period will be indicated by $P_1$; at the end of the second period by $P_2$; and so on.

| Original | | |
|---|---|---|
| principal | $P$ | $\$1000$ |
| Interest | $Pi$ | $1000 \times .04$ |
| $P_1$ | $P + Pi = P(1 + i)$ | $1000 + 1000 \times .04 = 1000(1.04)$ |
| Interest | $P(1 + i)i$ | $1000(1.04).04$ |
| $P_2$ | $P(1 + i) + P(1 + i)i$ | $1000(1.04) + 1000(1.04).04$ |
| | $= P(1 + i)(1 + i)$ | $= 1000(1.04)(1.04)$ |
| | $= P(1 + i)^2$ | $= 1000(1.04)^2$ |

If there were more periods, each new principal would be $(1 + i)$ times the preceding value. At the end of $n$ periods the final amount, for which the symbol is $S$, would equal the original principal times $(1 + i)^n$. This results in the basic formula for compound interest,

$$S = P(1 + i)^n \qquad (9)$$

$S = $ the amount at compound interest
$P = $ the principal
$i = $ the rate per conversion period
$n = $ the number of conversion periods

The factor $(1 + i)^n$ is called the **accumulation factor** or **Amount of 1**. It is sometimes designated by the symbol $s$. The numerical value of $(1 + i)^n$ can be computed by successive multiplication, by logarithms, or by the binomial theorem. In practical business usage it is usually obtained from previously computed tables. In this book, values of $(1 + i)^n$ for common interest rates will be found in the *Amount of* 1 column of Table 2. The columns of data in Table 2 have descriptive headings which tell what the various columns are in a few simple words. At the bottom of each column of data, symbols are given to help the student select the correct factor for a problem.

The usefulness of Table 2 is easily appreciated when we consider how much time it saves. Carrying a sum of money forward by getting the simple interest for each period and adding to the principal means two arithmetic operations for each period. This means a lot of work, and many chances to make mistakes if many periods are involved. Table 2 makes it possible to carry money forward 20, 30, or more periods just as easily as making one simple interest computation. The example on the next page shows how to get the correct factor from Table 2.

## 3.5   Finding *n*

When a sum of money earns interest from one date to another, the elapsed time must be obtained and converted into interest conversion periods or the value of *n*. One way to get elapsed time is to subtract the earlier calendar date from the later one.

EXAMPLE 1: How many semiannual conversion periods are there from June 1, 1969, to December 1, 1974?

SOLUTION: The dates are put in tabular form to simplify subtraction. After subtracting, the number of years is multiplied by the periods per year and the number of months is divided by the months in a period. These results are added to get the number of periods.

| YEAR | MONTH | DAY |
|------|-------|-----|
| 1974 | 12 | 1 |
| $-1969$ | $-6$ | $-1$ |
| 5 yrs. | 6 mos. | 0 days |

$$n = (5 \times 2) + 6/6 = 10 + 1 = 11$$

EXAMPLE 2: How many quarterly conversion periods are there from November 15, 1968, to August 15, 1977?

EXAMPLE: Find the amount of $6000 invested at 6% compounded semiannually for 20 years.

1. Get on the right page by either locating the rate per period at the top

or (better)

the frequency of conversion and the nominal annual rate in the marginal index. ──────

2. Find the column which gives the factor required in the particular problem. The columns are described at the top. Symbols at the bottom are the same as those used in the formulas. In this problem we want the *Amount of* 1 or the value of $(1 + i)^n$ so we look in the first column of factors.

3. Go down the *n* column to the correct number of periods. Be sure to convert the time in the problem to interest conversion periods. In 20 years there are 40 semiannual periods.

4. Find the factor in the proper line and column. ──────

5. Substitute the numerical value of the factor in the proper formula. To reduce arithmetic, answers in this book were obtained using factors rounded to the same number of decimal places as the number of digits in the sum of money. Substituting in (9),

$$S = P(1 + i)^n$$
$$= 6000.00(1 + .03)^{40}$$
$$= 6000.00(3.262\ 038)$$
$$= \$19,572.23$$

RATE

**3%**

.03

*per period*

ANNUALLY
If compounded
*annually*
nominal annual rate is

**3%**

SEMIANNUALLY
If compounded
*semiannually*
nominal annual rate is

**6%**

QUARTERLY
If compounded
*quarterly*
nominal annual rate is

**12%**

MONTHLY
If compounded
*monthly*
nominal annual rate is

**36%**

$i = .03$
$j_{(2)} = .06$
$j_{(4)} = .12$
$j_{(12)} = .36$

| P E R I O D S | AMOUNT OF 1 *How $1 left at compound interest will grow.* |
|---|---|
| 1 | 1.030 000 0000 |
| 2 | 1.060 900 0000 |
| 3 | 1.092 727 0000 |
| 4 | 1.125 508 8100 |
| 5 | 1.159 274 0743 |
| 6 | 1.194 052 2965 |
| 7 | 1.229 873 8654 |
| 8 | 1.266 770 0814 |
| 9 | 1.304 773 1838 |
| 10 | 1.343 916 3793 |
| 11 | 1.384 233 8707 |
| 12 | 1.425 760 8868 |
| 13 | 1.468 533 7135 |
| 14 | 1.512 589 7249 |
| 15 | 1.557 967 4166 |
| 16 | 1.604 706 4391 |
| 17 | 1.652 847 6323 |
| 18 | 1.702 433 0612 |
| 19 | 1.753 506 0531 |
| 20 | 1.806 111 2347 |
| 21 | 1.860 294 5717 |
| 22 | 1.916 103 4089 |
| 23 | 1.973 586 5111 |
| 24 | 2.032 794 1065 |
| 25 | 2.093 777 9297 |
| 26 | 2.156 591 2675 |
| 27 | 2.221 289 0056 |
| 28 | 2.287 927 6757 |
| 29 | 2.356 565 5060 |
| 30 | 2.427 262 4712 |
| 31 | 2.500 080 3453 |
| 32 | 2.575 082 7557 |
| 33 | 2.652 335 2384 |
| 34 | 2.731 905 2955 |
| 35 | 2.813 862 4544 |
| 36 | 2.898 278 3280 |
| 37 | 2.985 226 6778 |
| 38 | 3.074 783 4782 |
| 39 | 3.167 026 9825 |
| 40 | 3.262 037 7920 |
| 41 | 3.359 898 9258 |
| 42 | 3.460 695 8935 |
| 43 | 3.564 516 7703 |
| 44 | 3.671 452 2734 |
| 45 | 3.781 595 8417 |
| 46 | 3.895 043 7169 |
| 47 | 4.011 895 0284 |
| 48 | 4.132 251 8793 |
| 49 | 4.256 219 4356 |
| 50 | 4.383 906 0187 |
| 51 | 4.515 423 1993 |
| 52 | 4.650 885 8952 |
| 53 | 4.790 412 4721 |
| 54 | 4.934 124 8463 |
| 55 | 5.082 148 5917 |
| 56 | 5.234 613 0494 |
| 57 | 5.391 651 4409 |
| 58 | 5.553 400 9841 |
| 59 | 5.720 003 0136 |
| 60 | 5.891 603 1040 |
| n | $s = (1+i)^n$ |

SOLUTION: The dates are set up in the usual way to subtract the earlier date from the later one.

| YEAR | MONTH | DAY |
|------|-------|-----|
| 1977 | 8 | 15 |
| − 1968 | − 11 | − 15 |

Subtracting 11 months from 8 would result in a negative number. To avoid this, we borrow a year and add 12 to the 8 months. It is a good idea to keep a record of what is being done by striking out the numbers that are changed and replacing them with their new values. This procedure is illustrated below.

| YEAR | MONTH | DAY |
|------|-------|-----|
| 6 | 20 | |
| 1977 | 8 | 15 |
| − 1968 | − 11 | − 15 |
| 8 yrs. | 9 mos. | 0 days |

$$n = (8 \times 4) + 9/3 = 32 + 3 = 35$$

## 3.6   How Many Places?

The factors in Table 2 are given in 10 decimal places making them adequate for handling large sums of money. In the examples worked in the tables published by the Financial Publishing Company, the complete factor is used and the answer is rounded to the cent. If a calculator is available, as it usually is in a business, this is the sensible way to work a problem as it insures maximum accuracy without any troublesome questions about the number of decimal places to use to get answers correct to the nearest cent.

Since most students have to do calculations manually, we use simple sums in most problems to minimize routine arithmetic. To further conserve the student's time, we give answers which were obtained by rounding the factors to the same number of decimal places as there are digits in the sum of money given in the problem *including the cents*. Thus a principal of $25,000 would mean rounding the factor to 7 decimal places, while 4 places would be used for a principal of $25. This usually gives an answer that is the same as or within a penny or two of what would be obtained using the entire factor.

EXAMPLE 1: Find the compound amounts of $25, $2500, and $2,500,000 invested at 6% converted quarterly for 5 years.

SOLUTION:

$$25(1.015)^{20} = 25 \times 1.3469 = \$33.67$$
$$2500(1.015)^{20} = 2500 \times 1.346\ 855 = \$3367.14$$
$$2{,}500{,}000(1.015)^{20} = 2{,}500{,}000 \times 1.346\ 855\ 007 = \$3{,}367{,}137.52$$

EXAMPLE 2: A principal of $1000 is deposited at 4% for 10 years. What will be the compound amount and the compound interest if the interest is compounded annually, semiannually, quarterly, monthly?

SOLUTION: The required factors and final results are summarized below.

| FREQUENCY OF COMPOUNDING | RATE PER PERIOD $i$ | NUMBER OF CONVERSION PERIODS $n$ | AMOUNT OF 1 $(1 + i)^n$ | COMPOUND AMOUNT $S$ | COMPOUND INTEREST $S - 1000$ |
|---|---|---|---|---|---|
| Annually | .04 | 10 | 1.480 244 | $1480.24 | $480.24 |
| Semiannually | .02 | 20 | 1.485 947 | 1485.95 | 485.95 |
| Quarterly | .01 | 40 | 1.488 864 | 1488.86 | 488.86 |
| Monthly | .003333 | 120 | 1.490 833 | 1490.83 | 490.83 |

As the frequency of conversion is increased, interest is added to principal more often, so the depositor has a larger amount to his credit.

EXAMPLE 3: Banks and other savings institutions offer certificates of deposit and other savings instruments that permit deferral of interest payments until the deposit matures or is redeemed. This makes possible the automatic reinvestment of interest at the rate paid on the original investment. This rate is usually higher than the rate paid by the institution on its passbook accounts.

A man aged 60 put $10,000 in a deferred account paying 5% converted quarterly. The account is to mature in 5 years. Find the amount at that time.

SOLUTION: Substituting $P = 10{,}000$, $i = .0125$, and $n = 20$ in (9),

$$S = 10{,}000(1.0125)^{20} = 10{,}000 \times 1.282\ 0372 = \$12{,}820.37$$

EXAMPLE 4: A depositor planned to leave $2000 in a savings and loan association paying $4\frac{1}{2}$% compounded semiannually for a period of 5 years. However, at the end of $2\frac{1}{2}$ years he had to withdraw $1000. What will he have in his account at the end of the original 5-year period?

SOLUTION: We first get the amount in his account at the end of $2\frac{1}{2}$ years.

$$S = 2000(1.0225)^5 = 2000 \times 1.117\ 678 = \$2235.36$$

After withdrawing $1000, he has a remainder of $1235.36. During the remainder of the 5 years this will grow to

$$S = 1235.36(1.0225)^5 = 1235.36 \times 1.117\ 678 = \$1380.73$$

ALTERNATE SOLUTION: We could draw a time diagram, select a focal date, and solve using an equation of value.

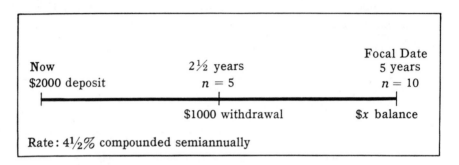

Carrying everything to the focal date,

$$x = 2000(1.0225)^{10} - 1000(1.0225)^5$$
$$= 2000 \times 1.249\ 203 - 1000 \times 1.117\ 678$$
$$= 2498.41 - 1117.68 = \$1380.73$$

In compound interest problems, the answer does not depend on the location of the focal date. By a skillful selection of focal date, a student can work problems and check results with a minimum of work.

### 3.7   Law of Organic Growth

The compound interest law is often called the *law of organic growth*. It can be applied to anything that is changing at a constant rate. There are many situations in nature, science, and business where the compound interest law is useful, provided good judgment is used in applying it. The investigator must be careful about extending past rates into the future. If something has been increasing at approximately a constant rate for several years, that rate can be useful for getting predicted values for the next few years. The same rate might lead to absurd long-term predictions. Rates determined under one set of conditions may not apply in another situation. Rats and bugs may increase at certain rates in the laboratory where they are protected from their natural enemies. But there is no justification for applying these rates to the usual environment with its cats, birds, and other limiting factors.

EXAMPLE 1: During the period 1960–1970, the population of a city increased at a rate of about 3% a year. If the population in 1970 was 300,000, what is the predicted population in 1980?

SOLUTION: Substituting $P = 300,000$, $i = .03$, and $n = 10$ in (9),

$$S = 300,000(1.03)^{10} = 300,000 \times 1.343\,916 = 403,175$$

In dealing with approximate data, the prediction should usually be rounded off to a reasonable value such as 403,000.

EXAMPLE 2: During the period 1966–1971 the net income per share of Columbia Gas System common stock increased about 5% a year compounded. The net income in 1971 was $2.90 per share. Assuming that the same rate of increase continues, predict the net income per share for 1975.

SOLUTION: Substituting $P = 2.90$, $i = .05$, and $n = 4$ in (9),

$$S = 2.90(1.05)^4 = 2.90 \times 1.216 = \$3.53$$

EXAMPLE 3: During the period 1960–1970, the population of a city increased 8%. If the population was 500,000 in 1970, what is the estimated population for 1990 assuming that the same rate of growth continues?

SOLUTION: The conversion period is the basic unit of time in compound interest problems. In financial problems, this is usually 1 year or less. In organic problems it may be many years or it may be a few seconds or less. In this problem it is a decade, so for 20 years, $n = 2$. Substituting in (9),

$$S = 500,000(1.08)^2 = 500,000 \times 1.166\,400 = 583,200$$

## 3.8 Nontabulated Rates

When a problem involves a rate not included in this text or even in the complete tables of the Financial Publishing Company, a desk calculator can be used to get the *Amount of* 1 factor. By the law of exponents, $(1 + i)^n \times (1 + i)^m = (1 + i)^{n+m}$, it is possible to get the answer in fast time. If we need $(1.052)^{15}$, we could multiply the factor by itself to get the square, multiply the 2nd power by itself to get the 4th power, multiply the 4th power by itself to get the 8th power, multiply the 8th power by itself to get the 16th power, and then divide the 16th power by the 1st power to give the 15th power. Sometimes the calculator manufacturer has instruction sheets which show how to reduce time and increase accuracy when making routine calculations. After $(1 + i)^n$ has been obtained, the other compound interest factors can be obtained using the relationships at the bottom of the columns in Table 2.

*EXERCISE 3a*

1. A finance company makes consumer loans at a nominal annual rate of 36% compounded monthly. Find $j$, $i$, and $m$.

$$(j = 36\% \text{ or } .36, \ i = 3\% \text{ or } .03, \ m = 12)$$

**2.** Fill in the conversion periods per year and the rate per period columns.

| Quoted or Nominal Rate | Conversion Periods per Year | Rate per Period $i$ | |
|---|---|---|---|
| $j$ | $m$ | Percent | Decimal |
| 4% | | | |
| 4% compounded semiannually | | | |
| 4% compounded monthly | | | |
| 5% compounded monthly | | | |
| $3\frac{1}{2}$% compounded semiannually | | | |
| $1\frac{3}{4}$% compounded semiannually | | | |

**3.** Find the compound amount and the compound interest if $1000 is invested for 10 years at 2%. ($1218.99; $218.99)

**4.** Find the compound amount and the compound interest if $24,500 is borrowed for 3 years at 5% converted monthly.

**5.** The day a boy was born, his father invested $200 at $3\frac{1}{2}$% compounded semiannually. Find the value of the fund on the boy's 18th birthday.

($373.48)

**6.** On a girl's 8th birthday her parents placed $250 in her name in an investment paying $3\frac{1}{2}$% compounded semiannually. How much will she have to her credit on her 21st birthday?

**7.** A town increased in population 2% a year during the period 1950 to 1960. If the population was 18,000 in 1960, what is the estimated population to the nearest hundred for 1970, assuming that the rate of growth remains the same? (21,900)

**8.** The sales of a business have been increasing at the rate of 3% a year. If the sales in 1968 are $250,000, what are the estimated sales to the nearest thousand dollars for 1973?

**9.** Find the amount of $6000 for 8 years at 4% nominal, compounded: (a) annually; (b) semiannually; (c) quarterly; (d) monthly.

[(a) $8211.41; (b) $8236.72; (c) $8249.65; (d) $8258.37]

**10.** Find the amount of $10,000 for 10 years at 6% compounded: (a) annually; (b) semiannually; (c) quarterly; (d) monthly.

**11.** What amount of money will be required to repay a loan of $6000 on December 31, 1974, if the loan was made on December 31, 1968, at a rate of 5% compounded semiannually? ($8069.33)

12. On June 1, 1965, a man incurred a debt of $3000 which was to be repaid on demand of the lender with interest at 3% converted semiannually. If the lender demanded payment on December 1, 1973, how much would he receive?

13. On June 30, 1974, a man put $15,000 in a deferred savings account paying 6% converted quarterly. Find the amount in the account when it matures on June 30, 1980.                                                                    ($21,442.54)

14. As part of her retirement program, a woman put $12,000 in a deferred savings account paying 5% converted quarterly. The investment was made on her 57th birthday on August 15, 1973. What will be the maturity value of this account if it matures on her 62nd birthday?

15. On June 30, 1966, a man deposited $850 in a building and loan paying $4\frac{1}{2}$% compounded semiannually. How much will he get if he draws out his money on June 30, 1973?                                                ($1160.66)

16. What amount of money will be required to repay a loan of $1835.50 on July 1, 1973, if the loan was made on October 1, 1969, at an interest rate of 5% compounded quarterly?

17. A person put $2500 in a savings and loan association paying 4% converted quarterly. He planned to leave the money there 6 years and then use it for a trip. At the end of 2 years he had to withdraw $500. What was the amount in his account at the end of the original 6-year period? ($2588.05)

18. What would be the answer to Problem 17 if the $500 withdrawal was made at the end of 4 years?

19. On July 1, 1969, a man put $5000 in a savings and loan association paying 4% converted semiannually. On January 2, 1971, he withdrew $2500 from his account. What was the balance in his account on January 2, 1974?
                                                                            ($3160.06)

20. Interest dates for a bank are May 1 and November 1. Interest on savings accounts is 4% converted semiannually. A depositor opens an account on May 1, 1970, with a deposit of $1500. He withdraws $500 on November 1, 1971, and deposits $1000 on May 1, 1973. What is the balance in his account on May 1, 1974?

21. During the period 1965 to 1970 the annual earnings per share of Standard Oil Company of California increased about 5% a year. If the earnings in 1970 were $5.36, the same rate of increase would result in what predicted per share earnings in 1975?                                                    ($6.84)

22. During the period 1967 to 1971 the annual earnings per share of The Clorox Company increased about 6% a year. If the earnings were $1.68 in 1971, the same rate of increase would result in what predicted per share earnings in 1975?

## 3.9   Daily Compounding

The Board of Governors of the Federal Reserve System establishes the maximum nominal rates that member banks may pay on time and savings deposits; the Federal Deposit Insurance Corporation has similar authority with respect to deposits in insured nonmember banks; and the Federal Home Loan Bank Board establishes the maximum rates paid by federally insured savings and loan associations. Since interest rates are the price of credit, this federal freeze on rates is one of our few peacetime examples of price controls. The greatest impact is on small savers. Affluent investors, who have more alternatives for investing money, can find higher rates in other investments.

Since there are no restrictions on the frequency of compounding, banks and savings and loan associations try to attract depositors by increasing the frequency of compounding when the demand for loanable funds is great. With a fixed nominal rate, more frequent compounding results in depositors earning more interest.

For a given nominal rate $j$ the *Amount of* 1 factor for a 360-day year is computed from the expression $[1 + (j/360)]^t$ where $t$ is the time in days. The *Amount of* 1 factor for a 365-day year is computed using $[1 + (j/365)]^t$.

EXAMPLE: Compute the *Amount of* 1 factor for 5% converted daily for 1, 2, and 3 days for 360 and 365 day years.

SOLUTION: For a 360-day year

$$(1 + j/360) = (1 + .05/360) = (1 + .000\ 138\ 8889)$$

We now raise this factor to a power equal to the number of days.

$$(1.000\ 138\ 8889)^1 = 1.000\ 138\ 8889$$
$$(1.000\ 138\ 8889)^2 = 1.000\ 277\ 7971$$
$$(1.000\ 138\ 8889)^3 = 1.000\ 416\ 7245$$

For a 365-day year, $(1 + j/365) = (1 + .05/365) = (1 + .000\ 136\ 9863)$. For 1, 2, and 3 days the *Amount of* 1 factors are

$$(1.000\ 136\ 9863)^1 = 1.000\ 136\ 9863$$
$$(1.000\ 136\ 9863)^2 = 1.000\ 273\ 9914$$
$$(1.000\ 136\ 9863)^3 = 1.000\ 411\ 0152$$

## 3.10   Continuous Compounding

To get an edge on the daily compounders, some institutions have gone to instantaneous or continuous compounding. This means that the money is growing continuously rather than in discrete jumps. This is not as strange as it sounds when we consider change in the natural world. Your foot, for example, got from its starting size to where it is now as a result of growth that was for practical purposes continuous, though not necessarily at a uniform rate.

An understanding of the mathematics involved in continuous compounding requires a knowledge of the calculus. This is discussed in Chapter 12 along with applications of continuous compounding to economic problems.

The Financial Publishing Company has published daily and continuous growth factor tables for 360- and 365-day years and common interest rates. Sample entries from these tables are shown on the next two pages. These tables are valuable time savers and enable anyone to get the amount of a sum earning daily or continuous interest with a simple table look-up and ordinary multiplication.

EXAMPLE 1: Savings and Loan Association A pays 5% compounded quarterly, B pays 5% compounded daily and C pays 5% compounded continuously. Find the interest earned in each case on $1000 for half a year.

SOLUTION:

| INSTITUTION AND RATE | AMOUNT OF 1 | AMOUNT OF $1000 | INTEREST |
|---|---|---|---|
| A. 5% comp. quarterly | 1.025 156 2500 | $1025.16 | $25.16 |
| B. 5% comp. daily | 1.025 313 3406 | 1025.31 | 25.31 |
| C. 5% comp. cont. | 1.025 315 1205 | 1025.32 | 25.32 |

While more frequent compounding increases interest, the gains for modest investments are not as large as one might expect from the advertising fanfare that accompanies the introduction of daily or continuous compounding.

Some institutions now pay interest from date of deposit to date of withdrawal regardless of when these occur. This can be of value to people, with temporarily idle funds, who might not earn any interest if the funds were in an account that paid interest only on fixed dates.

EXAMPLE 2: An institution advertises that they pay 5% compounded daily from date of deposit to date of withdrawal. A company deposits $150,000 on June 10 and withdraws it on July 15. Find the interest if computed on a 360-day basis.

SOLUTION:

| DATE | DAY OF YEAR |
|---|---|
| July 15 | 196 |
| June 10 | 161 |
| Elapsed time | 35 days |

Using the *Amount of* 1 factor from page 90,

$$S = 150,000 \times 1.004\ 8726063 = \$150,730.89$$
$$\text{Interest} = \$730.89$$

## 5% COMPOUNDED DAILY 360 DAY BASIS

| PERIOD | AMOUNT OF 1 | PERIOD | AMOUNT OF 1 | PERIOD | AMOUNT OF 1 |
|---|---|---|---|---|---|
| 1 | 1.000 138 8889 | 61 | 1.008 507 6198 | 121 | 1.016 946 3766 |
| 2 | 1.000 277 7971 | 62 | 1.008 647 6903 | 122 | 1.017 087 6191 |
| 3 | 1.000 416 7245 | 63 | 1.008 787 7802 | 123 | 1.017 228 8813 |
| 4 | 1.000 555 6713 | 64 | 1.008 927 8896 | 124 | 1.017 370 1631 |
| 5 | 1.000 694 6374 | 65 | 1.009 068 0185 | 125 | 1.017 511 4645 |
| 6 | 1.000 833 6227 | 66 | 1.009 208 1668 | 126 | 1.017 652 7855 |
| 7 | 1.000 972 6274 | 67 | 1.009 348 3347 | 127 | 1.017 794 1262 |
| 8 | 1.001 111 6514 | 68 | 1.009 488 5219 | 128 | 1.017 935 4865 |
| 9 | 1.001 250 6947 | 69 | 1.009 628 7287 | 129 | 1.018 076 8664 |
| 10 | 1.001 389 7573 | 70 | 1.009 768 9549 | 130 | 1.018 218 2660 |
| 11 | 1.001 528 8392 | 71 | 1.009 909 2006 | 131 | 1.018 359 6852 |
| 12 | 1.001 667 9404 | 72 | 1.010 049 4657 | 132 | 1.018 501 1240 |
| 13 | 1.001 807 0610 | 73 | 1.010 189 7504 | 133 | 1.018 642 5825 |
| 14 | 1.001 946 2008 | 74 | 1.010 330 0545 | 134 | 1.018 784 0607 |
| 15 | 1.002 085 3600 | 75 | 1.010 470 3781 | 135 | 1.018 925 5584 |
| 16 | 1.002 224 5385 | 76 | 1.010 610 7212 | 136 | 1.019 067 0759 |
| 17 | 1.002 363 7364 | 77 | 1.010 751 0838 | 137 | 1.019 208 6130 |
| 18 | 1.002 502 9536 | 78 | 1.010 891 4659 | 138 | 1.019 350 1697 |
| 19 | 1.002 642 1901 | 79 | 1.011 031 8675 | 139 | 1.019 491 7461 |
| 20 | 1.002 781 4460 | 80 | 1.011 172 2886 | 140 | 1.019 633 3422 |
| 21 | 1.002 920 7212 | 81 | 1.011 312 7292 | 141 | 1.019 774 9580 |
| 22 | 1.003 060 0157 | 82 | 1.011 453 1893 | 142 | 1.019 916 5934 |
| 23 | 1.003 199 3296 | 83 | 1.011 593 6689 | 143 | 1.020 058 2485 |
| 24 | 1.003 338 6628 | 84 | 1.011 734 1680 | 144 | 1.020 199 9232 |
| 25 | 1.003 478 0154 | 85 | 1.011 874 6867 | 145 | 1.020 341 6176 |
| 26 | 1.003 617 3874 | 86 | 1.012 015 2248 | 146 | 1.020 483 3318 |
| 27 | 1.003 756 7787 | 87 | 1.012 155 7825 | 147 | 1.020 625 0656 |
| 28 | 1.003 896 1893 | 88 | 1.012 296 3597 | 148 | 1.020 766 8190 |
| 29 | 1.004 035 6194 | 89 | 1.012 436 9564 | 149 | 1.020 908 5922 |
| 30 | 1.004 175 0688 | 90 | 1.012 577 5726 | 150 | 1.021 050 3851 |
| 31 | 1.004 314 5375 | 91 | 1.012 718 2084 | 151 | 1.021 192 1976 |
| 32 | 1.004 454 0256 | 92 | 1.012 858 8637 | 152 | 1.021 334 0299 |
| 33 | 1.004 593 5332 | 93 | 1.012 999 5386 | 153 | 1.021 475 8818 |
| 34 | 1.004 733 0600 | 94 | 1.013 140 2330 | 154 | 1.021 617 7535 |
| 35 | 1.004 872 6063 | 95 | 1.013 280 9469 | 155 | 1.021 759 6448 |
| 36 | 1.005 012 1719 | 96 | 1.013 421 6803 | 156 | 1.021 901 5559 |
| 37 | 1.005 151 7570 | 97 | 1.013 562 4333 | 157 | 1.022 043 4867 |
| 38 | 1.005 291 3614 | 98 | 1.013 703 2059 | 158 | 1.022 185 4371 |
| 39 | 1.005 430 9852 | 99 | 1.013 843 9980 | 159 | 1.022 327 4073 |
| 40 | 1.005 570 6284 | 100 | 1.013 984 8097 | 160 | 1.022 469 3973 |
| 41 | 1.005 710 2909 | 101 | 1.014 125 6409 | 161 | 1.022 611 4069 |
| 42 | 1.005 849 9729 | 102 | 1.014 266 4917 | 162 | 1.022 753 4363 |
| 43 | 1.005 989 6743 | 103 | 1.014 407 3620 | 163 | 1.022 895 4853 |
| 44 | 1.006 129 3951 | 104 | 1.014 548 2520 | 164 | 1.023 037 5542 |
| 45 | 1.006 269 1353 | 105 | 1.014 689 1614 | 165 | 1.023 179 6427 |
| 46 | 1.006 408 8949 | 106 | 1.014 830 0905 | 166 | 1.023 321 7510 |
| 47 | 1.006 548 6739 | 107 | 1.014 971 0391 | 167 | 1.023 463 8790 |
| 48 | 1.006 688 4723 | 108 | 1.015 112 0073 | 168 | 1.023 606 0268 |
| 49 | 1.006 828 2902 | 109 | 1.015 252 9951 | 169 | 1.023 748 1943 |
| 50 | 1.006 968 1274 | 110 | 1.015 394 0024 | 170 | 1.023 890 3815 |
| 51 | 1.007 107 9841 | 111 | 1.015 535 0294 | 171 | 1.024 032 5885 |
| 52 | 1.007 247 8602 | 112 | 1.015 676 0759 | 172 | 1.024 174 8153 |
| 53 | 1.007 387 7558 | 113 | 1.015 817 1420 | 173 | 1.024 317 0618 |
| 54 | 1.007 527 6707 | 114 | 1.015 958 2278 | 174 | 1.024 459 3280 |
| 55 | 1.007 667 6051 | 115 | 1.016 099 3331 | 175 | 1.024 601 6141 |
| 56 | 1.007 807 5590 | 116 | 1.016 240 4580 | 176 | 1.024 743 9198 |
| 57 | 1.007 947 5322 | 117 | 1.016 381 6025 | 177 | 1.024 886 2454 |
| 58 | 1.008 087 5250 | 118 | 1.016 522 7666 | 178 | 1.025 028 5907 |
| 59 | 1.008 227 5371 | 119 | 1.016 663 9503 | 179 | 1.025 170 9558 |
| 60 | 1.008 367 5687 | 120 | 1.016 805 1536 | 180 | 1.025 313 3406 |

## 5% COMPOUNDED CONTINUOUSLY 360 DAY BASIS

| PERIOD | AMOUNT OF 1 | PERIOD | AMOUNT OF 1 | PERIOD | AMOUNT OF 1 |
|---|---|---|---|---|---|
| 1 | 1.000 138 8985 | 61 | 1.008 508 2131 | 121 | 1.016 947 5633 |
| 2 | 1.000 277 8164 | 62 | 1.008 648 2934 | 122 | 1.017 088 8158 |
| 3 | 1.000 416 7535 | 63 | 1.008 788 3931 | 123 | 1.017 230 0880 |
| 4 | 1.000 555 7099 | 64 | 1.008 928 5124 | 124 | 1.017 371 3797 |
| 5 | 1.000 694 6856 | 65 | 1.009 068 6511 | 125 | 1.017 512 6911 |
| 6 | 1.000 833 6807 | 66 | 1.009 208 8092 | 126 | 1.017 654 0222 |
| 7 | 1.000 972 6950 | 67 | 1.009 348 9869 | 127 | 1.017 795 3728 |
| 8 | 1.001 111 7286 | 68 | 1.009 489 1839 | 128 | 1.017 936 7431 |
| 9 | 1.001 250 7816 | 69 | 1.009 629 4005 | 129 | 1.018 078 1330 |
| 10 | 1.001 389 8538 | 70 | 1.009 769 6366 | 130 | 1.018 219 5426 |
| 11 | 1.001 528 9454 | 71 | 1.009 909 8921 | 131 | 1.018 360 9718 |
| 12 | 1.001 668 0563 | 72 | 1.010 050 1671 | 132 | 1.018 502 4206 |
| 13 | 1.001 807 1866 | 73 | 1.010 190 4616 | 133 | 1.018 643 8891 |
| 14 | 1.001 946 3361 | 74 | 1.010 330 7755 | 134 | 1.018 785 3773 |
| 15 | 1.002 085 5050 | 75 | 1.010 471 1090 | 135 | 1.018 926 8851 |
| 16 | 1.002 224 6932 | 76 | 1.010 611 4620 | 136 | 1.019 068 4125 |
| 17 | 1.002 363 9007 | 77 | 1.010 751 8344 | 137 | 1.019 209 9596 |
| 18 | 1.002 503 1276 | 78 | 1.010 892 2264 | 138 | 1.019 351 5264 |
| 19 | 1.002 642 3738 | 79 | 1.011 032 6378 | 139 | 1.019 493 1128 |
| 20 | 1.002 781 6394 | 80 | 1.011 173 0688 | 140 | 1.019 634 7189 |
| 21 | 1.002 920 9243 | 81 | 1.011 313 5192 | 141 | 1.019 776 3447 |
| 22 | 1.003 060 2285 | 82 | 1.011 453 9892 | 142 | 1.019 917 9901 |
| 23 | 1.003 199 5521 | 83 | 1.011 594 4787 | 143 | 1.020 059 6552 |
| 24 | 1.003 338 8951 | 84 | 1.011 734 9877 | 144 | 1.020 201 3400 |
| 25 | 1.003 478 2574 | 85 | 1.011 875 5162 | 145 | 1.020 343 0445 |
| 26 | 1.003 617 6390 | 86 | 1.012 016 0642 | 146 | 1.020 484 7687 |
| 27 | 1.003 757 0400 | 87 | 1.012 156 6317 | 147 | 1.020 626 5125 |
| 28 | 1.003 896 4604 | 88 | 1.012 297 2188 | 148 | 1.020 768 2760 |
| 29 | 1.004 035 9002 | 89 | 1.012 437 8254 | 149 | 1.020 910 0592 |
| 30 | 1.004 175 3593 | 90 | 1.012 578 4515 | 150 | 1.021 051 8621 |
| 31 | 1.004 314 8378 | 91 | 1.012 719 0972 | 151 | 1.021 193 6848 |
| 32 | 1.004 454 3356 | 92 | 1.012 859 7624 | 152 | 1.021 335 5271 |
| 33 | 1.004 593 8529 | 93 | 1.013 000 4471 | 153 | 1.021 477 3891 |
| 34 | 1.004 733 3895 | 94 | 1.013 141 1514 | 154 | 1.021 619 2708 |
| 35 | 1.004 872 9455 | 95 | 1.013 281 8752 | 155 | 1.021 761 1722 |
| 36 | 1.005 012 5209 | 96 | 1.013 422 6186 | 156 | 1.021 903 0933 |
| 37 | 1.005 152 1156 | 97 | 1.013 563 3815 | 157 | 1.022 045 0342 |
| 38 | 1.005 291 7298 | 98 | 1.013 704 1640 | 158 | 1.022 186 9947 |
| 39 | 1.005 431 3633 | 99 | 1.013 844 9660 | 159 | 1.022 328 9750 |
| 40 | 1.005 571 0163 | 100 | 1.013 985 7876 | 160 | 1.022 470 9750 |
| 41 | 1.005 710 6886 | 101 | 1.014 126 6287 | 161 | 1.022 612 9947 |
| 42 | 1.005 850 3804 | 102 | 1.014 267 4894 | 162 | 1.022 755 0342 |
| 43 | 1.005 990 0915 | 103 | 1.014 408 3697 | 163 | 1.022 897 0933 |
| 44 | 1.006 129 8220 | 104 | 1.014 549 2695 | 164 | 1.023 039 1722 |
| 45 | 1.006 269 5720 | 105 | 1.014 690 1889 | 165 | 1.023 181 2709 |
| 46 | 1.006 409 3414 | 106 | 1.014 831 1279 | 166 | 1.023 323 3893 |
| 47 | 1.006 549 1302 | 107 | 1.014 972 0865 | 167 | 1.023 465 5274 |
| 48 | 1.006 688 9384 | 108 | 1.015 113 0646 | 168 | 1.023 607 6852 |
| 49 | 1.006 828 7660 | 109 | 1.015 254 0623 | 169 | 1.023 749 8629 |
| 50 | 1.006 968 6130 | 110 | 1.015 395 0796 | 170 | 1.023 892 0602 |
| 51 | 1.007 108 4795 | 111 | 1.015 536 1165 | 171 | 1.024 034 2773 |
| 52 | 1.007 248 3654 | 112 | 1.015 677 1730 | 172 | 1.024 176 5142 |
| 53 | 1.007 388 2707 | 113 | 1.015 818 2491 | 173 | 1.024 318 7708 |
| 54 | 1.007 528 1954 | 114 | 1.015 959 3447 | 174 | 1.024 461 0472 |
| 55 | 1.007 668 1396 | 115 | 1.016 100 4600 | 175 | 1.024 603 3433 |
| 56 | 1.007 808 1033 | 116 | 1.016 241 5949 | 176 | 1.024 745 6592 |
| 57 | 1.007 948 0863 | 117 | 1.016 382 7493 | 177 | 1.024 887 9949 |
| 58 | 1.008 088 0888 | 118 | 1.016 523 9234 | 178 | 1.025 030 3503 |
| 59 | 1.008 228 1108 | 119 | 1.016 665 1171 | 179 | 1.025 172 7255 |
| 60 | 1.008 368 1522 | 120 | 1.016 806 3304 | 180 | 1.025 315 1205 |

EXAMPLE 3: Find the interest for the above account at 5% compounded continuously.

SOLUTION: Using the *Amount of* 1 factor from page 91,

$$S = 150,000 \times 1.004\ 872\ 9455 = \$150,730.94$$
$$\text{Interest} = \$730.94$$

Since large sums of money can earn hundreds of dollars of interest in only a short time, corporate treasurers keep temporarily idle money to a minimum. As the preceding examples show, there is little practical difference between daily and continuous compounding for short-term investments.

## 3.11   Effective Interest Rates

To put different rates and frequencies of conversion on a comparable basis, we determine the **effective rate**, $r$. The effective rate is the rate converted annually that will produce the same amount of interest per year as the nominal rate $j$ converted $m$ times per year.

If the nominal rate is 6% converted annually, the effective rate will also be 6%. But if the nominal rate is 6% converted semiannually, the amount of $1 at the end of one year will be $(1.03)^2 = \$1.0609$. This is simply the accumulation factor for a rate per period of 3% and two periods. The interest on $1 for one year is then $\$1.0609 - 1.0000 = \$.0609$. This is equivalent to an annual rate of 6.09%. Thus 6.09% converted annually would result in the same amount of interest as 6% converted semiannually. The computations used to get the effective rate of 6.09% in this case can be summarized as follows:

$$1.0609 = (1.03)^2$$
$$r = 1.0609 - 1 = .0609 = 6.09\%$$

Putting the above relationship in the form of a general equation, we have

$$1 + r = (1 + i)^m$$
$$r = (1 + i)^m - 1 \qquad (10)$$

As $m$, the frequency of conversion is increased, the effective rate corresponding to a given nominal rate gets larger. However, the increase becomes less rapid with large value of $m$.

To get the effective rate for discrete compounding, we simply look up the *Amount of* 1 corresponding to the nominal rate and the number of conversions in a year and subtract 1 from this factor. For 5% converted monthly, the *Amount of* 1 factor for 12 periods is 1.051 161 and the effective rate is .051 161 or approximately 5.12%. For continuous compounding, we would go to the Daily Growth Factor tables for a full year and subtract 1 from the table entry.

The table below shows the effect of frequency of compounding on the effective rate and the corresponding interest on $10,000 for a year.

| IF THE NOMINAL RATE IS 5% COMPOUNDED: | THE EFFECTIVE RATE IS: | A YEAR'S INTEREST ON $10,000 IS: | ADDITIONAL INTEREST IS: |
|---|---|---|---|
| Annually | 5.000 0000% | $500.00 | — |
| Semiannually | 5.062 5000 | 506.25 | $6.25 |
| Quarterly | 5.094 5337 | 509.45 | 3.20 |
| Monthly | 5.116 1898 | 511.62 | 2.17 |
| Weekly | 5.124 5841 | 512.46 | .84 |
| Daily | 5.126 7496 | 512.67 | .21 |
| Hourly | 5.127 0946 | 512.71 | .04 |
| Continuously | 5.127 1096 | 512.71 | .00 |

While daily and continuous compounding may result in impressive advertisements, they do not mean much to the average depositor in terms of income. In a year, $10,000 earns $511.62 at 5% compounded monthly. With daily compounding, the interest is only $1.05 more. When an enterprising ad writer points out that if his institution gets to use your money, the interest will be compounded continuously, the cost to the borrower is not much more than for daily compounding. What can be of great value to depositors is the policy of some institutions of paying interest on deposits to the date of withdrawal.

Because three rates are used in compound interest work, it is well at this point to summarize the meaning of each.

The nominal rate (symbol $j$) is the quoted or stated rate. When a nominal rate is quoted, the frequency of compounding should be stated. Nominal rates are given in the marginal index of the compound interest tables.

The rate per period (symbol $i$) equals the nominal rate divided by the number of conversion periods per year $(j/m)$. The rate per period is the value used to compute compound interest factors. It is the rate at the top of the page in the compound interest tables.

The effective rate (symbol $r$) is the rate actually earned in a year. It is used to get different nominal rates and conversion periods on a common basis for comparison purposes.

EXAMPLE: Find the effective rate of interest equivalent to 8% converted semiannually.

SOLUTION: The rate per period = 4%, or .04, and $m = 2$. In getting the effective rate it is usually sufficiently accurate to take the *Amount of* 1 factor from Table 2 to four decimal places. Substituting in (10),

$$r = (1.04)^2 - 1$$
$$= 1.0816 - 1.0000 = .0816 = 8.16\%$$

Thus $8.16\%$ compounded annually will produce the same amount of interest as $8\%$ compounded semiannually.

### EXERCISE 3b

1. What is the effective rate of interest equivalent to $10\%$ converted (a) semi-annually; (b) quarterly?                                    [(a) $10.25\%$; (b) $10.38\%$]
2. What is the effective rate of interest equivalent to $7\%$ converted: (a) semi-annually; (b) quarterly?
3. Which gives the better annual return on an investment, $6\frac{1}{8}\%$ converted annually or $6\%$ converted quarterly? Show the figures on which you base your answer.                                         ($6\%$ converted quarterly)
4. Which rate of interest gives the better annual yield, $4\%$ compounded monthly or $4\frac{1}{2}\%$ compounded semiannually? Show the figures on which you base your answer.
5. A savings and loan association in California advertised that they are paying $5.25\%$ converted daily. According to the ad, this is equivalent to an effective rate of $5.39\%$. An investor in Ohio has his money in an account paying $5\%$ converted quarterly. If the Ohio investor transfers $10,000 to the California association, he will get about how much additional interest a year?     ($30)
6. A company has $50,000 to invest. What would be the difference in interest at the end of a year between earning $5\%$ converted semiannually and $5\%$ converted quarterly?
7. Complete the following table showing the effect of frequency of compounding on effective interest rates. Use the $3\%$ values as a check on your work. Answers not available in this text have been obtained from more extensive interest tables.

| NOMINAL ANNUAL RATE | EFFECTIVE RATE IF COMPOUNDED: | | |
|---|---|---|---|
| | SEMIANNUALLY | QUARTERLY | MONTHLY |
| $3\%$ | $3.02\%$ | $3.03\%$ | $3.04\%$ |
| 6 | | | |
| 9 | 9.20 | | |
| 12 | | | |
| 15 | 15.56 | 15.87 | |
| 18 | 18.81 | 19.25 | |
| 21 | 22.10 | 22.71 | |
| 24 | 25.44 | | |
| 27 | 28.82 | 29.86 | |
| 30 | 32.25 | 33.55 | |

## 3.12   Interest for Part of a Period

When deriving the compound interest formula, we assumed that the time would be an integral number of conversion periods. When there is a part of a period, the usual practice is to allow simple interest for this time on the compound amount at the end of the last whole period.

EXAMPLE: At 4% compounded semiannually, $2000 will amount to how much in 3 years and 5 months?

SOLUTION: The total time in this case is six whole periods and five months left over. The compound amount at the end of the six whole periods is

$$S = 2000(1.02)^6 = 2000 \times 1.126162 = \$2252.32$$

The simple interest for the remaining five months is

$$2252.32 \times \tfrac{5}{12} \times .04 = \$37.54$$

Therefore the amount at the end of 3 years and 5 months is

$$2252.32 + 37.54 = \$2289.86$$

Note that in getting the simple interest we use the nominal annual rate and the time in years. A common mistake is to use the rate per period.

The procedure used to get the total amount for a problem involving a part of a period is illustrated. The series of dots indicate that part of the time scale has been omitted.

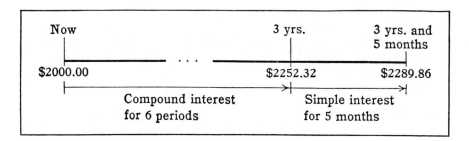

## 3.13   Amount at Changing Rates

If the interest rate on an investment changes, the final amount can be found by getting the amount each time there is a change in rate and then carrying this value forward at the new rate until there is another change. All that this means is that we have a series of compound interest problems. The amount at the end of one stage becomes the principal at the beginning of the next stage.

In this text when a problem has two or more stages, we round intermediate answers to the nearest cent. This makes the arithmetic as simple as possible. If a calculator is available, some people prefer to either carry more places in the intermediate steps or first multiply the factors together.

EXAMPLE: A principal of $900 earns 4% converted quarterly for 4 years and then 5% converted semiannually for 2 more years. Find the final amount.

SOLUTION: We first find the amount at the end of 4 years (16 periods) using a factor rounded to 5 decimal places.

$$900(1.01)^{16} = 900 \times 1.17258 = \$1055.32$$

We now go forward 2 more years at 5% converted semiannually. Since there are 6 digits in the new principal, we round the factor to 6 decimal places.

$$1055.32(1.025)^4 = 1055.32 \times 1.103\,813 = \$1164.88$$

If this problem were worked by first multiplying the complete factors together, we would have

$$900 \times 1.172\,578\,6449 \times 1.103\,812\,8906 = 900 \times 1.294\,307\,4241 = \$1164.88$$

## EXERCISE 3c

1. On June 30, 1967, Charles Moser borrowed $3000 at 4% converted semi-annually. How much would he have to repay on September 28, 1974? Use Bankers' Rule for simple interest computation. ($3998.02)
2. Find the amount of $750 for $4\frac{1}{2}$ years at 5% effective.
3. If $6000 is borrowed for 5 years and 4 months at $4\frac{1}{2}$% converted semi-annually, what amount would be required to repay the debt? ($7607.65)
4. What is the amount of $40,000 for 6 years and 3 months at $4\frac{1}{2}$% converted semiannually?
5. To what sum of money does $2000 accumulate in 3 years and 5 months at 6% compounded semiannually? ($2447.80)
6. On June 1, 1970, a debt of $4000 was incurred at a rate of 6%. What amount will be required to settle the debt on September 15, 1974? Use Bankers' Rule for simple interest computation.
7. A savings and loan association advertises "instant interest." Funds received by the 10th of the month earn interest from the 1st. Interest is paid at the rate of 4% converted quarterly. Interest dates are March 31, June 30, September 30, and December 31. Interest is paid to the date funds are withdrawn. A man deposits $2000 on January 7, 1972. If he closes out his account on January 30, 1974, how much will he get? Allow simple interest for 1 month. ($2172.93)

8. Another depositor put $5000 on April 8, 1970, in the savings and loan association in Problem 7. He closed out his account on November 30, 1973. What was the balance at that time? Allow simple interest for 2 months.

9. Four thousand dollars was invested for 12 years. During the first 5 years the interest rate was 5% converted semiannually. The rate then dropped to $4\frac{1}{2}$% converted semiannually for the remainder of the time. What was the final amount?                                                          ($6991.74)

10. A principal of $6500 earns 4% effective for 3 years and then $3\frac{1}{2}$% compounded semiannually for 4 more years. What is the amount at the end of the 7 years?

11. William H. Maguire bequeathed $400,000 to a university for the construction of a science building. The university got 4% on this investment for 9 years. The rate then dropped to $3\frac{1}{2}$%. If the building was built 25 years after the gift was received, how much was in the fund at that time?
                                                          ($987,201.12)

12. An investment of $3000 earns 3% for 2 years, then $2\frac{1}{2}$% compounded semiannually for 4 more years, then 4% compounded semiannually for 2 years. Get the amount at the end of the 8 years.

## 3.14   Present Value at Compound Interest

In business transactions there are many times when it is necessary to determine the **present value** of some sum of money due in the future. The present value is defined as the principal that will amount to the given sum at the specified future date. The difference between the future amount and its present value is the **compound discount**. To get the present value of a future amount, we simply solve the compound interest formula for $P$:

$$P = \frac{S}{(1 + i)^n}$$

This is often expressed using negative exponents:

$$P = S(1 + i)^{-n} \tag{11}$$

$P$ = the principal or present value
$S$ = the amount due in the future
$i$ = the rate per period
$n$ = the number of periods

The quantity

$$\frac{1}{(1 + i)^n}$$

or $(1 + i)^{-n}$ is called the **discount factor**, **Present Worth of 1**, or **Present Value of 1**. It is also indicated, particularly in insurance problems, by the symbol $v^n$. Numerical values of the discount factor for common interest rates are given in the *Present Worth of* 1 column in Table 2. In our examples we follow the common practice of using a negative exponent to indicate that a sum due in the future is to be discounted.

The *Present Worth of* 1 column gives the present or current value of a dollar to be paid in the future, taking into account compound interest. For example, at 5% compounded annually, $1 due in 5 years has a *Present Worth of* 1 factor of .783 526 1665. This means that $.78 will grow to $1.00 in 5 years if it earns 5% compounded annually. The present value of any sum due in the future can be obtained by simply multiplying the future amount by the *Present Worth of* 1 factor from Table 2.

The concept of present value is one of the most useful and powerful tools in economic analysis. It enables the analyst to take sums of money due in the future and determine how much they are worth now.

EXAMPLE 1: Find the present value of $5000 due in 4 years if money is worth 4% compounded semiannually.

SOLUTION: Substituting $S = 5000$, $i = .02$, and $n = 8$ in (11) and using the *Present Worth of* 1 factor from Table 2, we have

$$P = 5000(1.02)^{-8} = 5000 \times .853490 = \$4267.45$$

This means that if $4267.45 was put at interest for 4 years at 4% compounded semiannually, the amount would be $5000. A good exercise for students is to carry money backwards and forwards in this way to show that the results do check.

When the time involves a part of a conversion period, we bring $S$ back for the minimum number of periods that includes the given time and then compute the simple interest on the principal up to the point where the present value is wanted.

EXAMPLE 2: A note with a maturity value of $1000 is due in 3 years and 8 months. What is its present value at 6% compounded semiannually?

SOLUTION: We first bring the $1000 back 4 years or 8 periods, the minimum number of periods that includes 3 years and 8 months.

$$1000(1.03)^{-8} = 1000 \times .789 409 = \$789.41$$

This is now taken forward 4 months at simple interest.

$$789.41 \times .06 \times \tfrac{1}{3} = \$15.79$$

Adding principal and interest, we get $805.20 as the present value.

On problems like this where it is necessary to move money backwards and forwards, or keep track of several sums of money, it is good practice to make a time diagram which shows the dollar value of each inflow and outflow of money at the point in time where the flow occurs. A diagram for this problem is shown below.

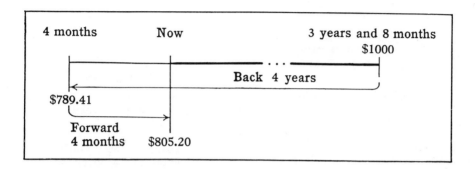

In the preceding examples the maturity value of the obligation was known and it was only necessary to discount this amount. Many times, however, the original debt will be interest-bearing and the maturity value will not be given. Then the *maturity value at the given interest rate must be determined.* Finally the present value of this maturity value is obtained by discounting at the rate specified for discounting. The two rates may be and frequently are different.

EXAMPLE 3: On August 5, 1964, Mr. Kane loans Mr. Hill $2000 at 6% converted semiannually. Mr. Hill gives Mr. Kane a note promising to repay the loan with accumulated interest in 6 years. On February 5, 1968, Mr. Kane sells the note to a buyer who charges an interest rate of 8% converted semiannually for discounting. How much does Mr. Kane get?

SOLUTION: We must first determine the maturity value of the debt.

$$S = 2000(1.03)^{12} = 2000 \times 1.425761 = \$2851.52$$

Now the original time and the original interest rate have no more bearing on the problem. All that the buyer of the note is interested in is the maturity value, how long he will have to wait to collect, and what the note is worth to him at his discount rate.

The note matures on August 5, 1970. From February 5, 1968, to this maturity date is $2\frac{1}{2}$ years or 5 periods of 6 months each. Therefore the value of the note at 8% compounded semiannually is

$$P = 2851.52(1.04)^{-5} = 2851.52 \times .821927 = \$2343.74$$

Note that the time for discounting is from the time the buyer buys the note to the maturity date. The time when the original debt was contracted does not enter into this part of the problem except to establish the maturity date. A time diagram will prevent many of the common errors with this type of problem.

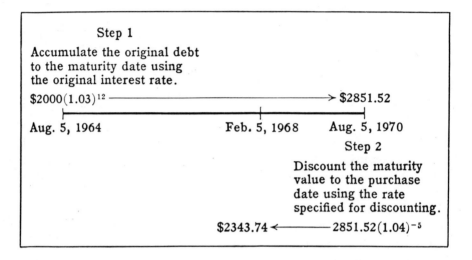

**Step 1**

Accumulate the original debt to the maturity date using the original interest rate.

$2000(1.03)^{12}$ ——————————————→ $2851.52

Aug. 5, 1964                    Feb. 5, 1968        Aug. 5, 1970

**Step 2**

Discount the maturity value to the purchase date using the rate specified for discounting.

$2343.74 ←————— $2851.52(1.04)^{-5}$

EXAMPLE 4: A man can buy a piece of property for $4500 cash or for $2000 down and $3000 in 3 years. If the man has money on which he is earning 4% converted semiannually, which is the better plan for him and by how much now?

SOLUTION: We get the present value at 4% compounded semiannually of $3000 due in 3 years.

$$P = 3000(1.02)^{-6} = 3000 \times .887\ 971 = \$2663.91$$

Adding this to the $2000 down payment makes the present value of the time payment plan $4663.91. By paying $4500 cash, the man saves $163.91 now.

EXAMPLE 5: A piece of property can be purchased for $2850 cash or for $3000 in 12 months. Which is the better plan for the buyer if money is worth 7% compounded quarterly to him? Give the cash (present value) equivalent of the savings made by adopting the better plan.

SOLUTION: Alternate purchase plans can be compared by bringing all payments to the same point in time and seeing which plan is better. While the comparison point can be anywhere in time, it is usually best to make the comparison on a present value basis. This gets all proposals on a now basis, the point in time when the decision is to be made.

Putting the focal date now and using (11) to discount the $3000 we have

$$P = 3000(1.0175)^{-4} = 3000 \times .932\ 959 = \$2798.88$$

The $2850 cash payment is simply $2850 at the focal date. Since the present value of the $3000 due in a year has a present value that is less than the cash payment, it is better to pay later. The cash equivalent of the savings is

$$2850.00 - 2798.88 = \$51.12$$

A different rate of interest could lead to a different decision. If the buyer could get only 4% compounded quarterly on his money, the present value of $3000 is

$$P = 3000(1.01)^{-4} = 3000 \times .960\ 980 = \$2882.94$$

It is now better to pay cash and save 2882.94 − 2850.00 = $32.94 on a cash basis.

### EXERCISE 3d

(Use Bankers' Rule for simple interest computations for part of a period when calendar dates are given.)

1. What principal is needed to accumulate $3000 in 8 years at $4\frac{1}{2}\%$ converted semiannually? ($2101.40)
2. What is the present value at $4\frac{1}{2}\%$ compounded semiannually of $3460 due in 18 months?
3. Find the present value of $5000 due in 5 years if money is worth 5% compounded semiannually. ($3905.99)
4. Find the present value of $450.80 due in $2\frac{1}{2}$ years if money is worth 6% compounded semiannually.
5. What is the present value at 4% compounded quarterly of $12,000 due in 18 months? ($11,304.54)
6. Find the present value of $3500 due in $4\frac{1}{2}$ years if money is worth 5%.
7. A man owns a note for $2500 due in 5 years. What should a buyer pay for the note if he wishes to earn 5% converted quarterly on his money? What is the compound discount? ($1950.02; $549.98)
8. An obligation of $5000 is due on December 1, 1977. What is the value of this obligation on July 16, 1972, at 4% compounded semiannually?
9. On September 3, 1972, Mr. Lovett buys some equipment for $3000 from the Excello Company. He signs a note promising to pay the $3000 with interest at 6% compounded semiannually in 18 months. On December 3, 1972, the Excello Company sells the note to a finance company that charges

an interest rate of 8% converted quarterly for discounting. How much does the Excello Company get for the note?                    ($2969.15)

10. A note dated June 1, 1969, calls for the payment of $850 in 6 years. On March 15, 1972, it is sold at a price that will yield the buyer 4%. How much is paid for the note?

11. Mr. Durkin gets a note which calls for repayment of $3000 in 5 years, together with compound interest at 4% converted quarterly. He immediately sells the note to a buyer who charges an interest rate of 6% converted semiannually for discounting. How much does Mr. Durkin get for the note?
($2723.81)

12. A note dated September 15, 1971, calls for the payment of $400 with interest at 6% per annum in 4 years. On December 20, 1973, the note is sold at a price that will yield $4\frac{1}{2}$% compounded semiannually. Compute the selling price.

13. A note for $800 is due in 5 years with interest at 4%. At the end of 3 years it is discounted at 5%. What are the proceeds at the time of discounting?
($882.83)

14. A debt of $2500 is due on September 15, 1974. What payment must be made on July 17, 1972, to repay the debt if the borrower is permitted to discount the debt at 3% compounded semiannually?

15. On August 9, 1972, Mr. Lufkin borrows $4000 from Mr. Feld. He gives Mr. Feld a note promising to repay the money in 5 years with interest at 5%. On February 9, 1974, Mr. Feld sells the note to a buyer who charges a rate of 7% compounded semiannually for discount purposes. How much does Mr. Feld get for the note?                    ($4012.59)

16. A note for $2000 dated June 1, 1972, is due with compound interest at 5% compounded semiannually 3 years after date. On December 1, 1973, the holder of the note has it discounted by a lender who charges 6% compounded semiannually. What are the proceeds?

17. Find the present value of $2000 due in 15 months if money is worth 7% converted semiannually.                    ($1835.46)

18. Thirty-five hundred dollars is due on October 30, 1974. At $4\frac{1}{2}$% compounded semiannually, what is the value of this obligation on August 1, 1972?

19. Mr. Wurtz sells the note on page 103 on March 16, 1973, to a lender who charges 6% compounded semiannually for discounting. How much does he receive?                    ($2005.66)

20. If the above note is discounted on September 21, 1973, by a lender who charges 8% converted quarterly, how much will Mr. Wurtz receive?

21. A man can buy a lot for $2800 cash or for payments of $1500 down and $1500 in 2 years. If he can earn $4\frac{1}{2}$% converted semiannually on his money, which plan is better?                    (Saves $72.26 now by paying cash)

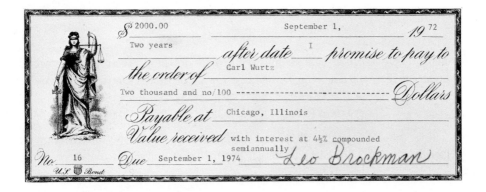

$2000.00                                     September 1, _____ 19 72

Two years
_____ *after date* ___ I ___ *promise to pay to*
*the order of* ___ Carl Wurtz

Two thousand and no/100 --------------------------------------- *Dollars*

*Payable at* ___ Chicago, Illinois

*Value received* with interest at 4½% compounded
semiannually
No. ___ 16 ___ *Due* ___ September 1, 1974 ___ *Leo Brockman*
U.S. Bond

**22.** What would be the better plan for the man in Problem 21 if he can earn 6% converted annually on his money?

## 3.15   Extension of the Tables

When a problem has a greater number of periods than is given in the tables, the tables can be extended by using the law of exponents for factors with a common base: $a^m \times a^n = a^{m+n}$. Applying this law in reverse order to the *Amount of* 1 factor, we get: $(1 + i)^{m+n} = (1 + i)^m \times (1 + i)^n$. Note that while the individual exponents add to the total exponent, the required factor is obtained by *multiplying* the individual factors.

EXAMPLE 1: Find the compound amount of $100 for 20 years at 6% compounded monthly.

SOLUTION: $n$ is 240 and the table goes only to 180. However, $(1.005)^{180} \times (1.005)^{60} = (1.005)^{240}$. Using these two factors, we have

$$S = 100 \times 2.45409 \times 1.34885 = \$331.02$$

When $n$ is an even number the work can be simplified by using the same factor more than once. In this example $(1.005)^{120} \times (1.005)^{120} = (1.005)^{240}$. Substituting accumulation factors, we have

$$S = 100 \times 1.81940 \times 1.81940 = \$331.02$$

The required multiplications may be done in any order.

EXAMPLE 2: In his will, an alumnus appointed a trust company to handle his estate. The decedent instructed the trust company to set aside a sum in a separate account sufficient to pay his alma mater $250,000 at the end of 40 years. What sum should the trust company deposit in the separate account if it earns 3% converted monthly?

SOLUTION: Substituting $S = 250,000$, $i = .0025$, and $n = 480$ in (11),

$$P = 250,000(1.0025)^{-480}$$

The *Present Worth of* 1 factor must be broken down into factors with powers no larger than 180 since this is the largest $n$ in our tables. One solution would be

$$250,000(1.0025)^{-180}(1.0025)^{-180}(1.0025)^{-120}$$

Since we are dealing with a large sum of money for a long time, complete factors were substituted and calculations made on a desk calculator.

$$P = 250,000 \times .637\ 986\ 3214 \times .637\ 986\ 3214 \times .741\ 095\ 6173 = \$75,411.40$$

To show how an alternate choice of factors would lead to the same result with less work, the problem is reworked below with the $n$ of 480 divided into 3 equal parts.

$$P = 250,000[(1.0025)^{-160}]^3 = 250,000(.670\ 654\ 7320)^3 = \$75,411.40$$

EXAMPLE 3: A sum of $75,411.40 was deposited in an account paying $3\%$ converted monthly. Find the amount at the end of 40 years. The result will be a check on our answer to Example 2.

SOLUTION: Substituting $P = \$75,411.40$, $i = .0025$, and $n = 480$ in (9),

$$S = 75,411.40(1.0025)^{480} = 75,411.40[(1.0025)^{160}]^3$$
$$= 75,411.40(1.491\ 080\ 2120)^3 = \$250,000.00$$

With a calculator, these calculations can be done quickly and we have a check on our work even though we are dealing with hundreds of thousands of dollars and hundreds of conversion periods.

### EXERCISE 3e

1. Find the compound amount if $250 is invested at $4\%$ compounded semi-annually for 40 years. ($1218.86)

2. What is the compound amount of $4500 invested at $5\%$ compounded monthly for 16 years?

3. If $35,000 is invested at $3\%$ compounded semiannually for 50 years, what will be the amount? ($155,121.59)

4. If $355.60 is invested at $5\%$ compounded quarterly, what will be the amount in 20 years?

5. Find the amount of $4000 invested for 25 years at $6\%$ converted monthly. ($17,859.89)

6. Find the amount of $14,000 invested at $4\%$ compounded monthly at the end of 22 years and 3 months.

7. How much must be invested today at $4\%$ compounded semiannually to amount to $10,000 in 50 years? ($1380.33)

8. How much must be invested today at 4% compounded quarterly to amount to $5000 in 25 years?

9. How much must be deposited now in an investment paying 3% converted monthly to amount to $100,000 in 20 years? ($54,922.27)

10. How much must be deposited now in an investment paying 4% converted monthly to amount to $100,000 in 20 years.

## 3.16 Finding the Rate

In the basic formula for compound interest, $S = P(1 + i)^n$, there are four quantities. We have shown how to determine the amount and the present value using Table 2. When the amount, principal, and time are known, the approximate rate can be found by linear interpolation. Since the rate is usually wanted only for information or purposes of comparison, this method is sufficiently accurate for most practical purposes. If a rate must be determined to several decimal places, refined methods of interpolation will be found in the Compound Interest and Annuity Tables published by the Financial Publishing Company. Logarithmic tables can also be used following the method given on page 126.

EXAMPLE: If $500 amounts to $700 in 5 years with interest compounded quarterly, what is the rate of interest?

SOLUTION: We substitute in (9) and get the *Amount of* 1 factor. Rate problems in this book are based on factors carried to 4 decimal places.

$$500(1 + i)^{20} = 700$$
$$(1 + i)^{20} = \tfrac{700}{500} = 1.4000$$

We must now find the value of $i$ for which $(1 + i)^{20} = 1.4000$. We go along line 20 in Table 2 until we find an *Amount of* 1 of 1.4000 or, as is usually the case, values on each side of the one we are looking for. We put the results in tabular form and let $d$ represent the desired difference.

$$\frac{d}{.250} = \frac{531}{679}$$

$$d = .250 \times \tfrac{531}{679} = .196$$

Therefore the desired rate per period is $1.500 + .196 = 1.696\%$. The nominal rate, compounded quarterly, is $4i$ or $4 \times 1.696 = 6.78\%$.

It is not necessary to write the difference between 1.4148 and 1.3469 as .0679. We can write 679 with the decimal point and zero understood. The number 679 is called the **tabular difference**. Omitting leading zeros is the usual practice and is the one we follow from now on.

If only the nominal rate is required, it is better to use the marginal index and work in terms of nominal rates. This eliminates multiplying the rate per period by the number of conversions in a year. The symbol $j_{(m)}$ stands for the nominal rate $j$ compounded $m$ times per year. With these simplifications, the problem becomes

$$
\begin{array}{ccc}
 & j_{(4)} \text{ in } \% & (1 + i)^{20} \\
 & 7 & 1.4148 \\
1 \quad d \begin{bmatrix} j \\ 6 \end{bmatrix} & & \begin{array}{c} 1.4000 \\ 1.3469 \end{array} \Big] 531 \quad \Big] 679
\end{array}
$$

$$
\frac{d}{1} = \frac{531}{679}
$$

$$
d = .78
$$

Therefore the nominal annual rate compounded quarterly is $6 + .78 = 6.78\%$.

### 3.17   Economic Analysis

An important concern of economists is forecasting the future performance of the economy. Business leaders use forecasts to help make investment, production and marketing decisions that are expected to result in profits for their companies. Based on forecasts, government administrators set policies to promote economic growth, full employment, and stable prices. In the 1967 Economic Report of the President, the Council of Economic Advisers stated:

...those concerned with national policies for economic growth have ... become aware of the power of compound interest. If the American economy continues to grow at 4 percent a year, output will double in 18 years, triple in 28, quadruple in 35. If that potential is wisely and efficiently shared among competing uses, great advances in the economic well-being of all Americans are assured.*

The American tendency to applaud material growth has resulted in too little attention to the less easily measured quality of life. This may be changing as concern over health care, nutrition, pollution, and other problems indicates a reordering of output priorities to emphasize quality as well as quantity. Consideration is being given to the establishment of a Council of Social Advisors to report to the President and the nation about social conditions in the same way that the Council of Economic Advisors reports on economic progress.

Because of many variables and uncertainties, economic forecasts involve risks that are not present in compound interest problems with definite rates.

* Economic Report of the President, January 1967, p. 135.

However, sound forecasting methods reduce risks by making predictions more dependable. Successful forecasting relies on careful and informed analysis of the past. If an economic time series plots as approximately a straight line on a semilogarithmic or ratio graph, the past rate of change was fairly constant. The compound interest law can be used to determine this rate which can then be used as a help in making forecasts.

Sometimes an economist is interested in monetary changes in the data he is studying. He then works with data expressed in current dollars. At other times he may be concerned with changes in real or actual output. This requires data which have been adjusted to eliminate the effect of price changes or changes in the value of money. Data deflated to base year prices or expressed in terms of dollars of constant purchasing power referred to a base year are a measure of volume of output.

An example of the type of time series with which economists are concerned is Gross National Product. GNP is the most important key measure of the performance of the economy. It is the total value at current market prices of all final goods and services produced by the nation's economy in a year or at an annual rate. To offset the effect of price changes, deflated GNP figures are also determined. They can be compared to show the year-to-year changes in constant dollars and are a good measure of changes in total physical output.

The graph below shows how the economy has grown in terms of dollars of constant purchasing power. While there were periods when there were serious drops in output, it is encouraging to note that during the last 20 years

How the United States Economy Has Grown
Gross National Product, 1958 Prices

Billions of Dollars (Ratio Scale)

Source: *1972 Economic Report of the President,* Table B-2.

declines have been small in relationship to total output. This may provide grounds for confidence in fairly stable growth in the future. Over the years, compounding at seemingly modest rates has resulted in impressive increases in goods and services. Because GNP in real terms has been increasing faster than population, we have been enjoying a rising standard of living. In 1950 the per capita GNP in 1958 dollars was $2333. The 1970 value, also in 1958 dollars, was $3525.

Some economists believe that government fiscal policy—taxing and spending programs—is the important determinant of economic progress. Others feel that monetary policy is the dominant influence on the economy. A monetary policy that is suggested by some economists is a steady rate of growth in the quantity of money. Controlling the amount of money is the responsibility of monetary authorities. The money supply must be increased fast enough to be adequate for carrying on the nation's business. But if the money supply is increased too rapidly, there is danger of inflation. An idea of desirable rates of increase can be obtained by studying past trends in relation to other economic variables.

EXAMPLE: If the money supply increased from $141.1 billions in 1960 to $170.3 billions in 1966, what was the annual compounded rate of increase?

SOLUTION: Substituting in the compound interest formula,

$$141.1(1 + i)^6 = 170.3$$

$$(1 + i)^6 = \frac{170.3}{141.1} = 1.207$$

$$\frac{d}{.5} = \frac{13}{35}$$

$$d = \frac{.5 \times 13}{35} = .2$$

$$i = 3.0 + .2 = 3.2\%$$

Efforts to forecast the future start with a search for regularities in data of the past. When a time series plots as approximately a straight line on semilogarithmic or ratio paper, the period-to-period rate of change has been about the same. Then the compound interest law becomes a promising tool for economic analysis and forecasting.

Because there is always uncertainty as to the extent to which past regularities will hold in the future, economic forecasting and the conduct of economic policy are partly an art. The art is to determine the timing and amount of policy changes to keep our large and complicated economy on a course that results in nearly full employment, relatively stable prices, and growth that includes quality of life as well as quantity of output.

Sometimes a ratio graph of a time series exhibits more than one linear pattern. During the 1960's the Consumer Price Index increased from 88.7 in 1960 to 116.3 in 1970, an annual compounded rate of increase of 2.7 percent. However, as the graph below shows, there were three fairly well-defined periods of approximately constant growth with quite different annual rates.

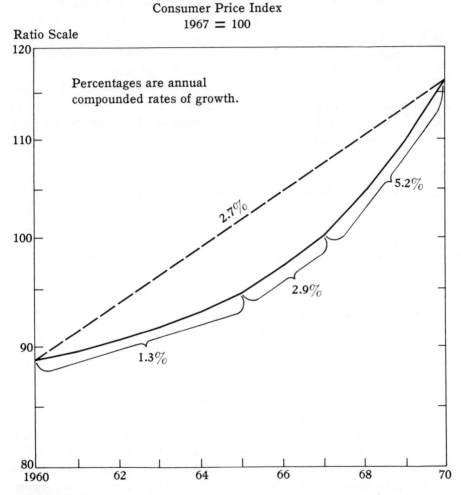

Consumer Price Index
1967 = 100

*EXERCISE 3f*

(In problems 1 to 4 get answer to two decimal places when expressed as a percent. In problems 5 to 18 get answer to one decimal place when expressed as a per cent.)

1. For a sum of money to double itself in 15 years, what must be the rate of interest converted annually? (4.72%)

2. If an investment increases from $5000 to $6000 in 5 years, what was the nominal rate of interest compounded semiannually?

3. If $750 accumulates to $850 in 6 years, find the nominal rate converted semiannually. (2.10%)

4. If an investment increases 50% in 12 years, what is the effective rate of interest?

5. The sales of a business increased from $30.4 million in 1967 to $43.5 million in 1972. What was the annual rate of increase, assuming that it was constant from year to year? (Answer to .1%.) (7.4%)

6. If the population of a city increases from 400,000 to 490,000 at approximately a constant rate during a decade, what is the annual rate of increase?

7. A firm organized in 1948 had sales of $30,000 that year. In 1968 the sales were $120,000. What was the annual rate of increase, assuming that it was approximately constant from year to year? (7.2%)

8. The sales of a business increased at approximately a constant rate from $5.8 million in 1962 to $7.9 million in 1967. What was the annual rate of increase?

9. A man bought a house for $8000. In addition to the cost of the house he paid $100 for legal fees and $50 for a survey. Three years later he sold the house for $10,000 from which the real estate agent deducted 5% commission. The increased net selling price represents what annual rate of return on the original total cost? (5.2%)

10. A man purchased 10 shares of Cincinnati and Suburban Bell Telephone Stock in 1957 when the price was $77 a share. Commissions and other buying costs totaled $10. He sold the stock in 1963 when the price was $104 a share. Selling costs totaled $12. Find the average annual increase in the net value of his investment.

11. During the period 1966 to 1970 the earnings per share of the Columbia Gas System increased at approximately a constant rate. If the earnings were $2.26 in 1966 and $2.80 in 1970, what was the annual compounded rate of increase? (5.5%)

12. During the period 1966 to 1971 the earnings per share of American Electric Power Company increased at approximately a constant rate from $1.90 in 1966 to $2.43 in 1971. Find the annual compounded rate of increase.

13. From 1950 to 1965 the gross national product in constant 1958 dollars increased from $355.3 billions to $616.7 billions. What was the annual compounded rate of growth? (3.7%)

14. From 1956 to 1966 GNP in current dollars increased from $419.2 billions to $743.3 billions. Find the annual compounded rate of growth.

**15.** Values of disposable personal income for selected years are

|  | DISPOSABLE |
| --- | --- |
|  | PERSONAL INCOME |
| YEAR | (BILLIONS) |
| 1960 | $350.0 |
| 1965 | 473.2 |
| 1970 | 687.8 |

Find the annual compounded rates of growth for 1960–1965; 1965–1970; 1960–1970.                                         (6.2%; 7.8%; 7.0%)

**16.** The average gross weekly earnings of factory production workers increased from $58.32 in 1950 to $133.73 in 1970. Find the annual compounded rate of growth.

**17.** Total mortgage debt on 1- to 4-family houses increased from $141.3 billions in 1960 to $280.2 billions in 1970. Find the annual compounded rate of growth.                                         (7.1%)

**18.** Personal consumption expenses went from $325.2 billions in 1960 to $615.8 billions in 1970. Find the annual compounded rate of growth.

**19.** The mathematics of finance is used in analyzing and comparing rates of change of economic time series. Refer to the latest *Economic Report of the President* and complete the table below to show how annual rates of change in the 1960's compare with the 1950's.

| | | | | ANNUAL COMPOUNDED RATE OF GROWTH | |
| --- | --- | --- | --- | --- | --- |
| TIME SERIES | 1950 | 1960 | 1970 | 1950–60 | 1960–70 |
| U.S. population, thousands | 152,271 | 180,684 | — | 1.7% | — |
| Gross National Product, current dollars, billions | $284.8 | $503.7 | — | 5.9% | — |
| Gross National Product, 1958 prices, billions | $355.3 | $487.7 | — | 3.2% | — |
| Consumer Price Index (1967 = 100) | 72.1 | 88.7 | — | 2.1% | — |
| Corporate after tax profits, billions | $24.9 | $26.7 | — | .7% | — |
| Average hourly earnings in manufacturing | $1.44 | $2.26 | — | 4.6% | — |
| Employed workers, thousands | 58,920 | 65,778 | — | 1.1% | — |
| Money supply, billions | $116.2 | $141.7 | — | 2.0% | — |

## 3.18   Finding the Time

We now find the time when the principal, amount, and rate are known. To do this we determine the numerical value of the *Amount of* 1 factor, $(1 + i)^n$, and then locate this factor, or the values on both sides of it, in Table 2. If no interest is allowed for part of a period, we can take $n$ corresponding to the factor closest to the computed value of $(1 + i)^n$. However, if we want at least a certain amount, we take the $n$ corresponding to the factor larger than the computed value. If simple interest is allowed for part of a period, we can use either the simple interest formula or interpolation to get the exact answer.

EXAMPLE 1: How long will it take $200 to amount to $350 at 3% compounded semiannually?

SOLUTION: Substituting in the compound interest formula, we have

$$200(1.015)^n = 350$$
$$(1.015)^n = \tfrac{350}{200}$$
$$(1.015)^n = 1.75$$

We now look under 1.5% for an accumulation factor of 1.75. As is usually the case, we do not find this exact value. If $n$ is 37 the factor is 1.735, and if $n$ is 38 the factor is 1.761. The nearest time is therefore 38 periods or 19 years. If this is a savings account or other investment on which interest is paid only on conversion dates, the closest amount to $350 would be $200(1.015)^{38} = \$352.16$.

If simple interest is allowed for a part of a period, we can get the compound amount at the end of 37 periods and then carry this forward a sufficient time to get $350. For 37 periods $S = 200(1.015)^{37} = 200 \times 1.73478 = \$346.96$. Now we must determine how long it takes this amount to draw $3.04 simple interest. Using the simple interest formula, $I = Prt$, we have $3.04 = 346.96 \times .03 \times t$. Solving this for $t$ we get .292 years or 105 days (based on a 360-day year). We can also get the answer by interpolating between the two values.

In the above diagram $d$ is used to indicate the desired difference. Since the periods in this problem are 180 days, we have

$$\frac{d}{180} = \frac{152}{260}$$

$$d = 180 \times \tfrac{152}{260} = 105$$

Thus the time for $200 to amount to $350 at 3% compounded semiannually is $18\frac{1}{2}$ years plus an additional 105 days if simple interest is allowed for a part of a period.

EXAMPLE 2: Draw a graph showing the time required to double your money if interest is compounded annually and no interest is allowed for part of a period.

SOLUTION: The time for any given rate is the smallest value of $n$ which results in an *Amount of* 1 factor of at least 2. For example, if the rate is 5% this occurs at 15 periods. More precisely, at the end of 15 years each dollar will grow to $2.08.

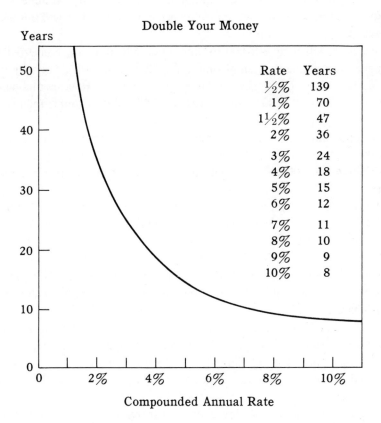

Double Your Money

Years

| Rate | Years |
|------|-------|
| ½% | 139 |
| 1% | 70 |
| 1½% | 47 |
| 2% | 36 |
| 3% | 24 |
| 4% | 18 |
| 5% | 15 |
| 6% | 12 |
| 7% | 11 |
| 8% | 10 |
| 9% | 9 |
| 10% | 8 |

Compounded Annual Rate

**EXERCISE 3g**

1. How long will it take an investment to increase at least 50% in dollar value if the interest rate is 5% converted annually. No interest for part of a period. (9 years)

2. Find the time required to triple your money if interest is compounded annually and no interest is allowed for a part of a period and the rate is: (a) 2%; (b) 3%; (c) 4%; (d) 5%; (e) 6%; (f) 7%; (g) 8%.

3. How long will it take $750 to accumulate to $1000 at 5% converted semi-annually? Give answer to the nearest period. (12)

4. How long will it take $4000 to amount to $5000 at $3\frac{1}{2}$% converted semi-annually? Give answer to the nearest period.

5. A child 8 years old is left $1600. Under the conditions of the will, the money is to be invested until it amounts to $2500. If the money is invested at $3\frac{1}{2}$%, how old will the boy be when he gets the $2500? Give answer to the nearest birthday. (21 years old)

6. A man invests $1000 at 6% compounded semiannually on June 1, 1964. No interest is allowed for a part of a period. On what date will this account have at least $2000 in it?

7. How long will it take $3000 to amount to $3600 at 3% converted semi-annually? Assume that simple interest is allowed for a fraction of a period and give answer to the nearest day. (6 years and 44 days)

8. In what time will $200 amount to $250 at 5%? Allow simple interest for a fraction of a period and get the answer to the nearest day.

9. The population of a city has been increasing at the rate of 3% a year. If the population is now 425,000, how long will it take the city to grow to a population of 500,000, assuming that the annual rate of increase remains at 3%? (5+ years)

10. The sales of a business have been increasing at approximately 7% a year. If the sales in 1970 were $14.2 million, when will sales reach $21 million assuming that the rate of increase remains at 7%? Give answer to the nearest year.

11. A loan company charges 36% a year compounded monthly on small loans. How long will it take to triple money at this rate? Give answer to the nearest month. (37 months)

12. An alumnus leaves $75,000 to a university with the provision that it is to be invested until it amounts to $100,000. From then on the interest is to be used each year for scholarships. If the school gets 3% compounded annually how many years after they receive the gift will the fund first amount to at least $100,000?

13. How long will it take an investment to increase 33% if it draws interest at 6% compounded quarterly? Answer to nearest period. (19 periods)

14. It is estimated that a piece of property will increase in value at the rate of 5% a year. If the property is purchased for $45,000 in 1971, what is its predicted value for the year 1976?

15. Five hundred dollars is put in a savings deposit on June 1, 1964. Interest

is allowed at $2\frac{1}{2}\%$ compounded semiannually, but no interest is paid for a part of a period. What is the date when this account will have at least $750 in it? What will be the amount at that time?        (Dec. 1, 1980; $753.37)

**16.** A man invests $2000 at $7\%$ compounded semiannually on September 1, 1965. No interest is allowed for a part of a period. On what date will this investment first amount to at least $3000 and what will be the amount at that time?

**17.** During the period 1966–1971, the dividends paid by Pacific Gas and Electric Company increased about $5\%$ a year. In 1971 a dividend of $1.64 per share of common stock was declared. If the $5\%$ rate of increase continues, when can the dividends be expected to reach $2.00 per share?        (1975)

**18.** Dividends paid by Union Electric Company have been increasing about $5\%$ a year. In 1966 a dividend of $1.14 was paid per common share. If the present rate of increase continues, when can the dividend be expected to reach $1.50?

## 3.19   Equations of Value

In business transactions it is often necessary to exchange one set of obligations for another set of different amounts due at different times. To do this it is necessary to bring all of the obligations to a common date called a **focal date**. We then set up an **equation of value** in which all of the original obligations at the focal date equal all of the new obligations at the focal date. This procedure is based on the fact that the value of any sum of money can be found at any time by accumulating it at compound interest if we take it into the future, or discounting it if we bring it back in time. The equation of value should be thoroughly understood because it is the most effective way to solve many investment problems, particularly the more complicated ones.

EXAMPLE 1: A man owes $200 due in 1 year and $300 due in 2 years. The lender agrees to let him settle both obligations with a cash payment. Before the problem can be worked, the two parties must agree on an interest rate or value of money to be used in setting up the equation of value. In this case we assume that the lender specifies that $4\%$ compounded semiannually will be used. If this is as much or more than the borrower can get elsewhere, he would be wise to use his cash to cancel the debts. Assume that the borrower is satisfied with this rate of interest and determine the size of the cash payment.

SOLUTION: The first thing to decide is the location of the focal date. In compound interest problems the answer will be the same regardless of the location of the focal date. Therefore, the only consideration is making the work a minimum. If there is only one unknown payment, putting the focal date at the time that payment is made will eliminate long division.

Most students find a sketch similar to the one below helpful in getting times correct in focal date problems. If the original obligations are put on one side of the time scale and the payments on the other side, the equation of value can be quickly and correctly determined from the sketch.

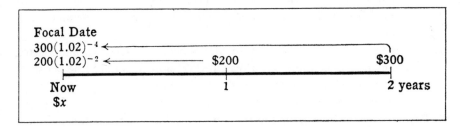

The sketch shows that the $200 must be discounted for 2 periods and the $300 for 4 periods to transfer them to the focal date. Because the focal date is at the point where the unknown payment is made, we can set up the equation of value:

$$x = 200(1.02)^{-2} + 300(1.02)^{-4}$$
$$= 200 \times .96117 + 300 \times .92385$$
$$= 192.23 + 277.16 = \$469.39$$

Thus a cash payment of $469.39 will equitably settle debts of $200 and $300 due in 1 and 2 years if money is worth 4% compounded semiannually.

Because the focal date method of solving problems is so useful in the mathematics of finance, it is important that students both understand and have confidence in this method. To show that we do have a fair and correct answer to this problem, let us consider it in another way. Suppose that the borrower had invested the $469.39 at 4% compounded semiannually, the rate he and the lender agreed on. At the end of 1 year this would amount to $469.39(1.02)^2$ or $488.35. If he deducts the $200 he now owes, this will leave a balance of $288.35. Carrying this forward for another year would result in an amount of $288.35(1.02)^2$ or $300.00. It is a good idea for students to check several problems in this way until they are convinced of the utility and the accuracy of the focal date and the equation of value.

EXAMPLE 2: A man owes $500 due now. The lender agrees to let him settle this obligation with 2 equal payments in 1 and 2 years respectively. Find the size of these payments if the settlement is based on 6%.

SOLUTION: Since there are 2 unknown payments, it will not be possible to avoid division in the final step. However, if the focal date is put at 2 years, the coefficient will be as simple as possible and the work will be less than if the focal date were put anywhere else. A sketch shows what factors are needed to get everything to the focal date.

Since the two payments are equal we shall designate each of them by $x$. The value of the first one *at the focal date* is $x(1.06)$. Since the second one is already at the focal date, its value at that point is $x$.

We now set up an equation of value in which the payments carried to the focal date equal the original obligation at the focal date.

$$x(1.06) + x = 500(1.06)^2$$
$$2.06x = 500 \times 1.12360 = 561.80$$
$$x = \frac{561.80}{2.06} = \$272.72$$

Thus payments of \$272.72 in one and two years will equitably settle a debt of \$500 due now if money is worth 6%. Sometimes students think that this answer should be accumulated or discounted from the focal date to the time the payment is made. This is incorrect. The equation of value gives the size of the payment at the time the payment is made.

EXAMPLE 3: A piece of property is sold for \$5000. The buyer pays \$2000 cash. He signs a noninterest bearing note for \$1000 due in 1 year, and a second noninterest bearing note for \$1000 due in 2 years. If the seller charges 8% compounded annually, what noninterest bearing note due in 3 years will pay off the debt?

SOLUTION: A time diagram of the debt and the payments shows that 3 years is a good location for the focal date.

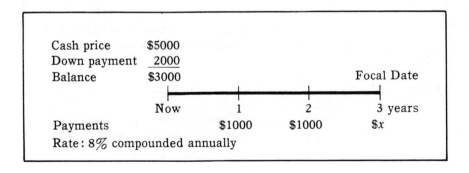

Carrying the $3000 balance and the payments to the focal date we get the equation of value,

$$x = 3000(1.08)^3 - 1000(1.08)^2 - 1000(1.08)$$
$$= (3000 \times 1.259712) - (1000 \times 1.166400) - (1000 \times 1.08)$$
$$= 3779.14 - 1166.40 - 1080.00$$
$$= \$1532.74$$

This problem can also be worked or checked using United States Rule.

| | |
|---|---:|
| Original debt | $3000.00 |
| Interest for 1 year | 240.00 |
| Amount due in 1 year | 3240.00 |
| Deduct first payment | 1000.00 |
| New balance | 2240.00 |
| Interest for 1 year | 179.20 |
| Amount due in 2 years | 2419.20 |
| Deduct second payment | 1000.00 |
| New balance | 1419.20 |
| Interest for 1 year | 113.54 |
| Amount due in 3 years | $1532.74 |

EXAMPLE 4: If any obligations bear interest, it is first necessary to compute the maturity values. A man owes $1000 due in 3 years with interest at 5% compounded quarterly, and $500 due in 5 years with interest at 4%. If money is worth 6%, what single payment 6 years hence will be equivalent to the original obligations?

SOLUTION: First get the maturity values of the debts:

$$1000(1.0125)^{12} = 1000 \times 1.160754 = \$1,160.75$$
$$500(1.04)^5 = 500 \times 1.21665 = \$608.33$$

Now sketch the problem and set up the equation of value:

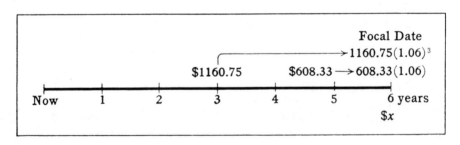

$$x = 1160.75(1.06)^3 + 608.33(1.06)$$
$$= (1160.75 \times 1.191016) + (608.33 \times 1.06)$$
$$= 1382.47 + 644.83 = \$2027.30$$

EXAMPLE 5: On June 1, 1971, a man obtained a $5000 loan. He is to pay $1000 a year on the principal plus 6% interest on the unpaid balance. The repayment schedule for this loan is given below.

| PAYMENT NUMBER | DATE | TOTAL PAYMENT | PAYMENT ON INTEREST | PAYMENT ON PRINCIPAL | BALANCE OF LOAN |
|---|---|---|---|---|---|
| | | | | | $5000 |
| 1 | June 1, 1972 | $1300 | $300 | $1000 | 4000 |
| 2 | June 1, 1973 | 1240 | 240 | 1000 | 3000 |
| 3 | June 1, 1974 | 1180 | 180 | 1000 | 2000 |
| 4 | June 1, 1975 | 1120 | 120 | 1000 | 1000 |
| 5 | June 1, 1976 | 1060 | 60 | 1000 | 0 |

On June 1, 1973, the lender sells this contract to a buyer who wants a yield of 8% converted annually. Find the sale price.

SOLUTION: The seller gets the payment due on June 1, 1973. The buyer will get the three remaining payments. A time diagram shows that June 1, 1973, is a good place for the focal date as this is the point in time when the purchase price is to be determined.

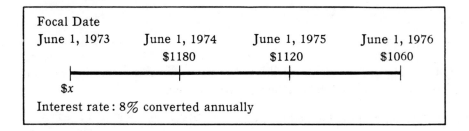

Discounting all payments to the focal date,

$$x = 1180(1.08)^{-1} + 1120(1.08)^{-2} + 1060(1.08)^{-3}$$
$$= (1180 \times .925926) + (1120 \times .857\,339) + (1060 \times .793\,832)$$
$$= 1092.59 + 960.22 + 841.46$$
$$= \$2894.27$$

EXAMPLE 6: A man stipulates in his will that $30,000 from his estate is to be placed in a fund from which his three children are to each receive an equal amount when they reach age 21. When the man dies, the children are ages 19, 16, and 14. If the fund is invested at 4% converted semiannually, how much does each receive?

SOLUTION: A sketch of the problem helps to get the required times.

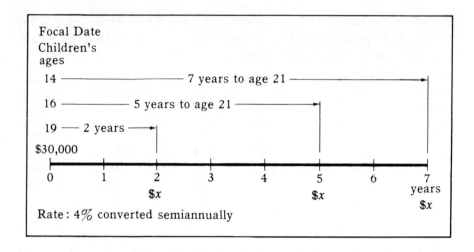

Focal Date
Children's
ages

14 ——————————— 7 years to age 21 ——————————————→

16 —————————— 5 years to age 21 ———————————→

19 —— 2 years ——→

$30,000

0      1      2      3      4      5      6      7
            $x                   $x          years
                                              $x

Rate: 4% converted semiannually

Bringing all sums to the focal date at $2\%$ a period,

$$x(1.02)^{-4} + x(1.02)^{-10} + x(1.02)^{-14} = 30,000.00$$
$$.923\ 8454x + .820\ 3483x + .757\ 8750x = 30,000.00$$

$$x = \frac{30,000.00}{2.502\ 0687}$$

$$= \$11,990.08$$

CHECK: The answer should be checked to be certain that everything will come out right with each child getting the same amount.

| | | |
|---|---|---|
| Amount in fund at end of 2 years | $= 30,000.00(1.02)^4 =$ | $32,472.96 |
| Pay oldest child | | 11,990.08 |
| | Balance in fund | $20,482.88 |
| Amount in fund after 3 more years | $= 20,482.88(1.02)^6 =$ | 23,067.05 |
| Pay second child | | 11,990.08 |
| | Balance in fund | $11,076.97 |
| Amount in fund after 2 more years | $= 11,076.97(1.02)^4 =$ | $11,990.07 |

The 1 cent difference is due to rounding. A problem like this shows the power of an equation of value which leads directly to the solution. It also shows why a lawyer may need an accountant or mathematical economist to help him set up a problem like this so it can be explained to the Surrogate Court Judge.

**EXERCISE 3h**

1. A man owes $300 due in 2 years and $500 due in 4 years. If money is worth 4% converted semiannually, what single payment 3 years hence will settle the obligations?                                                        ($792.71)

2. On June 1, 1971, a man owes $4000 which he is unable to repay. His creditor charges him 8% converted semiannually from that date. If the debtor pays $2000 on June 1, 1972, how much would he have to pay on June 1, 1973, to discharge the rest of his obligation?

3. Hull owes Graves $300 due at the end of 2 years and $300 due at the end of 3 years. He wishes to replace these two obligations with a single payment due at the end of $2\frac{1}{2}$ years. If the two agree that money is worth 5% converted semiannually, what will be the size of the payment?        ($600.18)

4. Wilson owes Smith $500 due at the end of 2 years and $1000 due at the end of 4 years. Both men agree that Wilson may settle his obligations with a single payment at the end of 3 years using an interest rate of 7%. Solve this problem putting the focal date at 3 years. Solve a second time using 4 years for the focal date.

5. A man leaves $10,000 to his 2 children with the provision that they are to get equal amounts when they reach age 21. If the children are 12 and 17 when the man dies, how much will each receive? The money is invested at $3\frac{1}{2}$% compounded semiannually.                                          ($6241.45)

6. A man leaves an estate of $30,000 which is invested at 4% compounded semiannually. At the time of his death, he has three children aged 13, 15, and 19. Each child is to receive an equal amount from the estate when he reaches age 21. How much does each get?

7. Suppose that the man in Problem 5 had left each child $5000 with the provision that the money be invested at $3\frac{1}{2}$% compounded semiannually and the compound amount given to each child upon reaching age 21. How much would each get?                (12-year old, $6832.66; 17-year old, $5744.41)

8. Assume that each of the three children in Problem 6 received $10,000 upon the father's death with the provision that the money was to be invested at 4% compounded semiannually until the child reaches age 21. How much would each receive?

9. A piece of property is sold for $10,000. The buyer pays $2000 cash. He signs a noninterest-bearing note for $4000 due in 1 year. If the seller charges 6% converted quarterly for credit, what noninterest-bearing note due in 2 years will pay off the debt?                                          ($4766.48)

10. Assume that the buyer in Problem 9 signs a noninterest-bearing note for $4000 due in 2 years. The remainder of the debt is to be met with a non-interest-bearing note due in 1 year. For how much should this note be drawn if the seller charges 6% converted quarterly?

**11.** Instead of taking $3000 cash, the beneficiary of an estate takes 2 equal payments due in 1 and 2 years respectively. If the investment pays interest at 3% converted quarterly, what will be the size of each payment?

($1568.60)

**12.** A father invests $2000 at 4% compounded semiannually on his son's 12th birthday. If the money is paid to the son in 4 equal annual payments starting on his 18th birthday, what will be the size of each payment?

**13.** A building is sold for $18,000. The buyer pays $3000 cash. He signs a note with a maturity value of $5000 due in 1 year, and a second note with a maturity value of $5000 due in 2 years. If the seller charges interest on the debt at 4%, what should be the maturity value of a third note due in 3 years that will pay off the remainder of the debt?       ($6264.96)

**14.** A man borrows $5000 on March 1, 1973, agreeing to pay 6% compounded semiannually. He pays $2000 on September 1, 1974. How much will he have to pay to settle the debt on October 16, 1975?

**15.** On August 1, 1972, a man bought $300 worth of merchandise and signed a note promising to pay the $300 without interest in 6 months. On November 1, 1972, he bought $500 worth of merchandise and signed a note promising to pay $500 without interest in 6 months. On December 1, 1972, the holder of the notes sold them to a finance company that charged 6% converted monthly. How much does the finance company pay for the notes?

($784.71)

**16.** On June 1, 1973, a man bought $400 worth of goods and gave a note for $400 to be paid in 6 months without interest. On August 1, 1973, he got $400 worth of goods and signed a 6 months noninterest-bearing note for this amount. On November 1, 1973, the company that holds the notes has them discounted by a finance company that charges 6% converted monthly. How much is received for the two notes?

**17.** A man owes $500 due now and $1000 due in 15 months. His creditor will allow him to pay both debts in 18 months provided the settlement is based on 8% converted quarterly. What payment in 18 months will settle both obligations?       ($1583.08)

**18.** A man buys machinery worth $6000. He pays $2000 down and agrees to pay the balance in 2 equal payments in 3 and 6 months respectively. If interest is charged at 6% converted monthly, what will be the size of each payment?

**19.** A piece of property can be purchased for $28,500 cash or for $10,000 down and two equal payments of $10,000 at the end of 1 and 2 years respectively. To pay cash, the buyer would have to withdraw the money from an investment which is paying him 4% converted semiannually. How much will the buyer save now by choosing the better method of payment?

(By paying cash he saves $350.14 now)

**20.** If the buyer in Problem 19 has his money in stocks which are currently yielding 6% on their market value, would you recommend that he sell the stocks and pay cash? Explain your answer in terms of probable savings by adopting your recommendation.

## 3.20   Negative Rates

The compound interest law also applies to quantities which are decreasing at a constant rate. A negative rate is sometimes called a decay coefficient. Negative rates are found in nature in the decay of radioactive substances. The book value of an asset, depreciated according to the double declining balance method (page 285), follows the compound interest law with a negative rate. The sales of a nonadvertised product may decline at approximately a constant rate. When only a limited number of periods is involved, calculations are easy to handle on a desk calculator.

EXAMPLE 1: A new car costs $3000 and depreciates 25% a year. Find the book value at the end of each year for 5 years and the annual depreciation in dollars.

SOLUTION: Substituting $P = 3000$ and $i = -.25$ in (9),

$$S = 3000(1.00 - .25)^n = 3000(.75)^n$$

where $n$ is the number of years. Since values are wanted for each year from 1 to 5, we simply multiply successively by .75.

| YEAR | BOOK VALUE | DEPRECIATION ALLOWANCE |
|---|---|---|
| 0 | $3000.00 | |
| 1 | 3000.00 × .75 = 2250.00 | $750.00 |
| 2 | 2250.00 × .75 = 1687.50 | 562.50 |
| 3 | 1687.50 × .75 = 1265.63 | 421.87 |
| 4 | 1265.63 × .75 = 949.22 | 316.41 |
| 5 | 949.22 × .75 = 711.92 | 237.30 |

With negative rates, the annual depreciation allowance is large at first and then gets progressively smaller. This corresponds to practical experience with many assets.

Negative rate problems can be solved using logarithms as shown in the appendix and in the example on page 129.

With discrete compounding, going forward at a negative rate is not the same as coming back with a positive rate having the same numerical value. For example, if a $1000 asset is decreasing 8% a year, its book value at the end of one year would be $1000(1.00 - .08) = \$920.00$. The *Present Worth of* 1 factor applied to a future amount of 1000 results in a present worth of 1000 × .925 926 = $925.93.

It is possible to use the compound interest table to handle negative rates if Table 2 has a rate with *Present Worth of* 1 factors equal to the depreciation factors for the negative rate. If the rate of decrease is $r$, we look for a rate $i$ in Table 2 such that $(1 - r) = (1 + i)^{-1}$.

EXAMPLE 2: An asset with an initial value of $1000 is decreasing in value 7.4% a year. Use Table 2 to find its value at the end of 5 years.

SOLUTION: $(1 - r) = (1 - .074) = .926$.

Looking in row 1 of the *Present Worth of* 1 column we find .925 925 for a rate of 8% per year. We can now use the *Present Worth of* 1 factors for 8% to get the depreciated value of an asset that is decreasing 7.4% a year. At the end of the 5 years the asset will be worth approximately,

$$1000(1.08)^{-5} = 1000 \times .680\ 583 = \$681$$

This method should be used with the complete Compound Interest Tables of the Financial Publishing Company to get the closest approximation to the required value.

## 3.21   Use of Logarithms

Logarithms can be used to solve problems when compound interest tables are not available or when the time or rate is not in the table. An explanation of logarithms will be found in the appendix.

When the total time is obtained using logarithms, the assumption is that compound interest is earned for the fraction of a period as well as for the number of whole periods. This will lead to slightly different results from those obtained using the factors from Table 2 and linear interpolation. If time is determined by logarithms and simple interest is to be used for the remaining fraction of a period, the amount should be determined for the integral number of periods. Then the simple interest formula can be used to get the additional time needed for this sum to equal the final amount.

When logarithms are used to get the rate, the result is theoretically correct and not an approximation, as was the case using factors from Table 2 and linear interpolation. Under ordinary business conditions when the rate is needed only for comparison purposes, Table 2 leads to sufficiently accurate results.

The examples below show how logs can be used to solve the four types of compound interest problems. Six-place tables have been used for these problems. Although the method remains the same, more extensive tables are needed to get accurate results with large sums of money.

EXAMPLE 1: Counterfeit notes seized by the Secret Service increased from $9.0 million in 1966 to $15.1 million in 1969. This is an annual compounded rate of increase of 19%. Forecast the 1975 value if this rate of increase continues.

SOLUTION: Substituting $P = 15.1$, $i = .19$, and $n = 6$ in (9),

$$S = 15.1(1.19)^6$$

Since 19% is not in Table 2, we take the logarithm of both sides.

$$\log S = \log 15.1 + 6 \log 1.19$$

| | |
|---|---|
| $\log 15.1 =$ | 1.17 8977 |
| $6 \log 1.19 = 6 \times .07\ 5547 =$ | .45 3282 |
| $\log S$ (adding) $=$ | 1.63 2259 |

Looking up the antilog of 1.63 2259, we find $S = \$42.9$ million. The answer is rounded since this is a forecast based on approximate data. However, the result is accurate enough to indicate that counterfeiting is an increasing threat to the integrity of the dollar.

EXAMPLE 2: Find the present value of $600 due in 8 years if money is worth 5.2% compounded semiannually.

SOLUTION: Substituting $S = 600$, $i = .026$, and $n = 16$ in (11), we have

$$P = 600(1.026)^{-16}$$

Taking the logarithm of both sides,

$$\log P = \log 600 - 16 \log (1.026)$$

| | |
|---|---|
| $\log 600$ | $= 2.778151$ |
| $16 \log (1.026) = 16 \times .011147 =$ | $.178352$ |
| $\log P$ (subtracting) | $= 2.599799$ |

Looking up the antilog of 2.599799, we have $P = \$397.92$.

EXAMPLE 3: How many years will it take $175 to amount to $230 at 4.4%?

SOLUTION: Substituting $S = 230$, $P = 175$, and $i = .044$ in (9), we have

$$230 = 175(1.044)^n$$

from which

$$(1.044)^n = \tfrac{230}{175}$$

Taking the logarithm of both sides,

$$n \log (1.044) = \log 230 - \log 175$$

$$n = \frac{\log 230 - \log 175}{\log 1.044} = \frac{2.361728 - 2.243038}{.018700} = 6.347 \text{ years}$$

This means that if compound interest is paid for a part of a period the time would be 6.347 years. Since this is not common in practice, the time would usually be used in one of the following ways. If the interest is paid only on conversion dates, we would say that the closest time is 6 years which would result in an amount somewhat less than $230. This means that if we want at least $230 the money would have to be left on deposit for 7 years. If simple interest is paid for part of a period, we would take the amount at the end of 6 years and use the simple interest formula to get the additional time necessary for this to accumulate to $230.

EXAMPLE 4: If a speculative investment increased in value from $30,000 to $80,000 in 5 years, what was the annual compounded rate of growth?

SOLUTION: Substituting $S = 80,000$, $P = 30,000$, and $n = 5$ in (9), we have

$$80,000 = 30,000(1 + i)^5$$

$$(1 + i)^5 = \frac{80,000}{30,000}$$

Taking logarithms of both sides,

$$5 \log (1 + i) = \log 80,000 - \log 30,000$$

$$\log (1 + i) = \frac{\log 80,000 - \log 30,000}{5}$$

$$= \frac{4.903090 - 4.477121}{5} = \frac{.425969}{5} = .085194$$

Looking up the antilog of .085194, we find that

$$1 + i = 1.2167$$

From which

$$i = .2167 = 21.67\%$$

## 3.22   Inflation

A common problem of people everywhere is too much month left over at the end of their money. Rapid rises in prices cause hardships for those on fixed money incomes. To help cope with rising prices, workers demand wage increases to compensate for both past and future losses of purchasing power. Increased costs of labor, material, and other inputs cause manufacturers to raise the prices of the final product.

Price changes are reported in terms of official cost-of-living or price indexes. The agency responsible for determining a price index must determine the types and quantities of goods on which the index will be based. The dollar values of the items in the index are determined for a base year or period. In subsequent years the total cost of the items on which the index is based is determined. This value is then expressed as a percentage of the total cost in the base period.

The domestic purchasing power of a nation's currency is computed from the reciprocal of the price index. When prices are increasing, as is the case now in most nations, the depreciation of money is measured by the rate of decline in the purchasing power of currency.

In the United States one of the most important statistics published by the Federal Government is the Consumer Price Index (CPI). The Consumer Price Index measures average changes in prices of goods and services usually bought by urban wage earners and clerical workers, both families and single persons living alone. It is based on prices of about 400 items which were selected to represent the movement of prices of all goods and services purchased by wage earners and clerical workers. Prices for these items are obtained in urban portions of 39 Standard Metropolitan Statistical Areas and 17 smaller cities, which were chosen to represent all urban places in the United States, including Alaska and Hawaii. They are collected from grocery and department stores, hospitals, filling stations, and other types of stores and service establishments which wage earners and clerical workers patronize.

To get the value of the dollar from the CPI, we substitute in the expression,

$$\text{Value of the dollar} = \frac{1}{\text{CPI}} \times 100 = \frac{100}{\text{CPI}}$$

When the CPI is 125, the value of the dollar is $\frac{1}{125} \times 100 = \$.80$ or 80 cents.

Movements of the price index and the value of the dollar are usually expressed as percentage changes rather than changes in index points because point changes are affected by the level of the index relative to its base period while percentage changes are not. To get the percentage change from one period to another, use the formula:

$$\text{Percentage change} = \frac{\text{Value for later period} - \text{value for previous period}}{\text{Value for previous period}} \times 100$$

When the CPI changes from 100 to 125 there is a 25 index point difference. There is also a 25 percent change as shown below:

$$\text{Percentage change} = \frac{125 - 100}{100} \times 100 = 25\%$$

When the CPI changes from 125 to 150 there is a 25 index point change. However, the percentage change is

$$\frac{150 - 125}{125} \times 100 = 20\%$$

The CPI change from 125 to 150 means a drop in the value of the dollar from $.80 to $.67 and a percentage change of

$$\frac{.67 - .80}{.80} = -16.2\%$$

Note that the percentage change in the value of the dollar is not equal to the corresponding percentage change in the price index. This frequently misunderstood point can be clarified by a simple example. If the CPI changes from 100 to 200, there is a 100 percent increase in prices. However, the corresponding drop in the value of the dollar is 50 percent.

Each year the First National City Bank of New York surveys rates of shrinkage in the value of money here and abroad. The results,* summarized on pages 130 and 131 show that other nations also have inflation problems, some much worse than that of the United States.

For countries in all stages of development, reasonable price stability is important for economic progress. Some countries have been more or less successful in slowing inflation with official stabilization policies—higher interest rates, increased taxes, and reduced public spending. The problem is to find policies that curb price increases without resulting in unacceptable levels of unemployment. As ways are sought to have relatively stable prices and nearly full employment, compound interest methods will be used to evaluate past results and predict future trends.

To analyze long-range trends in prices, values of the price index are substituted in the compound interest formula. When this formula is solved for the rate, we have the annual compounded rate of change in prices. The result is sometimes called the rate of inflation, particularly by the party not in office. When the value of money is substituted in the compound interest formula, we get the compounded rate of change in the purchasing power of money.

EXAMPLE: In 1966 the CPI was 97.2 and in 1970 it was 116.3. Both values are relative to 1967 = 100. Find the annual compounded rate of change of the CPI and the value of the dollar.

SOLUTION: Substituting the CPI values in (9),

$$97.2(1 + i)^4 = 116.3$$

$$(1 + i)^4 = \frac{116.3}{97.2}$$

* September 1971, *Monthly Economic Letter*, Economics Department, First National City Bank.

Taking logarithms of both sides,

$$4 \log (1 + i) = \log 116.3 - \log 97.2$$

$$\log (1 + i) = \frac{2.065580 - 1.987666}{4} = .019479$$

$$1 + i = \text{antilog of } .019479 = 1.046$$
$$i = 1.046 - 1 = .046 = 4.6\%$$

To get the annual percent change in the value of the dollar, we first get the value of the dollar as explained on page 127.

| YEAR | CONSUMER PRICE INDEX | VALUE OF THE DOLLAR |
|------|----------------------|---------------------|
| 1966 | 97.2 | $1.03 |
| 1970 | 116.3 | .86 |

Substituting in (9),

$$1.03(1 + i)^4 = .86$$

$$\log (1 + i) = \frac{\log .86 - \log 1.03}{4}$$

$$= \frac{(.934498 - 1) - (.012837)}{4}$$

When working with logarithms, we must end with a positive mantissa and an integral characteristic. To achieve this, we can change the form of a logarithm provided we do not change its numerical value. If we add 39 to the first term in the first logarithm and subtract 39 from the second term in the same logarithm, we can complete the problem.

$$\log (1 + i) = \frac{(39.934498 - 40) - (.012837)}{4}$$

$$= \frac{39.921661 - 40}{4} = 9.980415 - 10$$

$$1 + i = \text{antilog} (9.980415 - 10) = .956$$
$$i = .956 - 1 = -.044 = -4.4\%$$

Note that the rate of change in the value of the dollar is not numerically equal to the percentage change in the CPI. Here the difference is not large, but it can be as was shown in the example on page 128.

## DEPRECIATION OF MONEY IN INDUSTRIALIZED COUNTRIES

| | Indexes of value of money (1960 = 100) | | Rates of depreciation of money | | |
|---|---|---|---|---|---|
| | '65 | '70 | '60–'70* | '70 | '71† |
| Greece | 92 | 81 | 2.1% | 3.1% | 3.1% |
| Australia | 91 | 78 | 2.4 | 3.7 | 4.7 |
| Luxembourg | 90 | 78 | 2.5 | 4.4 | 4.2 |
| South Africa | 90 | 76 | 2.6 | 4.9 | 5.0 |
| Canada | 92 | 76 | 2.6 | 3.3 | 1.9 |
| Germany | 87 | 76 | 2.6 | 3.8 | 4.4 |
| United States | 94 | 76 | 2.6 | 5.6 | 4.4 |
| Belgium | 88 | 74 | 2.9 | 3.8 | 3.6 |
| Switzerland | 85 | 72 | 3.2 | 3.5 | 6.1 |
| Austria | 83 | 70 | 3.5 | 4.2 | 4.0 |
| New Zealand | 88 | 69 | 3.7 | 6.2 | 9.7 |
| Italy | 79 | 68 | 3.8 | 4.8 | 5.0 |
| France | 83 | 67 | 3.8 | 4.9 | 4.8 |
| Sweden | 84 | 67 | 3.8 | 6.6 | 7.2 |
| United Kingdom | 84 | 67 | 3.9 | 6.0 | 8.4 |
| Netherlands | 84 | 66 | 4.0 | 4.2 | 6.6 |
| Portugal | 88 | 65 | 4.3 | 6.0 | 8.6 |
| Norway | 82 | 64 | 4.3 | 9.7 | 6.5 |
| Ireland | 81 | 63 | 4.5 | 7.6 | 8.4 |
| Finland | 78 | 62 | 4.8 | 2.7 | 4.5 |
| Japan | 75 | 57 | 5.4 | 7.1 | 6.2 |
| Turkey | 84 | 57 | 5.5 | 7.3 | 10.2 |
| Denmark | 77 | 56 | 5.7 | 6.4 | 5.1 |
| Spain | 71 | 56 | 5.7 | 5.4 | 7.6 |
| Iceland | 59 | 33 | 10.6 | 11.3 | 9.7 |

* Compounded annually. † Based on average of monthly data available for 1971 compared with corresponding period of 1970. ‡ Less than one.

Note: As in the past, depreciation of money is measured by the rates of decline in the domestic purchasing power of national currencies (computed from reciprocals of official cost-of-living

## DEPRECIATION OF MONEY IN LESS-DEVELOPED COUNTRIES

| | Indexes of value of money (1960 = 100) | | Rates of depreciation of money | | |
| --- | --- | --- | --- | --- | --- |
| | '65 | '70 | '60–'70* | '70 | '71† |
| El Salvador | 99 | 94 | 0.7% | 2.8% | 1.1% |
| Guatemala | 99 | 92 | 0.8 | 2.3 | 0.3 |
| Venezuela | 99 | 92 | 0.9 | 2.1 | 2.7 |
| Iran | 91 | 84 | 1.7 | 2.1 | 1.9 |
| Thailand | 93 | 82 | 2.0 | 2.3 | 0.9 |
| Morocco | 82 | 80 | 2.2 | 1.3 | 3.2 |
| Costa Rica | 89 | 79 | 2.3 | 4.5 | 3.4 |
| Mexico | 91 | 77 | 2.6 | 4.9 | 4.6 |
| China | 89 | 72 | 3.3 | 3.5 | 3.9 |
| Pakistan | 88 | 71 | 3.4 | 5.1 | 4.5 |
| Jamaica | 87 | 67 | 3.9 | 8.9 | 6.7 |
| Ecuador | 82 | 65 | 4.2 | 4.9 | 8.9 |
| Philippines | 78 | 58 | 5.2 | 14.7 | 4.3 |
| Bolivia | 78 | 58 | 5.2 | 3.8 | 2.9 |
| Israel | 71 | 58 | 5.3 | 5.7 | 10.7 |
| India | 74 | 54 | 5.9 | 4.9 | 3.0 |
| Peru | 64 | 40 | 8.8 | 4.9 | 5.7 |
| Colombia | 56 | 35 | 10.1 | 6.4 | 6.2 |
| Yugoslavia | 53 | 31 | 10.9 | 11.3 | 12.4 |
| Korea | 49 | 27 | 12.1 | 13.8 | 13.1 |
| Argentina | 35 | 15 | 17.5 | 12.0 | 22.9 |
| Vietnam | 71 | 14 | 17.6 | 26.9 | 21.3 |
| Chile | 30 | 9 | 21.0 | 24.5 | 18.2 |
| Brazil | 9 | 3 | 30.6 | 16.0 | 17.2 |
| Indonesia | 2 | ‡ | 57.6 | 11.0 | 15.2 |

or consumer price indexes, not by rates of inflation). Since the quality of consumer price compilations varies considerably from country to country, calculations of comparative trends in the purchasing power of national currencies based on consumer price indexes are, at best, only approximate. Countries are ranked according to the index of value of money in 1970.

**EXERCISE 3i**

1. If an investment pays $9\frac{1}{2}\%$ return, what will be the amount of $100 in 5 years?                                                                                                ($157.42)

2. What will be the amount of $234.50 in 8 years at 4.8% compounded semiannually?

3. If an investment pays 10%, how much must be invested today to amount to $250 in 10 years?                                                                                ($96.39)

4. How much must be invested at 7.6% converted quarterly to amount to $500 in 4 years?

5. How long does it take $350 to amount to $500 at 4.15% converted annually? Give answer to the nearest year.                                                                (9 years)

6. How many years will it take $45,000 to amount to $72,000 at 3.8% converted annually?

7. How long does it take an investment to at least triple itself at 9.5% compounded annually?                                                                                (13 years)

8. How long will it take a principal of $42,000 to amount to $60,000 at 4.8% converted quarterly? Give answer to nearest period.

9. What is the annual rate of interest if an investment of $3500 amounts to $45,000 in 40 years?                                                                            (6.6%)

10. An investment of $6700 amounted to $32,000 in 14 years. What was the annual rate of return correct to .1%?

11. A piece of property was purchased in 1950 for $32,000. In 1965 it was sold for $255,000. What annual rate of return was received on this investment?                                                                                                (14.8%)

12. What is the nominal rate of return converted semiannually if $6780 amounts to $18,550 in $8\frac{1}{2}$ years?

13. Over the past several years a business has been increasing at an approximately constant rate of 10% a year. If the business had sales of $2.5 million in 1953, what are the estimated sales for 1963 assuming that the business continues to increase at about the same rate?                                        ($6.5 million)

14. The net income of a business has been increasing at about 12% a year. If the net income in 1964 was $23.6 million, what is the estimated net income for 1968?

15. A man estimates that a piece of property will be worth $185,000 in 6 years. If he expects a return of $8\frac{1}{2}\%$ on his investment, what is the property worth to him today to the nearest thousand dollars?                                ($113,000)

16. The estimated value of a piece of property in 5 years is $75,000. What would it be worth today to a speculator who expects a rate of return of 10% on his money?

**17.** An investor who bought 100 shares of International Business Machines Corporation common stock for $2750 in 1914 would have had 59,320 shares in 1972 worth $21,948,000. What was the compounded annual rate of increase in the value of this investment to the nearest percent?     (17%)

**18.** If the population of a country increases from 130 million to 144 million in 10 years, what is the annual rate of increase correct to .1%?

**19.** A man put $17,500 in a speculative investment in June 1960. In June 1974, the investment was valued at $75,000. What annual percent return did he earn on his investment?     (11%)

**20.** An illegal money lender makes a loan of $100. Three months later his victim repays $133.10. What rate of interest is the lender getting per month?

**21.** When Secretary of State William Seward purchased Alaska for less than 2 cents an acre in 1867, some dubbed it "Seward's Icebox," others "Seward's Folly." Since that time, Alaska has yielded nearly 100 times its price in gold alone. If the $7.2 million which the U.S. paid Russia for Alaska in 1867 had been invested at $4\frac{1}{2}\%$ compounded semiannually, how much did the investment amount to in 1967?     ($616.5 million)

**22.** In 1626, Peter Minuit bought Manhattan Island from the Indians for trinkets valued at 60 guilders or $24. Had this money been put into a savings account paying 4.6% converted semiannually, how much would be in the account in 1974? Answer to nearest $10,000.

**23.** From 1965 to 1970, the earnings per share of Bristol-Myers Company common stock increased from $1.32 to $2.42. What was the compounded annual rate of increase to the nearest percent?     (13%)

**24.** From 1966 to 1971, the earnings per share of International Business Machines Corporation common stock increased from $4.71 to $9.38. What was the compounded annual rate of increase to the nearest percent?

**25.** Get the year-to-year percentage changes:

|        |       |                            | YEAR-TO-YEAR CHANGE |                    |
| :----: | :---: | :------------------------: | :-----------------: | :----------------: |
| YEAR   | CPI   | VALUE OF<br>THE DOLLAR      | *Prices*            | *Value<br>of Money* |
| 1967   | 100.0 | $1.00                      | —                   | —                  |
| 1968   | 104.2 | .96                        | 4.2%                | −4.0%              |
| 1969   | 109.8 | .91                        | 5.4%                | −5.2%              |
| 1970   | 116.3 | .86                        | 5.9%                | −5.5%              |

**26.** Get the period-to-period percentage changes:

| | | | PERIOD-TO-PERIOD CHANGE | |
| | | VALUE OF | | *Value* |
| PERIOD | CPI | THE DOLLAR | *Prices* | *of Money* |
|---|---|---|---|---|
| 1 | 75 | | | |
| 2 | 100 | | | |
| 3 | 125 | | | |
| 4 | 150 | | | |

# 4

# Ordinary
# Annuities

## 4.1 Types of Annuities

When most people buy a home, they borrow money and agree to repay it in monthly payments over a period that may range from 10 to 30 years. It would be very laborious to have to compute the interest or discount on 120 to 360 payments one by one. Formulas and tables have been developed which make it possible to solve a problem of many payments as easily as a single sum was handled in Chapter 3.

The series of equal monthly payments which a person makes in buying a home is called an **annuity**. Interest payments on bonds, premiums on insurance, payments on installment purchases are familiar examples of annuities. In general, any set of equal payments made at equal intervals of time form an annuity.

Annuities are divided into **annuities certain** and **contingent annuities**. An **annuity certain** is one for which the payments begin and end at fixed times. The payments on a home form an annuity certain because the payments start on a fixed date and continue until the required number has been made. Even if the buyer of the home dies, any outstanding debt on the home must be paid.

A **contingent annuity** is one for which the date of the first or last payment or both depends upon some event. Pensions, social security, and many life insurance policies are examples of contingent annuities.

The **payment interval** or **rent period** is the length of time between successive payments. Payments may be made annually, semiannually, monthly, weekly, or at any fixed interval. The **term** of an annuity is the time between the start of the first rent period and the end of the last rent period. The **periodic rent** is the size of each payment in dollars and cents.

In this chapter we shall work with the **ordinary annuity** which has the periodic payments made at the *end* of each period. In the next chapter we discuss the **annuity due** which has the payments made at the *beginning* of each period.

## 4.2 Amount of an Ordinary Annuity

The final value or **amount of an annuity** is the sum of all the periodic payments and the compound interest on them accumulated to the end of the term. In the case of an ordinary annuity, this will be the value of the annuity on the date of the last payment.

EXAMPLE: Starting 1 year from now, a man deposits $500 a year in an account paying 4% compounded annually. What amount does he have to his credit just after making the 4th deposit?

SOLUTION: A sketch is often helpful in visualizing annuity problems. In this case we put the focal date at 4 years because we want the amount of all the payments at that time.

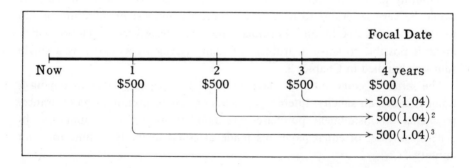

Starting with the last payment and accumulating all of them to the focal date, we have

| | |
|---|---|
| 4th payment | $500.00 |
| 3rd payment 500(1.04) | 520.00 |
| 2nd payment 500(1.04)$^2$ | 540.80 |
| 1st payment 500(1.04)$^3$ | 562.43 |
| Amount of the annuity | $2123.23 |

## 4.3  Amount Formula

If there are many payments, the above method for getting the amount would require too much work. We now derive a general formula for the amount of an annuity of $n$ payments of $1 each and a rate of $i$ per period. As in the preceding example, we accumulate each payment to the end of the term. At this point the last payment will, of course, be $1 as it has had no time to earn interest. The next to the last payment will be $1(1 + i)$ or simply $(1 + i)$ because it has earned interest for one period. The payment before this will amount to $(1 + i)^2$ and so on. The first payment will amount to $(1 + i)^{n-1}$ because it earns interest for one period less than the number of payments.

The diagram for this ordinary annuity of $1 per period is shown below. The dots show that some of the payments do not appear on the sketch. The symbol $s_{\overline{n}|}$ (read "$s$ sub $n$" or "$s$ angle $n$") is used to represent the amount of $n$ payments of $1 each when the interest rate per period is $i$. Students sometimes prefer to write this as $s_{\overline{n}|i}$ and put in the rate per period as they set up a problem. This helps them to remember what rate to use when they get the numerical value of the factor from Table 2. This practice is followed in some of the examples in this book.

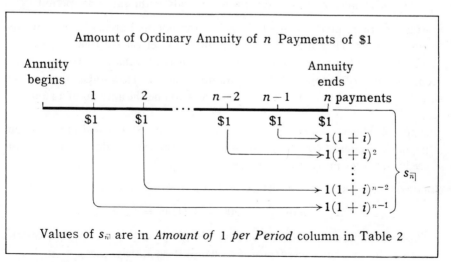

Amount of Ordinary Annuity of $n$ Payments of $1

Values of $s_{\overline{n}|}$ are in *Amount of 1 per Period* column in Table 2

Starting with the last payment and writing the sum of all the payments accumulated to the end of the annuity, we have

$$s_{\overline{n|}} = 1 + (1 + i) + (1 + i)^2 + \cdots + (1 + i)^{n-2} + (1 + i)^{n-1}$$

The expression on the right is a geometric progression in which the first term is 1, the common ratio is $(1 + i)$ and the number of terms is $n$. In algebra it is shown that the sum of the terms in a geometric progression is

$$s = \frac{a(r^n - 1)}{r - 1}$$

where $a$ is the first term and $r$ is the common ratio. Substituting values from the annuity problem in this general formula, we get

$$s_{\overline{n|}} = \frac{1[(1 + i)^n - 1]}{(1 + i) - 1} = \frac{(1 + i)^n - 1}{i}$$

Values of $s_{\overline{n|}}$ for common interest rates are given in the *Amount of 1 per Period* column of Table 2. This factor is also called *Amount of an Annuity of 1 per Period*. If the periodic rent is $\$R$ per period instead of $\$1$, we indicate the total amount of the payments by the symbol $S_n$. All we have to do to get the amount of an annuity of $\$R$ per period is to multiply $R$ by $s_{\overline{n|}}$. Thus the basic formula for the amount of an ordinary annuity is

$$S_n = Rs_{\overline{n|}} = R\frac{(1 + i)^n - 1}{i} \qquad \text{(12)}$$

$S_n$ = amount of an ordinary annuity of $n$ payments
$R$ = periodic payment or rent
$s_{\overline{n|}}$ = *Amount of 1 per Period* for $n$ periods at the rate $i$ per period

Many workers prefer to work with $j_{(m)}$, the nominal annual rate converted $m$ times a year. They use the marginal index to get on the right page of the compound interest and annuity tables. Numerical values of $s_{\overline{n|}}$ are in the second column of factors in Table 2. Example 1 under "How to Use the Amount of 1 Per Period Column in Table 2" shows how to find the amount of an annuity.

EXAMPLE 2: Starting 1 year from now, a man deposits $500 a year in an account paying 4% interest compounded annually. What amount does he have to his credit just after making the 4th deposit?

SOLUTION: Substituting $R = 500$, $n = 4$, and $i = 4\%$ in (12),

$$S_4 = 500s_{\overline{4|}4\%} = 500 \times 4.24646 = \$2123.23$$

This is the same as the problem on page 136 which took several multiplications and an addition when each deposit was handled separately.

EXAMPLE 1: Find the amount of an ordinary annuity of $500 every 3 months for 12 years at 6% compounded quarterly.

1. Get on the right page by locating the rate per period at the top ——————

or (better)

the frequency of conversion and the nominal rate in the marginal index. ——————

2. Find the column which has the required factor. The amount of an annuity of 1 per period is in the second column of factors. ——————

3. Calculate the number of payments. In an annuity of 4 payments a year for 12 years there are 48 payments. Find the numerical value of the factor in line 48. ——————

4. Substitute the value of $s_{\overline{48}|}$ in Formula (12).

$$S_{48} = Rs_{\overline{48}|}$$
$$= 500 \times 69.56522$$
$$= \$34,782.61$$

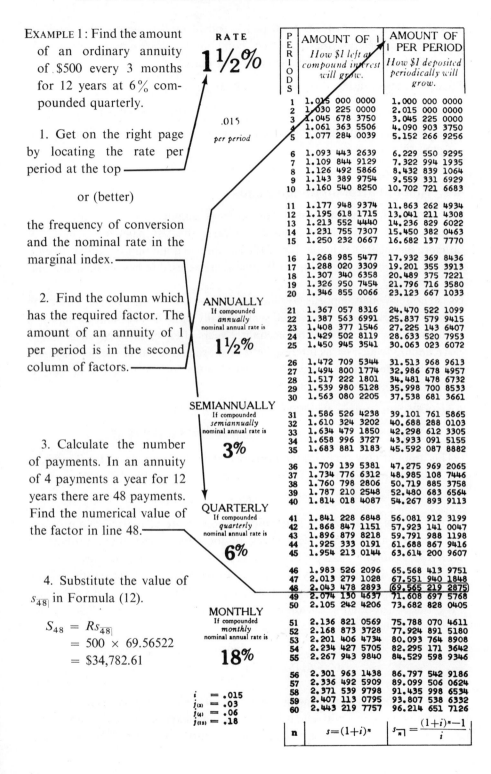

RATE

$1\frac{1}{2}\%$

.015
*per period*

ANNUALLY
If compounded
*annually*
nominal annual rate is

$1\frac{1}{2}\%$

SEMIANNUALLY
If compounded
*semiannually*
nominal annual rate is

$3\%$

QUARTERLY
If compounded
*quarterly*
nominal annual rate is

$6\%$

MONTHLY
If compounded
*monthly*
nominal annual rate is

$18\%$

$i \quad = .015$
$j_{(2)} = .03$
$j_{(4)} = .06$
$j_{(12)} = .18$

| P E R I O D S | AMOUNT OF 1 *How $1 left at compound interest will grow.* | AMOUNT OF 1 PER PERIOD *How $1 deposited periodically will grow.* |
|---|---|---|
| 1 | 1.015 000 0000 | 1.000 000 0000 |
| 2 | 1.030 225 0000 | 2.015 000 0000 |
| 3 | 1.045 678 3750 | 3.045 225 0000 |
| 4 | 1.061 363 5506 | 4.090 903 3750 |
| 5 | 1.077 284 0039 | 5.152 266 9256 |
| 6 | 1.093 443 2639 | 6.229 550 9295 |
| 7 | 1.109 844 9129 | 7.322 994 1935 |
| 8 | 1.126 492 5866 | 8.432 839 1064 |
| 9 | 1.143 389 9754 | 9.559 331 6929 |
| 10 | 1.160 540 8250 | 10.702 721 6683 |
| 11 | 1.177 948 9374 | 11.863 262 4934 |
| 12 | 1.195 618 1715 | 13.041 211 4308 |
| 13 | 1.213 552 4440 | 14.236 829 6022 |
| 14 | 1.231 755 7307 | 15.450 382 0463 |
| 15 | 1.250 232 0667 | 16.682 137 7770 |
| 16 | 1.268 985 5477 | 17.932 369 8436 |
| 17 | 1.288 020 3309 | 19.201 355 3913 |
| 18 | 1.307 340 6358 | 20.489 375 7221 |
| 19 | 1.326 950 7454 | 21.796 716 3580 |
| 20 | 1.346 855 0066 | 23.123 667 1033 |
| 21 | 1.367 057 8316 | 24.470 522 1099 |
| 22 | 1.387 563 6991 | 25.837 579 9415 |
| 23 | 1.408 377 1546 | 27.225 143 6407 |
| 24 | 1.429 502 8119 | 28.633 520 7953 |
| 25 | 1.450 945 3541 | 30.063 023 6072 |
| 26 | 1.472 709 5344 | 31.513 968 9613 |
| 27 | 1.494 800 1774 | 32.986 678 4957 |
| 28 | 1.517 222 1801 | 34.481 478 6732 |
| 29 | 1.539 980 5128 | 35.998 700 8533 |
| 30 | 1.563 080 2205 | 37.538 681 3661 |
| 31 | 1.586 526 4238 | 39.101 761 5865 |
| 32 | 1.610 324 3202 | 40.688 288 0103 |
| 33 | 1.634 479 1850 | 42.298 612 3305 |
| 34 | 1.658 996 3727 | 43.933 091 5155 |
| 35 | 1.683 881 3183 | 45.592 087 8882 |
| 36 | 1.709 139 5381 | 47.275 969 2065 |
| 37 | 1.734 776 6312 | 48.985 108 7446 |
| 38 | 1.760 798 2806 | 50.719 885 3758 |
| 39 | 1.787 210 2548 | 52.480 683 6564 |
| 40 | 1.814 018 4087 | 54.267 893 9113 |
| 41 | 1.841 228 6848 | 56.081 912 3199 |
| 42 | 1.868 847 1151 | 57.923 141 0047 |
| 43 | 1.896 879 8218 | 59.791 988 1198 |
| 44 | 1.925 333 0191 | 61.688 867 9416 |
| 45 | 1.954 213 0144 | 63.614 200 9607 |
| 46 | 1.983 526 2096 | 65.568 413 9751 |
| 47 | 2.013 279 1028 | 67.551 940 1848 |
| 48 | 2.043 478 2893 | 69.565 219 2875 |
| 49 | 2.074 130 4637 | 71.608 697 5768 |
| 50 | 2.105 242 4206 | 73.682 828 0405 |
| 51 | 2.136 821 0569 | 75.788 070 4611 |
| 52 | 2.168 873 3728 | 77.924 891 5180 |
| 53 | 2.201 406 4734 | 80.093 764 8908 |
| 54 | 2.234 427 5705 | 82.295 171 3642 |
| 55 | 2.267 943 9840 | 84.529 598 9346 |
| 56 | 2.301 963 1438 | 86.797 542 9186 |
| 57 | 2.336 492 5909 | 89.099 506 0624 |
| 58 | 2.371 539 9798 | 91.435 998 6534 |
| 59 | 2.407 113 0795 | 93.807 538 6332 |
| 60 | 2.443 219 7757 | 96.214 651 7126 |
| n | $s=(1+i)^n$ | $s_{\overline{n}|} = \dfrac{(1+i)^n-1}{i}$ |

EXAMPLE 3: A man deposits $300 at the end of each 6 months in a building and loan association that pays $3\frac{1}{2}\%$ compounded semiannually. How much will he have to his credit at the end of 10 years?

SOLUTION: Substituting $R = 300$, $n = 20$, and $i = 1\frac{3}{4}\%$ in (12),

$$S_{20} = 300s_{\overline{20}|1\frac{3}{4}\%} = 300 \times 23.70161 = \$7110.48$$

The deposits total $300 \times 20 = \$6000$. Thus the total compound interest is $1110.48.

## 4.4   Amount after an Annuity Ends

The formula for the amount of an ordinary annuity gives the value of all payments and accumulated interest just after the last payment is made. If no more payments are made, but if the accumulated amount continues to earn interest, the *Amount of* 1 column of Table 2 can be used to get the final amount.

EXAMPLE 1: A man deposits $300 at the end of each 6 months for 3 years in an account paying $3\%$ converted semiannually. If he makes no more deposits, how much will he have in his account 2 years after the last deposit is made? An annuity which earns interest for 2 or more periods after the last payment is called a **forborne** annuity. A special formula for the forborne annuity is given on page 188 of Chapter 5.

SOLUTION: Substituting $R = 300$, $n = 6$, and $i = 1\frac{1}{2}\%$ in (12),

$$S_6 = 300s_{\overline{6}|1\frac{1}{2}\%} = 300 \times 6.22955 = \$1868.87$$

This amount now becomes the principal which is accumulated for 2 years. Substituting $P = \$1868.87$, $n = 4$, and $i = .015$ in (9),

$$S = 1868.87(1.015)^4 = 1868.87 \times 1.061364 = \$1983.55$$

ALTERNATE SOLUTION: As an illustration of how a careful analysis of a problem can result in an independent check of the answer, the above problem is worked assuming that payments were also made during the last 2 years. This results in an ordinary annuity of 10 payments and makes the answer too large by the amount of the last 4 payments. The effect of these payments is offset by subtracting the amount of an annuity of 4 payments. This can all be done quite easily by subtracting factors as shown below.

$$S_6 = 300(s_{\overline{10}|} - s_{\overline{4}|}) = 300(10.70272 - 4.09090)$$
$$= 300(6.61182) = \$1983.55$$

While the theory of this method may be somewhat more complicated than the first method, the arithmetic is simpler. A time diagram, focal date approach helps to determine the most efficient way to work a problem. The sketch on this page shows how the addition and subtraction of fictitious payments enables us to solve the problem using only *Amount of 1 per Period* factors from Table 2.

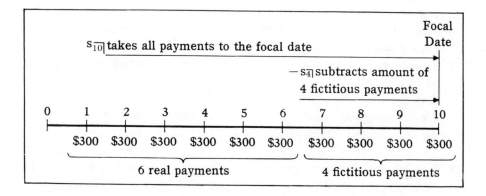

EXAMPLE 2: In 1933 a man was wrongfully convicted of killing a policeman and imprisoned. After a long investigation proved him innocent, he was granted a full pardon and released from prison in 1950. The legislature got around to making amends in 1965 and approved a settlement of $2000 for each year in prison. No allowance was made for interest. How much would the man have received in 1965 had interest been allowed at 4% converted annually and the problem worked as a forborne annuity?

SOLUTION: The amount of the annuity at the end of 17 years was

$$2000s_{\overline{17}|} = 2000 \times 23.697512 = \$47,395.02$$

Accumulating this for 15 more years,

$$47,395.02(1.04)^{15} = 47,395.02 \times 1.8009435$$
$$= \$85,355.75$$

**EXERCISE 4a**

1. Find the amount of an annuity of $5000 per year for 10 years at: (a) 3%; (b) 4%. Interest is compounded annually.    (a) $57,319.40; (b) $60,030.54

2. Find the amount of an annuity of $1200 at the end of each 6 months for 5 years if money is worth: (a) 4%; (b) 5%; (c) 6%. All rates are converted semiannually.

3. A man puts $100 every 3 months in a savings account that pays 5% compounded quarterly. If he makes his first deposit on June 1, 1964, how much will he have in his account just after he makes his deposit on December 1, 1973?    ($4986.62)

4. Every 3 months a family puts $50 in a savings account that pays 5% compounded quarterly. If they make the first deposit on August 1, 1964,

how much will be in their account just after they make their deposit on February 1, 1974?

5. What is the amount of an annuity of $100 at the end of each month for 6 years if money is worth 4% compounded monthly?            ($8122.26)

6. Find the amount of an annuity of $35 at the end of each month for 12 years if money is worth 5% converted monthly.

7. To provide for his son's education, a man deposits $150 a year at the end of each year for 18 years. If the money draws 3% interest, how much does the fund contain just after the 18th deposit is made? If no more deposits are made, but if the amount in the fund is allowed to accumulate at the same interest rate, how much will it contain in 3 more years?

($3512.17; $3837.84)

8. Two hundred dollars at the end of each year for 6 years is equivalent in value to what single payment at the end of 6 years if the interest rate is 6% effective?

9. A child 12 years old received an inheritance of $400 a year. This was to be invested and allowed to accumulate until the child reached the age of 21. If the money was invested at 4% effective and if the first payment was made on the child's 12th birthday and the last payment on his 21st birthday, what amount did he receive when he reached the age of 21?       ($4802.44)

10. A man deposits $125 at the end of each 3 months for 5 years in a fund that pays 5% converted quarterly. How much will he have to his credit just after the last deposit is made?

11. A man deposits $300 at the end of each year for 3 years in an investment paying 3% converted annually. He then allows his account to accumulate for 2 more years without making any more deposits. What is the amount in his account at the end of the 5 years?            ($983.74)

12. On March 1, 1968, a man deposited $150 in an investment that pays 3% converted semiannually. He continues to make $150 deposits every 6 months until September 1, 1974, when he makes his final deposit. If he lets the money continue to draw interest, how much will he have in his account on March 1, 1976?

13. A family has been paying $75.50 a month on their home. The interest rate on the mortgage is 5% compounded monthly. Because of sickness they miss the payments due on May 1, June 1, July 1, and August 1. On September 1 they want to make a single payment which will reduce their debt to what it would have been had they made all payments on time. What single payment on this date will be equivalent to the 5 payments from May to September inclusive?            ($380.66)

14. A dealer purchased merchandise and agreed to pay $200 on August 1, September 1, October 1, November 1, and December 1. He was to be charged 6% converted monthly on any payments not made on time. He made the

August payment, but let all the others go to December 1. At that time what payment did he have to make to settle all his obligations?

15. A person has an income of $250 every 3 months from preferred stocks. He deposits this in a savings and loan association paying 5% converted quarterly with interest dates on March 31, June 30, September 30, and December 31. If he makes his first deposit on June 30, 1965, and his last deposit on December 31, 1969, how much will be in his account just after he makes the last deposit?                                      ($5324.19)

16. In 1949, a man put $500 in common stocks. He continues to make the same deposit every year. If the stocks increase in market value at about 4% a year, what will be the value of the man's portfolio just after he makes his purchase in 1966?

17. To provide for a son's education, a man opens an account with a deposit of $300 in a savings and loan association which pays $4\frac{1}{2}\%$ converted semi-annually. The first deposit is made on the boy's 6th birthday on June 23, 1960. (This deposit will earn interest from July 1.) Additional deposits of $100 each are made every 6 months. How much will be in the account on the interest date immediately following the boy's 18th birthday?     ($3648.47)

18. The father in Problem 17 makes the last deposit on the boy's 16th birthday. How much will be in the account on July 1, 1972?

## 4.5   Present Value of an Ordinary Annuity

The **present value** of an annuity is the sum of the present values of all the payments of the annuity. To get the present value we shall assume an annuity of $n$ payments of $1 each and a rate of $i$ per period. We then discount each payment to the beginning of the annuity. The sum of these discounted values is designated by the symbol $a_{\overline{n}|}$.

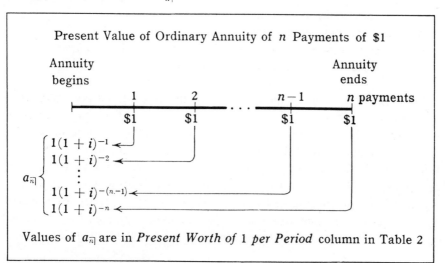

Present Value of Ordinary Annuity of $n$ Payments of $1

Values of $a_{\overline{n}|}$ are in *Present Worth of 1 per Period* column in Table 2

Writing the sum of all the payments discounted to the beginning of the annuity, we have

$$a_{\overline{n}|} = (1 + i)^{-1} + (1 + i)^{-2} + \cdots + (1 + i)^{-(n-1)} + (1 + i)^{-n}$$

The expression on the right is a geometric progression in which the first term is $(1 + i)^{-1}$, the common ratio is $(1 + i)^{-1}$, and the number of terms is $n$. Substituting these values in the formula for the sum of a geometric progression (page 138), we have

$$a_{\overline{n}|} = \frac{(1 + i)^{-1}\{[(1 - i)^{-1}]^n - 1\}}{(1 + i)^{-1} - 1}$$

Multiplying numerator and denominator by $(1 + i)$ gives

$$a_{\overline{n}|} = \frac{(1 + i)^{-n} - 1}{1 - (1 + i)} = \frac{(1 + i)^{-n} - 1}{1 - 1 - i} = \frac{(1 + i)^{-n} - 1}{-i}$$

$$= \frac{1 - (1 + i)^{-n}}{i} = \frac{1 - v^n}{i}$$

Values of $a_{\overline{n}|}$ are given in the *Present Worth of* 1 *per Period* column of Table 2. If the periodic rent is $\$R$ per period instead of $\$1$, we indicate the present value of the annuity by the symbol $A_n$. To get the value of $A_n$ in dollars all we need to do is to multiply $R$ by $a_{\overline{n}|}$. Thus the basic formula for the present value of an ordinary annuity is

$$A_n = Ra_{\overline{n}|} = R\,\frac{1 - (1 + i)^{-n}}{i} = R\,\frac{1 - v^n}{i} \qquad (13)$$

$A_n$ = present value of an ordinary annuity of $n$ payments
$R$ = periodic payment or rent
$a_{\overline{n}|}$ = *Present Worth of* 1 *per Period* for $n$ periods at the rate $i$ per period
$v^n$ = *Present Worth of* 1. Another symbol for $(1 + i)^{-n}$

Note that we have given the formulas for the amount and present value of an annuity in two forms—one using the factors $s_{\overline{n}|}$ and $a_{\overline{n}|}$, the other using the exponential form as obtained in the original derivation. Whenever possible, problems should be worked by using the $s_{\overline{n}|}$ and $a_{\overline{n}|}$ factors from Table 2. When the rate for a given problem is not in the table, the exponential form of the formula can be used and evaluated using logarithms or the laws of exponents. In practical business usage it is seldom necessary to calculate factors because the rate can usually be found in the extensive compound interest and annuity tables published by the Financial Publishing Company.

EXAMPLE 1: A man wants to provide a $300 scholarship every year for 10 years. The first scholarship is to be awarded one year from now. If the school can get a 4% return on their investment, how much money should the man give now?

SOLUTION: Substituting in the present value formula, we have

$$A_{10} = 300 \times a_{\overline{10}|}$$
$$= 300 \times 8.11090 = \$2433.27$$

Note that $3000 in scholarships will actually be paid from this gift. What happens is that the school will immediately invest the $2433.27 at 4%. At the end of the first year, interest will be added to the fund and the first $300 scholarship taken out. This will go on for 10 years when the last interest payment plus the balance in the fund at that time will be just sufficient for the last scholarship. When we consider amortization schedules in Chapter 6, this procedure will be illustrated in detail.

From the annuity problems worked thus far, the student should recognize that the annuity formulas, like the compound interest formulas, make it possible to shift financial obligations from one point in time to another point. This is so important that it is worth while restating in summary form the basic principles underlying the mathematics of finance. These are:

1. *Except in cash transactions, the date on which a given sum of money has a certain dollar value must be specified.*

2. *Once the dollar value on a certain date has been specified, the dollar value on any other date can be determined by using the stated interest rate and the appropriate formula.*

3. *Two or more items* must not be *equated unless they have been brought to the same point in time.*

EXAMPLE 2: Wilson agrees to pay Smith $1000 at the end of each year for 5 years. If money is worth 3%, what is the cash equivalent of this debt? If Wilson does not make any payments until the end of 5 years, how much should he pay at that time if this single payment is to be equivalent to the original payments using an interest rate of 3%?

SOLUTION: The original debt is $1000 at the end of each year. Thus *as each payment is made* it has a dollar value of $1000. If a payment is made before it is due, its dollar value will be less than $1000. If the entire debt is settled immediately, Smith will have the use of the money from one to five years sooner than would otherwise have been the case. Therefore, he will be willing to write off the entire debt if he gets the *present value* of the payments. This is given by (13):

$$A_5 = 1000a_{\overline{5}|3\%} = 1000 \times 4.579707 = \$4579.71$$

If a payment is made after it is due, the dollar value will be increased by the interest. If all of the debt is settled at the end of 5 years, Smith will expect the *amount* of the payments at that time. This is given by (12):

$$S_5 = 1000s_{\overline{5}|3\%} = 1000 \times 5.309136 = \$5309.14$$

Thus \$4579.71 now is *equivalent in value* to the five \$1000 payments at the end of each year if money is worth 3%. Likewise \$5309.14 in five years is *equivalent in value* to the original obligations. As an interesting check on our work let us see if \$4579.71 now is equivalent to \$5309.14 in 5 years. Substituting in (9), we have

$$4579.71(1.03)^5 = 4579.71 \times 1.159274 = \$5309.14$$

## 4.6   Finding *n*

In an annuity problem, *n* is the number of payments. When a problem is stated in terms of calendar dates, students often find that getting *n* is the most difficult step in solving the problem. The safest approach is to make a time diagram and a careful analysis of each problem.

EXAMPLE 1: An ordinary annuity starts on June 1, 1968, and ends on December 1, 1973. Payments are made every 6 months. Find *n*.

SOLUTION: By the definition of an ordinary annuity, a payment is made at the end of each period.

The elapsed time is found from the starting and terminal dates.

| YEAR | MONTH | DAY |
|---|---|---|
| 1973 | 12 | 1 |
| − 1968 | − 6 | − 1 |
| 5 yrs. | 6 mos. | 0 days |

Number of time periods $= (5 \times 2) + 6/6 = 10 + 1 = 11$.

Since there is a payment at the end of each period, $n = 11$.

EXAMPLE 2: An annuity has payments made every 3 months with the first payment on November 15, 1968, and the last payment on August 15, 1976. Find the number of payments.

SOLUTION: When the dates of the first and last payments are given, special care must be used in getting *n*. We start with a time diagram.

Subtracting the starting from the terminal date gives the elapsed time.

| YEAR | MONTH | DAY |
|---|---|---|
| 5 | 20 | |
| 197$\cancel{6}$ | $\cancel{8}$ | 15 |
| $-1968$ | $-11$ | $-15$ |
| 7 yrs. | 9 mos. | 0 days |

Number of time periods $= (7 \times 4) + 9/3 = 28 + 3 = 31$.

Since the problem starts and stops with a payment, $n = 32$, one more than the number of periods.

The following true story illustrates another way to tackle time problems. At a meeting of a group of scientists, the question came up of how long it would be until the next convention of a professional association. A renowned mathematician held up his hand, carefully ticked off the months on his fingers, and announced the right answer. When a similar problem is first given to a college class, it seems so simple that many students attempt it in their heads. Almost immediately the room is full of instant wrong answers.

Getting *n* can be so difficult that some students find a combination of time diagram and finger counting the most dependable method. Their solution to the preceding example would be

| | |
|---|---|
| Payments in 1968 (from the diagram) | 1 |
| From 1969 to 1975 inclusive there are 7 years (count them) | $7 \times 4 = 28$ |
| Payments in 1976 (from the diagram) | 3 |
| | $n = 32$ |

When this method is used, it is desirable to put all of the payments in the first and last years on the diagram.

## 4.7 Amount or Present Value?

A difficult problem is determining whether the single sum equivalent to a series of payments is an amount or a present value. When in doubt, draw a time diagram. If the payments follow the single sum, it is a present value. If the payments precede the single sum, it is an amount. The diagrams below show how the payments of an ordinary annuity are related to the equivalent single sums.

EXAMPLE: A person is paying $200 a month on a debt with the payments due the first of each month. He was unable to make the payments due on April 1 and May 1. Windfall income in May provides enough cash for him to make all payments which he owes plus prepaying the payments that will come due during the current year. If he and the lender agree to make a settlement on the basis of 6% compounded monthly, how much should he pay on June 1?

SOLUTION: A time diagram is drawn and the focal date located on June 1, the time of the unknown payment.

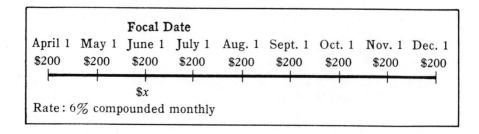

The April and May payments precede the single sum which will replace them on the focal date. These payments plus the June payment due on the focal date form an ordinary annuity of three payments for which we need the amount. The July-to-December payments follow the focal date, so these six payments form an ordinary annuity for which we need the present value. Combining these results in an equation of value we have

$$
\begin{aligned}
x &= 200s_{\overline{3}|} + 200a_{\overline{6}|} \\
&= 200 \times 3.01503 + 200 \times 5.89638 \\
&= 603.01 + 1179.28 \\
&= \$1782.29.
\end{aligned}
$$

### EXERCISE 4b

1. Find the present value of an ordinary annuity of $5000 per year for 10 years at: (a) 3%; (b) 4%. All rates are converted annually. Carry the present value for the 3% rate forward 10 years. How does the accumulated amount compare with the amount of an annuity of $5000 a year as determined in Problem 1 (a) in Exercise 4a?     [(a) $42,651.02; (b) $40,554.48]

2. Find the present value of an ordinary annuity of $750 at the end of each year for 8 years at: (a) 2%; (b) 4%; (c) 6%; (d) 8%.

3. Find the present value of an ordinary annuity of $1200 at the end of each 6 months for 5 years if money is worth: (a) 4%; (b) 5%; (c) 6%. All rates are converted semiannually.
                [(a) $10,779.10; (b) $10,502.48; (c) $10,236.24]

4. If money is worth $4\frac{1}{2}$% converted semiannually, what is the present value of $145.50 due at the end of each 6 months for 2 years?

5. A television set is bought for $50 cash and $18 a month for 12 months. What is the equivalent cash price if the interest rate is 24% converted monthly?                                                    ($240.36)

6. A refrigerator can be purchased for $57.47 down and $20 a month for 24 months. What is the equivalent cash price if the rate is 30% converted monthly?

7. Find the cash value of a car that can be bought for $400 down and $80 a month for 24 months if money is worth 18% converted monthly.
                                                                    ($2002.43)

8. An heir receives an inheritance of $500 every half year for 20 years, the first payment to be made in 6 months. If money is worth $4\frac{1}{2}$% converted semiannually, what is the cash value of this inheritance?

9. A contract for the purchase of a home calls for the payment of $81.90 a month for 20 years. At the beginning of the 6th year (just after the 60th

payment is made) the contract is sold to a buyer at a price which will yield 5% converted monthly. What does the buyer pay?                    ($10,356.68)

10. A man wants to provide a $3000 research fellowship at the end of each year for the next 4 years. If the school can invest money at 4%, how much should the man give them now to set up a fund for the 4 scholarships?

11. A home was purchased for $3000 down and $100 a month for 15 years. If the monthly payments are based on 6% converted monthly, what was the cash price of the house?                    ($14,850.35)

12. An apartment was purchased for $6000 down and $500 at the end of each 6 months for 8 years. If the payments are based on 5% converted semi-annually, what was the cash price of the apartment?

13. If a person can get 4% converted semiannually on his invested money, is it better for him to pay $11,500 cash or $3000 down and $1000 every 6 months for 5 years for a store building?

(Saves $482.59 now by paying cash)

14. Answer Problem 13 if the buyer can get 5% converted semiannually on his savings.

15. On page 144 the value of $a_{\overline{n}|}$ was obtained, using the formula for the sum of a geometric progression. Show that the value of $a_{\overline{n}|}$ can also be obtained by discounting $s_{\overline{n}|}$.

## 4.8    Extension of Tables

In some problems the number of payments is greater than can be found directly in the tables. Such problems can be solved by dividing the annuity into parts and then accumulating or discounting the amount or present value of each part of the annuity to the desired point in time.

EXAMPLE 1: Find the amount of an annuity of $100 at the end of each month for 30 years at 6% converted monthly.

SOLUTION: There are 360 payments, so we divide the annuity into 2 annuities of 180 payments each. The last 180 payments form an ordinary annuity which has an amount of

$$S_{180} = 100s_{\overline{180}|\frac{1}{2}\%} = 100 \times 290.818\,71 = \$29,081.87$$

The amount of the first 180 payments just after the 180th payment is also $29,081.87. At the time of the 180th payment, this single sum is equivalent in value to the 180 payments. From here on, all of the 180 payments can be moved at one time by simply moving this single sum. To get the value of the first 180 payments at the end of the term, we take this equivalent single sum forward at compound interest.

$$S = 29{,}081.87 \times (1.005)^{180}$$
$$= 29{,}081.87 \times 2.454\ 0936 = \$71{,}369.63$$

Adding the two amounts gives a total amount of $100,451.50.
A time diagram helps in analyzing and setting up problems of this type.

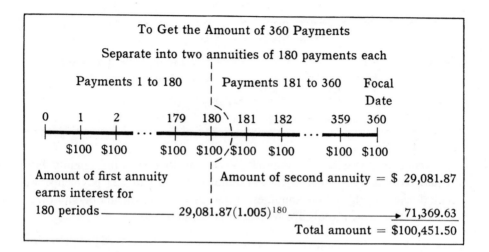

Had there been more than 360 payments, we would have separated the annuity into three or more annuities.

EXAMPLE 2: Find the present value of an annuity of $100 at the end of each month for 30 years at 6% converted monthly.

SOLUTION: We divide the annuity into 2 annuities of 180 payments each. The first 180 payments form an ordinary annuity which has a present value of

$$A_{180} = 100a_{\overline{180}|\frac{1}{2}\%} = 100 \times 118.503\ 51 = \$11{,}850.35$$

At a point in time one period before the 181st payment, the value of the last 180 payments is also $11,850.35. We now replace payments 181 to 360 with this single sum. To get the value of the last 180 payments at the beginning of the term, we discount this equivalent single sum.

$$P = 11{,}850.35(1.005)^{-180}$$
$$= 11{,}850.35 \times .407\ 4824 = \$4828.81$$

Adding the two results gives a total present value of $16,679.16.
A time diagram helps in finding a systematic solution of the problem.

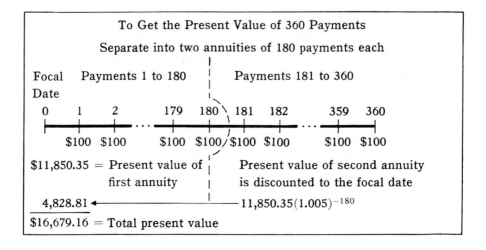

Whenever possible, the simplest solution is to divide the annuity into equal parts as was done in these examples. If we had 325 payments, we could separate them into annuities of 180 and 145 payments or any other combination which totals 325 with each part 180 or less.

EXAMPLE 3: Check the answers to Examples 1 and 2.

SOLUTION: Since both examples involved the same annuity, we check by taking the present value from Example 2 forward 30 years at 6% converted monthly.

$$S = 16,679.16(1.005)^{360} = 16,679.16(1.005)^{180}(1.005)^{180}$$
$$= 16,679.16(2.454\ 0936)^2 = \$100,451.50$$

This is the same as the amount in Example 1.

### EXERCISE 4c

1. Find the amount of an annuity of $40 at the end of each year for 80 years if money is worth 3%. ($12,854.52)
2. What is the amount of an annuity of $60 at the end of each month for 30 years at a rate of 5% converted monthly?
3. Find the present value of the annuity in Problem 1. ($1208.03)
4. Find the present value of the annuity in Problem 2.
5. A home can be purchased for $5000 down and $200 a month for 20 years. If the monthly payments are based on 5% converted monthly, find the total cash price of the house. ($35,305.06)
6. An apartment can be purchased for $10,000 down and $1000 every 3 months for 18 years. If the payments are based on 5% converted quarterly, find the total cash price.

## 4.9   Periodic Payment of an Annuity

In practical business problems the amount or present value of an annuity is frequently known and the periodic payment is to be determined. This can be done by solving the amount and present value formulas for $R$.

Solving (12), $S_n = R s_{\overline{n}|}$, for $R$,

$$R = \frac{S_n}{s_{\overline{n}|}} = S_n \times \frac{1}{s_{\overline{n}|}} \tag{14}$$

$R$ = periodic payment or rent

$S_n$ = amount of annuity of $n$ payments

$\dfrac{1}{s_{\overline{n}|}}$ = periodic deposit that will grow to \$1 in $n$ payments

Use (14) when the future amount is known.

Solving (13), $A_n = R a_{\overline{n}|}$, for $R$,

$$R = \frac{A_n}{a_{\overline{n}|}} = A_n \times \frac{1}{a_{\overline{n}|}} \tag{15}$$

$R$ = periodic payment or rent

$A_n$ = present value of annuity of $n$ payments

$\dfrac{1}{a_{\overline{n}|}}$ = periodic payment necessary to pay off a loan of \$1 in $n$ payments

Use (15) when the present value is known.

While $R$ could be found by dividing $S_n$ or $A_n$ by the correct factor, problems of this type occur so frequently in practice that the reciprocals of these factors have been determined. The numerical values of $1/s_{\overline{n}|}$ are given in the *Sinking Fund* column (third column of factors) of Table 2 and $1/a_{\overline{n}|}$ in the *Partial Payment* column (sixth column of factors). This means that the periodic rent can be determined by multiplying as indicated in the final form of (14) and (15). When setting up problems, the rate per period is often included as a subscript. If in doubt about which formula to use, draw a time diagram. If the payments precede the single sum, it is an amount. Use (14) and the *Sinking Fund* column. If the payments follow the single sum, it is a present value. Use (15) and the *Partial Payment* column.

EXAMPLE 1: If money is worth $4\%$ compounded semiannually, how much must a man save every 6 months to accumulate \$3000 in 4 years?

SOLUTION: A time diagram shows that the \$3000 is an amount in the future.

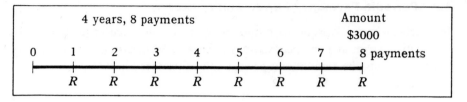

Substituting $S_8 = 3000$, $n = 8$, and $i = 2\%$ in (14),

$$R = 3000 \times \frac{1}{s_{\overline{8}|2\%}}$$

$$= 3000 \times .116510 = \$349.53$$

Note that 8 payments of $349.53 total $2796.24. The balance needed to produce an amount of $3000 comes from the accumulated interest on each payment from the time it is made to the end of the problem.

EXAMPLE 2: A man wants to buy a home costing $13,000. If he pays $3000 cash, how much will the monthly payments be if he gets a 15-year mortgage with a rate of $6\%$ compounded monthly?

SOLUTION: A time diagram shows that the $10,000 is a present value.

| Present value $10,000 | 15 years, 180 payments | | | | | |
|---|---|---|---|---|---|---|
| 0 | 1 | 2 | 3 | 178 | 179 | 180 payments |
| | R | R | R | ... R | R | R |

Substituting $A_{180} = 10,000$, $n = 180$, and $i = \frac{1}{2}\%$ in (15),

$$R = 10,000 \times \frac{1}{a_{\overline{180}|\frac{1}{2}\%}}$$

$$= 10,000 \times .0084386 = \$84.39$$

Note that 180 payments of $84.39 amount to $15,190.20 making the total interest $5190.20.

It is interesting to see what would happen if the man could borrow the $10,000 at $5\%$ compounded monthly.

$$R = 10,000 \times \frac{1}{a_{\overline{180}|\frac{5}{12}\%}} = \$79.08$$

A reduction of one percentage point in the rate results in a savings of $5.31 every month. Over 15 years this means total savings in interest of

$180 \times 5.31 = \$955.80$. This is not, of course, equivalent to a total cash savings of this amount as the savings are spread over 180 months at the rate of $5.31 per month. The equivalent cash savings will depend on the value of money to the person. For example, at $3\%$ converted monthly it would be

$$5.31 \times a_{\overline{180}|\frac{1}{4}\%} = 5.31 \times 144.805 = \$768.91$$

Whether we make the comparison on the basis of the total savings in interest or on the equivalent cash value of the savings, there is no doubt that before borrowing money, a person should shop around to find the most reasonable rate. An apparently small difference in the rate may mean saving hundreds of dollars.

Another thing to note in the above problem is that even with a $5\%$ rate, the interest totaled over $4000. Interest costs on a home loan can be reduced by making a larger down payment. Savings on interest provide an incentive for a couple to save money.

EXAMPLE 3: A savings and loan association pays $4\%$ converted quarterly. Their savings officer suggests to a couple that they set up a systematic plan for providing a retirement annuity of their own to supplement social security. The man is now 50 years old. The couple decides to deposit $200 at the end of each 3 months until the man is 65. Three months after the last deposit, they plan to start drawing down their account with equal withdrawals every 3 months over 15 years. Find the size of the withdrawals and the total interest.

SOLUTION: The amount which the couple will accumulate is obtained using (12).

$$S_{60} = 200 s_{\overline{60}|1\%} = 200 \times 81.66967 = \$16,333.93$$

This amount becomes the present value of an ordinary annuity. The couple will now receive 60 quarterly payments with the size determined by (15).

$$R = 16,333.93 \times \frac{1}{a_{\overline{60}|1\%}} = 16,333.93 \times .022\,2444 = \$363.34$$

Total retirement income $= 60 \times 363.34 = \$21,800.40$
Total deposits $= 60 \times 200 \qquad = \underline{\phantom{0}12,000.00}$
Total interest $= \$\phantom{0}9,800.40$

## 4.10   Extension of Tables

The simplest way to find the value of $1/s_{\overline{n}|}$ or $1/a_{\overline{n}|}$ for an $n$ beyond those given in the tables is to compute $s_{\overline{n}|}$ or $a_{\overline{n}|}$ using the method in Section 4.8 and then take the reciprocal.

To reduce arithmetic, examples and exercises involving extension of tables use factors rounded to the same number of decimal places as there are digits in the sum of money. When a calculator is available, it is good practice to use complete factors and round the final answer as suggested in Section 3.6, page 82.

EXAMPLE 1: How much must be deposited each quarter in an account paying 4% converted quarterly to accumulate $10,000 in 20 years?

SOLUTION: Substituting $S = 10,000$, $i = 1\%$, and $n = 80$ in (14),

$$R = 10,000 \times \frac{1}{s_{\overline{80}|1\%}}$$

We get $s_{\overline{80}|}$ by using 2 annuities of 40 payments each.

$$
\begin{aligned}
\text{Amount of last 40 payments} &= s_{\overline{40}|} &&= 48.886\ 3734 \\
\text{Amount of first 40 payments} &= s_{\overline{40}|}(1.01)^{40} \\
&= 48.886\ 3734 \times 1.488\ 8637 &&= \underline{72.785\ 1468} \\
&& s_{\overline{80}|} &= 121.671\ 5202
\end{aligned}
$$

If only one problem is to be solved, $R$ can be obtained by dividing 10,000 by $s_{\overline{80}|}$.

$$R = \frac{10,000}{121.671\ 5202} = \$82.19$$

If several problems are to be worked using the same factor, it will pay to get the reciprocal of $s_{\overline{80}|}$ and multiply.

$$\frac{1}{s_{\overline{80}|}} = \frac{1}{121.671\ 5202} = .008\ 2189$$

$$R = 10,000 \times .008\ 2189 = \$82.19$$

EXAMPLE 2: To help finance the purchase of a home, a couple borrows $20,000. The loan is to be repaid in equal monthly payments over 20 years. If the rate is 6% converted monthly, find the size of the monthly payment.

SOLUTION: Substituting $A_n = 20,000$, $i = \frac{1}{2}\%$, and $n = 240$ in (15),

$$R = 20,000 \times \frac{1}{a_{\overline{240}|\frac{1}{2}\%}}$$

We get $a_{\overline{240}|}$ using 2 annuities of 120 payments each. All payments are discounted to the present.

Present value of first 120 payments $= a_{\overline{120}|}$ $\qquad = 90.073\ 4533$
Present value of second 120 payments $= a_{\overline{120}|}(1.005)^{-120}$
$\qquad\qquad\qquad = 90.073\ 4533 \times .549\ 6327 = \underline{49.507\ 3153}$
$$a_{\overline{240}|} = 139.580\ 7686$$

Dividing 20,000 by $a_{\overline{240}|}$,

$$R = \frac{20,000}{139.580\ 7686} = \$143.29$$

Or using reciprocals,

$$\frac{1}{a_{\overline{240}|}} = \frac{1}{139.580\ 7686} = .007\ 1643$$

$$R = 20,000 \times .007\ 1643 = \$143.29$$

### EXERCISE 4d

1. A man wants to accumulate $3000 in 6 years. He makes equal deposits at the end of each 6 months in a savings account paying 4% converted semiannually. What is the size of each deposit?                    ($223.68)
2. Find the annual payment of an ordinary annuity if the amount is $5000, payments are made for 10 years, and the interest rate is 4%.
3. A man buys a refrigerator which sells for $350 cash. He pays $50 down and the balance in 24 equal monthly payments. If the seller charges 18% converted monthly for time payments, what is the size of the monthly payment?                    ($14.98)
4. A loan company charges 36% converted monthly for small loans. What would be the monthly payment if a loan of $150 is to be repaid in 12 payments?
5. A man buys a car which lists at $2500. He pays $1000 down and the balance in 24 monthly payments. If the interest rate is 12% converted monthly, what is the size of the payments?                    ($70.61)
6. What would be the monthly payment in Problem 5 if the rate is 24% converted monthly?
7. You are the accountant for a client who is selling a piece of property for $80,000. He is to get $30,000 down at date of sale. The remainder is to be paid with 12 noninterest-bearing notes of equal face value. The notes are due serially, one each 6 months from date of sale. If the settlement is based on 8% compounded semiannually, each note should be drawn for what amount?                    ($5327.61)
8. What would be the size of each note in Problem 7 if the rate is 6% compounded semiannually?

9. On June 1, 1973, a widow takes the $10,000 benefits from her husband's insurance policy and invests the money at 3% converted monthly with the understanding that she will receive 120 equal monthly payments. If she is to get her first check on July 1, 1973, what will be the size of each monthly payment?                                                     ($96.56)

10. If the widow in Problem 9 could invest the money at 4% converted monthly, how much would she get each month?

11. A couple expects to need about $3000 in 3 years for a down payment on a house. They plan to accumulate this amount by making equal payments every 6 months in a savings and loan association that pays $4\frac{1}{2}$% converted semiannually. If the first deposit is made on July 1, 1969, and the last deposit on July 1, 1972, what is the size of the semiannual payment? They want to have the $3000 just after the last deposit.          ($400.50)

12. Find the quarterly payment for an ordinary annuity to amount to $4500 in 4 years at 6% converted quarterly.

13. Eight thousand dollars is invested on June 1, 1973, at 5% converted monthly. The investment is to be paid out in 96 equal monthly payments with the first payment to be made on July 1, 1973. What is the size of the monthly payment?                                                     ($101.28)

14. If the investment in Problem 13 is paid out in 48 equal monthly payments, what would be the size of each payment?

15. A family needs a loan of $10,000 to buy a home. One lender charges 6% converted monthly. A second lender offers 5% converted monthly. If the monthly payments are to run for 12 years, what would be the total savings in interest if the borrower gets the 5% loan?          ($734.40)

16. A mortgage for $15,000 is to be repaid in monthly payments over a period of 15 years. What would be the total savings in interest if the loan is financed at 5% converted monthly rather than 6%?

17. A family buys a home costing $15,000. They pay $3000 down and get a 30-year mortgage for the balance at 5% converted monthly. What is the size of their monthly payments? What is the total interest that they will pay on this loan?                    ($64.42 a month; $11,191.20 interest)

18. A man gets a loan for $8000 to be repaid in monthly payments over a period of 25 years. If the interest rate is 6% converted monthly, what is the size of the monthly payment and the total interest?

19. A $30,000 life insurance policy matures on June 1, 1973, with the death of the insured. The beneficiary is to receive 192 equal monthly payments with the first payment on July 1, 1973. Find the size of the monthly payment and the date of the concluding payment if interest is earned at 3% converted monthly.                                   ($196.93, June 1, 1989)

20. What would be the size of the monthly payment if the money in Problem 19 earned 4% converted monthly?

**21.** A man wants to accumulate a $20,000 retirement fund. He plans to make semiannual deposits in a savings and loan association which pays 4% converted semiannually. If his first deposit is made on June 30, 1973, and his plan calls for the last deposit to be made on December 31, 2008, what should be the size of each deposit?                                  ($126.54)

**22.** Work Problem 21 if the man can get $4\frac{1}{2}\%$ converted semiannually.

## 4.11 Finding the Term of an Annuity

In some problems the amount or present value, the size of the payments, and the rate are specified. This leaves the number of payments to be determined. When an integral number of payments is not exactly equivalent to the original amount or present value, one of the following procedures is followed in practice. The last regular payment can be increased by a sum which will make the payments equivalent to the amount or present value. Or a smaller concluding payment can be made one period after the last full payment. In this book we follow the latter procedure unless the problem states that the last full payment is to be increased. Sometimes, when a certain amount of money is to be accumulated, a smaller concluding payment will not be required because the interest after the last full payment will equal or exceed the balance needed.

EXAMPLE 1: A man wants to accumulate $5000 by making payments of $1000 at the end of each year. If he gets 3% on his money, how many regular payments will he make and what is the size of the last payment?

SOLUTION: Using (12) for the amount of an annuity,

$$1000 s_{\overline{n}|3\%} = 5000$$

Solving for $s_{\overline{n}|}$,

$$s_{\overline{n}|3\%} = \tfrac{5000}{1000} = 5.0000$$

We look in Table 2 under 3% for the factor 5.0000 in the *Amount of 1 per Period* column. We find that for 4 periods the factor is 4.1836 and for 5 periods it is 5.3091. Therefore the man will have to make 4 deposits of $1000 and a fifth smaller deposit now to be determined. To get the size of this deposit we use an equation of value.

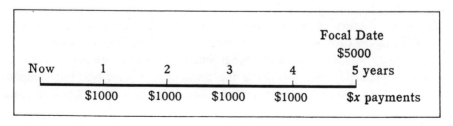

Instead of taking the four $1000 payments separately to the focal date, we get the amount of these four payments at the end of 4 years.

$$S_4 = 1000s_{\overline{4}|3\%}$$
$$= 1000 \times 4.183627 = \$4183.63$$

We now take this amount to the focal date using simple interest.

$$4183.63(1.03) + x = 5000.00$$
$$x = 5000.00 - 4309.14 = \$690.86$$

Thus, if the man deposits $1000 for four years and $690.86 at the end of 5 years, he will have exactly $5000 in his account. Note that in problems like this the last deposit will never be larger than the other deposits.

It is also possible to get the 4 payments to the focal date by looking up $s_{\overline{5}|}$ and subtracting 1 to allow for the fact that no full payment is made at the end. Then the amount becomes

$$1000(5.309136 - 1.000000) = \$4309.14$$

This leaves a balance of $690.86 to be paid at the end of 5 years.

This method will be discussed in more detail under annuities due in the next chapter.

EXAMPLE 2: A man wants to accumulate $9000 by annual payments of $1000 invested at 3%. How many full payments must he make and what will be the size of the concluding payment?

SOLUTION: Substituting in (12),

$$1000s_{\overline{n}|} = 9000$$

Solving for $s_{\overline{n}|}$,

$$s_{\overline{n}|} = 9.0000$$

The second column of Table 2 shows that an *Amount of* 1 *per Period* of 9.0000 lies between 8 and 9 payments. The amount of 8 full payments is

$$S_8 = 1000 \times 8.892\,336 = \$8892.34$$

Carrying this amount forward 1 year at simple interest,

$$8892.34(1.03) = \$9159.11$$

No smaller concluding payment is required.

EXAMPLE 3: A man dies and leaves his widow an estate worth $5000. Instead of taking the cash, she is to get monthly payments of $50. How many regular payments will she receive and what smaller payment one period after the last regular payment will settle the transaction equitably? The company will pay interest at 3% compounded monthly on the balance left with them.

SOLUTION: Using (13) for the present value of an annuity,

$$50a_{\overline{n}|\frac{1}{4}\%} = 5000$$

Solving for $a_{\overline{n}|}$,

$$a_{\overline{n}|\frac{1}{4}\%} = \frac{5000}{50} = 100$$

We look in Table 2 under $\frac{1}{4}\%$ for the factor 100 in the *Present Worth of 1 per Period* column. We find that for 115 periods the factor is less than 100 and for 116 periods it is greater. Therefore the widow will receive 115 payments of $50 and a 116th payment that is smaller than $50. To find the size of this concluding payment we set up an equation of value.

We first get the amount of the 115 regular $50 payments:

$$S_{115} = 50s_{\overline{115}|\frac{1}{4}\%}$$
$$= 50 \times 133.0450$$
$$= \$6652.25$$

We now take this amount and the $5000 to the focal date and set up the equation of value:

$$6652.25(1.0025) + x = 5000(1.0025)^{116}$$
$$x = 5000 \times 1.335944 - 6652.25(1.0025)$$
$$x = 6679.72 - 6668.88 = \$10.84$$

In this case the person will receive 115 payments of $50 and a 116th payment of $10.84.

As pointed out at the end of Example 1, it is also possible to get the 115 payments to the focal date by looking up $s_{\overline{116}|}$ and subtracting 1. The amount of 115 payments at the end of 116 periods then becomes

$$50(134.3776 - 1.0000) = \$6668.88$$

**EXERCISE 4e**

1. Mr. Freeman can afford to set aside $200 every 6 months from his salary. He plans to buy a resort cottage when he has accumulated $3600. How long will it take him if he can invest the money at $3\frac{1}{2}\%$ converted semi-annually? Give answer to the nearest payment.          (16 payments)

2. How many payments of $50 at the end of each month will be required to accumulate $3000 if interest is earned at 5% converted monthly? Give answer to the nearest payment.

3. How many annual payments of $12,000 each and what final smaller payment must be made to accumulate $35,000 if the money gets interest at 4%?

(Two full payments; a concluding payment of $9540.80)

4. A couple deposits $250 at the end of each 6 months in a savings and loan association paying 4% converted semiannually. To accumulate $4500, they must make how many full payments and what will be the size of the concluding payment if one is needed?

5. A man leaves his wife an estate of $25,000. The money is invested at 3% compounded monthly. How many monthly payments of $200 would the widow receive and what would be the size of the concluding payment?

(150 full payments; a concluding payment of $12.95)

6. An heiress invests her inheritance of $15,000 at 4% converted monthly. If she takes the money out in monthly payments of $125, how many full payments will she get and what will be the size of the concluding payment?

7. The present value of an annuity is $7500. Semiannual payments of $500 are made from the $7500 which is invested at 4% compounded semiannually. How many full payments will be made and what is the size of the concluding payment?   (18 full payments; a concluding payment of $5.80)

8. A man has $3000 in a savings and loan association. If he gets $4\frac{1}{2}$% converted semiannually, how many withdrawals of $500 can he make at the end of each 6 months and what will be the size of the concluding withdrawal if it is made 6 months after the last full withdrawal?

9. Since the concluding payment in Problem 7 would be so small if made one period after the last full payment, it might be sent with the last regular payment. If this is done what is the size of the last check received by the annuitant?                                                            ($505.69)

10. If, in Problem 5, the concluding payment was sent with the last regular payment, what total payment would the widow get at that time?

11. A man invests $20,000 on June 1, 1973, at 3% converted monthly. He is to receive monthly payments of $250 with the first payment to be made on July 1, 1973. How many full payments will he receive? What will be the size and date of the concluding payment if it is made 1 month after the last $250 payment?

(89 full payments; a concluding payment of $92.31 on December 1, 1980)

12. Ten thousand dollars is invested on August 1, 1974, at 3% converted monthly. The investment is to be paid out in monthly payments of $200 with the first payment to be made on September 1, 1974. How many full payments will be made and what will be the size and date of the last payment if it is made 1 month after the last full payment?

13. A house is for sale for $13,500. A couple can pay $4500 down and $80 a month. If they get a loan at 5% converted monthly, how many $80 payments must they make and what will be the size of the concluding payment?          (152 regular payments and a 153rd payment of $9.74)

14. How many full payments and what would be the size of the concluding payment in Problem 13 if the rate is 4% converted monthly?

15. A couple can save $150 at the end of each 6 months. How long will it take them to accumulate $3500 if they get 3% converted semiannually on their savings? If they need a partial deposit 6 months after the last $150 deposit, how large should it be? (20 full deposits; no partial deposit needed)

16. Work Problem 15 using a rate of 4% converted semiannually.

17. A piece of property is purchased for $360,000. The buyer pays $60,000 down and agrees to pay $40,000 at the end of each year. If the interest rate is 5%, how many full payments must be made and what will be the size of the concluding payment 1 year after the last full payment?
          (9 full payments and a concluding payment of $25,552.69)

18. A firm buys a store costing $180,000. They pay $30,000 down and $20,000 at the end of each year. If the interest rate is 4%, how many full payments must they make and what will be the size of the concluding payment?

## 4.12   Finding the Interest Rate

A very practical application of the amount and present value formulas is finding the interest rate. In many business transactions the true interest rate is concealed in one way or another, so it is desirable that the customer be able to determine the rate. In this way he can compare one proposition with another and select the one that is least expensive for him. The rate can be determined approximately, but with sufficient accuracy for most practical purposes, by linear interpolation using factors from Table 2.

EXAMPLE 1: Find the rate of interest per period and the nominal rate converted semiannually at which payments of $150 every 6 months will amount to $2000 in 6 years.

SOLUTION: Substituting in (12) for the amount of an annuity,

$$150s_{\overline{12}|} = 2000$$
$$s_{\overline{12}|} = \tfrac{2000}{150} = 13.3333$$

We refer to the *Amount of 1 per Period* column in Table 2 and go across the row for $n = 12$ until we find the factor 13.3333 or, as is usually the case, values on each side of this factor. We record these values below.

$$
\begin{array}{cc}
i \text{ in } \% & s_{\overline{12}|} \\
\end{array}
$$

$$
.25 \quad d \left[ \begin{array}{c} 2.00 \\ i \\ 1.75 \end{array} \right. \qquad \begin{array}{c} 13.4121 \\ 13.3333 \\ 13.2251 \end{array} \right] 1082 \quad \Bigg] 1870
$$

The rate per period in our problem lies between 1.75% and 2%. Using $d$ to indicate the difference between 1.75% and the desired rate, we set up the proportion

$$
\frac{d}{.25} = \frac{1082}{1870}
$$

$$
d = .25 \times \tfrac{1082}{1870} = .144
$$

From which

$$
i = 1.75 + .144 = 1.894\%
$$

This is the rate per period. To get the approximate nominal rate converted semiannually we double this value so that the final answer is

$$
2 \times 1.894 = 3.788 = 3.79\%
$$

If only the nominal rate is wanted, it is faster and simpler to interpolate between nominal rates as shown below.

$$
\begin{array}{cc}
j_{(2)} \text{ in } \% & s_{\overline{12}|} \\
\end{array}
$$

$$
.50 \quad d \left[ \begin{array}{c} 4.00 \\ j \\ 3.50 \end{array} \right. \qquad \begin{array}{c} 13.4121 \\ 13.3333 \\ 13.2251 \end{array} \right] 1082 \quad \Bigg] 1870
$$

$$
\frac{d}{.50} = \frac{1082}{1870}
$$

$$
d = .50 \times \tfrac{1082}{1870} = .29
$$

The nominal rate converted semiannually is $3.50 + .29 = 3.79\%$.

EXAMPLE 2: The winner of a lottery can take \$1000 cash or \$100 a month for 12 months with the first payment in one month. If he takes the monthly payments, what nominal rate of interest will he earn?

SOLUTION: Substituting in (13), we have

$$
100a_{\overline{n}|} = 1000
$$
$$
a_{\overline{n}|} = 10.0000
$$

We refer to Table 2 and look in row 12 until we find 10.0000 or factors on both sides of it in the *Present Worth of* 1 *per Period* column. The results are recorded below. Note that as $i$ increases, $a_{\overline{n}|}$ decreases.

$$
\begin{array}{llll}
& j_{(12)} \text{ in } \% & a_{\overline{12}|} \\
& \quad 30 & 10.2578 \\
6 & d \begin{array}{l} \\ -j \end{array} & 10.0000 \Big] 2578 & \Big] 3038 \\
& \quad 36 & 9.9540
\end{array}
$$

$$\frac{d}{6} = \frac{2578}{3038}$$

$$d = 6 \times \tfrac{2578}{3038} = 5.09$$

Nominal rate $= 30.0 + 5.1 = 35.1\%$ compounded monthly.

EXAMPLE 3: A used car can be purchased for $500 cash or for $50 down and $35 a month for 18 months. Find the nominal annual rate.

SOLUTION: Subtracting the down payment gives us a present value of $450. Substituting in (13) for the present value of an annuity, we have

$$35a_{\overline{18}|} = 450$$
$$a_{\overline{18}|} = \tfrac{450}{35} = 12.8571$$

We refer to Table 2 and look in row 18 until we find either 12.8571 or factors on both sides of this value in the *Present Worth of 1 per Period* column. The results are recorded below. Note that $a_{\overline{n}|}$ decreases as $i$ increases.

$$
\begin{array}{llll}
& j_{(12)} \text{ in } \% & a_{\overline{18}|} \\
& \quad 42 & 13.1897 \\
6 & d \begin{array}{l} \\ -j \end{array} & 12.8571 \Big] 3326 & \Big] 5304 \\
& \quad 48 & 12.6593
\end{array}
$$

$$\frac{d}{6} = \frac{3326}{5304}$$

$$d = 6 \times \tfrac{3326}{5304} = 3.76$$
$$j = 42.0 + 3.8 = 45.8\% \text{ compounded monthly}$$

Because rates on installment purchases and small loans are often quite high, a buyer should always check the true rate before signing a contract.

EXAMPLE 4: A trombone is priced on the tag at $100. It can be purchased for $8 down and $5 a week for 20 weeks. Or it can be obtained for cash at a 10% discount. What nominal interest rate converted weekly is charged the installment buyer?

SOLUTION: First we must get the *true* cash price which is not $100 but $100 less 10% or $90. This makes the original unpaid balance $82. ($90 less the $8 down payment.) Now we substitute in (13),

$$5a_{\overline{20}|} = 82$$
$$a_{\overline{20}|} = 16.4000$$

From which

| $i$ in % | | $a_{\overline{20}|}$ | | |
|---|---|---|---|---|
| | 1.75 | 16.7529 | | |

.25 $\left[\ d \left[\begin{array}{l} 1.75 \\ i \\ 2.00 \end{array}\right.\right.$    $\begin{array}{l} 16.7529 \\ 16.4000 \\ 16.3514 \end{array} \left.\begin{array}{l} \\ \end{array}\right] 3529$   4015

$$\frac{d}{.25} = \frac{3529}{4015}$$

$$d = .25 \times \tfrac{3529}{4015} = .22$$
$$i = 1.75 + .22 = 1.97\% \text{ per week}$$

This makes the approximate nominal rate $52 \times 1.97 = 102\%$.

EXAMPLE 5: A dealer extends credit on the basis of 6% add-on. This means that he takes the unpaid balance and adds 6% of the loan for each year that credit is to be extended. Then the total is divided by the number of months to get the monthly payment. If a $2000 loan is repaid over 2 years, what is the nominal interest rate?

SOLUTION:

$$\begin{array}{ll} \text{Unpaid balance} & = \$2000.00 \\ \text{Add-on} = .12 \times 2000 = & \underline{\phantom{0}240.00} \\ & \$2240.00 \end{array}$$

$$\text{Monthly payment} = 2240.00/24 = \$93.33$$

The problem is now an ordinary annuity with a present value of $2000 and a periodic payment of $93.33. Substituting in (13),

$$93.33a_{\overline{24}|} = 2000.00$$
$$a_{\overline{24}|} = 21.4293$$

Since only the nominal rate is required, we interpolate between the closest nominal rates in Table 2.

| $j_{(12)}$ in % | | $a_{\overline{24}|}$ | | |
|---|---|---|---|---|

3 $\left[\ d \left[\begin{array}{l} 9 \\ j \\ 12 \end{array}\right.\right.$    $\begin{array}{l} 21.8891 \\ 21.4293 \\ 21.2434 \end{array} \left.\begin{array}{l} \\ \end{array}\right] 4598$   6457

$$\frac{d}{3} = \frac{4598}{6457}$$

$$d = \frac{3 \times 4598}{6457} = 2.1$$

$$\text{Nominal rate} = 9.0 + 2.1 = 11.1\%$$

EXAMPLE 6: A lender makes loans on the basis of 6% discount. For a 1-year loan he subtracts 6% of the loan. The borrower receives the balance. The monthly payment is obtained by dividing the loan before the discount by the number of payments. Find the nominal rate paid by a person who borrows $1000 from this lender.

SOLUTION: The borrower receives $1000 - 1000 \times .06 = \$940$. Monthly payment $= 1000/12 = \$83.33$. The problem is now an ordinary annuity with a present value of $940 and a periodic payment of $83.33.

$$83.33a_{\overline{12}|} = 940.00$$

$$a_{\overline{12}|} = \frac{940.00}{83.33} = 11.2805$$

$$\frac{d}{3} = \frac{1544}{1798}$$

$$d = \frac{3 \times 1544}{1798} = 2.6$$

Nominal rate $= 9.0 + 2.6 = 11.6\%$

Monthly installment loans based on add-on or discount result in nominal rates that are about twice the stated value.

## 4.13  Truth in Lending

After several years of research and hearings by congressional committees, Truth in Lending became law on July 1, 1969. This law requires that the borrower be told the total finance charge in dollars (except for home loans) and the annual percentage rate. The finance charge includes all costs that must be paid to get credit. There are no distinctions among such items as interest, discount, the time-price differential, and other fees or charges made by the creditor. The annual percentage rate is based on the actuarial method which means that a rate is determined which makes the present value of the payments equal to the cash value of the loan. The law also includes the right to rescind certain credit transactions within three business days and the right to sue creditors for not obeying the law.

Since understanding credit costs is important for successful management of personal and family finances, the Truth in Lending Law can be helpful to consumers who are aware of the safeguards provided by the law. Borrowers can now compare financial terms offered by competing creditors. Since enforcement of the law depends in part on consumer awareness, it is important that consumers learn how the law can help them. As the number of informed borrowers increases, they will exert an influence that will result in a more competitive marketplace for credit that will benefit all borrowers.

A problem that Truth in Lending does not solve is that of comparing annual percentage rates when the same item is available for different cash prices and time payment plans. The example below shows how this situation can be analyzed using the methods developed in this chapter.

EXAMPLE: After a shopping trip a person returns home with the following information for the same item:

| STORE | CASH PRICE | DOWN PAYMENT | MONTHLY PAYMENT | NUMBER OF PAYMENTS | COST OF CREDIT | ANNUAL RATE |
|-------|-----------|--------------|-----------------|-------------------|---------------|-------------|
| A | $110.00 | $10.00 | $8.75 | 12 | $5.00 | 9% |
| B | 100.00 | 10.00 | 8.25 | 12 | 9.00 | 18% |

(a) Check the annual percentage rates claimed by the sellers.

(b) Get the total dollar cost for the two stores.

(c) The time payment plan for store A would represent what annual percentage rate if based on a cash price of $100?

SOLUTION: (a) On the basis of the tag price of $110, the borrower gets a loan of $100 after the down payment. Substituting in (13),

$$8.75a_{\overline{12}|} = 100.00$$
$$a_{\overline{12}|} = 11.4286$$

This is practically the *Present Worth of 1 per Period* factor for a nominal annual rate of 9% compounded monthly.

At the second store the buyer gets a loan of $90 to be repaid in 12 payments of $8.25. Substituting in (13),

$$8.25a_{\overline{12}|} = 90.00$$
$$a_{\overline{12}|} = 10.9091$$

This is the factor for 18% compounded monthly.

Both merchants are reporting the correct rate for their cash prices.

(b) Total dollar costs:

Store A

| Down payment | $ 10.00 |
|--------------|---------|
| 12 monthly payments of $8.75 | 105.00 |
| Total | $115.00 |

Store B

| | |
|---|---|
| Down payment | $ 10.00 |
| 12 monthly payments of $8.25 | 99.00 |
| Total | $109.00 |

Store B is the better place to make the purchase because the lower cash price more than offsets the apparently higher credit costs.

(c) If we use a cash price of $100 for store A, the borrower is getting a loan of $90 after the $10 down payment.

Substituting in (13),

$$8.75a_{\overline{12}|} = 90.00$$
$$a_{\overline{12}|} = 10.2857$$

Interpolating between the closest values in Table 2,

$$\begin{array}{ccc} & j_{(12)} \text{ in } \% & a_{\overline{12}|} \\ 3\left[\; d\left[\begin{array}{c} 27 \\ j \\ 30 \end{array}\right.\right. & & \left.\begin{array}{c} 10.4148 \\ 10.2857 \\ 10.2578 \end{array}\right]1291 \right]1570 \end{array}$$

$$\frac{d}{3} = \frac{1291}{1570}$$

$$d = \frac{3 \times 1291}{1570} = 2.5$$

Nominal rate $= 27.0 + 2.5 = 29.5\%$

Before buying an item on credit, a person should do comparison shopping for the total package—merchandise and credit. Neither the cash price alone nor the lender's annual percentage rate alone will necessarily indicate which is the best overall proposition. Had merchant A wanted his credit terms to sound even better, he could have run his "cash" price up to $115. Now a down payment of $10 and $8.75 a month for 12 months can be advertised as "no charge for credit." The rate is truly zero on the basis of the stated figures.

## 4.14 Check the Rate

Because most students will have to at least occasionally borrow money, it is important for them to know about the more common sources of credit. In this section we shall consider consumer loans and installment credit. Large loans for homes and businesses will be discussed in Chapter 6.

The following table gives common rates for various sources of small loans. While this will be a help in locating the most economical source of credit, the borrower should still check the rate himself as some lenders vary considerably from the typical values given below.

| SOURCE OF CREDIT | COMMON RATES |
| --- | --- |
| Insurance policies | 4–6% |
| Credit unions | 9–12% |
| Commercial banks | 6–18% |
| Automobile finance companies | 10–24% |
| Licensed small loan companies | 24–42% |
| Installment sellers | 0–24% and up! |
| Loan sharks | 120–500% and up! |

The person who borrows on his **life insurance** is in effect getting the use of his own cash reserve. This will be discussed in Chapter 10. While an insurance policy may be the cheapest source of a small loan, the borrower should remember that, if he dies, the benefits will be reduced by the amount of the loan.

A **credit union** is really a people's bank. The members of a business, union, church, or other group who have savings put the money on deposit in the credit union and receive interest. Members of the same group who need cash borrow from the credit union. Because operating, investigation, and collection costs are low, a credit union can make small loans at a rate that is usually lower than those charged by commercial sources of credit.

While consumer loan rates charged by **banks** are not high, as modern credit goes, they are likely to be considerably higher than a good money manager likes to pay.

**Automobile finance companies** usually charge rates that range from approximately 10 to 24% converted monthly. However, there are a few unethical companies in this field that resort to excessive packing (arbitrary amounts added to the financing charges) that can make the true interest rate much higher.

The **licensed small loan companies** charge rates which range from 2 to $3\frac{1}{2}$% a **month**. While these rates are high, perhaps unnecessarily so at times, these companies perform a useful service in granting credit to people who could not get a loan from one of the less expensive agencies mentioned above. People should not let the advertising emphasis of some of these companies on how easy it is to get a loan cause them to forget how hard it is to repay it at the usual rates.

Rates for **installment sales** vary from what is supposed to be zero when there is no charge for credit up to very high rates in other cases. However, if a discount can be obtained for cash, even the "no charge for credit" propositions may actually conceal a high rate of interest based on the *true* cash price.

**Loan sharks** operate outside the law and will charge whatever they can get away with. Because of their high rates and brutal methods, they should be avoided completely.

We can sum up the wise use of credit by saying that people should pay cash when possible, shop for credit if they must borrow, check the true rate of interest, and avoid being swindled by following the rule below:

*Read and understand the contract and check financing costs on both a dollar and a percentage basis before signing. Be sure that all blanks are filled in and get a complete copy of the contract.*

### EXERCISE 4f

1. The total cost of a car is $2673.54 cash. The down payment is $873.54. Payments of $70 a month are to be made for 30 months. What is the true annual interest rate converted monthly? Show answer between the two closest table values.                    (12–15% converted monthly)
2. A lathe priced at $120 was sold on easy terms for a down payment of $40 and 10 monthly payments of $9. What is the true annual interest rate converted monthly? Show answer between the two closest table values.
3. If $500 periodic payments per year for 8 years amount to $4500, what is the effective rate of interest?                    (3.34%)
4. Deposits in a building and loan association of $200 at the end of each 6 months for 5 years amounted to $2160. What was the average nominal rate of interest converted semiannually earned on this account?
5. A couple saves $200 every 6 months. They made their first deposit in June 1958. If they have $10,000 in their account just after making the deposit in June 1974, what nominal rate of interest converted semiannually did they earn on their savings?                    (4.92%)
6. At the end of each month for 5 years a man put $50 in an investment. If his account then amounted to $3300, what rate of interest converted monthly did he earn on his investment?
7. On his 26th birthday Walter Artmeyer put $300 in a savings account. He continues to deposit the same amount every year. If he has $27,000 in his account just after he makes his deposit on his 65th birthday, what average annual rate of return had he earned on his investment?                    (3.76%)
8. A rifle selling for $55 cash can be purchased for $10 down and $10 a month for 5 months. What is the nominal interest rate converted monthly rounded to the nearest .1%?

9. An electric range lists for $300. Sales tax is 3%. The range may be purchased on time for $25 down and 18 payments of $18.50 a month. What is the nominal interest rate?                                                        (20.8%)

10. A used car is priced at $730. It can be purchased for $64 down and $45 a month for 18 months. What is the nominal rate of interest converted monthly for this time payment plan? Round answer to the nearest .1%.

11. The cash price of a refrigerator is $360. A buyer can pay $160 down and $12 a month for 24 months. What is the nominal rate converted monthly?                                                                             (37.8%)

12. A sofa can be purchased for $100 cash. If it is bought on time the down payment is $10 and the balance is paid in 11 monthly payments of $9 each. Get the nominal interest rate rounded to .1%.

13. A suite of furniture for 3 rooms can be purchased for $431.47 cash, or for $31.47 down and 18 monthly payments of $26 each. What is the nominal rate converted monthly?                                                      (20.5%)

14. A refrigerator lists for $407.47. It can be purchased for $57.47 down and 24 monthly payments of $20 each. What is the nominal rate rounded to .1%?

15. A gravestone can be purchased for $180 cash or $45 down and $7.50 a month for 24 months. What is the nominal rate of interest?         (29.3%)

16. An engagement ring can be purchased for $110. Or it can be obtained with no down payment and monthly payments of $20 at the end of each month for 7 months. Get the nominal rate converted monthly rounded to .1%.

17. A store advertised a suite of furniture for $300. The ad said that there was no charge for easy terms since the furniture could be purchased for $50 down and $25 a month for 10 months. However, a cash customer could get a 10% discount by asking for it. What nominal rate of interest was actually paid by the installment buyer?                                            (28.7%)

18. A jewelry store advertised: "No carrying charge for time payments and no down payment." A watch with a price tag of $60 could be purchased for $5 a month for 12 months. When a customer asked for a cash discount, he got the watch for $50. Based on the true cash price, what was the nominal interest rate rounded to .1%?

19. A home freezer is listed at $350. If a customer pays $100 down, the balance plus a carrying charge of $20 can be paid in 12 equal monthly payments. If the customer pays cash, he can get a discount of 5% off the list price. What is the nominal rate converted monthly if the freezer is bought on time?                                                                       (28.6%)

20. A store offers to sell a watch for $60 or for $5 down and $5 a week for 11 weeks. If this same watch can be purchased for $50 cash at another store,

the first store is actually charging what nominal rate of interest under their "no carrying charge plan"?

21. A store claims that their credit costs are very low. For example, a $220 washing machine can be bought for $20 down and $17.20 a month for 12 months. Under this plan they claim that the buyer is paying only 6% interest. A competitor claims that these carrying charges are low only because the washing machine is overpriced by $15. If this is correct, what nominal interest rate converted monthly is paid by an installment buyer at the first store? (20.7%)

22. A man borrows $150 from a licensed small loan company and agrees to pay $15.07 a month for 12 months. What is the nominal rate of interest correct to the nearest per cent?

23. A man needs $75 immediately for medical care for one of his children. He gets the money from a small loan company and agrees to pay $9.02 a month for 10 months. What is the nominal rate of interest? (42%)

24. Shop for some item and get the following information:

Item.............................................

Cash price.......................................

Tax (if any).....................................

Total cost.......................................

Cash discount (if one is allowed)....................

Down payment....................................

Number and size of payments......................

Interest rate as stated by the seller..................

Now compute the nominal rate using Table 2.

25. You are preparing a report on consumer credit and want to include a table showing true rates corresponding to various stated values. Complete the following table. The given value is from Example 6, page 167.

*True Rates on Loans Repaid in 12 Monthly Payments*

| IF THE CHARGE FOR CREDIT PER YEAR IS: | THE QUOTED RATE IS: | THE TRUE RATE PER YEAR IS: | |
| --- | --- | --- | --- |
| | | *For add-on* | *For discount* |
| $4 per $100 | 4% | | |
| $6 per $100 | 6% | | 11.6% |
| $8 per $100 | 8% | | |

# 5

**Other
Annuities
Certain**

## 5.1  Annuity Functions

The *Amount of* 1 *per Period* function gives the amount of $n$ periodic deposits of \$1 at the time of the last deposit. The symbol for this function is $s_{\overline{n}|}$ and its numerical values are given in the middle column in the left-hand page of Table 2. The *Present Worth of* 1 *per Period* function gives the present worth of $n$ payments of \$1 at a point in time one period before the first payment. The symbol for this function is $a_{\overline{n}|}$ and its numerical values are given in the middle column on the right-hand page of Table 2.

Ordinary annuities have the payments made at the end of the time periods. The amount of an ordinary annuity is found by simply substituting the value of $s_{\overline{n}|}$ in (12), $S_n = Rs_{\overline{n}|}$. The present value of an ordinary annuity is found by substituting the value of $a_{\overline{n}|}$ in (13), $A_n = Ra_{\overline{n}|}$.

174

We now consider other types of annuities which are evaluated using Table 2. To solve these annuities, we modify or combine the ordinary annuity functions. Since this is a simple matter, publishers of compound interest tables print only numerical values of the ordinary annuity functions.

Before using Table 2 to solve other types of annuities, it is necessary to understand exactly what is meant by the tabled values of $s_{\overline{n}|}$ and $a_{\overline{n}|}$. The time diagram below shows the points in time at which the ordinary annuity functions give the value of a series of payments.

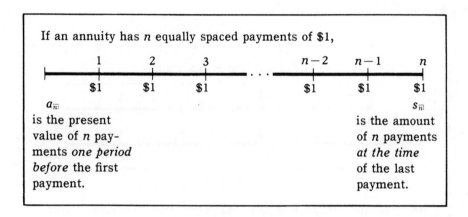

The value of an annuity may be needed at any point in time from several periods before the first payment to several periods after the last payment. The various possibilities and the corresponding annuity are shown below.

## 5.2   Annuity Due

An **annuity due** is one in which the payments are made at the beginning of the payment interval, the first payment being due at once. Insurance premiums and property rentals are examples of annuities due. To get the amount and present value formulas for the annuity due, we modify the formulas already derived for the ordinary annuity so that the ordinary annuity tables can be used with simple modifications.

The sketch below illustrates an annuity due. Note that it starts with a payment and ends one period after the last or $n$th payment. Also included in the sketch is the corresponding ordinary annuity.

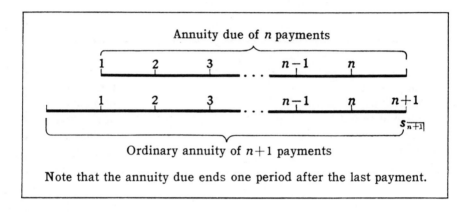

Note that the annuity due ends one period after the last payment.

The sketch shows that if we obtain the amount of an ordinary annuity of $n + 1$ payments, we would have the amount of the corresponding annuity due except that we have included a final payment which is not actually made at the end of the last period of the annuity due. Therefore all we have to do is subtract one payment to permit us to use the ordinary annuity tables to get the amount of an annuity due. This leads to the following formula:

$$S_n = Rs_{\overline{n+1}|} - R$$
$$S_n = R(s_{\overline{n+1}|} - 1) \qquad (16)$$

The rather complex appearing quantity which is to be multiplied by $R$ is quite simple to get. First we add 1 to the number of payments in the annuity due, and use the resulting value when we go to Table 2. This means that if there are 10 payments we look up the value for 11. Then we subtract 1 from the factor. For an interest rate of 2% and 11 periods the factor is 12.1687 (correct to 4 decimal places). To get the amount of an annuity due of 10 payments we would use 11.1687 for the factor. All of these steps can be done mentally.

To get the present value of an annuity due, we again make a sketch with the corresponding ordinary annuity.

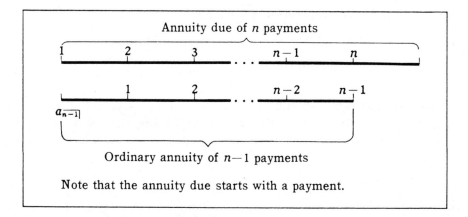

Annuity due of $n$ payments

Ordinary annuity of $n-1$ payments

Note that the annuity due starts with a payment.

We again match the annuity due with an ordinary annuity so we can get numerical factors from the Compound Interest and Annuity Tables. If we obtain the present value of an ordinary annuity of $n - 1$ payments, we would have the present value of the corresponding annuity due except that we would not be including a payment which is made at the beginning of the term of the annuity due. Therefore all we have to do is add this first payment. This leads to the following formula for the present value of an annuity due:

$$A_n = Ra_{\overline{n-1}|} + R$$
$$A_n = R(a_{\overline{n-1}|} + 1) \tag{17}$$

Again it is simple to use the ordinary annuity tables. First we subtract 1 from the number of payments in the annuity due, and use the resulting value when we go to the table. This means that if there are 8 payments in an annuity due we look up the value for 7. Then we add 1 to the factor. For an interest rate of $3\%$ and 7 periods the factor is 6.2303. We then change this to 7.2303 to get the present value of an annuity due of 8 payments and a rate of $3\%$.

EXAMPLE 1: A man invests $200 at the beginning of each year for 10 years. If he gets interest at $3\frac{1}{2}\%$ effective, how much does he have to his credit at the end of 10 years?

SOLUTION: Substituting $R = 200$, $n + 1 = 11$, and $i = 3\frac{1}{2}\%$ in (16),

$$S_{10} = 200(s_{\overline{11}|} - 1)$$
$$= 200 \times 12.14199 = \$2428.40$$

EXAMPLE 2: A student wants to have $600 four years from now. How much must he invest at the beginning of each year starting now if he gets 4% compounded annually on his savings?

SOLUTION: Substituting in (16) and solving for $R$,

$$600 = R(s_{\overline{5}|} - 1) = R \times 4.41632$$

$$R = \frac{600}{4.41632} = \$135.86$$

ALTERNATE SOLUTION: We can check the answer by using an equation of value with the focal date at the time of the last deposit. The 4 payments are brought to the focal date as an ordinary annuity, and the $600 is brought to the focal date by discounting it for one period.

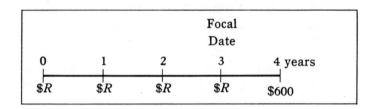

$$Rs_{\overline{4}|} = 600(1 + i)^{-1}$$

$$R = 600(1.04)^{-1} \times \frac{1}{s_{\overline{4}|}}$$

$$= 600 \times .96154 \times .23549 = \$135.86$$

This method requires an additional multiplication but no division.

EXAMPLE 3: The premium on a life insurance policy is $60 a quarter payable in advance. Find the cash equivalent of a year's payments if the insurance company charges 6% converted quarterly for the privilege of paying this way instead of all at once for the year.

SOLUTION: Substituting $R = 60$, $n - 1 = 3$, and $i = 1\frac{1}{2}\%$ in (17),

$$A_4 = 60(a_{\overline{3}|} + 1)$$
$$= 60 \times 3.9122 = \$234.73$$

While paying by the quarter is convenient, the savings represented by annual payments are substantial.

EXAMPLE 4: The beneficiary of a life insurance policy may take $10,000 cash or 10 equal annual payments, the first to be made immediately. What is the annual payment if money is worth $2\frac{1}{2}\%$?

SOLUTION: Substituting in (17) and solving for $R$,

$$10,000 = R(a_{\overline{9}|} + 1) = R \times 8.9708655$$

$$R = \frac{10,000}{8.9708655} = \$1114.72$$

ALTERNATE SOLUTION: An equation of value with the focal date at the time of the last payment enables us to check the above answer. The 10 payments are brought to the focal date as an ordinary annuity since the focal date is at the time of the last payment. The $10,000 is brought forward 9 (not 10) periods. A time diagram is very helpful in getting the correct values of $n$ in problems like this.

$$Rs_{\overline{10}|} = 10,000(1.025)^9$$

$$R = 10,000(1.025)^9 \times \frac{1}{s_{\overline{10}|}}$$

$$= 10,000 \times 1.248\ 8630 \times .089\ 2588 = \$1114.72$$

This method eliminates division, but requires an additional multiplication.

## 5.3 Outstanding Balance

A common financial problem is determining the outstanding balance on a loan after several payments have been made. The amount of an annuity due provides the easiest way to get the balance one period after a payment.

EXAMPLE 1: A $10,000 loan is to be amortized with payments of $1000 at the end of each year and a final concluding payment. Find the number of full payments and the size of the concluding payment if the rate is 6% converted annually.

SOLUTION: We first substitute in (13) for the present value of an ordinary annuity.

$$1000a_{\overline{n}|} = 10,000$$

$$a_{\overline{n}|} = 10$$

When we look for this factor in the *Present Worth of* 1 *per Period* column in Table 2, we find that there will be 15 full payments. We draw a time diagram and choose the time of the 16th (and unknown) payment as the focal date.

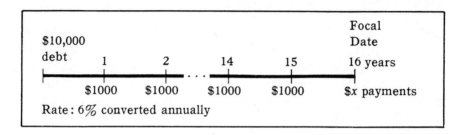

We get the concluding payment by taking the $10,000 forward as a single sum for 16 years and subtracting the amount of an annuity due of 15 payments.

$$10,000(1.06)^{16} = 10,000 \times 2.540\ 3517 = \$25,403.52$$
$$1000(s_{\overline{15+1}|} - 1) = 1000 \times 24.672\ 528 = \underline{24,672.53}$$
$$\text{Concluding payment} \quad \$\quad 730.99$$

A sharp practice that is sometimes used to take advantage of an unwary borrower is the balloon payment. An item is sold on time for a series of payments that the borrower can meet. At the end there is a much larger payment. If the buyer defaults on the balloon payment, the lender can repossess the merchandise and have both it and the payments that have been made.

EXAMPLE 2: A $2400 car is sold for $400 down, 17 payments of $100 a month, and an 18th balloon payment. If the interest rate is 24% converted monthly, find the size of the balloon payment.

SOLUTION: We draw a time diagram, put the focal date at 18 months, and carry everything to the focal date. Since the focal date is one period after the last regular payment, we use (16) for the amount of an annuity due.

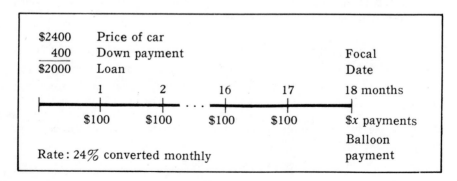

$$2000(1.02)^{18} = 2000 \times 1.428\ 246 = \$2856.49$$
$$100(s_{\overline{17+1}|} - 1) = 100 \times 20.41231 = \underline{\quad 2041.23}$$
$$\text{Balloon payment} = \$\ 815.26$$

## EXERCISE 5a

1. If money is worth 4% converted semiannually, what is the present value of an annuity due of $500 every 6 months for 5 years?  ($4581.12)

2. At 5% converted monthly, what is the present value of an annuity due of $45 every month for 12 years?

3. What is the amount of the annuity due in Problem 1?  ($5584.36)

4. What is the amount of the annuity due in Problem 2?

5. On July 6, 1967, a man deposited $250 in a savings and loan association paying $4\frac{1}{2}$% converted semiannually. Interest dates are June 30 and December 31, and deposits made by the 10th of a month earn interest for the entire month. This man continues to make $250 deposits every 6 months up to and including January 4, 1973, when he makes his last deposit. How much will be in his account after interest is credited on June 30, 1973?  ($3477.07)

6. On June 1, 1967, a man deposits $200 in a savings and loan association that pays $4\frac{1}{2}$% converted semiannually. He continues to make $200 deposits every 6 months. If he makes his last deposit on December 1, 1973, how much will be in his account on June 1, 1974? Interest dates are May 31 and November 30. Deposits made by the 10th of the month earn interest for the entire month.

7. A couple expects to need $4000 in June, 1974. In June, 1970, they made the first of 4 equal annual deposits in an investment paying 4%. What is the size of each deposit needed to accumulate the desired amount?  ($905.73)

8. A debt of $7500 is due in 10 years. The debtor agrees to settle this debt with 10 equal annual payments, the first payment to be made now. Find the size of the payment if money is worth 4%.

9. The premium on a life insurance policy is $15 a month payable in advance. A policy holder may pay a year's premium in advance. Find the annual premium if it is based on 6% converted monthly.  ($175.16)

10. A life insurance policy has premiums at the beginning of each month of $25. Find the equivalent annual premium at the beginning of each year if it is based on 9% converted monthly.

11. The annual premium on a life insurance policy is $250 payable in advance. However, payments may be made quarterly in advance in which case the insurance company charges interest at 6% converted quarterly. Find the size of the quarterly payment.  ($63.90)

12. The annual premium on a life insurance policy is $185 payable in advance. What would be the monthly premium based on 6% converted monthly?

13. A man has $5000 in a building and loan association which pays $4\frac{1}{2}\%$ compounded semiannually. If he withdraws $500 at the beginning of each half year, how many such withdrawals can he make? What will be the size of the concluding withdrawal?

>(Eleven $500 withdrawals and a 12th withdrawal of $85.45)

14. In Problem 13 how many $250 withdrawals could be made and what would be the size of the concluding withdrawal?

15. Instead of taking $5000 from an inheritance, a person decides to take 60 monthly payments with the first payment to be made immediately. If interest is allowed at $3\%$ converted monthly, what will be the size of each payment?                                        ($89.62)

16. Instead of taking $20,000 cash from an inheritance, the heir elects to receive quarterly payments for 10 years with the first payment to be made right away. If the money is invested at $4\%$ converted quarterly, what will be the size of each payment?

17. A man wants to take out enough life insurance to provide 120 monthly payments certain of $150 each to his family. If the first payment is to be made upon proof of the man's death, he should take out what size policy? Round the answer to the nearest $1000. The insurance company pays $3\%$ converted monthly on money left with them.                 ($16,000)

18. A man is planning an insurance program which will pay 180 monthly payments certain of $200 each to his widow. The insurance company will pay $3\%$ converted monthly on money left with them. If the first payment is to be made upon proof of the man's death, he should take out what size policy? Round answer to nearest $1000.

19. A store can be rented for $300 a month payable in advance. If the renter pays 3 months in advance, the owner will allow interest at $5\%$ converted monthly. What is the size of the payment at the beginning of each 3 months that is equivalent to $300 at the beginning of each month?       ($896.27)

20. A store can be rented for $350 per month payable in advance. The landlord will accept a single cash payment at the beginning of a year for a year's lease if interest is computed at $5\%$ converted monthly. What would be the cost of a year's lease?

21. A man knows that if he dies his wife will not get any social security benefits until she reaches age 60. He has several insurance policies. One for $10,000 is to be used to provide a monthly income for her between the time he dies and she reaches age 60. She is 53 at the time he dies and she elects to get 84 equal monthly payments from this policy with the first payment to be made immediately. What will be the size of each payment if $4\%$ converted monthly is paid on the proceeds of this policy?                 ($136.23)

22. The widow in Problem 21 decides to wait until age 62 to start receiving social security payments so they will be larger. She elects to get 108 equal

monthly payments from the $10,000 policy with the first payment to be made immediately. Find the size of the payments.

23. On June 1, 1967, a man opened a savings account for his daughter with a deposit of $25 in a bank paying 3% converted semiannually. If he continues to make semiannual deposits of $25 until December 1, 1974, when he plans to make the last deposit, how much will be in the account on June 1, 1975?
($455.04)

24. A man invests $300 every year, making his first deposit on August 1, 1962, and his last deposit on August 1, 1972. How much will be in his account on August 1, 1973, if he gets interest at 4% compounded annually?

25. A man aged 25 is considering two types of life insurance policies. The first is an ordinary life with an annual premium of $200 for a $10,000 policy. The second is a twenty-year endowment with an annual premium of $510. He decides to take out the ordinary life and deposit the difference in premiums each year in an investment paying 4% compounded annually. If he dies just before making his 17th deposit, how much will be in his savings account? Allow interest for the year after the 16th deposit.
($7036.23)

26. A man aged 30 is considering two $15,000 insurance policies. The first is an ordinary life with an annual premium of $277. The second is a 20-pay life with an annual premium of $410. He decides to take out the ordinary life and put the difference in premiums in an investment paying $3\frac{1}{2}$%. How much will his family get from this investment if he dies after interest is earned on the 15th deposit but before he makes the 16th deposit?

27. A factory owner has a fire insurance policy for which the annual premium is $300 payable in advance. If interest is 6% converted annually, what would be the equivalent single premium which would provide insurance for 5 years?
($1339.53)

28. A home owner has been paying his insurance at the beginning of each year. The annual premium is $60. At 8% converted annually, what would be the equivalent premium for a three-year policy?

29. A $2200 used car is sold for $200 down, 23 payments of $80 a month and a 24th balloon payment. If the interest rate is 18% converted monthly, what is the size of the balloon payment?
($648.33)

30. Find the size of the balloon payment in Problem 29 if the rate is 21% converted monthly.

## 5.4 Deferred Annuity

A **deferred annuity** is one in which the first payment is not made at the beginning or end of the first period but at some later date. When the first payment is made at the end of 10 periods, the annuity is said to be deferred 9 periods.

Similarly, an annuity which is deferred for 12 periods will have the first payment at the end of 13 periods. It is important to understand that *the interval of deferment ends one period before the first payment.* In practice this point causes considerable trouble because in some problems the interval of deferment is given, in others the time of the first payment. When the time of the first payment is given, the student must determine the interval of deferment before substituting in the present value formula. For example, if payments are made quarterly and the first payment is made in 4 years, the interval of deferment is 15 periods.

The sketch shows a deferred annuity of $n$ payments which is deferred for $m$ periods.

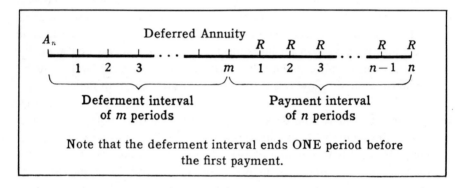

To get a formula for the present value of a deferred annuity, we begin by assuming that a payment is made at the end of each period during the interval of deferment. If this were the case, we would have an ordinary annuity of $m + n$ payments and the present value would be $Ra_{\overline{m+n}|}$. This value, of course, is too large because it includes the assumed payments during the interval of deferment. These assumed payments also form an ordinary annuity and their present value is $Ra_{\overline{m}|}$. Therefore, to get the present value of a deferred annuity all we have to do is subtract the present value of the $m$ assumed payments from the present value of the $m + n$ payments. This leads to

$$A_n = Ra_{\overline{m+n}|} - Ra_{\overline{m}|}$$

$$A_n = R(a_{\overline{m+n}|} - a_{\overline{m}|}) \tag{18}$$

To get the present value of a deferred annuity, we look up $a_{\overline{m+n}|}$ and $a_{\overline{m}|}$ in the *Present Worth of* 1 *per Period* column of Table 2, subtract the smaller from the larger, and multiply this difference by the periodic payment.

The present value of a deferred annuity can also be obtained by using (13) for the present value of an ordinary annuity to get the value of the payments one period before the first payment is made and then discounting this equivalent single sum for the $m$ periods in the interval of deferment. This leads to

$$A_n = Ra_{\overline{n}|}(1 + i)^{-m}$$

This form of the deferred annuity formula is useful when logarithms are used. It also makes it possible to obtain $R$ without dividing, since

$$R = A_n(1 + i)^m \times \frac{1}{a_{\overline{n}|}}$$

EXAMPLE 1: Find the present value of a deferred annuity of $500 a year for 10 years deferred 5 years. Money is worth 3%.

SOLUTION: The deferment interval is given and equals 5 years. The number of payments is also given and is 10. To get the present value all we need do is substitute in (18) and get values under *Present Worth of 1 per Period* in Table 2 for a rate of 3%.

$$\begin{aligned} A_{10} &= 500(a_{\overline{5+10}|} - a_{\overline{5}|}) \\ &= 500(11.93794 - 4.57971) \\ &= 500 \times 7.35823 = \$3679.12 \end{aligned}$$

EXAMPLE 2: Find the present value of an annuity of $50 every 3 months for 5 years if the first payment is made in 3 years. Money is worth 4% converted quarterly.

SOLUTION: Here $n = 20$ and $i$ is 1%. To get the interval of deferment we drop back 1 period from the first payment, so $m = 11$.

$$\begin{aligned} A_{20} &= 50(a_{\overline{11+20}|} - a_{\overline{11}|}) \\ &= 50(26.5423 - 10.3676) \\ &= 50 \times 16.1747 = \$808.74 \end{aligned}$$

EXAMPLE 3: A woman inherits $20,000. Instead of taking the cash, she invests the money at 3% converted semiannually with the understanding that she will receive 20 equal semiannual payments with the first payment to be made in 5 years. Find the size of the payments.

SOLUTION: The interval of deferment is 9 periods, the present value of the annuity is $20,000, and $i$ is $1\frac{1}{2}$%. Substituting in (18),

$$20,000 = R(a_{\overline{9+20}|} - a_{\overline{9}|}) = R(23.3760756 - 8.3605173)$$

$$R = \frac{20,000}{15.0155583} = \$1331.95$$

ALTERNATE SOLUTION: Using the expression derived on page 185,

$$R = A_n(1 + i)^m \times \frac{1}{a_{\overline{n}|}}$$

$$R = 20,000(1.015)^9 \times \frac{1}{a_{\overline{20}|}}$$

$$R = 20,000 \times 1.1433900 \times .0582457 = \$1331.95$$

This method eliminates division but requires 2 multiplications.

### EXERCISE 5b

1. Find the present value of a deferred annuity of $500 a year for 6 years deferred 5 years, if money is worth 4%.                    ($2154.33)
2. Find the present value of a deferred annuity of $250 every 6 months for 4 years deferred 5 years and 6 months, if the rate is 4% converted semiannually.
3. Find the value on September 1, 1972, of a series of $80 monthly payments, the first of which will be made on September 1, 1976, and the last on December 1, 1978, if money is worth 6% compounded monthly.

($1649.63)

4. Find the value on June 1, 1973, of a series of payments of $425 every 6 months if the first of these payments is to be made on December 1, 1976, and the last on June 1, 1983. Use an interest rate of $4\frac{1}{2}\%$ converted semi-annually.
5. What sum put aside on a boy's 12th birthday will provide 4 annual payments of $2000 for college expenses if the first payment is to be made on the boy's 18th birthday? The fund will earn interest at 4% compounded annually.                    ($5967.02)
6. What sum of money should be set aside today to provide an income of $150 a month for a period of 5 years if the first payment is to be made 4 years hence and money is worth 6% compounded monthly?
7. A child aged 12 wins $8000 on a quiz program. It is placed in a trust fund earning 4% converted annually. If she takes the money in 4 equal annual payments with the first payment to be made 6 years later, what will be the size of each payment?                    ($2681.41)
8. Under the terms of a will, a child on his 18th birthday will receive $12,000. He will get $2000 of this in cash. The remainder will be set aside to provide a monthly income from his 21st to his 25th birthday inclusive ($n = 49$). If the money is invested at 4% compounded monthly, what will be the size of the monthly payments?
9. On his wife's 59th birthday, her husband makes provision for her to receive $150 a month for 5 years with the first payment to be made on her 65th birthday. If the investment earns 4% converted monthly, how much money must be set aside?                    ($6430.90)

10. On his 57th birthday a man wants to set aside enough money to provide an income of $150 a month for 10 years with the first payment to be made on his 60th birthday. If he gets 3% compounded monthly on his money, how much will this pension plan cost on his 57th birthday?

11. On June 1, 1968, a man deposits $3000 in an investment paying 5% compounded annually. On June 1, 1974, he makes the first 4 equal annual withdrawals from his account. Find the size of the withdrawals so that the account will be closed with the last withdrawal.                 ($1079.78)

12. If the account in Problem 11 had earned 4% interest, what would be the size of the annual withdrawal?

13. A philanthropist gave a college $40,000 on September 1, 1959, with the provision that the money is to be used to provide annual scholarships of $4000 with the first scholarship to be awarded on the September 1 following his death. The money is invested at 4%. If the donor dies on June 18, 1974, how many full scholarships can be awarded?                 (30)

14. A widow decides to take the $10,000 proceeds from an insurance policy in payments of $200 a month with the first payment to be made in 5 years. How many full payments will she get if the insurance company allows 3% converted monthly on the money left with them?

15. On June 1, 1969, a minor received an inheritance of $6500. This was placed in a trust fund earning 3% compounded semiannually. On December 1, 1974, the child will reach age 18 and be paid the first of 8 equal semiannual payments from the fund. How much will each payment be?     ($1007.69)

16. A school receives $40,000 in 1968. This is to be used to provide annual scholarships of $3000 with the first scholarship to be awarded in 1974. If the money is invested at 4%, how many full scholarships can be awarded? How much will be left in the fund one year after the last full scholarship to apply to a partial scholarship?

## 5.5 Forborne Annuity

A **forborne annuity** earns interest for two or more periods after the last payment. The sketch below shows a forborne annuity of $n$ payments followed by $p$ periods during which interest is earned but no payments are made.

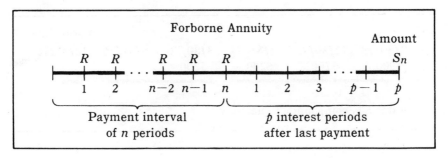

To get the formula for the amount of a forborne annuity, we begin by assuming a fictitious payment at the end of each period after the last regular payment. We now have an ordinary annuity of $n + p$ payments and an amount of $Rs_{\overline{n+p}|}$. This result is too large by the amount of the fictitious payments. These assumed payments also form an ordinary annuity and their amount is $Rs_{\overline{p}|}$. To get the amount of a forborne annuity, we subtract the amount of the $p$ assumed payments from the amount of the $n + p$ payments. This leads to

$$S_n = Rs_{\overline{n+p}|} - Rs_{\overline{p}|}$$
$$S_n = R(s_{\overline{n+p}|} - s_{\overline{p}|}) \qquad (19)$$

To get the amount of a forborne annuity, we look up $s_{\overline{n+p}|}$ and $s_{\overline{p}|}$ in the *Amount of 1 per Period* column of Table 2, subtract the smaller from the larger, and multiply the difference by the periodic payment.

The amount of a forborne annuity can also be obtained by using (12) for the amount of an ordinary annuity to get the value of the payments at the time of the last payment and then accumulating this equivalent single sum for $p$ periods. This leads to

$$S_n = Rs_{\overline{n}|}(1 + i)^p$$

This amount formula is useful when logarithms are used. It also makes it possible to obtain $R$ without dividing, since

$$R = S_n(1 + i)^{-p} \times \frac{1}{s_{\overline{n}|}}$$

EXAMPLE 1: A savings and loan association pays 5% converted quarterly on passbook accounts. Interest dates are March 31, June 30, September 30, and December 31. On September 30, 1973, a person opens an account with a deposit of $500. Every 3 months he adds $200 to his account. The last $200 deposit is made on March 31, 1976. The money is then left to accumulate interest until the amount is closed on December 31, 1978. Find the accumulated amount on that date.

SOLUTION: A time diagram is drawn to help determine the number of payments and interest periods.

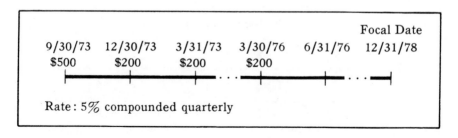

The \$500 is carried forward as a single sum from September 1973 to December 1978. The number of periods is found from:

| YEAR | MONTH |
|------|-------|
| 1978 | 12 |
| 1973 | 9 |
| 5 | 3 |

$$n = (5 \times 4) + (3/3) = 21$$

The number of \$200 payments is the same as the number of periods from September 1973 to March 1976.

| YEAR | MONTH |
|------|-------|
| 5 | 15 |
| 1976 | 3 |
| 1973 | 9 |
| 2 | 6 |

$$n = (2 \times 4) + (6/3) = 10$$

We now get the number of periods after the last payment.

| YEAR | MONTH |
|------|-------|
| 1978 | 12 |
| 1976 | 3 |
| 2 | 9 |

$$p = (2 \times 4) + (9/3) = 11$$

We use (9) to get the amount of the \$500 and (19) to get the amount of the forborne annuity.

$$500(1.015)^{21} = 500 \times 1.29806 \qquad\qquad = \$\ 649.03$$
$$200(s_{\overline{10+11}|} - s_{\overline{11}|}) = 200(23.84502 - 11.71394) = \underline{2426.22}$$
$$\text{Total on December 31, 1978} \quad \$3075.25$$

**EXERCISE 5c**

1. A bank pays 4% converted quarterly on passbook accounts. Interest dates are January 31, April 30, July 31, and October 31. Deposits by the first of the month earn interest for the entire month. On May 1, 1971, a man opens an account with a deposit of \$100. He continues to make \$100 deposits every 3 months until August 1, 1973, when he makes his last deposit. Find the amount in his account on November 1, 1975. (\$1144.24)
2. What would be the amount in Problem 1 if the rate is 5% converted quarterly?

3. A teacher arranges a home loan on which he pays $150 a month during the nine months, September to May inclusive, when he is paid by his school. The rate on the loan is 6% converted monthly. Because of sickness one year he is unable to make the March, April, and May payments. The lender allows him to defer these payments until September, provided he then makes a payment that will make the loan balance what it would have been had the payments been made on time. Find the total payment to be made in September, including the September payment.                     ($611.37)

4. What would be the amount in Problem 3 if the borrower misses only the April and May payments?

5. A saver wants to have $2000 in an account on December 31, 1975. He plans to make 4 equal deposits in an account paying 5% converted quarterly with interest payable on March 31, June 30, September 30, and December 31. If he makes his deposits on the four interest dates in 1974, what will the size of the deposits be?                     ($466.93)

6. Find the size of the deposit in Problem 5 if the rate is 4% converted quarterly.

## 5.6   Summary of Ordinary, Due, and Deferred Annuities

The most effective way for a student to solve an annuity problem is to make a sketch, determine at what point in time he wants the value of the annuity, and then substitute in the proper formula. This is much better than just reading a problem and then trying to "type" it. Students should recognize that the same series of payments might be treated as one type of annuity at one time and another type at another time. For example, if we want the value of a series of payments one period before the first payment we would use the present value formula for an ordinary annuity. But if we want the value of the same series of payments one period after the last payment, we would use the amount formula for an annuity due. By comparing his sketch with the diagram on page 191 the student can eliminate guesswork in solving annuity problems.

The focal date approach is very useful for annuity problems. The student should, of course, select a focal date that will minimize computations. Good judgment in choosing a focal date will come from observation and experience. Students should also note that even complicated problems can usually be broken down into simple parts. Too often students try to take a word problem of several sentences and immediately set up an equation that will give the final answer. Do one part at a time. Every problem can be broken down into single payments and annuities which can be moved to any point in time and an equation of value set up.

In this and the preceding chapter we discussed the common types of annuities certain. All of these have one thing in common—a series of equal payments equally spaced. The various formulas which were derived were for convenience in getting the value of the annuity at different times with a minimum of work. The sketch below shows how the formulas we now have enable us to get the value of an annuity at any time.

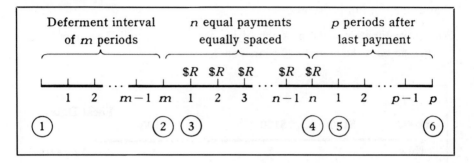

(1) To get the value two or more periods before the first payment use the present value formula for a deferred annuity:

$$A_n = R(a_{\overline{m+n}|} - a_{\overline{m}|}) \qquad \textbf{(18)} \text{ page } 184$$

(2) To get the value one period before the first payment use the present value formula for an ordinary annuity:

$$A_n = Ra_{\overline{n}|} \qquad \textbf{(13)} \text{ page } 144$$

(3) To get the value at the time the first payment is made use the present value formula for an annuity due:

$$A_n = R(a_{\overline{n-1}|} + 1) \qquad \textbf{(17)} \text{ page } 177$$

(4) To get the value at the time the last payment is made use the amount formula for an ordinary annuity:

$$S_n = Rs_{\overline{n}|} \qquad \textbf{(12)} \text{ page } 138$$

(5) To get the value one period after the last payment use the amount formula for an annuity due:

$$S_n = R(s_{\overline{n+1}|} - 1) \qquad \textbf{(16)} \text{ page } 176$$

(6) To get the amount two or more periods after the last payment use the amount formula for a forborne annuity:

$$S_n = R(s_{\overline{n+p}|} - s_{\overline{p}|}) \qquad \textbf{(19)} \text{ page } 188$$

Let us work an example to show how a step-by-step approach using focal dates can solve a problem that at first seems quite difficult.

EXAMPLE: A man deposits $2000 today at 3% interest. One year from now he makes the first of 19 annual deposits of $100 each in a fund paying 4%.

Twenty years from now he draws out both of his investments, adds $100 cash to their sum, and buys an annuity of $200 a month, the first payment to be made one month after he buys the annuity. The insurance company allows him 3% converted monthly on his deposit with them. How many $200 payments does he get? What is the size of the concluding payment 1 month after the last full payment?

SOLUTION: First we make a sketch of his deposits and find how much he has when he buys the annuity 20 years hence.

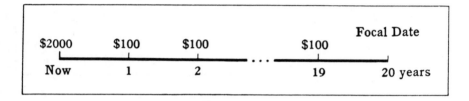

We put the focal date at 20 years and carry everything to that point. This means that we allow 3% compound interest on the $2000, get the amount of an annuity due of 19 payments at 4%, and add $100.

$$2000(1.03)^{20} = 2000 \times 1.806111 \quad = \$3612.22$$
$$100(s_{\overline{20}|4\%} - 1) = 100 \times 28.77808 = \quad 2877.81$$
$$\text{Final cash payment} \qquad\qquad\quad = \quad\quad 100.00$$
$$\text{Total for purchase of annuity} \quad \$6590.03$$

This $6590.03 now becomes the present value of an ordinary annuity of $200 per month. The student should note that the same sum of money may be an amount at one stage in the problem and a present value at another stage. Using (13), the present value formula for an ordinary annuity, we have

$$6590.03 = 200a_{\overline{n}|}$$
$$a_{\overline{n}|} = 32.95$$

Reference to the *Present Worth of 1 per Period* column of Table 2 shows that there will be 34 full payments and a smaller 35th payment. To get the size of the concluding payment we take the $6590.03 forward 34 periods and get the amount of an annuity of $200 a month for 34 months. We then allow simple interest on the difference for 1 month.

$$6590.03(1.0025)^{34} = 6590.03 \times 1.088602 \qquad = \$7173.92$$
$$200s_{\overline{34}|} = 200 \times 35.44064 \qquad\qquad\qquad = \quad 7088.13$$
$$\qquad\qquad\qquad\qquad\qquad\qquad\qquad\qquad\qquad\qquad 85.79$$
$$\text{Interest on } \$85.79 \text{ for 1 mo.} = 85.79 \times \tfrac{1}{12} \times .03 = \qquad .21$$
$$\qquad\qquad\qquad\qquad\qquad\qquad\qquad\qquad\qquad \$\quad 86.00$$

Thus the man will receive 34 payments of $200 and a 35th payment of $86.00.

To show how the same problem can be solved in more than one way, we could get the 35th payment by putting a focal date at this point and bring the 34 payments forward as an annuity due.

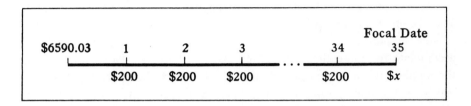

$$x = 6590.03(1.0025)^{35} - 200(s_{\overline{34+1}|} - 1)$$
$$= 6590.03 \times 1.091323 - 200 \times 35.52924$$
$$= 7191.85 - 7105.85 = \$86.00$$

In this problem the two methods gave exactly the same answer. Sometimes there will be a difference of a few cents if the answers to the intermediate steps are rounded to the nearest penny.

## 5.7 Perpetuities

In some investments only the interest is used and the principal is kept intact. For example, if a philanthropist wants to provide an annual scholarship of $1000 indefinitely, he must give as an endowment enough money to earn $1000 interest every year. When it is assumed that the regular payments will go on forever, the annuity is called a **perpetuity**. Other examples of perpetuities are dividends on noncallable preferred stock (provided all dividends are paid), interest on perpetual bonds, and the endowment funds of endowed institutions such as libraries, museums, etc., that are established with a sum of money that is supposed to maintain them "in perpetuity."

In practice all perpetuities must end sometime, but the *forever assumption* still underlies the mathematical treatment of perpetuities. It is, of course, impossible to get the accumulated amount of a perpetuity. Getting the present value is both possible and easy. We shall first consider the case where the interest period coincides with the payment period.

To get the present value of a perpetual scholarship of $1000 a year, we have to know what rate of interest can be expected on the endowment. Suppose the school can expect a return of 4%. Then the philanthropist would have to give $25,000 because it takes this amount to earn $1000 interest each year at 4%. As long as only the interest is used and the endowment earns 4%, the $1000 scholarships can be awarded indefinitely. In general terms we can say

$$A_\infty i = R$$

$$A_\infty = \frac{R}{i} \tag{20}$$

The subscript $\infty$ is the mathematical symbol for **infinity**. In this case $A_\infty$ denotes the present value of a series of payments that continue indefinitely. The size of each payment is $R and the rate per period is $i$.

Now suppose that instead of using the interest as it is earned, we let it accumulate for more than one period. We shall use the letter $n$ to indicate the number of conversion periods that elapse before the interest is drawn off leaving the original principal intact. Letting the present value of this perpetuity accumulate for $n$ periods we have an amount of

$$A_\infty(1 + i)^n$$

We now subtract the periodic payment and again have the original present value,

$$A_\infty(1 + i)^n - R = A_\infty$$

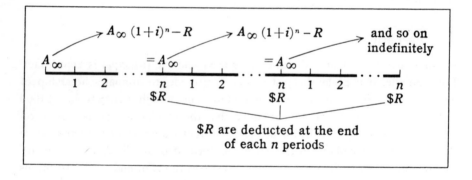

$R are deducted at the end
of each $n$ periods

To solve the above formula for $A_\infty$ we proceed as follows:

$$A_\infty(1 + i)^n - A_\infty = R$$

$$A_\infty[(1 + i)^n - 1] = R$$

$$A_\infty = \frac{R}{(1 + i)^n - 1}$$

Multiplying numerator and denominator by $i$ and rearranging, we have

$$A_\infty = \frac{R}{i} \times \frac{i}{(1 + i)^n - 1}$$

Since

$$\frac{i}{(1 + i)^n - 1} = \frac{1}{s_{\overline{n}|}}$$

this can be simplified as follows:

$$A_\infty = \frac{R}{i} \times \frac{1}{s_{\overline{n}|}} \tag{21}$$

We can now solve this type of perpetuity with a minimum of work because the factor $1/s_{\overline{n}|}$ can be obtained from the *Sinking Fund* column in Table 2.

EXAMPLE 1: An alumnus wants to provide a perpetual $400 a year scholarship with the first scholarship to be given in 1 year. If the money can be invested at 4%, how large must the grant be?

SOLUTION: This is the first type of perpetuity. Substituting in (20),

$$A_\infty = \frac{400}{.04} = \$10,000$$

EXAMPLE 2: If the money in Example 1 could be invested at 4% converted semiannually, how large a grant would be needed?

SOLUTION: Here we must use (21), the second perpetuity formula, because the interest is converted twice a year while it is used only once a year.

$$A_\infty = \frac{400}{.02} \times \frac{1}{s_{\overline{2}|2\%}}$$

$$= \frac{400}{.02} \times .4950495$$

$$= \$9900.99$$

It is interesting to see just how this initial grant provides the $400 annual scholarships.

| | |
|---|---|
| Initial grant | $9,900.99 |
| 2% interest for 6 months | 198.02 |
| New principal | 10,099.01 |
| 2% interest for the second 6 months | 201.98 |
| New principal | 10,300.99 |
| First scholarship is deducted | 400.00 |
| Principal at start of second year | $9,900.99 |

Thus the school will be able to provide annual scholarships of $400 indefinitely if they continue to get 4% converted semiannually on the original grant of $9900.99.

At even today's high interest rates, a very large endowment is needed to earn much of an income on a perpetual basis. This means that an organization, such as a private school, which does not have enough income from tuition to meet expenses, must conduct fund raising campaigns from time to time to provide funds for operation and expansion.

EXAMPLE 3: Find the nominal rate of return on a 4%, $100 preferred stock with dividends payable quarterly if the stock is selling at $105.

SOLUTION: In this problem the stock will pay 1% every 3 months on $100. Thus the person who gets the stock will obtain a perpetuity of $1 every 3 months regardless of what he pays for the stock. However, the rate of return on his investment will depend on the purchase price. The purchase price becomes the present value of the perpetuity and the $1 dividends are the periodic payments. Solving (20) for $i$, we have

$$i = \frac{R}{A_\infty} = \frac{1.00}{105} = .0095 = .95\%$$

The nominal rate is $4 \times .95 = 3.8\%$.

If the stock had been purchased for less than $100, the rate of return would be more than 4%.

EXAMPLE 4: How much must an alumnus give a college to provide an annual scholarship of $500 for an indefinitely long period if the endowment can be invested at 4% and if the first scholarship will be provided: (a) 1 year from now; (b) immediately; (c) 5 years from now?

SOLUTION: (a) If the first scholarship is to be awarded in 1 year, we use (20) to get the required grant.

$$A_\infty = \frac{500}{.04} = \$12,500$$

(b) If the first scholarship is to be awarded immediately the grant is the sum of the above perpetuity and $500 or $13,000.
(c) If the first scholarship is to be awarded in 5 years, the fund will have to contain $12,500 in 4 years. At that time it begins to function as a perpetuity and will earn $500 a year interest from then on. The question then is what sum will amount to $12,500 in 4 years at 4%. This can be obtained from (11).

$$P = 12,500(1.04)^{-4} = 12,500 \times .8548042 = \$10,685.05$$

In problems like this it is a good idea to use a time diagram to avoid errors in determining the various times that are involved. A sketch like the following shows each point in time and the corresponding dollar value of the endowment.

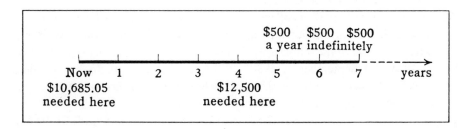

## EXERCISE 5d

1. A man wants to provide $1000 every 6 months indefinitely toward the support of an orphanage. If the first payment will be made in 6 months and if the fund draws interest at 4% converted semiannually, what size endowment will be needed?                                              ($50,000)

2. What is the present value of a perpetuity of $125 a month, if money is worth 6% converted monthly and the first payment is to be made in 1 month?

3. If money is worth 4% converted semiannually, find the present value of an annual scholarship of $1200 a year if the first scholarship is to be awarded 1 year from now? (Round answer to the nearest dollar.)
                                                                     ($29,703)

4. What is the present value of a perpetuity of $750 a year if the first payment is to be made in 1 year and the interest rate is 3% converted semiannually?

5. A man gives a school $15,000 to provide an annual scholarship indefinitely. The first scholarship is to be awarded 1 year after the grant is received. If the fund earns 4% converted semiannually, what will be the size of each scholarship? (When solving practical business problems, always look for the most direct method. While this is a perpetuity, the perpetuity formulas do not provide the easiest method of solution. Carry the original grant forward 1 year at compound interest and keep back a sum equal to the original grant. The difference will be the accumulated interest which can be given as a scholarship without touching the original principal.)   ($606.00)

6. If the institution in which the fund in Problem 5 is invested starts paying 4% compounded quarterly, what will be the size of the annual scholarship?

7. Mr. Berger wants to provide a research fellowship of $2000 annually. If money can be invested at 4% compounded semiannually, and if the first fellowship will be awarded in 5 years, how much should Mr. Berger give the school? ($42,252.00)

8. What sum of money invested at 4% converted semiannually will provide a perpetual income of $3000 at the end of each 2 years?

9. On September 1, 1970, a college receives a grant of $30,000 which is invested at 4%. If annual scholarships are awarded for 20 years from this grant, what is the size of the scholarship if the first one is awarded on (a) September 1, 1970; (b) September 1, 1980? If the scholarships are to be awarded indefinitely, what will be the size of the scholarship if the first one is awarded on (c) September 1, 1970; (d) September 1, 1980?

[(a) $2122.55; (b) $3141.89; (c) $1153.85; (d) $1707.97]

10. In 1960 an alumnus gave a university $20,000 which was invested at a rate that would provide $1000 scholarships at the end of each year indefinitely. (a) What interest rate was the school earning on the investment at that time? (b) After the scholarship was awarded in 1969, the school had to reinvest the fund at 4%. If they want to continue to award scholarships indefinitely, they will have to change the value of each scholarship to what amount? (c) If they want to continue to award $1000 scholarships, the fund will provide how many full scholarships at the new rate?

11. What is the present value of a perpetuity of $800 at the end of each year if money is worth: (a) 4%; (b) 4% compounded semiannually?

[(a) $20,000.00; (b) $19,801.98]

12. What would be the size of the grants in Problem 9 if the school can invest the money at 5%?

13. What sum of money invested at 5% converted semiannually, will provide $200 at the end of each 2 years indefinitely? ($1926.54)

14. How much will it take to provide a hospital with an annual research grant of $5000 indefinitely if the first grant is to be made immediately and if the endowment which is to make the grants possible can be invested at 4%?

15. A school can invest money at 4% converted semiannually. How large a grant would be needed to provide a $1500 research fellowship at the end of each year indefinitely? (Round answer to the nearest dollar.) ($37,129)

16. What size grant would provide the fellowship in Problem 15 if $4\frac{1}{2}$% compounded semiannually is earned on the invested funds?

17. A share of preferred stock has a par value of $100 and pays 6% dividends annually. If it is purchased for $94, what yield rate would the investor get? (6.38%)

18. If the stock in Problem 17 was purchased for $106, what would be the yield rate?

## 5.8 The General Case

When payments are made more or less frequently than the compounding period, the annuity comes under the **general case**. The first step in solving general annuity problems is to get the payments and the compounding periods to coincide. Then the problem can be completed by using the factors from Table 2 in the same way that we have been using them for simple annuities in which the payments are made at the time interest is earned.

One way to solve general annuities is to convert the given interest rate into an equivalent rate for which the conversion period is the same as the payment period. The second way is to change the original payments to equivalent payments made on the stated interest conversion dates. In this book we follow the latter practice of converting the original payments into equivalent payments which coincide with the compounding periods. This results in simpler computations in some cases.

We now consider problems which have interest compounded more frequently than payments are made. For example, payments may be made annually and interest compounded semiannually; or payments may be made semiannually and interest compounded monthly.

EXAMPLE 1: Find the amount of an ordinary annuity of $500 per year for 10 years if money is worth 4% compounded semiannually.

SOLUTION: A good way to analyze a problem of this type is to sketch one payment interval and the corresponding conversion periods.

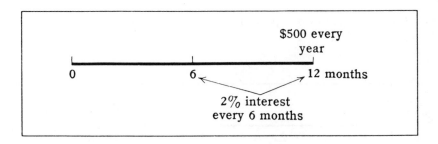

We now replace the original payments with payments of $R on each interest date.

Since the new payments form an ordinary annuity of $R per payment accumulating at 4% converted semiannually, we can set up the following equation of value using (14):

$$R = 500 \times \frac{1}{s_{\overline{2}|2\%}} = 500 \times .4950495 = \$247.52$$

(In the exercises and examples in this section we usually round the equivalent payment to the nearest cent. This results in answers that will be the same as those obtained by students who do not have access to computing machines and round intermediate answers to save time. In practical business situations where computing machines are available, entire factors can be used throughout the problem without additional labor and the final answer rounded to the cent.)

We now replace the original payments of $500 every year by payments of $247.52 every 6 months. The problem can then be completed as an ordinary annuity. Note in particular that there are 20 payments in the final annuity because each of the original 10 payments has been replaced by 2 payments. Therefore the final amount using (12) is

$$S_{20} = 247.52 s_{\overline{20}|2\%}$$
$$S_{20} = 247.52 \times 24.29737 = \$6014.09$$

EXAMPLE 2: Find the present value of an ordinary annuity of 20 semiannual payments of $1000 each if money is worth 6% converted monthly.

SOLUTION: A sketch of one payment interval shows that it contains 6 interest conversion periods.

The original payment is to be replaced by 6 equal monthly payments which are equivalent in value to $1000 at the end of 6 months. Substituting in (14),

$$R = 1000 \times \frac{1}{s_{\overline{6}|\frac{1}{2}\%}} = 1000 \times .164595 = \$164.60$$

We now have an annuity of $20 \times 6 = 120$ payments of \$164.60. At 6% converted monthly the present value of this annuity is

$$A_{120} = 164.60a_{\overline{120}|\frac{1}{2}\%} = 164.60 \times 90.07345 = \$14,826.09$$

We now consider problems in which payments are made more frequently than interest is compounded. For example, payments may be made semiannually and interest compounded annually; or payments may be made monthly and interest compounded semiannually.

The problem now is to convert the payments made during an interest conversion period into an equivalent single payment made on an interest conversion date. In doing this, as in all problems in the mathematics of finance, close attention must be given to practical conditions pertaining to the problem.

A typical illustration of the practical rules followed by a financial institution can be found in the passbook of a bank. We might find that a bank pays 3% compounded semiannually on May 1 and November 1. Money deposited between these dates earns simple interest. If money is deposited on the 10th or before, interest is credited from the 1st of that month. If deposited after the 10th, interest is credited from the 1st of the following month. Money withdrawn before the semiannual payment date gets no interest for that period. When we work a problem for this particular bank, these are the rules we must follow.

EXAMPLE 3: A man resolves to deposit \$100 from his pay at the end of each month in a bank which pays interest as described in the preceding paragraph. If he makes his first deposit on May 31, 1972, how much will he have in his account after interest is credited on May 1, 1977?

SOLUTION: The first step is to get the semiannual payment which is equivalent to the 6 monthly deposits. A time diagram for the first 6 deposits shows how long each deposit earns simple interest.

| | $100 | $100 | $100 | $100 | $100 | $100 |
|---|---|---|---|---|---|---|
| 0 | 1 | 2 | 3 | 4 | 5 | 6 months |
| 4/30/72 | 5/31/72 | 6/30/72 | 7/31/72 | 8/31/72 | 9/30/72 | 10/31/72 |

The diagram shows that the last deposit does not earn any simple interest, the 5th deposit earns interest for one month and so on. A table like the following one will simplify the interest computations:

| Deposit | Months Simple Interest Is Earned | Interest | Amount |
|---------|------------------------------------|----------|--------|
| 6th | 0 | 0 | $100.00 |
| 5th | 1 | $100 \times .03 \times \frac{1}{12} = .25$ | 100.25 |
| 4th | 2 | $100 \times .03 \times \frac{2}{12} = .50$ | 100.50 |
| 3rd | 3 | $100 \times .03 \times \frac{3}{12} = .75$ | 100.75 |
| 2nd | 4 | $100 \times .03 \times \frac{4}{12} = 1.00$ | 101.00 |
| 1st | 5 | $100 \times .03 \times \frac{5}{12} = 1.25$ | 101.25 |
|  | 15 | Total | $603.75 |

An equivalent and condensed way to get the simple interest is to assume that one deposit of $100 has earned 15 months interest.

$$100 \times .03 \times \tfrac{15}{12} = \$3.75$$

We now replace the 60 monthly deposits of $100 each with 10 semiannual deposits of $603.75 and work the problem as an ordinary annuity.

$$S_{10} = 603.75 s_{\overline{10}|1\frac{1}{2}\%} = 603.75 \times 10.70272 = \$6461.77$$

In the preceding example simple interest was credited for a part of a period. It is also possible to have compound interest for a part of a period. All that we need do is take the basic formula for compound interest, $S = P(1 + i)^n$, and substitute the proper value for $n$.

If $1 is placed at 6% compound interest for 6 months the amount would be

$$S = 1.00(1.06)^{\frac{1}{2}} = 1.02956$$

Values for $(1 + i)^n$ when $n$ is a fraction can be found using logarithms or in the auxiliary tables published by the Financial Publishing Company. In this text, values for compound interest for a part of a period for the more common interest rates are given in Table 3 under the column heading *Amount of* 1.

Going back to the above illustration, suppose that the dollar had been placed at 6% simple interest for 6 months. Then the amount would have been $1.03. This is more than the amount at 6% compound interest for 6 months. Most people know that money increases more rapidly at compound interest than at the same rate of simple interest if it is left on deposit for more than one interest period. This is the result of interest being earned on interest. But it is not generally known that for less than a conversion period, compound interest results in a smaller amount than simple interest. The difference is not great but it is one which should be taken into account.

Compound interest for a part of a period is used more frequently in annuity problems than in dealing with single sums. For such problems Table 3, Auxiliary

Tables taken from the extensive tables of the Financial Publishing Company, can be used to simplify computations. An example will show how these tables are used.

EXAMPLE 4: What is the amount of 60 payments of $100 at the end of each month at 3% converted semiannually, if compound interest is paid for part of a period?

SOLUTION: The interest conversion period is 6 months and the rate per period is $1\frac{1}{2}\%$. The time interval for payments is 1 month or $\frac{1}{6}$ of a conversion period. We now go to the auxiliary table for $1\frac{1}{2}\%$ and look opposite 1–6 where we find the factor 6.037391 in the *Equivalent per Period to a Payment of* 1 column. This means that a payment of $6.037391 every 6 months is equivalent to a payment of $1 every month if money is worth 3% compounded semiannually. Since our monthly payments are $100, the equivalent semi-annual payment is

$$100 \times 6.037391 = \$603.7391$$

and the amount of 60 deposits is

$$S_{10} = 603.7391 s_{\overline{10}|1\frac{1}{2}\%} = 603.7391 \times 10.70272 = \$6461.64$$

This example was worked using the factors to several decimal places to show that the auxiliary tables result in an answer close to, but not identical with the one obtained when simple interest is used for a part of a period. The answer to this example is 13 cents smaller than the answer to Example 3 which used the same data with simple interest for a part of a period. The fact that there is a difference, even if it is not large, shows that problems must be worked using rules which apply to the particular transaction.

EXAMPLE 5: An insurance company pays 3% compounded annually on money left with them. What would be the cost of an annuity of $200 at the end of each month for 10 years?

SOLUTION: In the 3% auxiliary table opposite 1–12, we find the factor 12.16412. Therefore, the annual payment equivalent to 12 monthly payments is

$$200 \times 12.16412 = \$2432.82$$

We now get the present value of an ordinary annuity of $2432.82 a year for 10 years at 3%.

$$A_{10} = 2432.82 a_{\overline{10}|3\%} = \$2432.82 \times 8.530203 = \$20,752.45$$

**EXERCISE 5e**

1. Find the present value and the amount of an annuity of $40 every 6 months for 12 years if money is worth 5% converted quarterly.

   ($714.32; $1296.74)

2. Find the present value and the amount of an annuity of $150 a year for 8 years at 3% converted semiannually.

3. What single payment now is equivalent at 6% converted monthly to payments of $100 at the end of each 6 months for 6 years?      ($993.19)

4. Compute the present value of an ordinary annuity of $50 at the end of each quarter for 7 years if money is worth 5% converted monthly.

5. Get the amount of the annuity in Problem 3.      ($1422.29)

6. Get the amount of the annuity in Problem 4.

7. Payments of $200 are made at the end of each month for 5 years in an investment paying 6% converted quarterly. Find the present value and amount of the annuity if: (a) simple interest is paid for part of a period; (b) compound interest is paid for part of a period.

   [(a) $10,352.69, $13,943.57; (b) $10,352.52, $13,943.34]

8. Payments of $50 are made at the end of each month for 6 years. The annuity earns 4% compounded semiannually. Find the present value and amount if: (a) simple interest is paid for part of a period; (b) compound interest is paid for part of a period.

9. Payments of $500 are made at the end of each 6 months for 10 years in an account paying 5% compounded annually. Find the present value and amount if: (a) simple interest is paid for part of a period; (b) compound interest is paid for part of a period.

   [(a) $7818.26, $12,735.12; (b) $7817.10, $12,733.23]

10. An insurance company pays 3% compounded annually on money left with them. What would be the cost of an annuity of $125 at the end of each month for 10 years if compound interest is paid for part of a period?

## 5.9   Finding the Periodic Payment

When the amount or present value of a general annuity is known, the **periodic payment** can be found by first getting the equivalent payment per interest conversion period and then converting this into the payments made on the actual payment dates.

EXAMPLE 1: A widow has $10,000 with which she wants to buy an annuity that will provide her a monthly income for 15 years. If she can get 3% converted semiannually on her money, what will be the size of the monthly payments, if compound interest is paid for a part of a period?

SOLUTION: First we get the equivalent payment at the end of each 6 months.

$$R = 10,000 \times \frac{1}{a_{\overline{30}|1\frac{1}{2}\%}} = 10,000 \times .0416392 = \$416.39$$

We must now convert this semiannual payment into an equivalent monthly payment. Since 6 payments are made during an interest period, we look in Table 3 for $1\frac{1}{2}\%$ and time interval of 1-6. The factor is 6.03739. Since this is for a payment of 1 per period our problem becomes

$$R \times 6.03739 = 416.39$$

$$R = \frac{416.39}{6.03739} = \$68.97$$

This problem can be solved without division by using the *Payment Equivalent to 1 per Period* column and multiplying. The payment at the end of each month equivalent to $1 at the end of each 6 months is $.16563. Therefore the payment every month equivalent to $416.39 every 6 months is

$$R = 416.39 \times .16563 = \$68.97$$

EXAMPLE 2: A couple would like to accumulate $3000 in 5 years by making deposits at the end of each month in an account paying $3\frac{1}{2}\%$ compounded semiannually. What is the size of each deposit?

SOLUTION: The equivalent semiannual deposit is

$$R = 3000 \times \frac{1}{s_{\overline{10}|1\frac{3}{4}\%}} = 3000 \times .092375 = \$277.13$$

Since 6 payments are made during each interest period, we look in Table 3 for $1\frac{3}{4}\%$ opposite 1-6 and find the factor .165464 in the *Payment Equivalent to 1 per Period* column.
  Therefore
$$R = 277.13 \times .165464 = \$45.86$$

### EXERCISE 5f

(Use compound interest for a part of a period.)
1. A man leaves his widow a $5000 insurance policy. What monthly income would this provide for 8 years if the insurance company pays 4% converted semiannually? Payments are made at the end of each month.     ($60.87)
2. The present value of an annuity is $12,000. It is to be used to provide a quarterly income for 6 years. What will be the size of the payments if the interest rate is 4% converted annually?

3. What periodic payment at the end of each month for 10 years will be required to accumulate $15,000 if the fund earns interest at 5% compounded quarterly?

($96.70)

4. A city wants to accumulate $250,000 in 15 years to redeem an issue of bonds. What payment will be required at the end of each 6 months to accumulate this amount if interest is earned at 3% converted annually?

## 5.10    Other General Annuities

Other types of general annuities also can be solved by first getting the equivalent payment on interest conversion dates and then solving a simple annuity. As shown in the following examples, time diagrams can be very helpful in the analysis and solution of general annuities.

EXAMPLE 1: Get the present value and the amount of an annuity due of $200 at the beginning of each year for 3 years if money is worth 6% compounded semiannually.

SOLUTION: First we make a time diagram of the problem.

We replace each of the $200 payments with a set of equivalent payments every 6 months. This can be done by letting the $200 be the present value of an ordinary annuity of 2 payments and getting the value of $R$ from (15).

$$R = 200 \times \frac{1}{a_{\overline{2}|3\%}} = 200 \times .52261 = \$104.52$$

The problem can now be illustrated by a diagram.

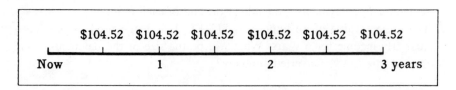

This is solved as a simple annuity.

From (13)

$$A_6 = 104.52 \times a_{\overline{6}|3\%} = 104.52 \times 5.41719 = \$566.20$$

From (12)

$$S_6 = 104.52 \times s_{\overline{6}|3\%} = 104.52 \times 6.46841 = \$676.08$$

CHECK: $566.20(1.03)^6 = 566.20 \times 1.19405 = \$676.07$.

EXAMPLE 2: Find the present value of an annuity of \$250 at the beginning of each month for 10 years if money is worth 4% converted semiannually.

SOLUTION: The six \$250 payments must be replaced with an equivalent payment made on an interest conversion date. A time diagram of the first 6 payments is a help in making this substitution.

| $250 | $250 | $250 | $250 | $250 | $250 | |
|------|------|------|------|------|------|------|
| Now | 1 | 2 | 3 | 4 | 5 | 6 months |

Again we emphasize that in a problem like this the practical conditions that pertain to the problem must be taken into account. Here are the possibilities:

(a) Simple interest is allowed for part of a period. The first payment earns interest for 6 months. Each payment earns interest for 1 month less until we get to the sixth payment which earns interest for 1 month. Adding the months from 1 to 6, we get a total of 21 months. Using the method described on page 202, we get simple interest on all payments with the single calculation:

$$I = 250 \times .04 \times \tfrac{21}{12} = \$17.50$$

We now have an equivalent semiannual payment of \$1517.50 which has a present value of

$$A_{20} = 1517.50 a_{\overline{20}|2\%} = 1517.50 \times 16.351\ 433 = \$24,813.30$$

(b) Compound interest is allowed for a part of a period. To find the equivalent payment we go to Table 3 for 2% and look opposite 1–6 because the payment interval is one sixth of a conversion period. Multiplying the *Equivalent per Period to a Payment of* 1 factor by the size of our payment we have

$$250 \times 6.049807 = \$1512.45$$

Since Table 3 gives us the equivalent payment at the time the last payment is made, we must allow interest on this value for $\tfrac{1}{6}$ of a period to get it to coincide with an interest conversion period. Using the *Amount of* 1 factor from Table 3 for 1–6 period, we have

$$1512.45 \times 1.003306 = \$1517.45$$

Note that this is a few cents smaller than the value for simple interest. We now use (13) to get the present value:

$$A_{20} = 1517.45a_{\overline{20}|2\%} = 1517.45 \times 16.351433 = \$24,812.48$$

### EXERCISE 5g

(Allow compound interest for a part of a period.)

1. Find the present value and the amount of an annuity due of $600 at the beginning of each year for 12 years if money is worth 3% converted semi-annually. ($6144.73; $8783.90)
2. Find the present value and the amount of payments of $500 at the beginning of each 6 months for 5 years if money is worth 5% converted monthly.
3. Four hundred dollars is invested at the beginning of each 3 months at 6% compounded annually. What is the amount at the end of 5 years?

($9355.04)
4. Two hundred dollars is invested at the beginning of each month at 5% compounded quarterly. What is the amount at the end of 3 years?
5. What is the present value of an annuity of $60 at the beginning of each month for 8 years, if money is worth 3% compounded annually? ($5136.10)
6. What is the present value of an annuity of $100 at the beginning of each month for 5 years, if money is worth 5% converted quarterly?

# 6

**Amortization
and
Sinking
Funds**

## 6.1  Amortization of a Debt

One of the most important applications of annuities in business transactions
is the repayment of interest-bearing debts. First we consider the **amortization**
method. When a debt is repaid by this method, a series of periodic payments,
usually equal in amount, pay the interest outstanding at the time the payments
are made and also repay a part of the principal. As the principal is gradually reduced in this way, the interest on the unpaid balance decreases. This means that
as time goes on, an increasing portion of the periodic payments is available to
reduce the debt. Sooner or later most of the students who study this material
will purchase a car, home, or other item on time and will amortize the debt.
An understanding of how debts are amortized, and the ability to determine the
costs involved, can save a person many dollars by enabling him to make a wise
selection of a lender and of a repayment plan.

The importance of amortization for the well-being of the economy is indicated by the following comment by economist Sumner H. Slichter.

By far the most important improvement in financial instruments during recent years has been the development of the long-term amortizable mortgage. This instrument has done much to encourage the flow of funds into housing. The development of the long-term amortizable mortgage was largely the result of the assumption of new functions by the federal government. In order to stimulate residential building during the depression, the federal government, through the Federal Housing Administration, undertook to insure long-term amortizable loans secured by residential properties. Later there was added the guarantee of similar mortgages by the Veterans Administration in connection with housing purchased by veterans.*

## 6.2   Finding the Payment

When a debt is amortized by equal payments at equal intervals, the debt becomes the present value of an annuity. We determine the size of the payment by the methods used to get the periodic rent in the annuity problems in the preceding chapters.

EXAMPLE 1: A man buys a $13,000 home and pays $5000 down. He gets a 10-year mortgage for the balance. If the lender charges 6% converted monthly, what is the size of the monthly payment?

SOLUTION: Here we have an ordinary annuity with $A_n = 8000$, $n = 120$, and $i = \frac{1}{2}\%$. From (15) on page 153 for the rent of an ordinary annuity we find

$$R = 8000 \times \frac{1}{a_{\overline{120}|\frac{1}{2}\%}}$$

$$= 8000 \times .011102 = 88.816$$

$$= \$88.82$$

When a debt is amortized, the common commercial practice is to round up any fraction of a cent. This insures complete amortization in the time specified. If each payment were low by a fraction of a cent, there would still be a small outstanding debt after the specified number of payments had been made. Instead of rounding up to the cent, a lender may round up to the dime, dollar, or other unit of money. This does not injure the borrower since the higher periodic payment will be offset by a smaller concluding payment.

* Sumner H. Slichter, *Economic Growth in the United States*, The Free Press, New York, 1966, page 154. Copyright 1961 by Louisiana State University Press. Reprinted with permission from The Macmillan Company.

EXAMPLE 2: A debt of $10,000 bearing interest at 5% converted semiannually is to be amortized in 20 semiannual payments. Find the concluding payment if the semiannual payment is rounded up to: (a) the cent; (b) the dime; (c) the dollar.

SOLUTION: Substituting $A_{20} = 10,000$; $i = 2\frac{1}{2}\%$; $n = 20$ in (15),

$$R = 10,000 \times \frac{1}{a_{\overline{20}|2\frac{1}{2}\%}} = 10,000 \times .064\ 1471 = 641.471$$

Making a time diagram, we see that the simplest method of solution is to set up an equation of value with the focal date at the 20th payment. Then the concluding payment is simply the difference between the $10,000 carried to the focal date and the amount of an annuity *due* of 19 regular payments. Formula (9) takes the $10,000 to the focal date and (16) brings forward the 19 payments.

(a) If the payment is rounded up to the cent,

$$x = 10,000(1.025)^{20} - 641.48(s_{\overline{20}|} - 1)$$
$$= 10,000(1.638\ 6164) - 641.48(24.54466)$$
$$= 16,386.16 - 15,744.91 = \$641.25$$

(b) If the payment is rounded up to the dime,

$$x = 10,000(1.025)^{20} - 641.50(s_{\overline{20}|} - 1) = \$640.76$$

(c) If the payment is rounded up to the dollar,

$$x = 10,000(1.025)^{20} - 642.00(s_{\overline{20}|} - 1) = \$628.49$$

## 6.3 Outstanding Principal

It is often important to know the principal outstanding at a certain time. The borrower may want to pay off the rest of the debt in a lump sum, or the lender may want to sell what is still owed him. To get the principal outstanding at any time we can get the value of the remaining payments at that time.

EXAMPLE 1: To pay off an $8000 mortgage, a man got a 10-year loan at 6% converted monthly. How much does he still owe on his home after he has paid on it for 5 years?

SOLUTION: In Example 1 in the preceding section, we found that the monthly payment is $88.82. To find the outstanding principal we use an equation of value and compare the original debt with the payments that have been made. We put the focal date at the 60th payment and bring everything to this point.

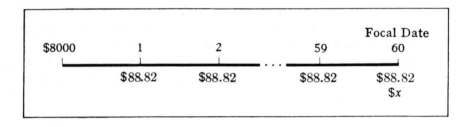

$$x = 8000(1.005)^{60} - 88.82 \times s_{\overline{60}|}$$
$$= 8000 \times 1.348850 - 88.82 \times 69.7700$$
$$= 10{,}790.80 - 6196.97 = \$4593.83$$

This means that the principal has been reduced by only $8000.00 - 4593.83 = \$3406.17$ although the man has paid $5329.20 (60 payments × $88.82). During the early years of a long-term amortization program, a large part of the money paid goes for interest. This leads to the practical point that the buyer of a home should try to borrow from a lender who offers the lowest rate of interest and who will permit the borrower to pay off the mortgage faster than the contract requires without charging a fee. Frequently a borrower will find that an increase in income or an inheritance will put him in a position to pay more per month on his mortgage than he had originally agreed. Since he probably cannot invest this money at as high a rate as he is paying on his mortgage, it is to his advantage to use it to reduce his debt. It is disconcerting to discover that a small print provision, which he had not read in his contract, imposes a penalty for this advance payment.

ALTERNATE SOLUTION: In this problem, we can get a good check on our answer by getting the present value of the remaining 60 payments which form an ordinary annuity.

$$A_{60} = 88.82a_{\overline{60}|\frac{1}{2}\%}$$
$$= 88.82 \times 51.7256$$
$$= \$4594.27$$

This differs by 44 cents from the preceding result because the monthly payment was rounded up to the nearest cent. Carrying the monthly payment to several decimal places would give a closer check, but there is no reason to do this since the payment must be rounded in practical problems.

This method of checking could not be used if the payment had been rounded up to the dime or dollar because then the concluding payment would differ greatly from the other payments.

EXAMPLE 2: On May 15, 1973, a man borrowed $10,000 at 6% converted monthly. He plans to repay the debt in equal monthly payments over 15 years with the first payment on June 15, 1973. The 12 payments during 1975 will reduce the principal by how much? What was the total interest paid in 1975?

SOLUTION: We use (15) to get the monthly payment.

$$R = 10,000 \times \frac{1}{a_{\overline{180}|\frac{1}{2}\%}} = \$84.39$$

The total reduction in principal in 1975 will be the difference between the outstanding principal in December, 1974, and December, 1975. A time diagram shows that the outstanding principal must be determined after the 19th and the 31st payments. This requires two equations of value using these points as focal dates.

Outstanding on 12/15/74 $= 10,000(1.005)^{19} - 84.39s_{\overline{19}|} = \$9316.34$
Outstanding on 12/15/75 $= 10,000(1.005)^{31} - 84.39s_{\overline{31}|} = \$8849.95$
Principal reduction during 1975 $= \$\ \ 466.39$

| | | Focal Date | Focal Date |
|---|---|---|---|
| 5/15/73 | 6/15/73 | 12/15/74 | 12/15/75 |
| $10,000 | 1 | 19 | 31 payments |
| | $84.39 | $84.39 | $84.39 |

To get the total interest paid in 1975, we subtract the amount applied to principal from the total payments which equal $12 \times 84.39 = \$1012.68$. Total interest $= 1012.68 - 466.39 = \$546.29$.

## 6.4  Owner's Equity

The owner's equity starts with the down payment and is gradually increased with that part of each monthly payment over and above the interest. On a long-term loan, equity in a home is built up slowly at first because of interest charges. The amount of the owner's equity can be found at any time by subtracting the outstanding principal from the original loan, and adding the down payment to this difference.

It should be recognized that owner's equity calculated in this way makes no allowance for increases or decreases in the value of the property. If a neighborhood or a piece of property deteriorates, an owner may not recover his investment when he sells. On the other hand, if the property increases in value, the calculated equity is less than the true value of the owner's investment. A long period of rising prices and favorable taxation of capital gains have resulted in attractive financial returns on many pieces of real estate.

EXAMPLE: A man buys a $14,000 home and pays $4000 down. He gets a 25-year, 6% loan for the balance. Monthly payments are $64.44. What is his equity after 10 years?

SOLUTION: The outstanding principal after the 120th payment is found by putting a focal date at that time and taking the original debt and the payments to that point.

$$\text{Outstanding principal} = 10,000.00(1.005)^{120} - 64.44s_{\overline{120}|}$$
$$= 18,193.97 - 10,560.39 = \$7,633.58$$
$$\text{Addition to owner's equity} = 10,000.00 - 7,633.58 = \$2,366.42$$

At the end of 10 years the man has paid a total of $120 \times 64.44 = \$7,732.80$ to get $2,366.42 worth of house. After 10 years the owner's equity is $4,000.00 + 2,366.42 = \$6,366.42$.

The table on page 216 shows how equity is built up in a number of typical loans. The graphs on page 215 show how cumulative total payments are distributed between interest and principal over the life of a long-term loan. Early payments go largely to interest. As the debt is reduced, the principal is repaid at an increasing rate. To reduce interest charges, it is often good money management to apply excess funds to outstanding debts.

As interest rates increase, the cost in dollars goes up even faster. In the preceding example the rate went from 6 to 8%, a $33\frac{1}{3}\%$ change in the rate. But the total interest charges increased from $9325 to $13,149, a 41% change.

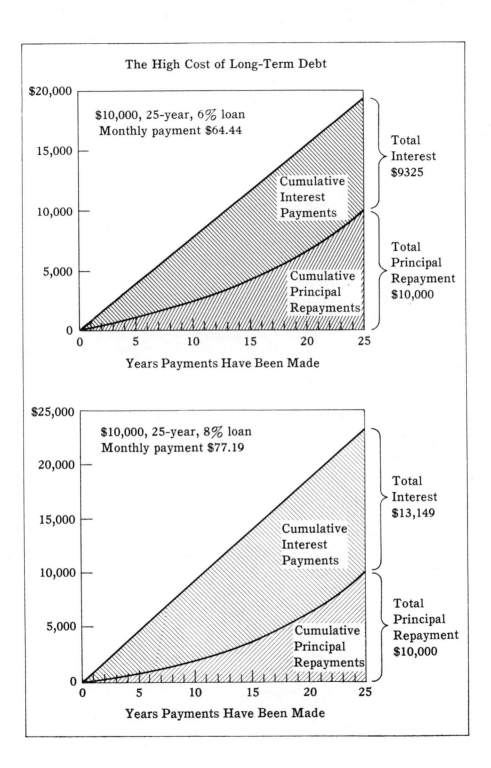

The High Cost of Long-Term Debt

$10,000, 25-year, 6% loan
Monthly payment $64.44

Cumulative Interest Payments

Total Interest $9325

Cumulative Principal Repayments

Total Principal Repayment $10,000

Years Payments Have Been Made

$10,000, 25-year, 8% loan
Monthly payment $77.19

Cumulative Interest Payments

Total Interest $13,149

Cumulative Principal Repayments

Total Principal Repayment $10,000

Years Payments Have Been Made

## Principal Repayments

| AFTER PAYING THIS MANY YEARS | THIS MUCH HAS BEEN REPAID ON A: | | | | |
|---|---|---|---|---|---|
| | 10-YR. LOAN | 15-YR. LOAN | 20-YR. LOAN | 25-YR. LOAN | 30-YR. LOAN |
| *$10,000 loan at 6%* | | | | | |
| 5 | $ 4,258 | $ 2,399 | $ 1,511 | $ 1,007 | $ 695 |
| 10 | 10,000 | 5,636 | 3,548 | 2,366 | 1,632 |
| 15 | | 10,000 | 6,296 | 4,199 | 2,896 |
| 20 | | | 10,000 | 6,672 | 4,602 |
| 25 | | | | 10,000 | 6,902 |
| 30 | | | | | 10,000 |
| *$10,000 loan at 7%* | | | | | |
| 5 | $ 4,136 | $ 2,259 | $ 1,374 | $ 884 | $ 588 |
| 10 | 10,000 | 5,462 | 3,323 | 2,137 | 1,420 |
| 15 | | 10,000 | 6,085 | 3,913 | 2,601 |
| 20 | | | 10,000 | 6,432 | 4,275 |
| 25 | | | | 10,000 | 6,648 |
| 30 | | | | | 10,000 |
| *$10,000 loan at 8%* | | | | | |
| 5 | $ 4,016 | $ 2,124 | $ 1,248 | $ 773 | $ 493 |
| 10 | 10,000 | 5,288 | 3,107 | 1,925 | 1,228 |
| 15 | | 10,000 | 5,877 | 3,642 | 2,323 |
| 20 | | | 10,000 | 6,199 | 3,954 |
| 25 | | | | 10,000 | 6,384 |
| 30 | | | | | 10,000 |

## 6.5   Amortization Schedule

When debts are repaid using the amortization method, it is important to know what portion of each payment goes for interest and how much is applied to reducing the principal. That interest can be a substantial part of the periodic payment can be seen from the following example.

EXAMPLE 1: A man buys a home and gets a 25-year, 6% mortgage for $10,000. The monthly payments are $64.44. When the buyer goes in to the lending institution to make his first monthly payment, he probably thinks he is buying a house with it. How much house is he getting?

SOLUTION: The interest rate is $\frac{1}{2}$% a month. The interest for the first month will be $50. Deducting this from the monthly payment means that the "home owner" gets only $14.44 worth of house with his payment of $64.44. Of course, things get brighter immediately. After the first payment the unpaid balance drops to $10,000.00 - 14.44 = \$9,985.56$. The second month's interest is figured on this principal and amounts to $49.93. With the second payment the buyer gets more house, 7 cents more as a matter of fact. As he continues the payments, more and more of each payment will be applied to the debt. When the debt gets down to approximately $2000 (this will take 22 years), the interest will be only about $10 and most of the payment will go for house.

A person who buys a home on an amortization plan should get a periodic statement from the lender showing how much interest he has paid and how much the mortgage has been reduced, or he should get an amortization schedule which will show exactly where he stands at any time. The interest column will show the buyer how much interest can be deducted in a calendar year when computing his income tax. The same column will show the lender how much he must report as income. Since there is not space here to show an amortization schedule for 300 periods, we use a shorter problem. The schedule for this problem will include all the steps necessary to construct any amortization schedule.

EXAMPLE 2: A debt of $5000 is to be amortized by 5 semiannual payments made at the end of each six months. If interest is charged at the rate of 6% convertible semiannually, find the periodic payment and construct an amortization schedule. Round the payment up to the cent.

SOLUTION: Substituting in (15),

$$R = 5000 \times \frac{1}{a_{\overline{5}|3\%}} = \$1091.775 = \$1091.78$$

*Amortization Schedule*

| PAYMENT NUMBER | TOTAL PAYMENT | PAYMENT ON INTEREST | PAYMENT ON PRINCIPAL | BALANCE OF LOAN |
|---|---|---|---|---|
| | | | | $5000.00 |
| 1 | $1091.78 | $150.00 | $ 941.78 | 4058.22 |
| 2 | 1091.78 | 121.75 | 970.03 | 3088.19 |
| 3 | 1091.78 | 92.65 | 999.13 | 2089.06 |
| 4 | 1091.78 | 62.67 | 1029.11 | 1059.95 |
| 5 | 1091.75 | 31.80 | 1059.95 | — |
| | $5458.87 | $458.87 | $5000.00 | |

The final payment equals the preceding loan balance plus interest on this balance for the last period. When determining the periodic payment, lenders customarily round up. This insures that the final payment will be equal to or less than the other payments.

**EXERCISE 6a**

Unless stated otherwise, periodic payments were obtained by rounding up to the cent. Outstanding balances were obtained by carrying all obligations and payments forward to a focal date.

1. A $6000 loan is to be amortized with 6 equal annual payments. If the interest rate is 5%, find the annual payment and construct an amortization schedule. $(R = \$1182.11)$

2. A loan of $1200 is to be amortized with 12 equal monthly payments. Find the monthly payment and construct a schedule if the rate is 12% converted monthly.

3. A debt of $30,000 with interest at 6% is to be amortized with 4 equal annual payments. Find the size of the payment and construct an amortization schedule. $(R = \$8657.75)$

4. Construct an amortization schedule for a debt of $30,000 to be repaid with equal payments at the end of each 6 months over a 5-year period. The rate is 4% converted semiannually.

5. A debt of $8000 with interest at 6% converted semiannually is being amortized with 10 equal semiannual payments. Find the size of the periodic payment and the outstanding principal just after the fifth payment.

    ($937.85; $4295.01)

6. A debt of $8500 with interest at 5% converted monthly is being amortized with monthly payments over a period of 15 years. Find the size of the payment and the outstanding principal just after the 90th payment.

7. A man buys a $13,000 home and pays $3000 down. He gets a 12-year mortgage for the balance. (a) If the lender charges 6% converted monthly, determine the monthly payment rounded up to the nearest dime. (b) How much of the first payment goes for interest and how much toward reducing the principal? (c) How much does the man still owe just after making the 72nd payment? (d) How much of the 100th payment goes for interest and how much for principal?

    $\begin{bmatrix} \text{(a) } \$97.60; \quad \text{(b) } \$50.00 \text{ interest, } \$47.60 \text{ principal} \\ \text{(c) } \$5886.93; \text{ (d) } \$19.61 \text{ interest, } \$77.99 \text{ principal} \end{bmatrix}$

8. A house worth $16,000 is purchased with a down payment of $6000 and monthly payments for 15 years. If the interest rate is 6% compounded monthly, find the size of the monthly payment rounded up to the nearest dime. Complete the first three lines of the amortization schedule. How much is still owed on the house just before making the 90th payment?

9. A $2400 car is purchased with a down payment of $800 and equal monthly payments for 24 months. If the interest rate is 12% compounded monthly, find the size of the monthly payment and complete the first three lines of the amortization schedule. How much is still owed on the car just before making the 12th payment?                    ($R$ = $75.32; $923.00 still owed)

10. Work Problem 9 for a rate of 24% converted monthly.

11. A man purchases a home costing $13,300 and makes a down payment of $2300. He gets a mortgage for the balance at 6% converted monthly. This is to be repaid in equal monthly payments over a 15-year period. If he gets the loan in September, 1973, and makes the first monthly payment one month later, how much interest can he deduct when preparing his income tax statement for 1973? By how much is the mortgage reduced in 1973? Base your answers on an amortization schedule.

(Tax deduction $164.43; principal reduced by $114.06)

12. A family buys a home for $13,000. They make a 20% down payment and get a 10-year, 4% loan for the balance which is to be paid off in equal monthly payments. If they make their first payment in November, 1974, how much interest can they deduct when they prepare their income tax report for 1974?

13. A debt of $20,000 bearing interest at 4% converted quarterly is to be amortized with payments every 3 months for 10 years. Find the concluding payment if the quarterly payment is rounded up to (a) the cent; (b) the dime; (c) the dollar.                    [(a) $608.72; (b) $604.89; (c) $566.58]

14. Work Problem 13 for a rate of 5% converted quarterly.

15. A mobile home is a complete dwelling unit built on a chassis and capable of being towed by truck. The increased size and amenities of mobile homes have resulted in their becoming widely acceptable for family living. Their lower cost makes home ownership available to more people, so that mobile homes now account for the majority of homes under $15,000. Mobile home loans are often made as installment loans. This means higher interest rates and shorter terms than conventional mortgage loans.

   A couple buys a $12,000 mobile home and pays $4000 down. The balance is financed at 12% converted monthly over 5 years. Find the monthly payment and the balance due after the 30th payment.    ($177.96; $4592.47)

16. Find the answers to Problem 15 if the couple could get the loan at 9% converted monthly.

## 6.6 Refinancing

After a long-term loan has been partially paid off, it is sometimes possible to get the balance due refinanced at a lower rate which will result in a considerable reduction in the total interest charges. The present value of these interest savings should be balanced against any costs involved in refinancing to see if the change would be a profitable one.

EXAMPLE: A man purchased a home and signed a mortgage contract for $10,000 which required repayment in equal monthly payments over 12 years based on 6% converted monthly. Just after making the 60th payment, he has the balance refinanced at 5% converted monthly. If the number of payments remains unchanged, what will be the new monthly payment and what will be the total savings in interest?

SOLUTION: Using (15) to get the monthly payment,

$$R = 10,000 \times \frac{1}{a_{\overline{144}|\frac{1}{2}\%}} = \$97.59$$

Outstanding balance after 60 payments $= 10,000(1.005)^{60} - 97.59 s_{\overline{60}|\frac{1}{2}\%} =$ 13,488.50 − 6808.85 = $6679.65.

This balance becomes the present value of an ordinary annuity of 84 payments. From (15) the new monthly payment is

$$R = 6679.65 \times \frac{1}{a_{\overline{84}|\frac{5}{12}\%}} = \$94.42$$

The difference per month is $3.17 making the total savings in interest $266.28 over 84 months. If money is worth about 4% converted monthly to the person, the present value of these savings is, $3.17 \times a_{\overline{84}|\frac{1}{3}\%} = \$231.91$.

If the cost of refinancing is less than $231.91, it will pay the man to refinance. In this analysis, no allowance was made for the concluding payments being slightly smaller than the regular payments since the difference would be about the same for both plans.

## 6.7 Amortization with Specified Payments

In some transactions the size of the payment is specified. Often this will be some rounded value such as $50, $1000, etc. This means that the number of payments must be determined.

EXAMPLE 1: A debt of $6000 is to be amortized with payments of $1000 at the end of each year. Find the number of payments if the interest rate is 5%.

SOLUTION: Substituting in (13),

$$6000 = 1000 a_{\overline{n}|}$$

$$a_{\overline{n}|} = \tfrac{6000}{1000} = 6.00$$

Reference to Table 2 shows that the factor 6.00 lies between 7 and 8 periods. Thus 7 full payments plus a part of a payment will be required to amortize the debt.

The concluding irregular payment may be added to the last regular payment or it may be made one interval after the last full payment. If the concluding payment is small, some lenders prefer to add it to the last full payment. In this book, unless the problem specifies otherwise, follow the common practice of making this payment one period after the last full payment, regardless of size. This means that simple interest must be computed on the unpaid balance after the last full payment.

EXAMPLE 2: Find the size of the concluding payment in Example 1 if the last full payment is to be increased by the amount of the outstanding debt.

SOLUTION: A time diagram shows that the time of the last full payment is a good place to put the focal date.

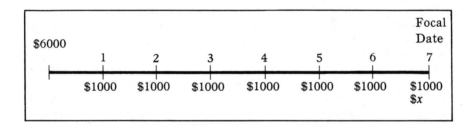

The equation of value is

$$x = 6000(1.05)^7 - 1000s_{\overline{7}|} = 8442.60 - 8142.01 = \$300.59$$

The debt would be liquidated with a 7th payment of $1300.59.

EXAMPLE 3: Find the size of the concluding payment in Example 1 if it is made one period after the last full payment.

SOLUTION: The focal date is put at the time of the 8th payment and the 7 full payments are brought forward as an annuity due.

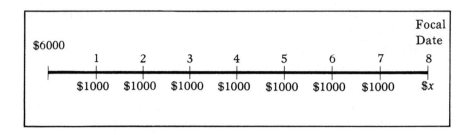

The equation of value is

$$x = 6000(1.05)^8 - 1000(s_{\overline{8}|} - 1) = 8864.73 - 8549.11 = \$315.62$$

This problem could also be worked by taking the $300.59 balance after the 7th payment in Example 2 forward at simple interest.

$$x = 300.59 + 300.59 \times .05 = 300.59 + 15.03 = \$315.62$$

EXAMPLE 4: Construct an amortization schedule for Problem 3.

*Amortization Schedule*

| | ($6000, 5% loan with annual payments of $1000) | | | |
|---|---|---|---|---|
| PAYMENT NUMBER | TOTAL PAYMENT | PAYMENT ON INTEREST | PAYMENT ON PRINCIPAL | BALANCE OF LOAN |
| | | | | $6000.00 |
| 1 | $1000.00 | $ 300.00 | $ 700.00 | 5300.00 |
| 2 | 1000.00 | 265.00 | 735.00 | 4565.00 |
| 3 | 1000.00 | 228.25 | 771.75 | 3793.25 |
| 4 | 1000.00 | 189.66 | 810.34 | 2982.91 |
| 5 | 1000.00 | 149.15 | 850.85 | 2132.06 |
| 6 | 1000.00 | 106.60 | 893.40 | 1238.66 |
| 7 | 1000.00 | 61.93 | 938.07 | 300.59 |
| 8 | 315.62 | 15.03 | 300.59 | 0.00 |
| | $7315.62 | $1315.62 | $6000.00 | |

## 6.8   The Point System

On FHA and VA loans, there are legal ceilings on interest rates. On conventional (nongovernment insured or guaranteed) mortgages, some states specify a rate ceiling under antiusuary laws. An interesting system called "charging points" is sometimes used by lenders to get additional revenue. Here is how it works.

Assume that a house is for sale for $14,000. A buyer can pay $4000 down. He can get a 6%, 20-year loan for the balance from a lender who charges

5 points. Each point is a 1% discount from the face amount of the loan. Five points or 5% means a lender would advance only $95 for each $100 of mortgage to be repaid. Who pays the points? If the borrower absorbs the points, it increases the true interest rate he pays. In this case the borrower would have to take out and repay a loan of $10,526.32. This is obtained by dividing 10,000 by .95. Note that 5% of 10,526.32 is $526.32 which is deducted from the face amount of the loan to provide the $10,000 which the borrower needs. Over the term of the loan the lender will get back $10,526.32 plus interest.

If the seller absorbs the points, the amount he receives is reduced by the amount of the discount. If the seller absorbs all the points in the above example, the borrower would get a loan of $10,000 but the seller would receive only $9500 from the lender. To offset this charge, the seller may raise the asking price of the house so that after the loan based on the asking price is discounted, he will receive what he wanted to get in the first place.

Sometimes the buyer and seller split the points, each paying part of the discount. No matter who pays the points, the lender comes out ahead.

EXAMPLE 1: A borrower gets a $10,000, 5-year, 6% loan from a lender who charges 2 points. If the borrower pays the points, what is the true interest rate?

SOLUTION: The lender charges 2% of $10,000. This means that the borrower receives $9800. However, the monthly payment is based on $10,000. From (15),

$$R = 10,000 \times \frac{1}{a_{\overline{60}|\frac{1}{2}\%}} = \$193.33$$

The problem is now an ordinary annuity with a present value of $9800 (what the borrower actually receives) and 60 payments of $193.33. Substituting in (13),

$$193.33a_{\overline{60}|} = 9800.00$$

$$a_{\overline{60}|} = \frac{9800.00}{193.33} = 50.6905$$

Reference to the *Present Worth of 1 per Period* column in Table 2 shows that the nominal rate is between 6 and 7%.

$$
\begin{array}{cccc}
 & j_{(12)} & a_{\overline{60}|} & \\
 & 6 & 51.7256 & \\
1 \quad d & j & 50.6905 \quad 1.0351 & 1.2236 \\
 & 7 & 50.5020 &
\end{array}
$$

$$d = \frac{1.0351}{1.2236} = .85$$

$$j = 6.00 + .85 = 6.85\%$$

Because many students will be confronted with the point problem in their shopping for a home loan, true interest rates corresponding to typical loans and point charges are given on page 225.

These data show the importance of getting the true rate when shopping for credit. Suppose one lender offers to make a 15-year loan at 6% but charges the borrower 5 points. A second lender will make the loan at $6\frac{1}{2}$% but not charge any points. The table shows that the $6\frac{1}{2}$% loan is the better deal for the borrower.

Because points are charged at the beginning of the loan, none of this charge is recovered if the loan is prepaid. The result is that borrowers who pay off a loan ahead of time pay even higher rates than those shown in the table.

EXAMPLE 2: A man gets a $10,000, 6% loan to be repaid over 20 years. The monthly payment is $71.65. The lender charges 5 points. At the end of 5 years the borrower sells the house and pays off the mortgage. What true rate did he pay?

SOLUTION: After paying the 5 points, the borrower actually received $9500. The table shows that if he repaid the loan over 20 years, the true rate would be 6.65%. To find the true rate if he prepays the loan, we first get the unpaid balance. A focal date is put at 5 years and the $10,000 and the 59 payments are brought to this point at the stated rate of 6% converted monthly using the indicated formulas.

(9) $\qquad$ $10,000(1.005)^{60} = \$13,488.50$
(16) $\qquad$ $71.65(s_{\overline{60|}} - 1) = \underline{\quad 4,927.37}$
$\qquad$ $\$ 8,561.13$

Now it is necessary to analyze the problem on a cash flow basis. At the beginning of the loan there was an inflow of $9500 from the borrower's standpoint. There have been 59 monthly outflows of $71.65 each and a single outflow of $8561.13 at the end of 5 years. A time diagram helps to get an overall view of the problem.

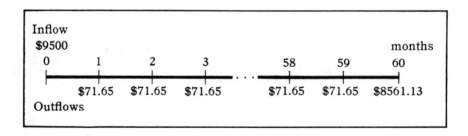

The focal date is put at time zero and trial and error used to find a rate which makes the discounted value of the outflows equal to the $9500 inflow. We use (13) to get the present value of the periodic payments and (11) to discount the single sum. At 6% converted monthly the discounted values are,

$$71.65a_{\overline{59}|} + 8561.13(1.005)^{-60} = 3653.02 + 6346.98 = \$10,000.00$$

## True Interest Rates on Discounted Loans

| STATED RATE | POINTS CHARGED | 15-YEAR LOAN | 20-YEAR LOAN | 25-YEAR LOAN | 30-YEAR LOAN |
|---|---|---|---|---|---|
| 6% | 1 | 6.16% | 6.13% | 6.11% | 6.09% |
| | 2 | 6.32 | 6.25 | 6.21 | 6.19 |
| | 3 | 6.48 | 6.38 | 6.32 | 6.29 |
| | 4 | 6.64 | 6.51 | 6.44 | 6.38 |
| | 5 | 6.81 | 6.65 | 6.55 | 6.49 |
| | 6 | 6.98 | 6.78 | 6.66 | 6.59 |
| | 7 | 7.15 | 6.92 | 6.78 | 6.69 |
| | 8 | 7.33 | 7.06 | 6.90 | 6.80 |
| | 9 | 7.51 | 7.20 | 7.02 | 6.90 |
| | 10 | 7.69 | 7.34 | 7.14 | 7.01 |
| 6½% | 1 | 6.66 | 6.63 | 6.61 | 6.60 |
| | 2 | 6.82 | 6.76 | 6.72 | 6.70 |
| | 3 | 6.99 | 6.89 | 6.83 | 6.80 |
| | 4 | 7.15 | 7.02 | 6.95 | 6.90 |
| | 5 | 7.32 | 7.16 | 7.06 | 7.00 |
| | 6 | 7.49 | 7.30 | 7.18 | 7.11 |
| | 7 | 7.67 | 7.44 | 7.30 | 7.22 |
| | 8 | 7.85 | 7.58 | 7.42 | 7.32 |
| | 9 | 8.03 | 7.72 | 7.55 | 7.43 |
| | 10 | 8.21 | 7.87 | 7.67 | 7.54 |
| 7% | 1 | 7.16 | 7.13 | 7.11 | 7.10 |
| | 2 | 7.33 | 7.26 | 7.22 | 7.20 |
| | 3 | 7.49 | 7.40 | 7.34 | 7.30 |
| | 4 | 7.66 | 7.53 | 7.46 | 7.41 |
| | 5 | 7.83 | 7.67 | 7.58 | 7.52 |
| | 6 | 8.01 | 7.81 | 7.70 | 7.62 |
| | 7 | 8.19 | 7.96 | 7.82 | 7.73 |
| | 8 | 8.37 | 8.10 | 7.95 | 7.85 |
| | 9 | 8.55 | 8.25 | 8.07 | 7.96 |
| | 10 | 8.74 | 8.40 | 8.20 | 8.08 |

This is really a check on our work. The payments and the balance were computed on the basis of a present value of $10,000 and a 6% rate, so the sum of their discounted values should be $10,000.

To get a present value less than $9500, it is necessary to go to a higher rate. At 9% converted monthly, the present value of the outflows is

$$71.65a_{\overline{59}|} + 8561.13(1.0075)^{-60} = 3405.86 + 5467.99 = \$8873.85$$

Linear interpolation can now be used to get an approximate value of the true rate.

$$
\begin{array}{c}
\qquad\qquad Nominal \qquad Present\ Value \\
\qquad\qquad Rate \qquad\quad of\ Outflows
\end{array}
$$

$$
3 \left[ d \left[ \begin{array}{c} =6\% \\ j \end{array} \right. \quad \begin{array}{c} 10,000.00 \\ 9,500.00 \end{array} \left. \right] 500 \quad 1126.15 \right.
$$
$$
\qquad\qquad\quad 9\% \qquad\quad 8,873.85
$$

$$d = \frac{3 \times 500}{1126.15} = 1.33$$

$$\text{True rate} = 6.00 + 1.33 = 7.33\%$$

## EXERCISE 6b

(Round periodic payments up to the cent unless the problem states otherwise.)

1. A 10-year mortgage for $8000 is being amortized with monthly payments at 6% converted monthly. Just after making the 60th payment, the borrower has the balance refinanced at 5% converted monthly with the term of the loan to remain the same. What will be the total savings in interest?

$$
\begin{bmatrix}
\text{Original monthly payment} & \$88.82 \\
\text{New monthly payment} & \$86.70 \\
\text{Total savings in interest} & \$127.20
\end{bmatrix}
$$

2. A man gets a $10,000 mortgage on a new home to be repaid in 144 monthly payments at 6% converted monthly. Instead of making the regular 96th payment, he applied $2000 from an inheritance on the mortgage. At the same time he gets the balance of the debt refinanced at 5% converted monthly with the first payment under the new plan to be made in 1 month. If the duration of the loan remains the same, what is the size of the new monthly payment? If the size of the payments remains the same, how many full payments must he make to pay off the balance and what will be the size of the final payment?

3. On September 15, 1970, a couple buys a home. Their loan is to be repaid in 180 payments of $50 each with the first payment to be made on October 15, 1970. If the rate is 5% converted monthly, how much would it cost to

pay off the debt on July 15, 1975? Include the payment due on July 15, 1975. ($4824.41)

4. On May 1, 1965, a family borrowed $15,000 at 6% converted monthly to finance the purchase of a home. The term of the loan was 15 years. The first payment was made on June 1, 1965. All payments were made on time up to and including the one on August 1, 1974. On September 1, 1974, the borrower paid $1000 instead of the usual monthly payment and arranged with the lender to refinance the balance at 5% converted monthly. On October 1, 1974, he is to make the first of 60 equal monthly payments under the new conditions. What is the size of the new monthly payment?

5. A debt of $8000 is to be amortized with annual payments of $500. How many full payments will be required and what will be the size of the concluding payment 1 year after the last full payment if: (a) the rate is 4%; (b) the rate is 5%?

$$\left[ \begin{array}{l} \text{(a) At 4\%, 26 full payments and a 27th payment of \$24.84} \\ \text{(b) At 5\%, 32 full payments and a 33rd payment of \$493.62} \end{array} \right]$$

6. A debt of $6500 is to be amortized with semiannual payments of $500. How many full payments will be required and what will be the size of the concluding payment 6 months after the last full payment if: (a) the rate is 6% compounded semiannually; (b) the rate is 7% compounded semiannually?

7. A widow inherits an estate of $12,000 on March 1, 1973. Instead of taking the cash, she immediately invests the money at 3% converted monthly with the understanding that she will be paid $125 monthly, with the first payment to be made on April 1, 1973. How many $125 payments will she receive? Get the size and date of the concluding payment.

(109 full payments; $114.00 on May 1, 1982)

8. Work Problem 7 if the widow could get 4% converted monthly.

9. A borrower gets a 5-year, $10,000, 6% loan to be repaid in equal monthly payments. If the lender charges 3 points, what is the true nominal interest rate? (7.28%)

10. A person gets a 5-year, $5000, 6% loan to be repaid in equal monthly payments. If the lender charges 4 points, what is the true nominal interest rate?

## 6.9 Sinking Funds

When a sum of money will be needed at some future date, it is good practice to accumulate systematically a fund that will equal the desired sum at the time it is needed. The money accumulated in this way is called a **sinking fund**.

Sinking funds are used to redeem bond issues, pay off other debts, replace worn-out equipment, or provide money for the purchase of new equipment.

Sinking funds are used to retire some loans because the borrower is not allowed to make payments on the principal until the entire debt is due. The creditor may want it this way so that he will not have the problem of reinvesting a part of his capital every few months. Aside from the extra bother, there is also the possibility that he may have to make the new loan at a lower rate.

While the deposits to a sinking fund may be unequal and at unequal intervals of time, this is usually not done because the problem then must be worked sum by sum using the focal date procedure in Chapter 3. A much more common and systematic procedure is to accumulate the fund by equal deposits at equal intervals. Each periodic deposit is invested on the specified date and allowed to accumulate until the final maturity value is needed. This is the method we shall use.

Since the amount needed in the sinking fund, the time it is needed, and the interest rate which the fund will earn are known, a sinking fund becomes simply an ordinary annuity in which the size of the payment is to be determined. When a sinking fund is used to retire a debt, the borrower continues to owe the entire principal on which he pays interest as it falls due to the creditor. The sinking fund is an entirely separate account and the interest rate it earns will probably be different from the rate paid on the debt.

EXAMPLE: A man wants to have $2000 to purchase a new car in three years. How much must he deposit every 6 months in an account paying 3% converted semiannually?

SOLUTION: Substituting in (14),

$$R = S_n \times \frac{1}{s_{\overline{n}|}} = 2000 \times \frac{1}{s_{\overline{6}|1\frac{1}{2}\%}} = \$321.05$$

It is sometimes desirable to have a schedule to show how much is in the sinking fund at any time. The schedule for the above example is shown on the following page.

It is well to note the advantage of this systematic way of providing for some future purchase. First of all, the buyer avoids the very high interest rates commonly charged on installment loans. Second, he gets interest on his own savings. Third, there is a good chance that he will be able to get a discount when he is in a position to pay cash for the item he wants.

*Sinking Fund Schedule*

| PERIOD | AMOUNT IN FUND AT START OF PERIOD | INTEREST EARNED ON SINKING FUND DURING PERIOD | DEPOSIT AT END OF PERIOD | AMOUNT IN THE FUND AT END OF PERIOD |
|---|---|---|---|---|
| 1 | — | — | $ 321.05 | $ 321.05 |
| 2 | $ 321.05 | $ 4.82 | 321.05 | 646.92 |
| 3 | 646.92 | 9.70 | 321.05 | 977.67 |
| 4 | 977.67 | 14.67 | 321.05 | 1313.39 |
| 5 | 1313.39 | 19.70 | 321.05 | 1654.14 |
| 6 | 1654.14 | 24.81 | 321.05 | 2000.00 |
| | | $73.70 | $1926.30 | |

## 6.10   Total Periodic Charge

In the above example we assumed a case in which a person was simply saving money for a future purchase. The most common use of sinking funds is to make provision for retiring a debt. In such cases the borrower must meet two charges—the interest when it is due and the periodic deposits to the sinking fund. Note that there is no relation between the interest on the debt and the interest earned on the sinking fund. The interest on the debt is not paid from the sinking fund. The two are entirely separate. However, for accounting purposes we can add the two to get the total periodic charge. This is illustrated by an example.

EXAMPLE: A man borrows $2000 for 3 years at 5 % interest payable semiannually. He makes periodic deposits into a sinking fund earning 3 % converted semi-annually. Get the total periodic payment and construct a schedule.

SOLUTION: The interest every 6 months will be $2\frac{1}{2}$ % of $2000 or $50. From (14), the deposit every 6 months to the sinking fund is

$$R \doteq 2000 \times \frac{1}{s_{\overline{6}|1\frac{1}{2}\%}} = \$321.05$$

Thus the total cost to the borrower every 6 months will be the sum of these two or $371.05. Note that the $50 and the $321.05 may be paid to different persons or institutions. However, when the amount in the sinking fund reaches $2000 it will be drawn out and paid to the lender, probably with the last interest payment.

*Sinking Fund and Interest Schedule*

| PERIOD | AMOUNT IN FUND AT START OF PERIOD | INTEREST EARNED ON SINKING FUND DURING PERIOD | DEPOSIT AT END OF PERIOD | AMOUNT IN FUND AT END OF PERIOD | INTEREST ON DEBT | TOTAL PERIODIC PAYMENT |
|---|---|---|---|---|---|---|
| 1 | — | — | $ 321.05 | $ 321.05 | $50.00 | $371.05 |
| 2 | $ 321.05 | $ 4.82 | 321.05 | 646.92 | 50.00 | 371.05 |
| 3 | 646.92 | 9.70 | 321.05 | 977.67 | 50.00 | 371.05 |
| 4 | 977.67 | 14.67 | 321.05 | 1313.39 | 50.00 | 371.05 |
| 5 | 1313.39 | 19.70 | 321.05 | 1654.14 | 50.00 | 371.05 |
| 6 | 1654.14 | 24.81 | 321.05 | 2000.00 | 50.00 | 371.05 |
| | | $73.70 | $1926.30 | | | |

### EXERCISE 6c

(Round periodic deposits up to the cent.)

1. A firm expects to need $50,000 on May 1, 1978, to replace some machine tools. To provide this amount the firm makes equal annual deposits into a fund that is invested at 4%. If the first deposit is made on May 1, 1973, and the last deposit on May 1, 1978, what will be the size of each deposit? Prepare a schedule for this problem.  $(R = \$7538.10)$

2. A sinking fund of $6000 is to be accumulated with 5 equal annual deposits at the end of each year. If interest is earned at 3%, get the size of the deposit and prepare a schedule.

3. A couple would like to accumulate $4000 for a down payment on a home by August 1, 1976. They plan to make semiannual deposits in a building and loan with the first deposit to be made on August 1, 1972, and the last deposit on February 1, 1976. If the building and loan pays 4% compounded semiannually on February 1 and August 1, the couple should deposit how much every 6 months?  (Payments of $456.91 will amount to $4000.08)

4. What would be the semiannual deposit in Problem 3 if the rate is $4\frac{1}{2}\%$ compounded semiannually?

5. A company borrows $80,000 at 4% for 12 years. If they set up a sinking fund at 3% to repay the debt, what is the total annual cost of this obligation?  ($8836.97)

6. A man borrows $5500 for 6 years at 7%. To be sure that he will be able to repay the debt, he makes equal deposits at the end of each year in an investment paying 4% compounded annually. What is the total annual cost of this loan?

## 6.11   Sinking Fund with Specified Deposit

In some transactions the size of the payment to the sinking fund is specified, and the problem is to determine the number of payments. Usually in such cases an integral number of payments will not give the exact result desired. This means that an irregular deposit must be made either at the time of the last regular deposit or one period later. In this book we shall assume the latter procedure unless the problem specifies otherwise.

EXAMPLE: A man wants to accumulate $10,000 to start a business. If he can save $750 every six months, how long will it take him to accumulate $10,000? He is able to put his savings at the end of each 6 months in an investment paying 5% compounded semiannually.

SOLUTION: Substituting in (12),

$$10,000 = 750 s_{\overline{n}|2\frac{1}{2}\%}$$

$$s_{\overline{n}|} = \frac{10,000}{750} = 13.33$$

From Table 2 we find that he will have to make 11 deposits of $750 plus a smaller 12th deposit. To get the size of the concluding deposit, the most direct procedure is to get the amount of an annuity due of 11 deposits and subtract this from the $10,000.

$$S_n = R(s_{\overline{n+1}|} - 1)$$
$$= 750(s_{\overline{11+1}|} - 1) = 750(13.79555 - 1)$$
$$= 750 \times 12.79555 = \$9,596.66$$
$$\text{12th payment} = 10,000 - 9,596.66 = \$403.34$$

The student should note that this or any similar problem can be worked by setting up a focal date and an equation of value.

---

**Focal Date**
**Need $10,000**
**here**

| 1 | 2 | 3 | | 10 | 11 | 12 payments |

$750  $750  $750  $\cdots$  $750  $750  Have amount of annuity
due of eleven $750 payments

Balance needed $= 10,000 -$
$750(s_{\overline{11+1}|} - 1)$

---

## 6.12   Comparison of Amortization and Sinking Funds

When a debt is amortized, each payment pays the outstanding interest at that time and the balance is used to reduce the principal. When a sinking fund is used, the entire principal remains unpaid until the due date of the debt. Each interest period, the debtor pays only the interest to the lender. Then he makes a separate deposit into a sinking fund which will accumulate to an amount that will retire all or a portion of the debt.

The amortization method has the advantage of being more convenient as it requires only a single payment each period. Which method will be cheaper depends on the rates of interest. If the rate received on the sinking fund is the same as that charged on the debt the total periodic cost of the two methods will be the same. If the sinking fund earns a lower rate of interest than is charged on the debt, the periodic cost for the sinking fund method will be greater than for the amortization method. The reason is that the buyer will be paying one rate of interest on his debt while receiving a lower rate on his savings. Conversely, if the borrower can get more interest on the sinking fund than he is paying on the debt, he would be ahead to use a sinking fund. Since such a situation would be very unusual for most borrowers, it is usually better for a person to amortize a debt. The effect of different interest rates on the total periodic cost can be shown by an example.

EXAMPLE 1: A man borrows $1000 to be repaid in equal annual installments at the end of each year for 3 years. Find the total annual cost under the following conditions:

(a) The debt is amortized at $4\%$.
(b) Interest at $4\%$ is paid on the debt and a sinking fund is set up at $3\%$.
(c) Interest at $4\%$ is paid on the debt and a sinking fund is set up at $4\%$.
(d) Interest at $4\%$ is paid on the debt and a sinking fund is set up at $5\%$.

SOLUTION:

| a | b |
|---|---|
| $R = 1000 \dfrac{1}{a_{\overline{3}\mid 4\%}} = \$360.35$ | $\text{Int.} = .04 \times 1000 = \$ 40.00$ |
| This is the total annual cost as it includes both interest and principal. | $R = 1000 \times \dfrac{1}{s_{\overline{3}\mid 3\%}} = 323.53$ |
| | Total    $\$363.53$ |

| c | | d | |
|---|---|---|---|
| Interest | $ 40.00 | Interest | $ 40.00 |
| $R = 1000 \times \dfrac{1}{s_{\overline{3}|4\%}} =$ 320.35 | | $R = 1000 \times \dfrac{1}{s_{\overline{3}|5\%}} =$ 317.21 | |
| | $360.35 | | $357.21 |
| Note that this is the same as the amortization plan. | | | |

Note that all of the above plans result in the entire debt, principal and interest, being paid in 3 years. Besides simplifying the transaction and usually having a lower periodic cost, the amortization plan has another practical advantage for most borrowers. It literally forces the borrower to reduce the principal as he goes along. If most people tried to pay future debts by setting up sinking funds they would probably spend some of the periodic deposits instead of saving them. The result would be that when the debt comes due they would not have enough in the sinking fund to pay it. That is why most home mortgages today are paid off with amortization or direct reduction loans.

EXAMPLE 2: A company wants to borrow $1,000,000. One possibility is to borrow the money at 6% converted semiannually and set up a sinking fund at 5% converted semiannually to retire the debt in 10 years. At what rate, converted semiannually, would it be less expensive to amortize the debt?

SOLUTION: Get the total periodic payment.

Interest $\qquad 1,000,000 \times .03 = \$30,000.00$

Payment to sinking fund $\qquad 1,000,000 \times \dfrac{1}{s_{\overline{20}|2\frac{1}{2}\%}} = 39,147.13$

Total payment every 6 months $\qquad = \$69,147.13$

The total periodic payment becomes the rent of an ordinary annuity with a present value of $1,000,000. Substituting in (13),

$$69,147.13 a_{\overline{20}|} = 1,000,000$$

$$a_{\overline{20}|} = \frac{1,000,000}{69,147.13} = 14.4619$$

Interpolating between the closest nominal rates in Table 2,

$$
1 \left[ d \left[ \begin{array}{c} -6 \\ -j \\ -7 \end{array} \right. \right.
\begin{array}{c} \dfrac{j_{(2)}}{} \end{array}
\qquad
\begin{array}{c} a_{\overline{20}|} \\ 14.8775 \\ 14.4619 \\ 14.2124 \end{array}
\left. \begin{array}{c} \\ 4156 \\ \end{array} \right] \; 6651
$$

$$
\frac{d}{1} = \frac{4156}{6651}
$$

$$
d = .62
$$

Nominal rate $= 6.00 + .62 = 6.62\%$ compounded semiannually

If the company can borrow money at less than 6.62% compounded semi-annually, it will be less expensive than a straight loan at 6% and a 5% sinking fund.

Because of the importance of a thorough understanding of the amortization and sinking fund methods, the two are sketched below for a debt of $1000 to be repaid with three annual payments.

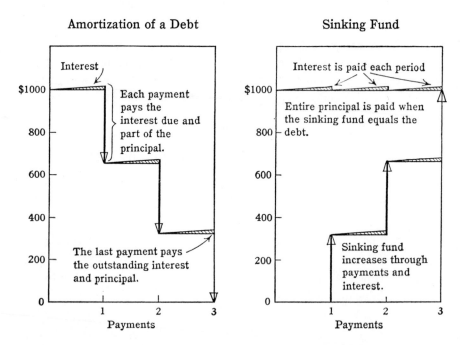

**Amortization of a Debt**

Interest

$1000

Each payment pays the interest due and part of the principal.

800

600

400

The last payment pays the outstanding interest and principal.

200

0

1   2   3

Payments

**Sinking Fund**

Interest is paid each period

$1000

Entire principal is paid when the sinking fund equals the debt.

800

600

400

Sinking fund increases through payments and interest.

200

0

1   2   3

Payments

**EXERCISE 6d**

(Round periodic payments up to the cent.)

**1.** A debt of $4000 is due at the end of 5 years. To be certain that he will have this amount when it is due, the borrower decides to set up a sinking fund by making deposits at the end of each year into an account paying $3\frac{1}{2}\%$. Construct a schedule showing how this fund accumulates.   $(R = \$745.93)$

2. A sinking fund is set up to accumulate \$8500 in 6 years. If the fund earns $4\%$ converted annually, what is the size of the deposit at the end of each year? Construct a schedule.

3. A man wants to accumulate \$8000 to start a business. If he can save \$800 every 6 months and can invest these savings at $3\%$ compounded semi-annually, how long will it take him? What is the size of the concluding deposit?                  (9 full deposits; 10th deposit of \$237.82)

4. A couple wants to accumulate \$2500 for a down payment on a home. If they can deposit \$250 at the end of each 6 months in a savings and loan association paying $4\%$ converted semiannually, how many full deposits must they make and what will be the size of the concluding deposit?

5. The management of a factory wants to set up a sinking fund to provide \$40,000 for the replacement of a machine at the end of 6 years. If equal deposits are made at the end of each 6 months in a fund earning $4\%$ converted semiannually, find the size of each deposit. If the machine has to be replaced at the end of 4 years, how much will be in the fund at that time?
          $(R = \$2982.39;$ At the end of 4 years fund contains \$25,597.76)

6. Work Problem 5 for a rate of $3\%$ converted semiannually.

7. A man borrows \$5000 to be repaid in equal annual installments at the end of each year for 6 years. Find the total annual cost under the following conditions.
   (a) The debt is amortized at $5\%$.
   (b) Interest at $5\%$ is paid on the debt and a sinking fund is set up at $3\%$.
   (c) Interest at $5\%$ is paid on the debt and a sinking fund is set up at $5\%$.
   (d) Interest at $5\%$ is paid on the debt and a sinking fund is set up at $6\%$.
          [(a) \$985.09; (b) \$1022.99; (c) \$985.09; (d) \$966.82]

8. Get the total annual cost for a loan of \$12,000 repaid in 4 equal annual payments under the following conditions.
   (a) The debt is amortized at $3\%$.
   (b) Interest at $3\%$ is paid on the debt and a sinking fund is set up at $2\frac{1}{2}\%$.
   (c) Interest at $3\%$ is paid on the debt and a sinking fund is set up at $3\%$.
   (d) Interest at $3\%$ is paid on the debt and a sinking fund is set up at $3\frac{1}{2}\%$.

9. A firm can borrow \$10,000 at $6\frac{1}{2}\%$ per annum for 5 years. A sinking fund could be set up at $5\%$ converted annually to repay the debt. At what rate would an amortization plan have the same annual cost?      (7.32%)

10. A company can borrow \$100,000 at $6\%$ for 10 years. To repay the debt at the end of 10 years, a sinking fund would be set up at $5\%$ converted annually. Another lender will provide the money at $6\frac{1}{2}\%$ and permit the loan

to be amortized with 10 annual payments. Which plan would you choose for the company? Show data on which you base your answer.

## 6.13   Aids to Computation

In most businesses, a calculator is available for doing the arithmetic in mathematics of finance problems. It is a good idea to get from the manufacturer's representative the instruction sheets pertaining to the types of problems encountered in the business. These instruction sheets describe the most efficient way to solve problems with the particular make of machine. In some cases, a valuable built-in check is included as a part of the suggested procedure. If a short amortization schedule using equal payments is prepared on a desk calculator, the work can be checked by noting if the last payment is within a few cents of the other payments. If a person is preparing a long schedule by line-by-line simple interest computations, an error early in the work will be serious if it is not discovered quickly. By using the method of Section 6.3, the outstanding principal can be computed for certain lines, such as every 12th one, before doing the detailed computations. Then an error will be discovered as soon as the simple interest computations do not agree with the previously computed principal for that line. Differences of a few cents due to rounding entries to the penny may occur, in which case the value to retain is the one resulting from the line-by-line computations.

Because of the labor required to prepare long amortization schedules, the work is often done today by specialists in the field such as the Financial Publishing Company. With modern electronic computing equipment, schedules can be prepared quickly at reasonable cost. A few lines from such a schedule are shown on page 237. The final entry in each line (except the last) is the outstanding principal after the numbered payment has been made. The last entry in the schedule is the concluding payment. The schedule shows exactly how much of each payment goes to principal and how much to interest. This schedule is for a $10,000 loan at 6% converted monthly to be repaid with payments of $100 a month. The schedule shows that 138 full payments and a 139th payment of $97.63 will be required to amortize the loan.

## 6.14   Some Practical Points

Most students will some day borrow several thousand dollars to buy a home. Here are a few rules that can save hundreds of dollars.

1. *Look for a Low Rate.* Throughout this text, many problems have been worked using different rates to show that a small difference in the rate may mean hundreds of dollars difference in interest. For example, on a $10,000 loan at $6\frac{1}{2}\%$ to be repaid monthly over 20 years, the total interest is $7893.

## Schedule of Direct Reduction Loan

| RATE %<br>6.00 | PAYMENT $<br>100.00 | | LOAN $<br>10,000.00 | TERM: YEARS<br>11 | MONTHS<br>7 | | PERIODS<br>139 |
|---|---|---|---|---|---|---|---|
| Payment<br>Number | Payment on<br>Interest | Principal | Balance<br>of Loan | Payment<br>Number | Payment on<br>Interest | Principal | Balance<br>of Loan |
| 1 | 50.00 | 50.00 | 9,950.00 | 61 | 32.56 | 67.44 | 6,444.09 |
| 2 | 49.75 | 50.25 | 9,899.75 | 62 | 32.22 | 67.78 | 6,376.31 |
| 3 | 49.50 | 50.50 | 9,849.25 | 63 | 31.88 | 68.12 | 6,308.19 |
| 4 | 49.25 | 50.75 | 9,798.50 | 64 | 31.54 | 68.46 | 6,239.73 |
| 5 | 48.99 | 51.01 | 9,747.49 | 65 | 31.20 | 68.80 | 6,170.93 |
| 56 | 34.22 | 65.78 | 6,777.96 | 135 | 2.45 | 97.55 | 392.73 |
| 57 | 33.89 | 66.11 | 6,711.85 | 136 | 1.96 | 98.04 | 294.69 |
| 58 | 33.56 | 66.44 | 6,645.41 | 137 | 1.47 | 98.53 | 196.16 |
| 59 | 33.23 | 66.77 | 6,578.64 | 138 | .98 | 99.02 | 97.14 |
| 60 | 32.89 | 67.11 | 6,511.53 | 139 | .49 | 97.14 | 97.63* |

The final payment is usually somewhat different from the regular payment, and is shown starred on the last line.

Prepared by Financial Publishing Company, Boston.

On the same loan at 6% the total interest would be $7193. When a difference of only $\frac{1}{2}$% can save $700 on a typical loan, it is easy to see why a little time should be spent looking for the best available rate. If it is necessary to make a loan at a relatively high rate, do not overlook the possibility of having it refinanced later at a lower rate.

2. *Pay Off Quickly.* As long as you owe several thousand dollars, you will be paying a lot of interest every year even though you have a relatively low rate. The sooner a loan is paid off, the less the interest. A $10,000 loan paid off in 20 years at 6% will cost $7193 in interest. If the same loan is paid off in 10 years, the interest will drop to $3322, a difference of $3871. Interest charges for common rates and payment periods are shown on page 239.

3. *Keep Payments Within Your Means.* The preceding paragraph pointed out the savings that result from paying a loan off quickly. But be careful not to commit yourself to payments that are beyond your means. The table on the following page shows how the monthly payment varies with the rate and payment period.

4. *Avoid Penalty Clauses.* Fortunately there is a way to keep the monthly payments within your means and yet be able to pay the loan off quickly if your income increases or you receive a sum of money from an inheritance or other source. Get a loan which has a monthly payment you can afford but

*Monthly Payment on a $10,000 Amortization Loan*
*(Payment is rounded up to the cent)*

| PAYMENT PERIOD | | NOMINAL ANNUAL RATE | | | | |
|---|---|---|---|---|---|---|
| *Years* | *Months* | $3\%$ | $3\frac{1}{4}\%$ | $3\frac{1}{2}\%$ | $3\frac{3}{4}\%$ | $4\%$ |
| 10 | 120 | $ 96.57 | $ 97.72 | $ 98.89 | $100.07 | $101.25 |
| 15 | 180 | 69.06 | 70.27 | 71.49 | 72.73 | 73.97 |
| 20 | 240 | 55.46 | 56.72 | 58.00 | 59.29 | 60.60 |
| 25 | 300 | 47.43 | 48.74 | 50.07 | 51.42 | 52.79 |
| 30 | 360 | 42.17 | 43.53 | 44.91 | 46.32 | 47.75 |
| | | $4\frac{1}{4}\%$ | $4\frac{1}{2}\%$ | $4\frac{3}{4}\%$ | $5\%$ | $5\frac{1}{4}\%$ |
| 10 | 120 | $102.44 | $103.64 | $104.85 | $106.07 | $107.30 |
| 15 | 180 | 75.23 | 76.50 | 77.79 | 79.08 | 80.39 |
| 20 | 240 | 61.93 | 63.27 | 64.63 | 66.00 | 67.39 |
| 25 | 300 | 54.18 | 55.59 | 57.02 | 58.46 | 59.93 |
| 30 | 360 | 49.20 | 50.67 | 52.17 | 53.69 | 55.23 |
| | | $5\frac{1}{2}\%$ | $5\frac{3}{4}\%$ | $6\%$ | $6\frac{1}{4}\%$ | $6\frac{1}{2}\%$ |
| 10 | 120 | $108.53 | $109.77 | $111.03 | $112.29 | $113.55 |
| 15 | 180 | 81.71 | 83.05 | 84.39 | 85.75 | 87.12 |
| 20 | 240 | 68.79 | 70.21 | 71.65 | 73.10 | 74.56 |
| 25 | 300 | 61.41 | 62.92 | 64.44 | 65.97 | 67.53 |
| 30 | 360 | 56.78 | 58.36 | 59.96 | 61.58 | 63.21 |
| | | $6\frac{3}{4}\%$ | $7\%$ | $7\frac{1}{4}\%$ | $7\frac{1}{2}\%$ | $7\frac{3}{4}\%$ |
| 10 | 120 | $114.83 | $116.11 | $117.41 | $118.71 | $120.02 |
| 15 | 180 | 88.50 | 89.89 | 91.29 | 92.71 | 94.13 |
| 20 | 240 | 76.04 | 77.53 | 79.04 | 80.56 | 82.10 |
| 25 | 300 | 69.10 | 70.68 | 72.29 | 73.90 | 75.54 |
| 30 | 360 | 64.86 | 66.54 | 68.22 | 69.93 | 71.65 |
| | | $8\%$ | $8\frac{1}{4}\%$ | $8\frac{1}{2}\%$ | $8\frac{3}{4}\%$ | $9\%$ |
| 10 | 120 | $121.33 | $122.66 | $123.99 | $125.33 | $126.68 |
| 15 | 180 | 95.57 | 97.02 | 98.48 | 99.95 | 101.43 |
| 20 | 240 | 83.65 | 85.21 | 86.79 | 88.38 | 89.98 |
| 25 | 300 | 77.19 | 78.85 | 80.53 | 82.22 | 83.92 |
| 30 | 360 | 73.38 | 75.13 | 76.90 | 78.68 | 80.47 |

## Total Interest on a $10,000 Amortization Loan

| PAYMENT PERIOD | | NOMINAL ANNUAL RATE | | | | |
|---|---|---|---|---|---|---|
| Years | Months | 3% | $3\frac{1}{4}\%$ | $3\frac{1}{2}\%$ | $3\frac{3}{4}\%$ | 4% |
| 10 | 120 | $ 1,587 | $ 1,726 | $ 1,866 | $ 2,007 | $ 2,149 |
| 15 | 180 | 2,430 | 2,648 | 2,868 | 3,090 | 3,314 |
| 20 | 240 | 3,310 | 3,613 | 3,919 | 4,229 | 4,543 |
| 25 | 300 | 4,225 | 4,618 | 5,017 | 5,423 | 5,834 |
| 30 | 360 | 5,176 | 5,665 | 6,167 | 6,670 | 7,184 |
| | | $4\frac{1}{4}\%$ | $4\frac{1}{2}\%$ | $4\frac{3}{4}\%$ | 5% | $5\frac{1}{4}\%$ |
| 10 | 120 | $ 2,292 | $ 2,437 | $ 2,582 | $ 2,728 | $ 2,875 |
| 15 | 180 | 3,541 | 3,770 | 4,000 | 4,234 | 4,470 |
| 20 | 240 | 4,861 | 5,183 | 5,508 | 5,838 | 6,171 |
| 25 | 300 | 6,251 | 6,673 | 7,101 | 7,537 | 7,976 |
| 30 | 360 | 7,708 | 8,240 | 8,777 | 9,322 | 9,874 |
| | | $5\frac{1}{2}\%$ | $5\frac{3}{4}\%$ | 6% | $6\frac{1}{4}\%$ | $6\frac{1}{2}\%$ |
| 10 | 120 | $ 3,023 | $ 3,172 | $ 3,322 | $ 3,473 | $ 3,626 |
| 15 | 180 | 4,707 | 4,946 | 5,189 | 5,433 | 5,679 |
| 20 | 240 | 6,509 | 6,850 | 7,193 | 7,541 | 7,893 |
| 25 | 300 | 8,422 | 8,870 | 9,325 | 9,789 | 10,252 |
| 30 | 360 | 10,440 | 11,007 | 11,581 | 12,160 | 12,752 |
| | | $6\frac{3}{4}\%$ | 7% | $7\frac{1}{4}\%$ | $7\frac{1}{2}\%$ | $7\frac{3}{4}\%$ |
| 10 | 120 | $ 3,779 | $ 3,933 | $ 4,088 | $ 4,244 | $ 4,401 |
| 15 | 180 | 5,929 | 6,178 | 6,431 | 6,685 | 6,943 |
| 20 | 240 | 8,248 | 8,607 | 8,969 | 9,334 | 9,701 |
| 25 | 300 | 10,723 | 11,202 | 11,679 | 12,169 | 12,655 |
| 30 | 360 | 13,349 | 13,943 | 14,556 | 15,163 | 15,782 |
| | | 8% | $8\frac{1}{4}\%$ | $8\frac{1}{2}\%$ | $8\frac{3}{4}\%$ | 9% |
| 10 | 120 | $ 4,559 | $ 4,718 | $ 4,878 | $ 5,039 | $ 5,201 |
| 15 | 180 | 7,201 | 7,461 | 7,724 | 7,989 | 8,256 |
| 20 | 240 | 10,072 | 10,448 | 10,825 | 11,205 | 11,590 |
| 25 | 300 | 13,149 | 13,650 | 14,151 | 14,660 | 15,176 |
| 30 | 360 | 16,412 | 17,042 | 17,670 | 18,308 | 18,955 |

which can be paid off more rapidly *without a penalty* if you are able at any time to make larger payments. The borrower who has prepaid a part of his loan may be helped later if sickness or temporary loss of income prevents him from making some of the regular monthly payments.

5. *Avoid Escalation Clauses.* Some mortgages have a sleeper called a rate-escalation clause. This gives the lender contractual liberty to increase the rate on an existing mortgage. Adding a half per cent or one per cent to the rate can result in extending a mortgage for several years at an additional cost of thousands of dollars. If a contract has this clause, have it removed. A verbal statement that it is only a "formal thing that is never used" is no comfort if the clause is invoked.

6. *Watch Out for Points.* If you are thinking of borrowing from a lender who charges points, be sure to compare the true rate of interest on his loan with other sources of credit. It may be that a "6%" loan with points is more expensive than a true $6\frac{1}{4}$ or $6\frac{1}{2}\%$ from another lender.

7. *Make a Large Down Payment.* The larger the down payment, the less you will have to borrow and the less you will pay in interest. However, don't make the mistake of putting all of your cash into the down payment. Moving expenses, needed equipment for a new home, and other expenses involved in getting settled may amount to many hundred dollars. If you have to get a small loan from a bank or loan company or buy on the installment plan, you may have to pay 12% or more interest a year as was pointed out in Chapter 4. Too many people try to buy a home with a minimum down payment. It is far better for them to save money so that they will be able to make a large down payment. The rate of interest charged on a home mortgage is sometimes related to the percentage the down payment bears to the cost of the house. A larger down payment may reduce the rate on the unpaid balance.

8. *Contact Several Lenders.* Mortgage loans are made by many types of lenders—commercial and savings banks, savings and loan associations (sometimes called building and loan associations), insurance companies, private individuals, and others. Their lending practices, rates, appraisals, closing costs, and down payment requirements vary, so it will pay you to talk with several lenders when you are in the market for a loan. Before you apply for a loan, as in all installment buying, read the application carefully. You may be required to pay a fee even if you decide to get the loan elsewhere. If you are interested in an FHA or VA loan, remember that the money is still supplied by a private lender. No matter where you get a loan, be sure that the principal is reduced as payments are made.

9. *Know What You Owe.* Always know how much you still owe and how much of your payments have gone to principal and how much to interest. Home buyers should be sure to claim any tax advantages to which they are

entitled. One way to determine how much interest has been paid is to get periodic statements from the lender. Another way is to get an amortization schedule. A portion of a schedule is presented below to show how much valuable information is contained in a schedule of this type.

This schedule is for a conventional mortgage loan to be repaid over 25 years. The rate is 6% converted monthly. The monthly payment rounded up to the cent is $64.44. Borrowers who get a Federal Housing Administration insured mortgage pay, in addition to the interest, a mortgage insurance premium of $\frac{1}{2}$% a year on the average scheduled balance of loan principal outstanding during the year. FHA insurance protects the lender against loss on the loan. It does not protect the borrower against loss; but because of the insurance, lenders are able and willing to make loans on terms that bring home ownership within the reach of many families who otherwise could not afford it. The schedule shows that during the first year $595.17 goes to interest leaving only $178.11 to reduce the debt.

10. *Allow for Closing Costs.* Attorney fees, title insurance, property survey, recording fees, lender's service charges, and other items may mean last-minute cash outlays when a house is purchased. Closing costs may run from nothing to several hundred dollars. Get an estimate from the lender and add the money required for closing to your other cash needs.

*Amortization Schedule*

| | LOAN $10,000 | TERM 25 YEARS | RATE 6% | PAYMENT $64.44 | |
|---|---|---|---|---|---|
| *Payment Number* | *Total Payment* | *Payment to Interest* | *Payment to Principal* | *Balance of Loan* |
| | | | | | $10,000.00 |
| 1 | $64.44 | $50.00 | $14.44 | 9,985.56 |
| 2 | 64.44 | 49.93 | 14.51 | 9,971.05 |
| 3 | 64.44 | 49.86 | 14.58 | 9,956.47 |
| 4 | 64.44 | 49.78 | 14.66 | 9,941.81 |
| 5 | 64.44 | 49.71 | 14.73 | 9,927.08 |
| 6 | 64.44 | 49.64 | 14.80 | 9,912.28 |
| 7 | 64.44 | 49.56 | 14.88 | 9,897.40 |
| 8 | 64.44 | 49.49 | 14.95 | 9,882.45 |
| 9 | 64.44 | 49.41 | 15.03 | 9,867.42 |
| 10 | 64.44 | 49.34 | 15.10 | 9,852.32 |
| 11 | 64.44 | 49.26 | 15.18 | 9,837.14 |
| 12 | 64.44 | 49.19 | 15.25 | 9,821.89 |
| | $773.28 | $595.17 | $178.11 | |

Below is the schedule for the 13th year. After the 150th payment, the halfway point in time, the borrower still owes over two-thirds of the loan. The 150 payments, which total $9666.00, have reduced the mortgage by only $3214.42. Payments to interest are still greater than the amount going to principal.

| | | | |
|---|---|---|---|
| 145 | $64.44 | $34.83 | $29.61 | $6,935.88 |
| 146 | 64.44 | 34.68 | 29.76 | 6,906.12 |
| 147 | 64.44 | 34.53 | 29.91 | 6,876.21 |
| 148 | 64.44 | 34.38 | 30.06 | 6,846.15 |
| 149 | 64.44 | 34.23 | 30.21 | 6,815.94 |
| 150 | 64.44 | 34.08 | 30.36 | 6,785.58 |
| 151 | 64.44 | 33.93 | 30.51 | 6,755.07 |
| 152 | 64.44 | 33.78 | 30.66 | 6,724.41 |
| 153 | 64.44 | 33.62 | 30.82 | 6,693.59 |
| 154 | 64.44 | 33.47 | 30.97 | 6,662.62 |
| 155 | 64.44 | 33.31 | 31.13 | 6,631.49 |
| 156 | 64.44 | 33.16 | 31.28 | 6,600.21 |
| | $773.28 | $408.00 | $365.28 | |

The 25th year has finally arrived. The borrower has 288 payments behind him. He is almost a home owner. Because the payment was rounded up, the last payment is less than the regular payment. The last line gives the 25-year totals.

| Payment Number | Total Payment | Payment to Interest | Payment to Principal | Balance of Loan |
|---|---|---|---|---|
| 289 | $64.44 | $3.71 | $60.73 | $681.73 |
| 290 | 64.44 | 3.41 | 61.03 | 620.70 |
| 291 | 64.44 | 3.10 | 61.34 | 559.36 |
| 292 | 64.44 | 2.80 | 61.64 | 497.72 |
| 293 | 64.44 | 2.49 | 61.95 | 435.77 |
| 294 | 64.44 | 2.18 | 62.26 | 373.51 |
| 295 | 64.44 | 1.87 | 62.57 | 310.94 |
| 296 | 64.44 | 1.55 | 62.89 | 248.05 |
| 297 | 64.44 | 1.24 | 63.20 | 184.85 |
| 298 | 64.44 | .92 | 63.52 | 121.33 |
| 299 | 64.44 | .61 | 63.83 | 57.50 |
| 300 | 57.79 | .29 | 57.50 | 0.00 |
| | $766.63 | $24.17 | $742.46 | |
| | $19,325.35 | $9,325.35 | $10,000.00 | |

## EXERCISE 6e

1. Look up the complete Compound Interest and Annuity Tables in your school or public library and complete the following table for a loan specified by your instructor.

*Monthly Payments for a Loan of $_____*

| PAYMENT PERIOD | | RATE | | | | |
|---|---|---|---|---|---|---|
| *Years* | *Months* | 6% | 6½% | 7% | 7½% | 8% |
| 10 | | | | | | |
| 12 | | | | | | |
| 15 | | | | | | |
| 18 | | | | | | |
| 20 | | | | | | |
| 25 | | | | | | |
| 30 | | | | | | |

2. Determine the total interest for the loan in Problem 1. Values may be rounded to the nearest dollar.

*Total Interest Paid on a Loan of $_____*

| PAYMENT PERIOD | | RATE | | | | |
|---|---|---|---|---|---|---|
| *Years* | *Months* | 6% | 6½% | 7% | 7½% | 8% |
| 10 | | | | | | |
| 12 | | | | | | |
| 15 | | | | | | |
| 18 | | | | | | |
| 20 | | | | | | |
| 25 | | | | | | |
| 30 | | | | | | |

# 7

# Bonds

## 7.1 Bonds and Stocks

When a corporation or government needs money for an extended period of time, the amount required may be too large to obtain the money from a single bank or other lender. This situation can be met by issuing **bonds** which are purchased by individuals, insurance companies and other investors. Thus the buyer of a bond lends money to the organization that issued the bond. A stockholder, on the other hand, is a part owner of the corporation. Interest must be paid on bonds before dividends are declared on stocks. The *face value* or *par value* of a bond, the *interest rate*, and the *term* or *maturity* are quoted in the bond itself. Therefore, we are able to use the compound interest and annuity formulas and tables to get either the price to yield a desired return, or the return corresponding to a quoted price.

## 7.2   Kinds of Bonds

There are several ways in which bonds may be classified. A bond may be **registered** or **unregistered**. Registered bonds have the name of the owner on them and are valueless to anyone except the person whose name is registered with the issuing company or government. Unregistered or bearer bonds do not have the owner's name printed on them. Bearer bonds and bonds registered only as to principal are printed with attached coupons, which are dated serially with the dates on which interest is due. To get his interest the holder of a coupon bond clips each coupon and presents it to his bank or broker for collection.

A coupon bond consists of two parts:

1. The bond itself which is redeemable on the stated date (see illustration on page 246).

2. Coupons which can be cashed periodically (see page 247).

Bonds may also be subdivided according to the security back of them. A **mortgage bond** is secured by a mortgage issued against property of the corporation. A **debenture bond** is secured only by the general credit of the corporation, that is the reputation of the firm for meeting its obligations. Other types exist but we shall not go into them here because the computations involved in getting the value of a bond are not affected by the security behind it.

Interest on a bond may accumulate and be paid in one lump sum when the bond matures. Government savings bonds are the most common example of this type of bond. Since the value of government savings bonds at any time after issue is fixed and is printed on the bond, we shall not discuss them further. Our discussion will be limited to those bonds which have interest payments made periodically, usually semiannually.

Interest earned on corporation bonds and on bonds issued by the federal government is subject to federal income taxes. State and local government bonds, which are known as **municipal bonds**, are exempt from federal income taxes. Municipals are issued not only by states, towns, and cities, but also by housing authorities, port authorities, and other local government agencies responsible for providing and maintaining community facilities. Most states give preferential tax treatment to their own municipal bonds. However, interest on bonds issued by other states may be subject to tax. Municipals are a favored investment of people in the higher tax brackets. A person in the 50% tax bracket would get the same net return from a municipal paying 6% as he would get from a stock that pays a dividend equal to 12% of the purchase price, and probably with less risk.

The **face value** or **denomination** of a bond is usually some simple figure such as $100, $500, or $1000. Most bonds are redeemed at **face value** or **par** at maturity.

NUMBER
1263

DOLLARS
1000

UNITED STATES OF AMERICA

STATE OF OHIO

COUNTY OF TRUMBULL

# CITY OF WARREN

**STORM SEWER BOND**

*Know All Men by These Presents,* that the City of Warren in the County of Trumbull, State of Ohio, acknowledges itself to owe and for value received hereby promises to pay to bearer the sum of

## ONE THOUSAND DOLLARS

on the first day of June, 1967, with interest thereon from the date hereof at the rate of two (2%) per cent per annum, payable June 1, 1950, and semi-annually thereafter on the first day of June and the first day of December in each year, as evidenced by the coupons hereto attached, until the principal sum is paid. The principal sum and interest thereon are payable in lawful money of the United States of America at the office of the City Treasurer in Warren, Ohio, upon presentation and surrender of this bond and the coupons hereto attached as they respectively mature.

This bond is one of an issue of 1,950 serial bonds of like tenor and effect, except as to maturity, numbered from 1 to 1,950, both inclusive, all of said bonds being of the denomination of $1,000 each, aggregating in amount $1,950,000, and issued for the purpose of making the following storm sewer improvements: Hoyt Run No. 2 Storm Relief Sewer; Red Run Combined Sewer (West Branch); Hoyt Run No. 1, Storm Relief Sewer; Grandview and Catalpa Street, S. E. Storm Relief Sewer; Harrison Street, N. E., Storm Relief Sewer; Dickey Run Storm Sewer; Red Run Combined Sewer (East Branch); Hoyt Street Run Storm Sewer, under authority of the general laws of the State of Ohio, particularly the Uniform Bond Act of the General Code, and by virtue of a 65% majority vote of the electors of said city voting upon said proposition at the regular election held on November 4, 1947, and pursuant to Ordinance No. 3851, duly adopted by the Council of the City of Warren, on August 1, 1949.

AND IT IS HEREBY CERTIFIED AND RECITED that all acts, conditions and things necessary to be done precedent to and in the issuing of these bonds in order to make them legal, valid and binding obligations of said City of Warren, have been done, have happened and have been performed in regular and due form as required by law; that the full faith, credit and revenue of said city is hereby irrevocably pledged for the prompt payment of the principal and interest thereof at maturity; that no limitation of indebtedness or taxation, either statutory or constitutional, has been exceeded in issuing these bonds; and that due provision has been made for levying and collecting an unlimited, annual ad valorem tax upon all of the taxable property in said city sufficient in amount to pay the interest on these bonds as it falls due and to provide a fund for the redemption of said bonds at maturity.

*In Witness Whereof,* the City of Warren, County and State aforesaid, has caused this bond to be officially signed by its Mayor and City Auditor, the corporate seal to be hereto affixed and the coupons attached hereto to bear the facsimile signature of the City Auditor as of the first day of October, 1949.

MAYOR

CITY AUDITOR

## 7.3 Call Provision

The issuer of a bond may have the option of calling the bond before maturity. This **call provision** gives the issuer of the bond the advantage of being able to time repayments to suit his financial needs and objectives as they develop. If interest rates decline, a call provision enables a company to call in old bonds and replace them with bonds paying a lower rate. The redemption price of a bond called before maturity is a previously specified percentage of the par value. A $1000 bond redeemable at 102 during a certain year would have a redemption price of $1020 during that year. From the bond owner's standpoint, a call provision has the disadvantage that the call premium may not be enough to compensate him for having to reinvest funds at a lower rate of interest. To protect buyers of new bonds from early call, most bonds have a stated number of years, typically 5 or 10, of protection against early redemption of the bond. The prospectus which describes a bond issue lists the dates when the bond may be called and corresponding redemption prices.

## 7.4 Bond Transactions

Bonds are traded on the New York Stock Exchange, the American Stock Exchange, and other exchanges throughout the country. Many large blocks of bonds are traded in the "Over-the-counter" market. This is not a place but a method of doing business by private negotiation among dealers who use the telephone to buy and sell securities.

Many newspapers publish tables of bond information. Bonds are listed alphabetically by type: corporation, foreign, municipal, and government.

Symbols and abbreviations, which vary with different papers, are explained in footnotes. The table below from the August 16, 1972 issue of *The Wall Street Journal* is a good illustration of information given in bond tables.

## Corporation Bonds

Sales for the day on a par value basis.————  ( **Volume, $18,650,000** )

### A-B-C

Highest and lowest prices during the indicated period. Bond quotations are on a basis of 100. Most corporation bonds have a face value of $1000. For a $1000 bond a quotation of 107½ means $1075.00.

Abbreviated name of the company. In this case American Airlines.

Annual interest rate and year bond matures. This $1000 bond pays $48.00 a year interest and matures in 1987.

"cv" means the bond is convertible into the company's common stock. Details of the conversion can be obtained from a broker.

For this bond the high for the day was 48⅝, the low was 47⅞, and the closing price was 48⅝. The bond closed 1⅝ points or $16.25 above the previous closing price.

| —1972— High | Low | Bonds | Sales in $1,000 | High | Low | Close | Net Chg. |
|---|---|---|---|---|---|---|---|
| 107½ | 104¾ | Abex Corp 8¾s77 | 10 | 106 | 106 | 106 | −1 |
| 113 | 108 | AddresMult 9⅜s95 | 10 | 112 | 112 | 112 | ..... |
| 88½ | 69½ | AirReduc cv3⅞s87 | 6 | 76¾ | 76½ | 76¾ | ..... |
| 111½ | 106 | AlaPow 9s2000 | 145 | 107⅝ | 107⅜ | 107⅝ | ..... |
| 102¾ | 102¼ | AlaPow 7⅞s2002 | 5 | 104 | 104 | 104 | +1¼ |
| 204½ | 98 | Alaska Int cv6s96 | 321 | 171½ | 162 | 170 | +6½ |
| 90⅛ | 72 | Alexandr cv5½s96 | 6 | 74 | 74 | 74 | +1½ |
| 77 | 69¼ | AllghyLud cv4s81 | 5 | 77⅛ | 77⅛ | 77⅛ | + ⅛ |
| 82 | 78½ | Allied Chm 5.20s91 | 10 | 80¾ | 80 | 80 | ..... |
| 83 | 78½ | Allied Prod 7s84 | 7 | 82½ | 81½ | 82½ | ..... |
| 132 | 108 | Allied Str cv4½s81 | 1 | 113 | 113 | 113 | +2 |
| 93 | 80½ | Allied Str cv4½s92 | 20 | 82 | 82 | 82 | + ½ |
| 73¾ | 60 | AlliedSup cv5¾s87 | 6 | 62⅛ | 62⅛ | 62⅛ | + ⅛ |
| 102¾ | 97¾ | Alcoa 7.45s96 | 7 | 101¼ | 101¼ | 101¼ | ..... |
| 90½ | 81¾ | Alcoa cv5¼s91 | 22 | 87¼ | 85½ | 85½ | −2 |
| 80½ | 76 | Alcoa 3⅞s83 | 10 | 77¼ | 77¼ | 77¼ | + ¾ |
| 112½ | 110½ | AlumCoCan 9½s95 | 4 | 111⅞ | 111⅞ | 111⅞ | ..... |
| 92½ | 76⅞ | Amer Esna cv5s92 | 2 | 84 | 84 | 84 | +1¼ |
| 93 | ·88¼ | AmradHess 6¾s96 | 27 | 90⅝ | 90⅛ | 90⅝ | + ⅝ |
| 176½ | 144 | AmAirFilt cv6s90 | 3 | 183 | 183 | 183 | +6½ |
| 119 | 114 | AmAirlln 11s88 | 1 | 117⅛ | 117⅛ | 117⅛ | − ⅞ |
| 117¼ | 112⅜ | AmAirlin 10⅞s88 | 1 | 115½ | 115½ | 115½ | +1¼ |
| 119½ | 85¼ | AmAirlln cv4¼s92 | 127 | 90 | 89¼ | 89¼ | −1¾ |
| 108¼ | 102¾ | Am Brands 8⅞s75 | 1 | 106⅞ | 106⅞ | 106⅞ | − ⅜ |
| 74¼ | 72½ | Am Brands 4⅝s90 | 15 | 74¼ | 73⅝ | 74¼ | + ⅝ |
| 100 | 89½ | ACenMtg cv6¾s91 | 18 | 93 | 92¼ | 92¼ | + ½ |
| 68 | 64½ | Am Dist 4⅜s86 | 4 | 68 | 67½ | 67½ | − ½ |
| 53¼ | 17 | A Exprt cv5¼s93f | 88 | 25 | 24 | 24½ | − ⅜ |
| 57½ | 48 | AmForPow 5s2030 | 19 | 50 | 49¾ | 49¾ | − ¼ |
| 59½ | 48½ | AmForPw (4.80s87) | 7 | 51⅞ | 51¾ | 51¾ | + ¾ |
| 86 | 75 | Am Hoist cv5½s93 | 10 | 85 | 85 | 85 | ..... |
| 107¼ | 104½ | AmInvest 9½s76 | 2 | 105⅞ | 105⅞ | 105 ⅞+ | ⅞ |
| 102½ | 94 | AmMedicp cv5s97 | 5 | 95¾ | 95¾ | 95¾ | + ¼ |
| 73 | 69½ | Am Smelt 4⅝s88 | 15 | 70⅛ | 70⅛ | 70⅛ | + ⅜ |
| 75 | 71⅝ | AmSugar 5.30s93 | 3 | 72½ | 72¼ | 72¼ | − ¼ |
| | | AmSug 5.30s93reg | 2 | 72¼ | 72¼ | 72¼ | ..... |
| 112 | 109¼ | AmT&T 8¾42000xw | 273 | 111 | 107⅞ | 111 | ..... |
| 111¼ | 109 | Am T&T 8.70s2002 | 17 | 110¾ | 110½ | 110¾ | ..... |
| 107⅞ | 104⅞ | AmT&T 7.75s77 | 16 | 106¼ | 105⅞ | 105⅞ | − ¼ |
| 99⅞ | 94⅛ | AmT&T 7s2001 | 140 | 97½ | 97 | 97¼ | ..... |
| 78⅞ | 76 | AmT&T 4⅜s85 | 32 | 78 | 77½ | 77½ | ..... |
| 69⅜ | 66 | AmT&T 3⅞s90 | 17 | 67½ | 67½ | 67½ | −1 |
| 98 | 95¼ | AmT&T 3⅜s73 | 14 | 97½ | 97½ | 97½ | ..... |
| 91 | 88¾ | AmT&T 2¾s75 | 84 | 90⅞ | 90½ | 90¾ | − ¼ |
| 78⅛ | 73 | AmT&T 2¾s80 | 15 | 75⅛ | 75⅛ | 75⅜ | − ⅛ |
| 72½ | 69 | AmT&T 2¾s82 | 15 | 70⅞ | 70¾ | 70¾ | − ⅛ |
| 62¾ | 60 | Am T&T 2⅝s 86 | 9 | 62 | 61⅝ | 61⅝ | ..... |
| 116 | 95½ | AMF Inc cv4½s81 | 1 | 104⅞ | 104⅞ | 104⅞ | ..... |
| 111 | 98½ | Amfac cv5¼s94 | 5 | 98½ | 98½ | 98½ | −1¼ |
| 70½ | 45 | Ampex cv5½s94 | 49 | 48⅝ | 47⅞ | 48⅝ | +1⅝ |
| 88 | 78 | Apco Oil cv5s88 | 111 | 86⅛ | 83⅝ | 86⅛ | +3⅛ |
| 121⅞ | 90⅞ | APL Cp cv5¼s88 | 3 | 96 | 96 | 96 | − ⅞ |
| 107½ | 105 | Appal Pw 9s75 | 10 | 106 | 106 | 106 | ..... |
| 108 | 105 | Appal Pw 8⅝s76 | 25 | 106¾ | 106¾ | 106¾ | ..... |
| 138¼ | 120½ | ARA Svc cv4⅝s96 | 49 | 132½ | 132½ | 132½ | +1 |
| 100⅝ | 99 | AirzPSv 7.45s2002 | 2 | 99⅝ | 99⅝ | 99⅝ | − ¼ |
| 64¼ | 53 | ArlansDStr cv6s94 | 2 | 55 | 55 | 55 | − ½ |
| 129 | 90 | ArenRltyD cv5s86 | 3 | 99½ | 99½ | 99½ | + ½ |
| 109 | 105¼ | Armco Stl 8.70s95 | 10 | 107¾ | 107¾ | 107¾ | − ¼ |
| 76 | 73 | Armour&Co 5s84 | 4 | 74½ | 74½ | 74½ | ..... |

## 7.5   Valuation of a Bond

A fundamental bond problem is the determination of the price an investor can pay for a bond to give him the yield he wants on his purchase price. This problem involves two rates of interest. One is the rate which the issuing organization pays on the face value of the bond. The other is the yield to maturity which the purchaser gets on his investment. For example, several years ago when interest rates were lower than today, a corporation issued a $1000, 5% bond with semi-annual interest payments. The owner of this bond will get $25 every six months regardless of what he paid for the bond. If an investor expects more than 5% on money invested in bonds, he must purchase this 5% bond for less than $1000. We shall determine what the price would be to produce a specific yield to maturity such as 8%.

Over the years a special terminology has grown up in connection with the buying and selling of bonds. Since bond valuation is based on formulas already obtained for single sums and annuities, the main problem for students is to gain an understanding of bond terminology including the symbols defined below.

$F$ = the face or par value of the bond.

$C$ = the redemption price of the bond. This will be the same as the par value of the bond unless the problem states otherwise.

$r$ = interest rate paid on the bond per period.

$Fr$ = amount of each coupon or interest payment. From now on we use the word coupon for any periodic interest payment. Computations are the same whether the bond-holder clips a coupon or the company mails him a check for the interest.

$n$ = number of interest conversion periods from the given date to the redemption date or the maturity date of the bond.

$i$ = yield or investor's rate per period. This is the rate of interest actually earned by the investor on his investment.

$V$ = value of the bond.

$P$ = premium.

$D$ = discount.

We now get the value of a bond on a coupon date. This is a day on which the organization that issued the bond pays interest. The seller will keep the coupon that is due on that date. The buyer pays for the present value of the redemption price of the bond and the present value of all future interest payments. These present values are to be *computed at the yield rate* because this is the return the investor wants on his investment. The bond rate is used only to calculate the periodic interest payment or coupon.

Adding the present value of the redemption price of the bond and the present value of the annuity formed by the coupons gives us the basic formula for the value of a bond.

$$V = C(1 + i)^{-n} + Fra_{\overline{n}|i} \qquad (22)$$

The buyer of a bond gets two things:
   1. The redemption price of the bond
   2. Each coupon as it comes due

$C(1+i)^{-n}$ ⎤
                ⎬  The value of a bond is the sum of the present
$Fra_{\overline{n}|i}$ ⎦  values of the redemption price and the
                   coupons, both discounted at the yield rate.

EXAMPLE 1: Find the value of a $1000 bond with interest at 4% payable semi-annually if the bond is bought 3 years before maturity to yield 7% on the investment. This is sometimes referred to as a 7% basis.

SOLUTION: The semiannual interest payments are 2% of $1000 or $20. The buyer of this bond gets the present value at 7% of $1000 due in 3 years, and the present value at 7% of the 6 interest payments of $20 each. We assume that the yield or investment rate is compounded at the same time as the interest is paid on the bond. This will make the yield rate per period $3\frac{1}{2}\%$ and the problem looks like this:

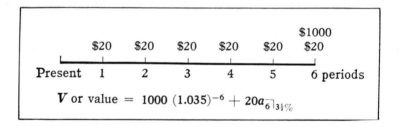

$V$ or value $= 1000\,(1.035)^{-6} + 20a_{\overline{6}|3\frac{1}{2}\%}$

$$V = (1000 \times .813\ 501) + (20 \times 5.3286)$$
$$= 813.50 + 106.57 = \$920.07$$

If a buyer pays $920.07 for this bond, he is getting it at a *discount* or less than the par value because he wants a yield rate that is higher than the interest rate on the face of the bond (the "coupon rate"). The buyer will get 7% converted semiannually on his investment of $920.07. The company that issued the bond will continue to pay 2% every 6 months on the $1000 face value of the bond regardless of who owns the bond and what he paid for it.

In the case of callable bonds, there is an element of doubt in determining the value because there is no way to know in advance if and when the bond will be called. An investor who wants a certain yield can get the value of the bond assuming both redemption on the earliest call date and redemption at maturity. The lower of these values would be a safe price to insure the desired yield.

EXAMPLE 2: An Atlantic Richfield Company $1000, $8\frac{5}{8}\%$ debenture is due on April 1, 2000. Interest is payable on April 1 and October 1. Find the value of this bond on October 1, 1974, to a buyer who wants a return on his investment of $8\%$ converted semiannually, assuming: (a) The bond is called at 105.05 on April 1, 1980; (b) The bond is redeemed at par on April 1, 2000.

SOLUTION: (a) We get the number of periods from the purchase date to the call date.

| YEAR | MONTH |
|------|-------|
| 79 | 16 |
| 19~~80~~ | ~~4~~ |
| 1974 | 10 |
| 5 | 6 |

$$n = (5 \times 2) + 6/6 = 11$$

The semiannual interest payments are $43.12 and the call price is $1050.50. The dated money flows are shown below.

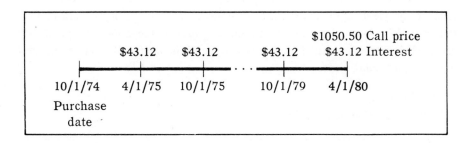

Substituting in (22),

$$V = 1050.50(1.04)^{-11} + 43.12a_{\overline{11}|4\%}$$
$$= (1050.50 \times .649\,581) + (43.12 \times 8.760\,5)$$
$$= 682.38 + 377.75 = \$1060.13$$

(b) Get the number of periods from the purchase date to the due date.

| YEAR | MONTH |
|------|-------|
| 1999 | 16 |
| ~~2000~~ | ~~4~~ |
| 1974 | 10 |
| 25 | 6 |

$$n = (25 \times 2) + 6/6 = 51$$

The time diagram now goes to the due date of the bond.

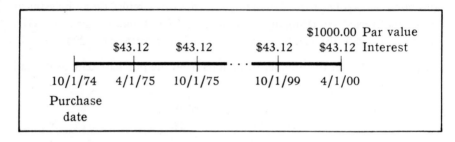

Substituting in (22),

$$V = 1000.00(1.04)^{-51} + 43.12a_{\overline{51}|4\%}$$
$$= (1000.00 \times .135\ 301) + (43.12 \times 21.617\ 5)$$
$$= 135.30 + 932.15 = \$1067.45$$

If the purchaser of this bond can get it for $1060, his yield will be 8% if the bond is called, and slightly more than this if the bond is not redeemed until the due date.

In this example the bond is priced at a *premium* or more than the par value because the yield rate is lower than the coupon rate. In the investment market the price of a bond depends on the interest rate of the bond, the yield rate acceptable to investors, the time to maturity, and the degree of safety associated with the particular bond.

### EXERCISE 7a

Compute the value of the following bonds.

| No. | FACE VALUE | REDEMPTION CONDITIONS | ANNUAL BOND RATE INTEREST PAID SEMIANNUALLY | YIELD RATE COMPOUNDED SEMIANNUALLY | ANSWER |
|-----|-----------|----------------------|-----------------------------|-----------------------------|--------|
| 1. | $1000 | 8 yrs. at par | 4% | 6% | $874.39 |
| 2. | 1000 | 6 yrs. at par | 5% | $4\frac{1}{2}\%$ | |
| 3. | 500 | 10 yrs. at 102 | $3\frac{1}{2}\%$ | 4% | 486.28 |
| 4. | 5000 | 5 yrs. at 101 | 5% | 7% | |

5. A Bethlehem Steel Corporation $1000, 9% debenture is due on May 15, 2000. Interest is payable on May 15 and November 15. The bond may be called at 104 on May 15, 1980. Find the value of this bond on May 15, 1974, if the yield rate is to be 8% converted semiannually assuming: (a) The bond is called at 104 on May 15, 1980; (b) The bond is redeemed at par on May 15, 2000.                    [(a) $1071.91; (b) $1108.74]

6. A Kroger Company $1000, 9% debenture is due on May 1, 1995. Interest is payable on May 1 and November 1. The bond may be called at 104 on May 1, 1980. Find the value of this bond on May 1, 1973, if the yield rate is to be 8% converted semiannually assuming: (a) The bond is called at 104 on May 1, 1980; (b) The bond is redeemed at par on May 1, 1995.

7. A Dana Corporation $1000, 6% debenture is due on December 1, 1991. Interest is payable on June 1 and December 1. The bond may be called at 103 on December 1, 1976. Find the value of this bond on June 1, 1973, if the yield is to be 8% converted semiannually assuming: (a) The bond is redeemed at 103 on December 1, 1976; (b) The bond is redeemed at par on December 1, 1991.                    [(a) $962.78; (b) $808.58]

8. A Pacific South West Airlines $1000, 6% debenture is due on October 1, 1987. Interest is payable on April 1 and October 1. The bond may be called at 102 on October 1, 1977. Find the value of this bond on April 1, 1974, if the yield is to be 8% converted semiannually assuming: (a) The bond is called at 102 on October 1, 1977; (b) The bond is redeemed at par on October 1, 1987.

9. A National Steel Corporation $1000, 8% bond is due on December 1, 1995. Interest is payable on June 1 and December 1. The bond may be called at 104 on December 1, 1980. Find the value of this bond on June 1, 1974, if the yield is to be 7% converted semiannually assuming: (a) The bond is called at 104 on December 1, 1980; (b) The bond is redeemed at par on December 1, 1995.                    [(a) $1077.09; (b) $1110.32]

10. A Standard Oil Company of Indiana, 6% debenture is due on January 15, 1998. Interest is payable on January 15 and July 15. The bond may be called at 103 on January 15, 1978. Find the value of this bond on July 15, 1973, if the yield is to be 7% converted semiannually assuming: (a) The bond is called at 103 on January 15, 1978; (b) The bond is redeemed at par on January 15, 1998.

## 7.6 Premium and Discount

We now develop simplified formulas which can be used for bond valuation when it is assumed that the bond will be paid at par at maturity. If the interest rate on the bond is greater than the yield rate on the purchase price, the buyer will pay more than the par value of the bond. This difference is called the premium and can be obtained as follows.

Since the value at maturity equals the par value, we can substitute $F$ for $C$ in (22).

$$V = F(1 + i)^{-n} + Fra_{\overline{n}|i}$$

Because the premium is the difference between the value at the yield rate and the face value, we can say

$$P = V - F$$

Substituting the value for $V$ obtained above, we have

$$
\begin{aligned}
P &= F(1 + i)^{-n} + Fra_{\overline{n}|i} - F \\
&= Fra_{\overline{n}|i} - F + F(1 + i)^{-n} \\
&= Fra_{\overline{n}|i} - F[1 - (1 + i)^{-n}]
\end{aligned}
$$

Multiplying the last term by $i/i$ will not change the value of the fraction and will enable us to replace $[1 - (1 + i)^{-n}]/i$ with $a_{\overline{n}|i}$.

$$P = Fra_{\overline{n}|i} - Fi\,\frac{[1 - (1 + i)^{-n}]}{i}$$

$$
\begin{aligned}
&= Fra_{\overline{n}|i} - Fia_{\overline{n}|i} \\
P &= (Fr - Fi)a_{\overline{n}|i}
\end{aligned}
\tag{23}
$$

We now have to look up only one factor to get the value of a bond. Also, as the examples will show, the computations will be simplified. Note that in (23), $Fr$ is the coupon and $Fi$ is the face value of the bond times the *yield* rate.

EXAMPLE 1: Find the value on September 1, 1972, of a $1000, 5% bond maturing at par on March 1, 1979, if it is to yield 4% compounded semiannually.

SOLUTION: In this problem $Fr = 1000 \times .025 = 25$, $Fi = 1000 \times .02 = 20$, and $n = 13$. Substituting in (23),

$$P = (25 - 20)a_{\overline{13}|2\%} = 5 \times 11.348 = \$56.74$$

From which the purchase price $= \$1056.74$.

When the buyer of a bond wants a higher rate of return on his investment than the interest rate of the bond, he must get the bond at less than the par value or at a **discount**. This discount equals the par value minus the value at the yield rate.

$$D = F - V$$

To get an equation for the discount we substitute the value of $V$ from (22) and proceed as we did in getting the formula for the premium.

$$
\begin{aligned}
D &= F - F(1 + i)^{-n} - Fra_{\overline{n}|i} \\
&= F[1 - (1 + i)^{-n}] - Fra_{\overline{n}|i} \\
&= Fi\,\frac{[1 - (1 + i)^{-n}]}{i} - Fra_{\overline{n}|i} \\
&= Fia_{\overline{n}|i} - Fra_{\overline{n}|i} \\
D &= (Fi - Fr)a_{\overline{n}|i} \tag{24}
\end{aligned}
$$

EXAMPLE 2: Find the value on October 1, 1972, of a \$1000, 3% bond maturing at par on October 1, 1987, if it is to yield $3\frac{1}{2}$% compounded semiannually.

SOLUTION: $Fi = 1000 \times .0175 = 17.50$, $Fr = 1000 \times .015 = 15$, and $n = 30$. Substituting in (24),

$$D = (17.50 - 15.00)a_{\overline{30}|1\frac{3}{4}\%} = 2.50 \times 23.186 = \$57.97$$

From which the purchase price = \$942.03.

### EXERCISE 7b

1. A \$1000, $4\frac{1}{2}$% Chesapeake and Ohio Railroad bond is due on March 1, 1992. Interest is payable on March 1 and September 1. Find the value on September 1, 1973, to yield 7% converted semiannually. (\$742.87)
2. A \$1000, 5% Columbia Gas System bond is due on October 1, 1982. Interest is payable on April 1 and October 1. Find the value on April 1, 1973, to yield 8% converted semiannually.
3. A Dana Corporation \$1000, 7.30% debenture is due on February 1, 1996. Interest is payable on February 1 and August 1. Find the value on February 1, 1974, to yield 8% converted semiannually. (\$928.08)
4. A \$1000, 5% General Motors Acceptance debenture is due on September 1, 1980. Interest is payable on March 1 and September 1. Find the value on September 1, 1973, to yield 7% compounded semiannually.
5. A \$1000, $8\frac{1}{2}$% Kansas City Gas and Electric bond is due on March 1, 2000. Interest is payable on March 1 and September 1. Find the value on March 1, 1974, to yield 8% converted semiannually. (\$1054.37)
6. An American Telephone and Telegraph \$1000, 8.7% debenture is due on December 1, 2002. Interest is payable on June 1 and December 1. Find the value on December 1, 1973, to yield 8% converted semiannually.
7. A Jersey Central Power and Light \$1000, $7\frac{1}{4}$% bond is due on October 1, 1998. Interest is payable on April 1 and October 1. Find the value on April 1, 1974, to yield 7% converted semiannually. (\$1029.10)

**8.** A Household Finance $1000, $7\frac{1}{4}\%$ debenture is due on January 1, 1990. Interest is payable on January 1 and July 1. Find the value on July 1, 1973, to yield 7% converted semiannually.

## 7.7 Amortization of the Premium

When the purchase price of a bond is higher than the maturity value, the buyer's capital can be kept intact by setting aside enough from the interest payments to equal the premium when the bond is redeemed. A systematic way to do this is to compute the interest at the yield rate on the *book value* of the bond (the value at which the bond is carried on the books of the owner), subtract this from the bond interest, and apply this difference to periodically reducing the book value. Under this plan the bond will have a gradually decreasing book value that will equal the face value of the bond when it matures. This method insures that the investment always earns its yield rate and what remains from the bond coupon is used to amortize the premium. An example will show how this is done.

EXAMPLE: A $1000, 5% bond maturing at par in two years was bought on June 1, 1973, to yield 4%. The interest is paid on June 1 and December 1. Construct a schedule for the amortization of the premium.

SOLUTION: Substituting $Fr = 25$, $Fi = 20$, and $n = 4$ in (23),

$$\text{Premium} = (25 - 20)a_{\overline{4}|2\%} = 5 \times 3.808 = \$19.04$$

Thus the purchase price of the bond is $1019.04. This is the initial investment on which the buyer wants to realize 4%. At the end of 6 months, he cashes a coupon worth $25. However, 2% of $1019.04 is only $20.38. Thus in effect the buyer has received from his coupon $20.38 in interest while the difference between this and the $25, which is $4.62, can be looked on as a partial return of his premium. This $4.62 is capital for reinvestment and is no longer considered part of the investment in the bond. These partial returns of the capital will equal the total premium when the bond matures so that the buyer's capital remains intact. Each period then shows a decreased investment in the bond and an increased part of the bond interest applied to the amortization of the premium. The money invested in the bond at any time is the book value of the bond. The following schedule shows how the book value finally equals the face value of the bond. Long schedules of this type are often prepared on electronic computers.

*Amortization of the Premium*

| DATE | INTEREST ON BOOK VALUE AT YIELD RATE | INTEREST ON BOND | AMOUNT FOR AMORTIZATION OF PREMIUM | BOOK VALUE |
|---|---|---|---|---|
| June 1, 1973 | — | — | — | $1019.04 |
| Dec. 1, 1973 | $20.38 | $25.00 | $4.62 | 1014.42 |
| June 1, 1974 | 20.29 | 25.00 | 4.71 | 1009.71 |
| Dec. 1, 1974 | 20.19 | 25.00 | 4.81 | 1004.90 |
| June 1, 1975 | 20.10 | 25.00 | 4.90 | 1000.00 |
| | | | $19.04 | |

## 7.8   Accumulation of the Discount

If the bond is bought below par, the bond interest will not equal the desired return on the investment. This means that a portion of the desired interest will not be received with the bond payments but will be obtained when the bond matures at more than the purchase price. Rather than picking up the increase in the value of the bond all at once, the deficit between the desired interest and the bond interest can be applied each period to raise the book value from the purchase price to the maturity value.

EXAMPLE: A $1000, 5% bond maturing at par in two years was bought on June 1, 1973, to yield 6%. The interest is paid on June 1 and December 1. Construct a schedule for the accumulation of the discount.

SOLUTION: Substituting $Fi = 30$, $Fr = 25$, and $n = 4$ in (24),

$$\text{Discount} = (30 - 25)a_{\overline{4}|3\%}$$
$$= 5 \times 3.717 = \$18.59$$

Thus the purchase price of the bond is $981.41. This is the investment on which the buyer wants to realize 6%. At the end of six months the owner cashes a coupon worth $25. However, 3% of $981.41 is $29.44. The $4.44 in excess of the bond interest must come from the increase in the book value of the bond. The following schedule shows how these periodic differences result in the book value of the bond finally equaling the maturity value.

## Accumulation of the Discount

| DATE | INTEREST ON BOOK VALUE AT YIELD RATE | INTEREST ON BOND | AMOUNT FOR ACCUMULATION OF DISCOUNT | BOOK VALUE |
|---|---|---|---|---|
| June 1, 1973 | — | — | — | $ 981.41 |
| Dec. 1, 1973 | $29.44 | $25.00 | $4.44 | 985.85 |
| June 1, 1974 | 29.58 | 25.00 | 4.58 | 990.43 |
| Dec. 1, 1974 | 29.71 | 25.00 | 4.71 | 995.14 |
| June 1, 1975 | 29.86 | 25.00 | 4.86 | 1000.00 |
| | | | $18.59 | |

### EXERCISE 7c

1. A $5000 bond with interest at 4%, payable January 1 and July 1, is to mature at par on July 1, 1976. Construct a schedule showing the amortization of the premium if the bond is bought on July 1, 1973, to yield 3% converted semiannually. (Purchase price $5142.43)

2. A $500, 6% bond with coupons payable on March 1 and September 1 is to mature at par on March 1, 1976. Construct a schedule showing the amortization of the premium if the bond is bought on September 1, 1973, to yield 5%, compounded semiannually.

3. A $1000, 3% bond with semiannual coupons on April 1 and October 1 will mature on October 1, 1977. Construct a schedule showing the accumulation of the discount if the bond is bought on April 1, 1974, to yield 4%. (Purchase price $967.64)

4. A $10,000 bond with interest at $2\frac{1}{2}$%, payable annually on June 1, is to mature at par on June 1, 1982. It is bought on June 1, 1973, to yield 3%. Construct a schedule showing the accumulation of the discount.

## 7.9   Bonds Purchased Between Coupon Dates

In all of the problems worked so far to get the purchase price of a bond, the bond was purchased on a coupon date. The seller kept the coupon that was due on that date and the buyer had to hold the bond for a full period before he could cash his first coupon. In practice, of course, bonds are usually purchased between coupon dates. This means that the purchaser will get the full value of the next coupon even though he has not had his money invested during all of the interest period. The seller, on the other hand, has had his money tied up for part of a coupon period but he will not collect any of his interest from the company that issued the bond. The logical solution to this problem, and the one usually followed in practice, is for the buyer to pay the seller for the accrued portion of the current coupon.

When the buyer pays the interest that has accrued since the last interest payment date, the purchase price includes both the quoted or listed price of the bond and the accrued interest. Thus bonds are sold at a quoted price "and interest." The price that is quoted on the bond market, sometimes called the **market** or **and interest** price, is the price of the bond itself to yield a certain return. The total cost of a bond includes the *and interest* price, the accrued interest, and, if the bond is traded in the secondary market, the broker's commission.

EXAMPLE: A $5000, 6% bond with interest payable semiannually on June 1 and December 1 matures on June 1, 1975. This bond was purchased on October 1, 1973, to yield 4% converted semiannually. What was the purchase price?

SOLUTION: To get the *quoted* or *and interest* price, we will first determine the value of the bond on the coupon dates immediately preceding and following the purchase date. Then we interpolate to get the *and interest* price on the purchase date.

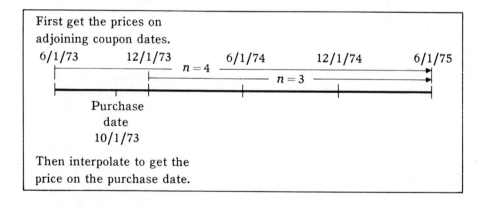

For June 1, 1973 the premium $= (150 - 100)a_{\overline{4}|2\%} = \$190.39$
For Dec. 1, 1973 the premium $= (150 - 100)a_{\overline{3}|2\%} = \$144.19$

Thus the price on a coupon date drops from $5190.39 on June 1, 1973 to $5144.19 on December 1, 1973. This is a decrease of $46.20. We now interpolate to find what part of this decrease has occurred on October 1. Since

October 1 is $\frac{4}{6}$ of the way from June 1 to December 1, we simply multiply $46.20 by this ratio giving us $30.80.

This makes the quoted price on October 1, $5190.39 − $30.80 = $5159.59. But on October 1, $\frac{4}{6}$ of a coupon has also accrued. This ratio applied to the total interest payment of $150 equals $100. Thus the actual selling price on October 1 would be $5159.59 + 100 = $5259.59. Note that the buyer on this date has to wait only 2 months until he gets a full coupon of $150. At this time he is reimbursed for the extra $100 he paid the seller.

The sketch uses the data from the preceding example to show the relationship between the various prices in bond problems. Note that the *quoted* or *and interest* price approaches the par value of the bond and finally equals it on the maturity date. The actual price equals the *and interest* price only on interest dates.

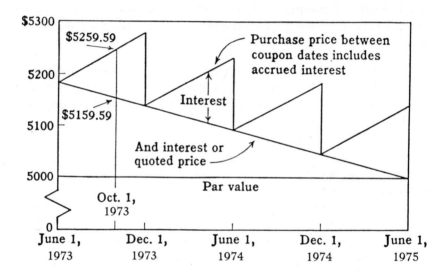

The sketch shows why the quoted price of a bond does not include the accrued interest. If the actual purchase price were quoted, there would be a big change in the price before and after an interest date that would be caused by the paying of the bond interest rather than to any change in the value of the bond itself.

Sometimes bonds are traded **flat**. This means without interest. The market price is the full price paid by the purchaser. A bond may be traded flat when it is in default on interest payments or when there is doubt about the ability of the borrower to meet future interest payments. **Income bonds**, which pay interest only when earned, are also traded flat.

**EXERCISE 7d**

1. A Florida Power Corporation $1000, 5% bond is due on June 1, 1989. Interest is payable on June 1 and December 1. Get the *and interest* price and the price including accrued interest if the bond is sold on August 1, 1973, to yield 7% converted semiannually. ($810.42, $818.75)

2. A General Motors Acceptance $1000, 5% debenture is due on March 15, 1981. Interest is payable on March 15 and September 15. Get the *and interest* price and the price including accrued interest if the bond is sold on July 15, 1973, to yield 7% converted semiannually.

3. A Lucky Stores $1000, $8\frac{1}{2}$% debenture is due on April 15, 1996. Interest is payable on April 15 and October 15. Get the *and interest* price and the price including accrued interest on September 15, 1973, to yield 8% converted semiannually. ($1051.87, $1087.29)

4. An American Metal Climax $1000, $8\frac{1}{2}$% debenture is due on March 1, 1996. Interest is payable on March 1 and September 1. Get the *and interest* price and the price including accrued interest on July 1, 1973, to yield 8% converted semiannually.

5. An American Telephone and Telegraph $1000, 6% debenture is due on August 1, 2000. Interest is payable on February 1 and August 1. Get the *and interest* price and the price including accrued interest if the bond is sold on September 1, 1973, to yield 8% converted semiannually.
($780.27, $785.27)

6. A Boeing Company $1000, 5% debenture is due on August 1, 1978. Interest is payable on February 1 and August 1. Get the *and interest* price and the price including accrued interest if the bond is sold on April 1, 1974, to yield 10% converted semiannually.

7. A Gulf Oil Corporation $1000, $8\frac{1}{2}$% debenture is due on November 15, 1995. Interest is payable on May 15 and November 15. Get the *and interest* price and the price including accrued interest if the bond is sold on September 15, 1974, to yield 8% converted semiannually. ($1050.62, $1078.95)

8. A Shell Oil Company $1000, $8\frac{1}{2}$% debenture is due on September 1, 2000. Interest is payable on March 1 and September 1. Get the *and interest* price and the price including accrued interest if the bond is sold on December 1, 1973, to yield 8% converted semiannually.

## 7.10 Finding the Yield Rate

Up to now we have been determining the value of a bond to yield a certain rate of return on the investment. In practice, the quoted or the *and interest* price is often given without stating the yield rate. Since the purchaser is interested in the return he will get on his investment, it is necessary to determine the yield rate. The yield which we get is known as *yield to maturity* by investment dealers. It is the true overall rate of return which an investor gets on his invested capital. Another yield which is sometimes used is the *current yield* obtained by dividing the annual return in dollars by the current price. This is very simple to compute but is not a true measure of return on invested capital. For this reason, whenever yield rate is used in this text, it means yield to maturity. We get the yield rate in two ways. The first is the Bond Salesman's Method which is simple and usually leads to fairly accurate results.

EXAMPLE 1: A $1000, 5% bond which matures in 10 years has interest payable semiannually. The quoted price is $1050. What is the yield rate?

SOLUTION: Here we have a bond which has a book value of $1050 now and $1000 in 10 years or 20 periods:

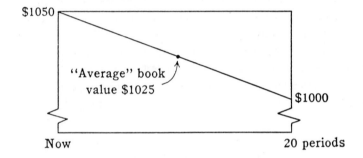

We add these two values and divide by 2 to get an "average" investment or book value.

$$\frac{1050 + 1000}{2} = \$1025$$

The periodic interest on this bond is $25. But it has been purchased at a premium of $50 which must be amortized over the 20 periods. The "average" amortization per period = 50/20 = $2.50. This is deducted from the interest payments so that our return per period is $22.50 on an average investment of $1025. This makes the approximate yield rate 22.50/1025 = 2.2% per period or 4.4% nominal.

If a more accurate value for the yield rate is desired, we use trial and error until we find two adjacent yield rates which bracket the given price. We then find the yield rate by interpolation. The Bond Salesman's Method showed that the yield rate is close to 2.2% per period. We try the closest table value to this and compute the purchase price.

With our table this is $4\frac{1}{2}\%$ a year or $2\frac{1}{4}\%$ a period. Using (23) for bond premium, we get

$$P = (25.00 - 22.50)a_{\overline{20}|2\frac{1}{4}\%} = 2.50(15.964) = \$39.91$$

This would make the purchase price $1039.91. Since the actual purchase price was $1050, the yield rate must be less than $2\frac{1}{4}\%$. The closest table value lower than this is $2\%$, so we compute the purchase price at $2\%$.

$$P = (25 - 20)a_{\overline{20}|2\%} = 5(16.351) = \$81.76$$

and

$$V = \$1081.76$$

We now have a purchase price below the quoted price and another one above. Since our tables do not permit any closer approximations, we interpolate

| | $i$ in $\%$ | Quoted Price | | |
|---|---|---|---|---|
| | 2.00 | \$1081.76 | | |
| .25 | $d$ | | 31.76 | 41.85 |
| | $i$ | 1050.00 | | |
| | 2.25 | 1039.91 | | |

$$\frac{d}{.25} = \frac{31.76}{41.85}$$

$$d = .19$$
$$i = 2.00 + .19 = 2.19\%$$

$$\text{Nominal annual yield} = 2i = 4.38\%$$

What this method of determining the yield rate comes down to is finding two adjacent rates in the table such that the quoted price of the bond lies between the prices determined using the two tabular rates. In practical investment work it is usually possible to simplify computations by using bond tables which will be described later. We shall work one more example to show how the yield rate is determined if the bond is bought at a discount or between interest dates.

EXAMPLE 2: A $1000, $4\%$ bond with coupons payable semiannually on April 1 and October 1 matures on April 1, 1989. On June 1, 1974, this bond is quoted at 94. What is the yield rate?

SOLUTION: First we use the approximate method to get an estimate of the yield rate assuming that the bond was quoted on the nearest interest date, in this case April 1, 1974. Averaging the quoted price and the redemption price gives

$$\frac{940 + 1000}{2} = \$970$$

The semiannual coupon is $20. In addition to the interest there will be an increase of $60 in the value of the bond. Averaged over 30 periods this amounts to $2 per period. Therefore we have an average return of $22 on an average investment of $970. This makes the approximate yield rate

$$\frac{22}{970} = 2.3\% \text{ per period or } 4.6\% \text{ nominal}$$

If we want a more accurate answer, it is necessary to make trial computations using assumed yield rates. We use the value obtained above as a guide in selecting trial rates.

First we try $2\frac{1}{4}\%$ ($4\frac{1}{2}\%$ nominal).

| DATE | DISCOUNT | QUOTED PRICE |
|------|----------|--------------|
| April 1, 1974 | $(22.50 - 20.00)a_{\overline{30}|} = \$54.11$ | $945.89 |
| June 1, 1974 | | ? |
| Oct. 1, 1974 | $(22.50 - 20.00)a_{\overline{29}|} = 52.83$ | 947.17 |

(with bracket: $d$ and 1.28)

Since June 1 is $\frac{2}{6}$ of the way from April 1 to October 1, the interpolation to get the June 1 price is

$$\frac{d}{1.28} = \frac{2}{6}$$

$$d = .43$$

And the June 1 price for a yield rate of $2\frac{1}{4}\%$ per period is

$$\$945.89 + .43 = \$946.32$$

This shows that the true yield rate must be more than $2\frac{1}{4}\%$ so we repeat the above procedure with a trial rate of $2\frac{1}{2}\%$.

| DATE | DISCOUNT | QUOTED PRICE |
|------|----------|--------------|
| April 1, 1974 | $(25.00 - 20.00)a_{\overline{30}|} = \$104.65$ | $895.35 |
| June 1, 1974 | | ? |
| Oct. 1, 1974 | $(25.00 - 20.00)a_{\overline{29}|} = 102.27$ | 897.73 |

(with bracket: $d$ and 2.38)

$$\frac{d}{2.38} = \frac{2}{6}$$

$$d = .79$$

From which the June 1, 1974, price for a yield rate of $2\frac{1}{2}\%$ per period is

$$\$895.35 + .79 = \$896.14$$

We can now summarize the results as follows:

*Yield Rate*    *Quoted Price on*
*per period*    *June 1, 1974*

$$\begin{array}{c} .25 \end{array} \left[ \begin{array}{c} d \left[ \begin{array}{c} 2.25 \\ i \\ 2.50 \end{array} \right. \end{array} \right. \qquad \begin{array}{c} \$946.32 \\ 940.00 \\ 896.14 \end{array} \left] 6.32 \right] 50.18 $$

$$\frac{d}{.25} = \frac{6.32}{50.18}$$

$$d = .03$$

From which $i = 2.25 + .03 = 2.28\%$ and the nominal yield rate is

$$2 \times 2.28 = 4.56\% \text{ converted semiannually}$$

**EXERCISE 7e**

(Use Bond Salesman's Method for Problems 1 to 4. Interpolate between closest table values for Problems 5 to 10.)

1. A \$1000, 3% bond with semiannual coupons matures at par in 10 years. If this bond is bought for \$960.00, what is the nominal yield rate, converted semiannually? (3.5%)
2. A \$500, 4% bond with semiannual coupons matures at par in 5 years. If this bond is bought for \$480, what is the nominal yield rate, converted semiannually?
3. A \$1000, 5% bond with semiannual coupons matures at par in 10 years. If this bond is bought for \$1080, what is the nominal yield rate, converted semiannually? (4.0%)
4. A \$5000, $4\frac{1}{2}$% bond with semiannual coupons matures at par in 10 years. If this bond is bought for \$5300, what is the nominal yield rate, converted semiannually?
5. Get the nominal yield rate for a \$1000, 4% bond quoted at 98 on June 1, 1972, if the bond is to mature at par on December 1, 1979. Coupons are payable on June 1 and December 1. (4.32%)
6. A \$1000, 6% bond with coupons payable semiannually on March 1 and September 1 is issued on March 1, 1964, to mature in 20 years. On September 1, 1972, this bond is quoted at 102. If purchased at this price, what would be the nominal yield rate converted semiannually?
7. A \$1000, 5% bond issued on August 1, 1966, is to mature at par on August 1, 1976. Coupons are payable semiannually on February 1 and August 1. If this bond is quoted at 95 on February 1, 1974, what is the nominal yield rate converted semiannually? (7.22%)

8. A $1000, 4% Baltimore and Ohio RR bond matures on September 1, 1980. Coupon dates are March 1 and September 1. If this bond was quoted at 70 on September 1, 1973, what was the nominal yield rate converted semiannually?

9. A $500, 5% bond with coupons payable on January 1 and July 1 matures at par on July 1, 1977. It is purchased on February 1, 1973, for $530 plus accrued interest. What is the yield rate?                    (3.52%)

10. A $1000, 4% bond with coupons payable on March 1 and September 1 matures at par on March 1, 1978. It is purchased on May 1, 1973, for $960 plus accrued interest. What is the yield rate?

## 7.11 Bond Tables

Companies that buy and sell bonds reduce the computations required to get the price of a bond or the yield rate by using bond tables that cover most of the cases that arise in practice. Bond tables are available in large volumes with answers to 4 or 6 decimal places and in pocket-size books with values to 2 decimal places. The tables give the *and interest* prices of bonds for a wide range of yield and coupon rates and lengths of time until the maturity date of the bond. A sample page from the 6-place tables of the Financial Publishing Company is shown on page 267, and a sample page from the pocket-size book is shown on page 268. The examples below are based on page 267 which is for a $100, $2\frac{3}{4}$% bond with interest paid semiannually. The yield rate in the left column is the nominal annual rate converted semiannually.

EXAMPLE 1: A $1000, $2\frac{3}{4}$% bond with interest payable semiannually matures in 23 years. What is the purchase price for a yield rate of 1.5% converted semiannually?

SOLUTION: We simply go down the yield rate column to 1.50 and read the purchase price of $124.239 for a $100 bond. A $1000 bond will cost $1242.39.

EXAMPLE 2: A $1000, $2\frac{3}{4}$% bond with interest payable semiannually matures in 23 years and 3 months. What is the purchase price for a yield rate of 5% converted semiannually?

SOLUTION: Since the bond is not being purchased on a coupon date, we must first obtain the *and interest* price and then add the accrued interest. Both of these can be obtained directly from the table. The *and interest* price is $692.70. From the bottom of the table we get $.6875 for the accrued interest for 3 months on $100. On $1000 it will be $6.88. Adding the two gives a purchase price of $699.58.

Facsimile of Portion of a Page of Bond Tables

## 2¾% COUPON  23 YEARS

| Yield | Even | 1 Month | 2 Months | 3 Months | 4 Months | 5 Months |
|---|---|---|---|---|---|---|
| .00 | 163.250000 | 163.479167 | 163.708333 | 163.937500 | 164.166667 | 164.395833 |
| .05 | 161.736617 | 161.958989 | 162.181360 | 162.403732 | 162.626104 | 162.848477 |
| .10 | 160.239532 | 160.455235 | 160.670938 | 160.886643 | 161.102349 | 161.318057 |
| .15 | 158.758557 | 158.967716 | 159.176817 | 159.386041 | 159.595207 | 159.804376 |
| .20 | 157.293510 | 157.496247 | 157.698989 | 157.901735 | 158.104486 | 158.307241 |
| .25 | 155.844208 | 156.040644 | 156.237088 | 156.433538 | 156.629995 | 156.826459 |
| .30 | 154.410472 | 154.600726 | 154.790990 | 154.981264 | 155.171547 | 155.361840 |
| .35 | 152.992124 | 153.176312 | 153.360514 | 153.544729 | 153.728958 | 153.913199 |
| .40 | 151.588989 | 151.767227 | 151.945482 | 152.123754 | 152.302043 | 152.480349 |
| .45 | 150.200894 | 150.373294 | 150.545715 | 150.718158 | 150.890622 | 151.063107 |
| .50 | 148.827667 | 148.994340 | 149.161039 | 149.327765 | 149.494516 | 149.661293 |
| .55 | 147.469139 | 147.630195 | 147.791282 | 147.952400 | 148.113549 | 148.274729 |
| .60 | 146.125144 | 146.280689 | 146.436271 | 146.591890 | 146.747546 | 146.903238 |
| .65 | 144.795515 | 144.945656 | 145.095840 | 145.246066 | 145.396335 | 145.546646 |
| .70 | 143.480091 | 143.624931 | 143.769820 | 143.914758 | 144.059745 | 144.204781 |
| .75 | 142.178708 | 142.318349 | 142.458046 | 142.597799 | 142.737608 | 142.877472 |
| .80 | 140.891208 | 141.025751 | 141.160357 | 141.295026 | 141.429758 | 141.564553 |
| .85 | 139.617433 | 139.746977 | 139.876591 | 140.006276 | 140.136031 | 140.265856 |
| .90 | 138.357228 | 138.481870 | 138.606590 | 138.731388 | 138.856264 | 138.981218 |
| .95 | 137.110438 | 137.230273 | 137.350195 | 137.470202 | 137.590296 | 137.710476 |
| 1.00 | 135.876912 | 135.992035 | 136.107252 | 136.222564 | 136.337970 | 136.453472 |
| 1.05 | 134.656500 | 134.767002 | 134.877608 | 134.988317 | 135.099129 | 135.210045 |
| 1.10 | 133.449052 | 133.555024 | 133.661110 | 133.767308 | 133.873618 | 133.980041 |
| 1.15 | 132.254422 | 132.355954 | 132.457609 | 132.559386 | 132.661284 | 132.763304 |
| 1.20 | 131.072465 | 131.169645 | 131.266958 | 131.364401 | 131.461976 | 131.559682 |
| 1.25 | 129.903037 | 129.995952 | 130.089009 | 130.182206 | 130.275545 | 130.369025 |
| 1.30 | 128.745998 | 128.834732 | 128.923618 | 129.012655 | 129.101844 | 129.191183 |
| 1.35 | 127.601207 | 127.685844 | 127.770643 | 127.855603 | 127.940726 | 128.026010 |
| 1.40 | 126.468525 | 126.549147 | 126.629942 | 126.710908 | 126.792048 | 126.873359 |
| 1.45 | 125.347817 | 125.424504 | 125.501375 | 125.578429 | 125.655667 | 125.733087 |
| 1.50 | 124.238946 | 124.311779 | 124.384806 | 124.458027 | 124.531443 | 124.605052 |
| 1.55 | 123.141780 | 123.210836 | 123.280097 | 123.349564 | 123.419237 | 123.489114 |
| 1.60 | 122.056186 | 122.121542 | 122.187115 | 122.252904 | 122.318911 | 122.385134 |
| 1.65 | 120.982035 | 121.043765 | 121.105725 | 121.167914 | 121.230331 | 121.292976 |
| 1.70 | 119.919196 | 119.977376 | 120.035797 | 120.094459 | 120.153361 | 120.212504 |
| 5.00 | 69.451559 | 69.389843 | 69.329321 | 69.269989 | 69.211842 | 69.154874 |
| 5.05 | 68.918721 | 68.856348 | 68.795184 | 68.735224 | 68.676462 | 68.618895 |
| 5.10 | 68.391188 | 68.328179 | 68.266394 | 68.205828 | 68.146474 | 68.088329 |
| 5.15 | 67.868901 | 67.805279 | 67.742894 | 67.681742 | 67.621818 | 67.563116 |
| 5.20 | 67.351804 | 67.287588 | 67.224625 | 67.162909 | 67.102434 | 67.043196 |
| 5.25 | 66.839840 | 66.775052 | 66.711530 | 66.649270 | 66.588265 | 66.528511 |
| 5.30 | 66.332953 | 66.267612 | 66.203553 | 66.140768 | 66.079254 | 66.019004 |
| 5.35 | 65.831089 | 65.765215 | 65.700637 | 65.637348 | 65.575343 | 65.514617 |
| 5.40 | 65.334192 | 65.267805 | 65.202727 | 65.138953 | 65.076477 | 65.015293 |
| 5.45 | 64.842209 | 64.775327 | 64.709769 | 64.645529 | 64.582601 | 64.520978 |
| 5.50 | 64.355086 | 64.287729 | 64.221709 | 64.157021 | 64.093658 | 64.031616 |
| 5.55 | 63.872771 | 63.804956 | 63.738493 | 63.673375 | 63.609597 | 63.547152 |
| 5.60 | 63.395213 | 63.326957 | 63.260068 | 63.194538 | 63.130362 | 63.067532 |
| 5.65 | 62.922358 | 62.853680 | 62.786383 | 62.720458 | 62.655901 | 62.592704 |
| 5.70 | 62.454157 | 62.385074 | 62.317385 | 62.251083 | 62.186161 | 62.122614 |

| Accrued Interest on $100 | 5 Months 1.145833 | 4 Months .916667 | 3 Months .687500 | 2 Months .458333 | 1 Month .229167 |
|---|---|---|---|---|---|

*Bond tables used by courtesy of the Financial Publishing Co., Boston, Mass.*

## Pocket-size Bond Tables

| 2¾% | | YEARS AND MONTHS | | | | | | |
|---|---|---|---|---|---|---|---|---|
| Mat. Yield | 14-1 | 14-2 | 14-3 | 14-4 | 14-5 | 14-6 | 14-7 | 14-8 |
| .50 | 130.56 | 130.73 | 130.91 | 131.08 | 131.26 | 131.43 | 131.61 | 131.78 |
| .60 | 128.99 | 129.16 | 129.32 | 129.49 | 129.65 | 129.81 | 129.98 | 130.14 |
| .70 | 127.45 | 127.60 | 127.76 | 127.91 | 128.06 | 128.22 | 128.37 | 128.53 |
| .75 | 126.68 | 126.83 | 126.98 | 127.13 | 127.28 | 127.43 | 127.58 | 127.73 |
| .80 | 125.92 | 126.07 | 126.21 | 126.36 | 126.50 | 126.65 | 126.79 | 126.93 |
| .85 | 125.17 | 125.31 | 125.45 | 125.59 | 125.73 | 125.87 | 126.01 | 126.15 |
| .90 | 124.42 | 124.55 | 124.69 | 124.82 | 124.96 | 125.10 | 125.23 | 125.36 |
| .95 | 123.67 | 123.81 | 123.94 | 124.07 | 124.20 | 124.33 | 124.46 | 124.59 |
| 1.00 | 122.94 | 123.06 | 123.19 | 123.31 | 123.44 | 123.57 | 123.69 | 123.82 |
| 1.05 | 122.20 | 122.32 | 122.44 | 122.57 | 122.69 | 122.81 | 122.93 | 123.05 |
| 1.10 | 121.47 | 121.59 | 121.71 | 121.82 | 121.94 | 122.06 | 122.17 | 122.29 |
| 1.15 | 120.75 | 120.86 | 120.97 | 121.09 | 121.20 | 121.31 | 121.42 | 121.54 |
| 1.20 | 120.03 | 120.14 | 120.25 | 120.35 | 120.46 | 120.57 | 120.68 | 120.79 |
| 1.25 | 119.31 | 119.42 | 119.52 | 119.63 | 119.73 | 119.84 | 119.94 | 120.04 |
| 1.30 | 118.60 | 118.70 | 118.80 | 118.91 | 119.01 | 119.11 | 119.21 | 119.30 |
| 1.35 | 117.90 | 118.00 | 118.09 | 118.19 | 118.28 | 118.38 | 118.48 | 118.57 |
| 1.40 | 117.20 | 117.29 | 117.38 | 117.48 | 117.57 | 117.66 | 117.75 | 117.84 |
| 1.45 | 116.51 | 116.59 | 116.68 | 116.77 | 116.86 | 116.95 | 117.03 | 117.12 |
| 1.50 | 115.82 | 115.90 | 115.98 | 116.07 | 116.15 | 116.23 | 116.32 | 116.40 |
| 1.55 | 115.13 | 115.21 | 115.29 | 115.37 | 115.45 | 115.53 | 115.61 | 115.69 |
| 1.60 | 114.45 | 114.52 | 114.60 | 114.68 | 114.75 | 114.83 | 114.90 | 114.98 |
| 1.65 | 113.77 | 113.84 | 113.92 | 113.99 | 114.06 | 114.13 | 114.21 | 114.28 |
| 1.70 | 113.10 | 113.17 | 113.24 | 113.31 | 113.37 | 113.44 | 113.51 | 113.58 |
| 1.75 | 112.43 | 112.50 | 112.56 | 112.63 | 112.69 | 112.76 | 112.82 | 112.88 |
| 1.80 | 111.77 | 111.83 | 111.89 | 111.95 | 112.01 | 112.08 | 112.14 | 112.20 |
| 1.85 | 111.11 | 111.17 | 111.23 | 111.28 | 111.34 | 111.40 | 111.46 | 111.51 |
| 1.90 | 110.46 | 110.51 | 110.57 | 110.62 | 110.67 | 110.73 | 110.78 | 110.83 |
| 1.95 | 109.81 | 109.86 | 109.91 | 109.96 | 110.01 | 110.06 | 110.11 | 110.16 |
| 2.00 | 109.16 | 109.21 | 109.26 | 109.30 | 109.35 | 109.40 | 109.45 | 109.49 |
| 2.05 | 108.52 | 108.57 | 108.61 | 108.65 | 108.70 | 108.74 | 108.78 | 108.83 |
| 2.10 | 107.89 | 107.93 | 107.97 | 108.01 | 108.05 | 108.09 | 108.13 | 108.17 |
| 2.15 | 107.26 | 107.29 | 107.33 | 107.37 | 107.40 | 107.44 | 107.48 | 107.51 |
| 2.20 | 106.63 | 106.66 | 106.69 | 106.73 | 106.76 | 106.80 | 106.83 | 106.86 |
| 2.25 | 106.01 | 106.03 | 106.06 | 106.10 | 106.13 | 106.16 | 106.19 | 106.21 |
| 2.30 | 105.39 | 105.41 | 105.44 | 105.47 | 105.45 | 105.52 | 105.55 | 105.57 |
| 2.35 | 104.77 | 104.79 | 104.82 | 104.84 | 104.87 | 104.89 | 104.91 | 104.94 |
| 2.40 | 104.16 | 104.18 | 104.20 | 104.22 | 104.24 | 104.26 | 104.28 | 104.30 |
| 2.45 | 103.55 | 103.57 | 103.59 | 103.61 | 103.62 | 103.64 | 103.66 | 103.68 |
| 2.50 | 102.95 | 102.97 | 102.98 | 102.99 | 103.01 | 103.03 | 103.04 | 103.05 |
| 2.55 | 102.35 | 102.36 | 102.37 | 102.39 | 102.40 | 102.41 | 102.42 | 102.43 |
| 2.60 | 101.76 | 101.77 | 101.77 | 101.78 | 101.79 | 101.80 | 101.81 | 101.82 |
| 2.65 | 101.17 | 101.17 | 101.18 | 101.18 | 101.19 | 101.20 | 101.20 | 101.21 |
| 2.70 | 100.58 | 100.58 | 100.59 | 100.59 | 100.59 | 100.60 | 100.60 | 100.60 |
| 2.75 | 100.00 | 100.00 | 100.00 | 100.00 | 100.00 | 100.00 | 100.00 | 100.00 |
| 2.80 | 99.42 | 99.42 | 99.41 | 99.41 | 99.41 | 99.41 | 99.40 | 99.40 |
| 2.85 | 98.85 | 98.84 | 98.83 | 98.83 | 98.82 | 98.82 | 98.81 | 98.81 |
| 2.90 | 98.27 | 98.27 | 98.26 | 98.25 | 98.24 | 98.23 | 98.23 | 98.22 |
| 2.95 | 97.71 | 97.70 | 97.68 | 97.67 | 97.66 | 97.65 | 97.64 | 97.63 |
| 3.00 | 97.14 | 97.13 | 97.12 | 97.10 | 97.09 | 97.08 | 97.06 | 97.05 |
| 3.05 | 96.58 | 96.57 | 96.55 | 96.54 | 96.52 | 96.51 | 96.49 | 96.47 |
| 3.10 | 96.03 | 96.01 | 95.99 | 95.97 | 95.95 | 95.94 | 95.92 | 95.90 |

472

EXAMPLE 3: A \$1000, $2\frac{3}{4}\%$ bond which matures in 23 years is quoted at \$1250. What is the nominal yield rate?

SOLUTION: The equivalent price for a \$100 bond is \$125. From the table we see that the yield rate is between 1.45 and 1.50%. If a more accurate answer is needed, we interpolate

*Yield Rate in* %　　*Quoted Price*

$$
.05\% \quad \left[ d \left[ \begin{array}{l} 1.45 \\ \text{Rate} \\ 1.50 \end{array} \right. \right. \qquad \left. \begin{array}{l} 125.35 \\ 125.00 \\ 124.24 \end{array} \right] .35 \right] 1.11
$$

$$\frac{d}{.05} = \frac{.35}{1.11}$$

$$d = .016$$

Yield rate $= 1.45 + .016 = 1.466\%$ converted semiannually

The following examples are based on the pocket-size tables.

EXAMPLE 4: A $100, $2\frac{3}{4}\%$ bond matures in 14 years and 6 months. Find the *and interest* price to yield 3% converted semiannually.

SOLUTION: Opposite 3% under 14–6 we find the answer to be $97.08.

EXAMPLE 5: A $2\frac{3}{4}\%$ bond which matures in 14 years and 3 months is quoted at 105. What is the yield rate?

SOLUTION: The table shows that the rate is between 2.30 and 2.35%. This narrow range is a satisfactory answer for many purposes. Interpolation could be used to get a closer approximation to the true yield rate.

EXAMPLE 6: A $1000, $2\frac{3}{4}\%$ bond matures in 14 years and 6 months. What should be the quoted price to yield 2%?

SOLUTION: The table value is 109.40 for a $100 bond. Therefore the value of a $1000 bond would be $1094.00.

### EXERCISE 7f

(Use the sample bond table on page 267. All yield rates are converted semiannually.)

1. A $1000, $2\frac{3}{4}\%$ bond with interest payable semiannually matures at par in 23 years. What is the purchase price for a yield rate of 5% converted semi-annually? ($694.52)
2. Work Problem 1 for a yield rate of 1.6% converted semiannually.
3. A $1000, $2\frac{3}{4}\%$ bond with interest payable semiannually matures at par in 23 years and 5 months. Get the *and interest* and the purchase price for a yield rate of 5% converted semiannually. ($691.55; $693.84)
4. A $500, $2\frac{3}{4}\%$ bond with semiannual coupons matures at par in 23 years and 5 months. Get the *and interest* and the purchase price for a yield rate of 1.5% converted semiannually.
5. A $1000, $2\frac{3}{4}\%$ bond which matures at par in 23 years is sold for $670. What is the nominal yield rate? (5.23%)
6. A $500, $2\frac{3}{4}\%$ bond matures at par in 23 years. If a buyer pays $630 for this bond, what rate of return will he get on his money?

## 7.12   Buying Bonds

Lenders who say, "Here's my money for 30 years," expect a better return than would be earned on shorter investments of comparable safety. When savings accounts are paying 5%, high grade bonds may be paying 8% and more. To help students determine when and how bonds can be attractive, we now consider bond facts which are important to investors.

Classified according to the issuing organization, important types of bonds are:

*United States Treasury Bonds.* These bonds have behind them no tangible assets to guarantee either the payment of interest or the return of invested capital. Yet millions of investors have put billions into Treasury bonds with complete confidence because they know that behind these bonds lies the integrity of the United States. For many years the maximum rate which Congress permitted on long term debt was $4\frac{1}{4}\%$. Since this rate has not been competitive for several years, the government stopped issuing $4\frac{1}{4}\%$ bonds. Outstanding Treasury bonds with $2\frac{1}{2}$ to $4\frac{1}{4}\%$ coupons are now traded at deep discounts. In 1971 Congress authorized the issue of 10-year, 7% bonds. These are now traded at small premiums. Some Treasury bonds are redeemable at par and accrued interest for payment of federal estate taxes if the bonds were owned by the decedent and are part of his estate. A person can now buy these bonds at a discount for a safe income while he is living and a lessening of the tax bite for his heirs after he dies. Because of their potential tax benefits, these bonds have lower yields to maturity than comparable issues without the estate-tax advantage.

*Bonds of Government Agencies and Sponsored Corporations.* Bonds issued by Federal agencies and sponsored corporations are not direct obligations of the Treasury but in one way or another the bonds involve federal sponsorship or guarantee. They are recognized as investment quality obligations and many of them are actively traded in secondary markets, enabling owners to combine a high degree of safety and liquidity. Yields are slightly higher than on Treasury bonds of comparable maturity.

*Municipal Bonds.* These bonds are issued by state and local governments, housing and port authorities, and local government agencies for roads, schools, water works, public housing, and other community services. Regardless of what local government or authority issues the bonds, they are called municipals. The interest income from municipals is exempt from federal income tax and is often exempt from state and local income taxes in the state where the bonds are issued. Municipals are issued in denominations of $1000 and up with $5000 being the most common.

It is the tax-free feature of municipal bonds that makes them attractive to people in the higher tax brackets. To find the rate which a person would have to earn on a taxable investment to produce the same dollar return as a municipal, we substitute in the formula,

$$\text{Required taxable rate} = \frac{\text{rate on municipal}}{1 - \text{tax rate}}$$

To have an after-tax income equivalent to a 7% return from a municipal bond, a person in the 20% tax bracket would need an investment paying

$$\frac{.07}{1 - .20} = \frac{.07}{.80} = .0875 = 8.75\%$$

The table below shows the equivalent taxable rate for several tax brackets and tax free rates.

*Taxable Equivalent Yields*

| TAX BRACKET* | TAXABLE RATE REQUIRED TO PRODUCE SAME AFTER-TAX INCOME AS A TAX-FREE RATE OF: | | |
|---|---|---|---|
| | 5% | 6% | 7% |
| 20% | 6.25% | 7.50% | 8.75% |
| 30 | 7.15 | 8.59 | 10.00 |
| 40 | 8.33 | 10.00 | 11.67 |
| 50 | 10.00 | 12.00 | 14.00 |
| 60 | 12.50 | 15.00 | 17.50 |
| 70 | 16.67 | 20.00 | 23.33 |

* Total of federal rate and any state and local income taxes which do not apply to municipal bonds.

When a person gets into the 30% and higher tax brackets, municipal bonds can be very attractive investments.

*Industrial and Utility Bonds.* These bonds are issued by companies from corporate giants down to small local concerns. The usual denomination is $1000, but "baby bonds" of $500 and less are sometimes sold. Some companies also issue convertible bonds which give the owner the privilege of converting the bond into a specified number of shares of common stock of the same corporation. From the company's standpoint, convertibles offer lower cost financing since rates on convertibles are less than on other bonds of similar quality. These hybrid securities combine features of a stock and a bond. The buyer can count on his interest while having a chance of additional profit if the stock of the issuing company goes up. Some companies have been so successful that their convertible bonds now trade at 200 or higher.

## 7.13 Long-term Interest Rates

Over the years there have been large changes in interest rates on bonds. As the graph below shows, returns on different types of top-grade securities tend to go up and down together.

Long-term Interest Rates

Source: *1972 Economic Report of the President,* Table B-57.

A bond is a promise to do two things—make periodic interest payments and redeem the bond at maturity. This promise is only as good as the outfit making it. Bond quality ranges from bonds with the least investment risk to those with the greatest investment risk. Bonds are rated by two investment services and gradations of investment quality are indicated by rating symbols, each symbol representing a group in which the quality characteristics are broadly the same. Starting with the highest investment quality, the ratings are:

| MOODY'S INVESTORS SERVICE, INC. | STANDARD AND POOR'S. CORP. |
|:---:|:---:|
| Aaa | AAA |
| Aa | AA |
| A | A |
| Baa | BBB |
| Ba | BB |
| B | B |
| Caa | CCC–CC |
| Ca | C |
| C | DDD–D |

In general, the higher the quality the lower the yield, as shown by the 1970 averages below.

| MOODY'S RATINGS | CORPORATE BONDS | MUNICIPAL BONDS |
|:---:|:---:|:---:|
| Aaa | 7.64% | 6.12% |
| Aa | 8.13 | 6.28 |
| A | 8.48 | 6.49 |
| Baa | 9.12 | 6.75 |

Beginners and conservative investors are wise to buy bonds of A and higher ratings. The safety and peace of mind provided by high-grade bonds are likely to be more important than the chance of a higher yield. As a person gains experience and funds, he may prefer to move down the scale with the hope of increasing his return from speculative buys.

Bonds are usually bought and sold through brokers. The buyer does not pay a commission on bonds of a new issue when it is first offered to the public. When an outstanding bond is sold, both buyer and seller pay a commission which is currently $5.00 for a $1000 corporation bond.

As interest rates rise, bond prices drop. The reverse is also true up to a point close to the price at which a corporation may call its bonds. If the call price as of a certain date is 106, this becomes in effect a ceiling on the market price of the bond. A bond whose price is being held down because of call provisions is sometimes referred to as a "stymied" bond. Before buying a new issue, it is a good idea to check on the number of years of call protection. Today this is usually 5 years for utility bonds and 10 years for industrial obligations.

One way to avoid call problems and get desired due dates is to buy seasoned issues, bonds that have been on the market for several years. Since these bonds were issued when rates were lower than today, they are now selling at discounts and so there is no danger of their being called. The yield to maturity on seasoned issues constantly adjusts to the going rate for new issues. At any particular time the yield on older issues may be somewhat lower than the yield on new issues but that will be offset in part by the lower income taxes on the capital gains between purchase price and redemption price. Yields to maturity can be checked using the methods in Section 7.10.

Bond buyers should be aware of the forms of bond ownership. In the case of bonds *registered as to both principal and interest*, the name of the holder appears on the bond and interest checks are mailed by the paying agent to the registered owner. Bonds *registered as to principal only* have the owner's name on the bond. There are coupons attached to the bond and these are fully negotiable. Both types of registered bonds have the owner's name recorded on the books of the paying agent and transfer of ownership may be made only through this agent. Dealers who handle bond sales and purchases usually take care of this transfer in registration. *Bearer bonds* do not carry the owner's name nor is his name recorded on the books of the paying agent. Possession of a bearer bond implies ownership. Replacing a lost or stolen registered bond entails bother and expense but it can be done. The loss or theft of a bearer bond is a disaster comparable to losing cash.

## 7.14 You Never Know

While the interest rate and redemption price of a bond are fixed, the market price is quite sensitive to changes in interest rates and economic trends. Bonds of the highest quality may have wide price movements while retaining their gilt-edge investment status. Bond buyers must be willing to assume a price level risk that can make life unpleasant if bonds must be sold to get cash. For example, *U.S. News and World Report* in the November 6, 1967, issue had an article headed "Bargains in Bonds—A Look at Today's Record Yields," which said in part:

Prices of bonds in the open market, dropping month after month, are now in many cases at the lowest levels ever. For investors, the result is an array of offerings that carry record-high yields.

In large type the article pointed out:

Many yields are at their highest levels in 46 years. Some are the biggest in nearly a century.

The article included an extensive table of different types of bonds with their yields to maturity. Among the mouth-watering yields (in 1967) were Shell Oil $4\frac{5}{8}\%$ Triple A bonds of 1986 selling at 84.375 for a yield to maturity of 5.98%. Do not feel bad if you did not call your broker to order bargain bonds a few years ago. Interest rates have since set new records with the inevitable result of lower prices for fixed income securities. In 1971 the Shell bond was down to 76.125. The person who bought this bond in 1967 and sold it in 1971 would have made about $3\frac{1}{4}\%$ on his investment.

While a large drop in the market value of a bond is depressing, the owner of a bond in a sound company knows that if he holds the bond it will eventually appreciate as it approaches maturity. Even this limited consolation is denied the poor soul who has bonds for which economic or political developments indicate a bleak future. In 1967 Pennsylvania Railroad $4\frac{1}{4}\%$ bonds were rated Ba and were quoted around 80. In 1971 these bonds had a new rating of Caa and were sold flat at about 17. Speculators who buy at this price may eventually do very well if the railroad gets back on a profitable basis. People who have less to hope for are holders of Czarist Russian bonds of 1916, Imperial Chinese Government Hukuang Railways Bonds, and other IOUs which have been in default for decades. There is still active trading in bonds issued by pre-Communist governments in countries now behind the Iron Curtain. Some of the price swings have been spectacular. When Lenin annulled foreign loans, Czarist bonds dropped to $7.50 for a $1000 bond. Early in World War II the price dropped to $2.50. Then up to over $200 at the time of the Yalta Conference. Currently you can get one of these bonds for a few dollars. The speculative interest in old and defaulted bonds is based on the hope that some settlement of ancient debts will be made. Even bonds for which there is no such hope have some trading value as material for papering playrooms.

# 8

Capital
Budgeting
and
Depreciation

## 8.1 Gross National Product

One of the most important measures of the health of the nation's economy is gross national product. GNP is the total value at current prices of all final goods and services produced for sale plus the estimated value of certain imputed outputs. Major components of GNP are shown on page 277.

## 8.2 Business Investment

Capital expenditures, money spent by business for structures and the tools of production, amount to about one-tenth of GNP. But this relatively small investment in productive capital plays a particularly important role in determining whether the economy will be in a state of boom or recession. Jobs for

276

|  | 1971 | | 1970 | |
| --- | --- | --- | --- | --- |
|  | *Billions of Dollars* | *Per Cent of Total* | *Billions of Dollars* | *Per Cent of Total* |
| Personal consumption expenses | 662.2 | 63.2 | 615.8 | 63.2 |
| Gross private domestic investment | | | | |
| Business structures and equipment | 99.8 | 9.5 | 95.9 | 9.8 |
| Farm structures and equipment | 8.4 | .8 | 6.3 | .7 |
| Residential structures | 40.6 | 3.9 | 30.4 | 3.1 |
| Changes in business inventories | 2.1 | .2 | 2.8 | .3 |
| Government purchases of goods and services | 233.1 | 22.3 | 219.4 | 22.5 |
| Net exports of goods and services | .7 | .1 | 3.6 | .4 |
|  | 1046.9 | 100.0 | 974.2 | 100.0 |

Source: 1972 Economic Report of the President, Tables B-1 and B-11.

a growing labor force, a rising standard of living, stable prices, all depend on maintaining capital formation at a rate that is high enough to meet future needs, yet not so high that inflation results.

Unlike personal consumption expenditures, which are relatively stable through good times and bad, capital expenditures are volatile with cyclical swings several times as large in percentage terms as the changes in outlays for consumer goods. As the graph on page 278 shows, business investment in plant and equipment almost disappeared in the depths of the depression. From 1957 to 1958 business investment dropped 12 per cent in one year. The 5-year boom period from 1961 to 1966 saw a 69 per cent rise in business investment. The instability of investment and the attendant financial fluctuations provide plenty of opportunities either to go broke or to get rich. The mathematics of finance can help to put investment planning for individuals, financial and other organizations on sound, rational, and profitable bases.

## 8.3   Where the Money Comes From

Investment requires saving, that is, consumption of less than total income. Americans are great savers. Year in and year out individuals and families save on the average 5 to 8 cents out of each dollar of disposable income, the income that is left after taxes. Saving is good for the economy, provided the savings are borrowed and put to work by others who have reason to spend more than their incomes.

In exceptional years the savings pattern changes. During wartime, when incomes are high and spending opportunities are low, as much as a quarter

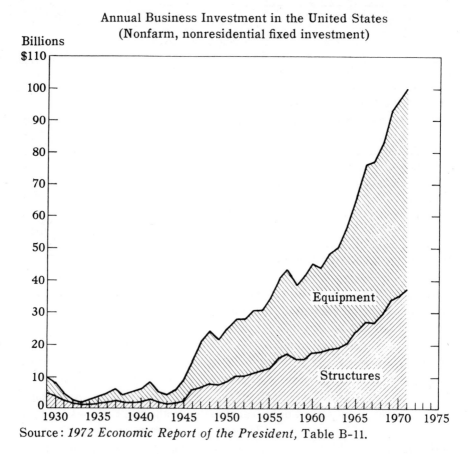

Annual Business Investment in the United States
(Nonfarm, nonresidential fixed investment)

Source: *1972 Economic Report of the President,* Table B-11.

of each dollar may be saved. In hard times, such as the depression of the 30's, some people dissave or spend more than they take in. During these years many families were forced to borrow or use past savings. The graph on page 279 shows both the great fluctuations in abnormal times and the relative stability of the savings rate in normal years, particularly since World War II.

While household savings out of take-home pay are usually close to the 6.4% average prevailing since 1950, misgivings about the future can cause marked changes in the savings rate. When families become jittery about the economy, particularly unemployment and inflation, they start squirreling away money. In the second quarter of 1971, the savings rate hit a 20-year high of 8.6%. With disposable income at an annual rate of about $700 billion, even a one percentage point increase in the savings rate means $7 billion less spent on goods and services. As consumer confidence returns, the savings rate drops and more money is pumped into the spending stream. As this increased spending works

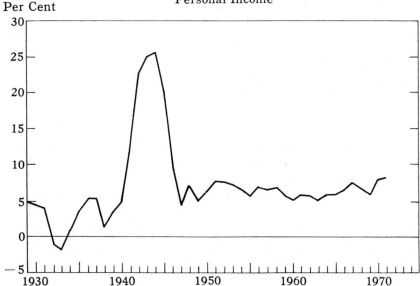

Source: *1972 Economic Report of the President,* Table B-15.

its way through the economy, after-tax income is increased. Since consumption expenditures account for nearly two-thirds of GNP, consumer behavior is an important determinant of the country's gross national product.

Not all money saved by consumers is used to increase investment. Much of the savings of individuals is used to pay off mortgages and other debts. However, as old debt is extinguished, new debt may be created. Money hoarded at home is not financing a new machine. Money can be transferred from household savings to business investment if it is put in financial intermediaries such as banks and insurance companies. These efficient financial mechanisms pay interest for the use of the savings of individuals and then make investment loans to businesses in need of funds for the purchase of productive capital. They also help provide liquidity for the whole economy.

Personal savings also become available to finance investment when the savings are used to buy new corporate bonds and stocks. Once bonds and stocks have been issued, they are traded in the various securities markets. This transfer of existing securities does not provide new funds for investment in capital goods. A person buying stock on the stock exchange may say that he is investing. This may be true in a personal sense, but it is not business investing because the purchase price is transferred to the seller of the stock rather than being used to buy plant or equipment. Although security exchanges do not provide a market-place for the sale of new securities, the exchanges do result in a high degree of liquidity for stocks and bonds and thereby make it easier for firms to raise new funds.

While the savings of individuals are important for investment they are only a part of investment funds in a progressive economy. Corporations are important savers, too. They save by not paying out to their stockholders their entire net income. Funds for capital projects are also obtained from depreciation allowances. In 1970, nonfarm, nonfinancial corporations obtained $20.3 billions from bonds, $11.7 billions from mortgages and bank and other loans, and $6.8 billions from new stock issues. These are substantial sums from external sources but their total is less than funds from internal sources which included $53.8 billions from depreciation allowances and $12.3 billions of retained earnings.

Net cash flow, the sum of depreciation allowances and retained earnings, has financed about two-thirds of corporate investment over the years. However, in the last few years there has been a marked drop in the percentage of investment financed with internally generated funds. This is the result, as shown below, of a drop in retained earnings that has resulted in stagnation in corporate cash flow.

Increased use of external sources of money, along with restricted credit supplies, has helped to carry interest rates to record highs. Money and capital

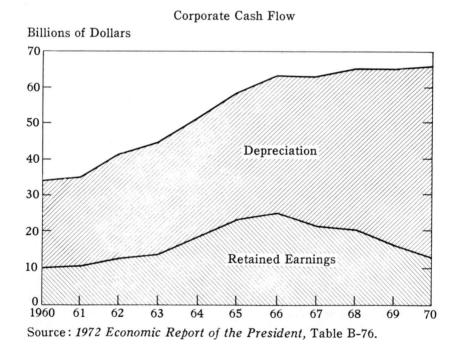

Corporate Cash Flow

Source: *1972 Economic Report of the President,* Table B-76.

markets are sensitive to changes in prices, business earnings, consumer spending, and other major economic variables.

Regardless of the source of funds—new stock issues, loans, profits, or depreciation—the question to which management seeks an answer is the same. Will a proposed investment show an acceptable profit? Adequate returns are the key requirement for raising the vast sums needed by an advanced technology if it is to become more productive. Individual firms usually have several alternative proposals for the use of limited funds. Present value analysis, using compound interest, can help a decision maker allocate funds in a way that will result in acceptable rates of return on invested capital.

Jobs, as well as profits, depend on investment. Managers of factories and offices tend to employ the number of workers required for efficient operation with the use of equipment on hand. A new job in manufacturing can require an additional investment of $20,000 or more. An adequate level of capital formation is necessary to provide jobs for an increasing labor force.

## 8.4 Will It Pay?

"Will it pay?" is an important and difficult question which the management of a business must face when planning for the future. It is particularly important to find the right answer when management is considering a capital expenditure, that is, a major replacement or addition to plant capacity. Since several years may be required to recover the large initial outlays involved in capital expenditures, errors in capital budgeting can have serious consequences for a company.

As Stewart S. Cort, President of Bethlehem Steel Corporation, has said: "Of all business activities, capital spending requires the most careful planning. The lives of capital assets are comparatively long and the time lag between the decision to make a particular investment and the beginning of its productive use is usually substantial."*

There may be as much as a 6-year lag between the time a utility orders a power plant and the time the plant is on line and producing electricity. Because of its size and permanence, a capital spending mistake can affect earnings for a long time. Even after it is written off the books, the memory may linger to prejudice future financing.

Experience and good judgment are essential for making sound capital spending decisions. Although they cannot take the risks and uncertainties out of capital budgeting, correct compound interest methods can help in the analysis and judicious comparison of capital projects.

The combination of the focal date technique developed in earlier chapters with the depreciation methods discussed in this chapter, results in useful

* *Wall Street Journal*, October 6, 1966, page 16.

methods for evaluating proposed capital expenditures. As is the case through-out the mathematics of finance, our analysis is based on the fact that money has a *time value*. A sum of money expected in the future must be discounted if it is to be compared with a cash outlay at another time. Discounting is usually done at a rate which is high enough to include both a reasonable return on the investment and an allowance for risk.

In capital budgeting, the comparison of expenses and income on a present value basis is called *discounted cash flow analysis*. Cash flows include some or all of the following:

| Cash Outflows | Cash Inflows |
|---|---|
| Initial investment | Expected benefits: |
| Continuing costs | Increased revenues |
| in future years | Lower costs |
| | Depreciation allowances |
| | Salvage value |

Since some of the expenses and all of the revenues occur in the future, we discount future cash flows before we compare proposed projects or estimate the rate of return to be expected on an investment. Because the future contains many uncertainties, the returns from a proposed investment depend to a considerable extent on forecasting judgment relative to sales, prices, and other variables. Thus in discounted cash flow analysis we have estimates, not the mathematical certitude that we had in earlier chapters when dealing with fixed payments and annuities certain. Predicting cash flows is the most complex and difficult aspect of the capital budgeting process. Once these estimates have been made, it is relatively easy to use mathematics of finance to compare proposed projects and to estimate rates of return.

In predicting the future, two types of risk are involved. One is that the asset may not perform as expected because of early breakdown, high maintenance costs, low productivity, or early obsolescence. The other risk is that future economic conditions and the demand for the product may not develop as expected.

Important in all capital budgeting problems is the recovery of invested capital. Determining the best method of capital recovery requires an understanding of the depreciation methods discussed in the following sections.

## 8.5   Depreciation Is an Expense

The cost of a machine, building, or other tangible asset is an expense to be recovered out of revenue during the useful life of the asset. All machinery is headed for the junk heap, and its cost should be recovered before it gets there. As income-producing plants and equipment are used up, depreciation is the allocation of cost which a company writes off against profits.

The earnings of a business are dependent on having adequate capital, materials, and labor. If the costs of assets are not recovered by the end of their useful lives, a company may find itself in serious financial trouble.

One cause of depreciation is wear and tear resulting from use of the asset. Another cause is obsolescence, which means that the asset is out of date because of the development of a better machine, an increase in demand which the present asset cannot meet, or a big decrease in demand for the products which the asset has been producing. A change in the costs of the factors of production may cause obsolescence. For example, increased labor costs may result in the installation of more efficient machinery before the old machinery is worn out.

The importance of allowing for depreciation can be illustrated by a simple example. A man buys a heavy-duty dump truck for $12,000. Contractors will pay $75 a day for his services and the use of the truck. From this $75 he must pay maintenance and operating expenses, his wages, and earn a reasonable return after taxes on his invested capital. And, if he hopes to remain in business, he should also recover the $12,000 by the end of the useful life of the truck. Eventually this truck, like any machine, will have to be replaced because it wears out or becomes obsolete. Regardless of the reason for replacement, the capital invested in an asset should be recovered from the income of the business. This recovery of invested capital is an expense, and it should be met from current income in the same way that labor, materials, interest, and other costs are recovered from the sale of the goods or services sold by a company.

The terms that will be used in depreciation problems are:

$C$ = the **original cost** of the asset.

$S$ = the **scrap, salvage,** or **residual value** of the asset at the end of its useful life.

$n$ = the **useful life** of the asset in years.

$W$ = the **wearing value** of the asset. It is the difference between cost and scrap value. $W = C - S$.

$R$ = the **periodic depreciation charge**. This is usually an annual charge. It may or may not be equal from year to year depending on the method of depreciation.

Both the estimated life of an asset and its scrap value are estimates made by authorities who are familiar with the particular asset. Since the rate of depreciation is based on judgment of how long an asset will be useful, there may be disagreements as to how much depreciation may be charged against income in any year. In 1962, the Internal Revenue Service published guidelines for depreciation allowances. Industry was classified into about 50 groups and depreciable lives assigned to assets in each group. If a company departs substantially from guideline useful lives, it may be necessary to show that the claimed depreciation rate is reasonable for their business.

While money recovered through depreciation allowances may be put into securities or other investments to build up a fund which will be used to replace the asset, a much more common practice is to use recovered funds in the operation of the business. In the modern corporation, depreciation charges are a major source of funds for capital projects. Used to purchase currently needed assets, the recovered funds usually earn a higher rate of return than could be obtained from income on securities.

The value at which an asset is shown on the accounting records of a company is called **carrying value** or **book value**. Initially the book value is the cost of the asset. After the first year it equals the amount of capital still invested in the property and which must be recovered in the future through depreciation charges and salvage value. As an asset depreciates, it is carried at a decreasing book value. The depreciation allowance each year offsets the decrease in book value. The sum of the depreciation allowances is called the total accumulated depreciation. At all times the book value plus the total accumulated depreciation should equal the cost of the asset.

In general, depreciation charges are on an annual basis. If a company acquires or disposes of property during a year, regular depreciation is allowable for that part of the year the company owns the asset. For example, a company whose accounting year is the calendar year would depreciate an asset purchased on March 1 an amount equal to the first full year's depreciation times 10/12. To simplify calculations in the examples and exercises in this book, it is assumed that assets were purchased in time to claim a full year's depreciation for the first year.

Practices differ regarding the handling of scrap values. Some accountants claim that because salvage estimates often require forecasts many years into an uncertain future plus the fact that removal costs may offset recovery income, the best practice is to assume zero scrap value. If this is done and the fully depreciated asset is eventually sold, any receipts from salvage sales would then be reported as income and taxes paid at that time. Others claim that if salvage is likely to be positive, the assumption of zero scrap value is not a sound practice. Since the student may in his later work encounter either or both practices, we assume in some problems that the company will get something for the asset when they dispose of it, while in other cases we depreciate on the assumption of zero scrap value.

There are several ways of allowing for depreciation which meet government regulations. We first discuss three methods based on time: *straight line, declining balance*, and *sum of the years digits*.

## 8.6  Straight Line Method

The simplest method of allowing for depreciation is the straight line method. This method spreads depreciation evenly over the useful life of the property. The periodic depreciation charge is obtained by simply dividing the wearing value by the useful life.

$$R = \frac{W}{n} \qquad (25)$$

As an asset is depreciated, the book value at any time equals

Original cost − (periodic charge $x$ number of charges)

EXAMPLE: A machine costs $5000 and has an estimated scrap value of $500 at the end of 5 years. Find the annual depreciation charge and the book value at the end of 3 years.

SOLUTION:

$$W = C - S = 5000 - 500 = \$4500$$

$$R = \frac{W}{n} = \frac{4500}{5} = \$900$$

Book value at the end of 3 years $= 5000 - (3 \times 900) = \$2300$

In many cases the scrap value is assumed to be zero, and a rate is determined from the estimated life of the asset. For an asset with a 5-year life, the rate would be 1/5 or 20% and the annual depreciation under the straight line method would be 20% of the cost.

## 8.7  Declining Balance Method

Under this method the depreciation allowance for each year is a constant per cent of the undepreciated or book value of the asset. Since the book value decreases each year, the depreciation charges are largest at first and then become progressively smaller.

New assets having a life of at least 3 years can be depreciated under this method at twice the straight line rate assuming no salvage value. If it is anticipated that a particular asset will have a significant scrap value, depreciation should stop when cost less this salvage has been recovered even though this occurs before the end of the useful life. A taxpayer using the 200% or double declining balance method can change to the straight line method at any time. If the asset has no salvage value, a shift will have to be made at some time to the straight line method since the declining balance method cannot depreciate an asset to zero.

If the declining balance method is applied to used, tangible property acquired after 1953, the rate per year may not exceed 150% of the straight line method, and a change to the straight line method requires the consent of the Internal Revenue Service.

EXAMPLE: A new machine costs $5000 and has an estimated scrap value of $500 at the end of 5 years. Find the annual depreciation allowances if the double declining balance method is used for 3 years and the straight line method is used for the last 2 years.

SOLUTION: The double declining balance rate is 40% since it is twice the straight line rate of 20% based on a life of 5 years with no allowance for salvage. Putting the problem in tabular form is a help in making the year-to-year calculations. The last entry in the Book Value column should equal the scrap value.

| YEAR | DEPRECIATION CHARGE | ACCUMULATED DEPRECIATION | BOOK VALUE |
|------|---------------------|--------------------------|------------|
| 0 | | | $5000 |
| 1 | $2000* | $2000 | 3000 |
| 2 | 1200* | 3200 | 1800 |
| 3 | 720* | 3920 | 1080 |
| 4 | 290** | 4210 | 790 |
| 5 | 290** | 4500 | 500 |

\* .40 × book value at end of preceding year.

\*\* Straight line charge $= \dfrac{1080 - 500}{2} = 290.$

## 8.8 Sum of the Years Digits

This is a simple method for making the depreciation allowances large during the early years of the useful life of the asset. The depreciation for each year is a fraction of the wearing value. The denominator of the fraction is obtained by numbering the years of useful life and adding. For example, if the estimated life is 4 years, the denominator $= 1 + 2 + 3 + 4 = 10$. The numerator for the first year is the estimated useful life. Each year the numerator is reduced by 1.

EXAMPLE 1: A machine costs $5000. It has an estimated scrap value of $500 at the end of 5 years. Get the annual depreciation allowances using the sum of the years digits.

SOLUTION: The sum of the digits is $1 + 2 + 3 + 4 + 5 = 15$. Depreciation allowances are:

| YEAR | DEPRECIATION ALLOWANCE | |
|------|------------------------|---|
| 1 | $4500 \times 5/15 =$ | $1500 |
| 2 | $4500 \times 4/15 =$ | 1200 |
| 3 | $4500 \times 3/15 =$ | 900 |
| 4 | $4500 \times 2/15 =$ | 600 |
| 5 | $4500 \times 1/15 =$ | 300 |
| | | $4500 |

Note that most of the cost is recovered early in the life of the asset.

EXAMPLE 2: A store building costs $510,000 and has an estimated life of 50 years. Assume zero salvage value and use the sum of the years digits to get the first two years' and the last two years' depreciation allowances.

SOLUTION: Since the digits from 1 to 50 form an arithmetic progression, we can get their sum quickly and easily by using the formula developed in algebra for the sum of an arithmetic progression.

$$S = \frac{n}{2}(t_1 + t_n)$$

where

$S =$ the sum
$n =$ number of terms
$t_1 =$ the first term
$t_n =$ the last term

Substituting the values in this problem, we have:

$$S = \tfrac{50}{2}(1 + 50) = 1275$$

Since the first term in the sum of the years digits is 1 and the last term is $n$, we can write the sum as:

$$S = \frac{n}{2}(1 + n) = n\left(\frac{n + 1}{2}\right) = \frac{n^2 + n}{2}$$

An individual may prefer one form of this formula over the others because it is easier for him to remember and use. In our problem, we have

$$S = \frac{(50 \times 50) + 50}{2} = \frac{2550}{2} = 1275$$

| YEAR | DEPRECIATION ALLOWANCE |
|:---:|:---|
| 1 | $510,000 \times 50/1275 = \$20,000$ |
| 2 | $510,000 \times 49/1275 = \phantom{0}19,600$ |
| ⋮ | |
| ⋮ | |
| 49 | $510,000 \times 2/1275 = \phantom{00,}800$ |
| 50 | $510,000 \times 1/1275 = \phantom{00,}400$ |

Since the depreciation allowances form an arithmetic progression with a decrease of $400 each year, a simple way to get each year's depreciation is to subtract $400 from the preceding year's value.

## 8.9   Comparison of Different Methods

The tables and sketches on page 289 show how the depreciation is accumulated and the book value reduced under the three methods. All are for an asset costing $5000 with a scrap value of $500 at the end of 5 years.

## 8.10   Determining the Best Method

The objective of all depreciation methods is the eventual recovery of the money invested in an asset, but there are differences in the rate of recovery. This is an important consideration because the value of a sum of money depends not only on the dollar amount but also on when it is received. Another consideration is the maximization of a company's net earnings after taxes.

An advantage of the straight line method is its simplicity. There are times when the straight line method offers not only simplicity but also financial advantages. The taxes of an individual are dependent on his tax bracket. In a new business, the owners may be in a low tax bracket while the business is getting established. Large depreciation charges then may be less desirable than later when the owners expect to be in a higher tax bracket.

The declining balance and the sum of the years digits result in a quick recovery of a large part of the money in an asset. Since depreciation charges reduce the income reported for tax purposes, high depreciation during the early years means savings on income tax during these years. This decrease in tax liability results in more money available sooner for use in the business. A dollar received now is worth more than a dollar to be received in several years because it can be put to use sooner to repay debts, expand the business, or it can be invested at interest.

Accelerated depreciation methods result in large depreciation allowances when the asset is new and repair costs are low and smaller depreciation allowances later when maintenance costs are higher. The result is a better matching of revenues with expenses throughout the life of the asset.

### Straight Line Method

| Year | Periodic Depreciation Charge | Total Accumulated Depreciation | Book Value |
|------|------|------|------|
| 0 |  |  | $5000 |
| 1 | $900 | $ 900 | 4100 |
| 2 | 900 | 1800 | 3200 |
| 3 | 900 | 2700 | 2300 |
| 4 | 900 | 3600 | 1400 |
| 5 | 900 | 4500 | 500 |

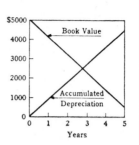

### Double Declining Balance
### (40% a year for 3 years and then straight line)

| Year | Periodic Depreciation Charge | Total Accumulated Depreciation | Book Value |
|------|------|------|------|
| 0 |  |  | $5000 |
| 1 | $2000 | $2000 | 3000 |
| 2 | 1200 | 3200 | 1800 |
| 3 | 720 | 3920 | 1080 |
| 4 | 290 | 4210 | 790 |
| 5 | 290 | 4500 | 500 |

### Sum of the Years Digits

| Year | Periodic Depreciation Charge | Total Accumulated Depreciation | Book Value |
|------|------|------|------|
| 0 |  |  | $5000 |
| 1 | $1500 | $1500 | 3500 |
| 2 | 1200 | 2700 | 2300 |
| 3 | 900 | 3600 | 1400 |
| 4 | 600 | 4200 | 800 |
| 5 | 300 | 4500 | 500 |

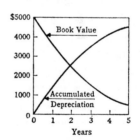

In times of rising prices with resulting decreases in the purchasing power of the dollar, a rapid write-off may mean that dollars recovered early have more purchasing power than dollars recovered after additional price increases. In many cases, this may be offset at least partially since newer and more expensive machines are also more productive.

Different depreciation methods can be compared on a present value basis by discounting all the depreciation charges. This is done in the table below for the $5000 asset discussed in the preceding section. The comparison is based on the assumption that money will earn 8% for the company. The nonuniform payments of the declining balance and sum of the years digits must be discounted one by one using the *Present Worth of* 1 factor. For comparison purposes, we have also used this factor for the straight line method although one would usually get the total present value with one computation using the *Present Worth of* 1 *per Period* factor. Factors which are taken to three decimal places result in answers that are adequate for comparison purposes.

| | | ANNUAL DEPRECIATION CHARGE | | | PRESENT WORTH OF ANNUAL CHARGE | | |
|---|---|---|---|---|---|---|---|
| YEAR | PRESENT WORTH OF 1 AT 8% | *Straight Line* | *Double Declining Balance* | *Sum of Years Digits* | *Straight Line* | *Double Declining Balance* | *Sum of Years Digits* |
| 1 | .926 | $900 | $2000 | $1500 | $833 | $1852 | $1389 |
| 2 | .857 | 900 | 1200 | 1200 | 771 | 1028 | 1028 |
| 3 | .794 | 900 | 720 | 900 | 715 | 572 | 715 |
| 4 | .735 | 900 | 290 | 600 | 662 | 213 | 441 |
| 5 | .681 | 900 | 290 | 300 | 613 | 197 | 204 |
| | | 500* | 500* | 500* | 340** | 340** | 340** |
| | | $5000 | $5000 | $5000 | $3934 | $4202 | $4117 |

\* Estimated salvage value.
\*\* Present worth of estimated salvage value.

Note that all three methods result in total depreciation charges plus salvage value equal to the cost of the asset. Regardless of method, depreciation enables a taxpayer to recover from income the cost of equipment which is used up in his business.

Since the timing of depreciation charges depends on the method, there are differences in the total present value of the depreciation charges. Both the double declining balance and the sum of the years digits result in a greater present value than the straight line method.

People who are responsible for preparing income tax reports for a business should understand the various methods of depreciation and be familiar with current tax regulations. Using the most advantageous system of depreciation will result in timing depreciation charges so that they will be of greatest benefit to the business.

If a business grows steadily, accelerated depreciation results in a more or less permanent grant of deferred taxes which may be used for company purposes. This has contributed to industrial growth in the United States.

### EXERCISE 8a

1. A truck costs $7000 and has an estimated scrap value of $1000 at the end of 5 years. Prepare depreciation schedules and graphs showing the total

accumulated depreciation and book value for the straight line, double declining balance shifting to straight line at the end of 3 years, and sum of the years digit methods.

2. A taxi costs $2500 and has an estimated scrap value of $500 at the end of 3 years. Prepare depreciation schedules and graphs showing the total accumulated depreciation and book value for the straight line, double declining balance shifting to straight line at the end of 1 year, and sum of the years digits methods.

3. An electric generator costs $39,000. It has an estimated life of 12 years and no scrap value. Compute the first two years' depreciation allowances for the straight line, double declining balance, and sum of the years digits.

$$\begin{bmatrix} \text{Straight line: } \$3250.00; \ \$3250.00 \\ \text{Double declining balance: } \$6500.00; \ \$5416.67 \\ \text{Sum of the years digits: } \$6000.00; \ \$5500.00 \end{bmatrix}$$

4. A sewing machine costs $400. It has an estimated life of 14 years and a salvage value of $50. Compute the first two years' depreciation allowances under straight line, double declining balance, and sum of the years digits methods.

5. An apartment building costs $82,000. Assume a life of 40 years and no scrap value and get the first two years' depreciation allowances under straight line, double declining balance, and sum of the years digits methods.

$$\begin{bmatrix} \text{Straight line: } \$2050.00; \ \$2050.00 \\ \text{Double declining balance: } \$4100.00; \ \$3895.00 \\ \text{Sum of the years digits: } \$4000.00; \ \$3900.00 \end{bmatrix}$$

6. A warehouse costs $366,000. It has an estimated life of 60 years and no scrap value. Compute the first two years' depreciation under straight line, double declining balance, and sum of the years digits methods.

7. When a $13,000 machine was purchased, the estimated life was 8 years and the estimated salvage value was $1000. However, soon after the machine was put into operation, it became advisable to replace it with a greatly improved model. The replacement was made after the third annual depreciation charge. What was the total accumulated depreciation at this time if depreciation was handled using: (a) straight line; (b) double declining balance; (c) sum of the years digits?

[(a) $4500.00; (b) $7515.63; (c) $7000.00]

8. A machine which cost $7500 has an estimated scrap value of $300 at the end of 12 years. At the end of 5 years, the machine becomes obsolete because of the development of a better machine. What will be the total accumulated depreciation at this time if the depreciation was handled using: (a) straight line; (b) double declining balance; (c) sum of the digits?

**9.** A used truck was purchased for $3000. It has an estimated life of 4 years and a scrap value of $600. Find the first two years' depreciation allowances under: (a) straight line; (b) 150% declining balance; (c) sum of the years digits.

$$\begin{bmatrix} \text{Straight line: } \$600.00; \$600.00 \\ 150\% \text{ declining balance: } \$1125.00; \$703.12 \\ \text{Sum of the years digits: } \$960.00; \$720.00 \end{bmatrix}$$

**10.** A farmer paid $2000 for a used tractor. It has an estimated life of 8 years and a scrap value of $200. Find the first two years' depreciation allowances under: (a) straight line; (b) 150% declining balance; (c) sum of the years digits.

## 8.11   Depreciation Based on Use

The depreciation methods discussed so far have been based on the asset having an assumed life in years. We now consider a method which is based on the hours an asset is used or the number of units it produces. This method allows for more depreciation during a busy period when a factory may be working two or three shifts as compared to one shift during normal times.

EXAMPLE 1: A machine costs $5000 and has an estimated scrap value of $200. Machines of this type have an estimated operating life of 20,000 hours. This machine has been run as follows: first year, 2200 hours; second year, 4000 hours; third year, 1800 hours; fourth year, 3000 hours, fifth year, 4000 hours. Prepare a table showing the depreciation for each year.

SOLUTION: The total wearing value is $4800. The depreciation charge for the first year is

$$4800 \times \frac{2200}{20,000} = \$528$$

Continuing this for successive years, we have:

| YEAR | FRACTION OF USEFUL LIFE | PERIODIC DEPRECIATION CHARGE | ACCUMULATED DEPRECIATION | BOOK VALUE |
|---|---|---|---|---|
| 0 | | | | $5000 |
| 1 | 2200/20,000 | $528 | $ 528 | 4472 |
| 2 | 4000/20,000 | 960 | 1488 | 3512 |
| 3 | 1800/20,000 | 432 | 1920 | 3080 |
| 4 | 3000/20,000 | 720 | 2640 | 2360 |
| 5 | 4000/20,000 | 960 | 3600 | 1400 |

EXAMPLE 2: A machine costs $5000 and has an estimated scrap value of $200. It is estimated that this machine will produce 50,000 units. The annual production has been: first year 8000 units; second year 5000 units; third year 12,000 units; fourth year 10,000 units; fifth year 5000 units. Prepare a table showing the depreciation for each year.

SOLUTION: The total wearing value is $4800. The depreciation charge for the first year is

$$4800 \times \frac{8000}{50,000} = \$768$$

Continuing this for successive years, we have

| YEAR | FRACTION OF ESTIMATED PRODUCTION | PERIODIC DEPRECIATION CHARGE | ACCUMULATED DEPRECIATION | BOOK VALUE |
|------|------|------|------|------|
| 0 | | | | $5000 |
| 1 | 8,000/50,000 | $ 768 | $ 768 | 4232 |
| 2 | 5,000/50,000 | 480 | 1248 | 3752 |
| 3 | 12,000/50,000 | 1152 | 2400 | 2600 |
| 4 | 10,000/50,000 | 960 | 3360 | 1640 |
| 5 | 5,000/50,000 | 480 | 3840 | 1160 |

### EXERCISE 8b

1. A piece of machinery costs $8000 and has an estimated scrap value of $2000. Machines of this type have an estimated working-hour life of 10,000 hours. This machine is used as follows: first year 3000 hours; second year 1200 hours; third year 1000 hours; fourth year 2000 hours. Prepare a depreciation schedule for the 4 years this machine has been in use.

2. A machine costs $30,000 and has an estimated scrap value of $4000. It is estimated that this machine will produce 120,000 units during its useful life. The machine produces the following outputs during the first 5 years it is in use: first year 20,000 units; second year 15,000 units; third year 25,000 units; fourth year 10,000 units; fifth year 18,000 units. Prepare a depreciation schedule.

## 8.12 Determining Cash Flows

Cash flows, both expenses and revenues, may occur at any time during a time period, or more or less continuously during a period. The common practice in capital budgeting is to value all cash flows during a year as if they occur at the end of the year. This simplifies computations, is realistic, and is in accord with the practice of making major decisions in business on an annual basis.

Therefore, before starting numerical computations, it is a good procedure to combine all cash flows during a year into a single net cash flow for that year. The analyst should take into account expected revenues, expenses, depreciation allowances, taxes, and any other factors that affect the final cash flow for that year.

Depreciation is not only the largest single source of investment funds, it is also the most confusing. The reason is that depreciation is both a non-cash expense and a net inflow of cash for the current year. When a company buys a capital asset—a building or a machine—a certain amount of it is used up each year and a cost must be charged for this wear and tear if the company is to keep its capital intact. If no allowance were made for depreciation, a company would be overstating its profits. Depreciation is a legitimate accounting procedure used to arrive at net profits. Inadequate depreciation allowances can contribute to a firm's eventual failure.

But unlike the costs for labor, materials, and taxes, the company does not send anyone a check or cash to take care of depreciation. Depreciation costs are handled with entries in the company books which show that the plant or machine is worth so much less than a year ago. This takes care of the non-cash expense aspect of depreciation.

However, there was a time in the past when the asset was paid for. As the asset is used up in production, it becomes a legitimate expense that is a part of the total cost of production. Depreciation allowances spread the cost of the asset over its life and the company must charge enough for its product to cover this cost as well as the costs of labor, material, taxes, and so on. By pricing goods high enough, revenue is derived from sales to cover the cost of depreciation. The depreciation bookkeeping charge against earnings results in the company being able to reduce current income by writing off assets as they are used up in the business. The depreciation charge before taxes results in the net cash inflow aspect of depreciation.

Note in the examples how net cash inflow from operations is determined. We first get the depreciation which is deducted as a cost or expense from income. Then taxes are calculated on income less depreciation. Finally the charge for depreciation is added to income after taxes to get the net cash inflow from operations.

Sometimes capital budgeting studies are made on the basis of flows before taxes. This is reasonable when analyzing government proposals or investment in human capital. However, corporate tax rates are responsible for large cash outflows. For this reason, it is best to use after tax flows when analyzing private business investments. The examples in this book are based on a tax rate of 48%. This rate may be changed in the future as it has been in the past. Fiscal policy may result in a lower rate when the economy needs such a fiscal stimulus to head off a recession or to initiate a recovery. At other times a higher rate may be desired to slow down an overheated economy that seems headed for inflation.

In some cases, it may also be necessary to allow for state taxes. However, the methods apply regardless of rates. The example below shows how both depreciation and taxes are taken into account in determining the net cash flow for each year.

EXAMPLE 1: A company is considering the purchase of a machine which costs $15,000 and has an estimated salvage value of $3000 at the end of its useful life of 3 years. Annual operating costs are expected to be about $1000 a year. Additional revenue expected from the machine is $7000 a year. Get the net cash flows for this machine assuming a 48% tax rate and (a) straight line depreciation; (b) double declining balance for the first year and straight line for the next two years; (c) sum of the years digits.

STRAIGHT LINE:
Net income before taxes and depreciation =
    additional revenue − additional costs           $7000 − 1000 = \$6000$

Annual depreciation allowance                       $\dfrac{15,000 - 3000}{3} = 4000$

Taxable income = net income − depreciation          $6000 - 4000 = 2000$
Income after taxes = .52 × taxable income*           $.52 \times 2000 = 1040$
Net cash flow = income after taxes + depreciation    $1040 + 4000 = 5040$

The year-by-year determination of cash flows can be presented quite well in tabular form. The net cash flow for year zero is the cost of the asset and is negative. For subsequent years, the net cash flow is the sum of the depreciation allowance and the income after taxes.

| (1) | (2) | (3) | (4) | (5) | (6) |
|---|---|---|---|---|---|
| YEAR | NET INCOME BEFORE TAXES AND DEPRECIATION | DEPRECIATION ALLOWANCE | TAXABLE INCOME (2) − (3) | INCOME AFTER TAXES .52 × (4) | NET CASH FLOW (3) + (5) |
| 0 | − $15,000 | | | | − $15,000 |
| 1 | 6,000 | $4,000 | $2,000 | $1,040 | 5,040 |
| 2 | 6,000 | 4,000 | 2,000 | 1,040 | 5,040 |
| 3 | 6,000 | 4,000 | 2,000 | 1,040 | 8,040** |
| | | $12,000 | $6,000 | $3,120 | $3,120 |

* Some authors first multiply the taxable income by the tax rate. The tax in dollars is then subtracted from taxable income to get the income after taxes. In capital budgeting problems it is easier and faster to get the after-tax income by multiplying the taxable income by $(1 - \text{tax rate})$. With a tax rate of 48%, the after tax factor becomes $(1.00 - .48) = .52$.
** Includes $3000 salvage value. The salvage value is added to cash inflow after taxes and depreciation.

DOUBLE DECLINING BALANCE: The first year's depreciation is 2/3 of the purchase price, or $10,000. This is more than the net income for the year, resulting in a taxable income of −$4000. If the company has other income, as will usually be the case, the excess depreciation on this machine can be used to reduce reported earnings by $4000. This will result in a tax shield or tax offset of .48 × 4000 = $1920. This means that the income after taxes from this asset will be −$2080. Since this is what we get from .52(−4000), we can use the same procedure for getting income after taxes whether the taxable income is plus or minus. If this machine represented all of the company's operations, there could be a carry back or carry forward of the loss.

| (1) | (2) | (3) | (4) | (5) | (6) |
|---|---|---|---|---|---|
| | NET INCOME | | TAXABLE | INCOME AFTER TAXES | NET CASH FLOW |
| | BEFORE TAXES AND | DEPRECIATION | INCOME | | |
| YEAR | DEPRECIATION | ALLOWANCE | (2) − (3) | .52 × (4) | (3) + (5) |
| 0 | −$15,000 | | | | −$15,000 |
| 1 | 6,000 | $10,000 | −$4,000 | −$2,080 | 7,920 |
| 2 | 6,000 | 1,000 | 5,000 | 2,600 | 3,600 |
| 3 | 6,000 | 1,000 | 5,000 | 2,600 | 6,600* |
| | | $12,000 | $6,000 | $3,120 | $3,120 |

* Includes $3000 salvage value. The salvage value is added to cash inflow after taxes and depreciation.

SUM OF THE YEARS DIGITS: The denominator of the annual fraction = 1 + 2 + 3 = 6.

| (1) | (2) | (3) | (4) | (5) | (6) |
|---|---|---|---|---|---|
| | NET INCOME | | TAXABLE | INCOME AFTER TAXES | NET CASH FLOW |
| | BEFORE TAXES AND | DEPRECIATION | INCOME | | |
| YEAR | DEPRECIATION | ALLOWANCE | (2) − (3) | .52 × (4) | (3) + (5) |
| 0 | −$15,000 | | | | −$15,000 |
| 1 | 6,000 | $6,000 | $ 0 | $ 0 | 6,000 |
| 2 | 6,000 | 4,000 | 2,000 | 1,040 | 5,040 |
| 3 | 6,000 | 2,000 | 4,000 | 2,080 | 7,080* |
| | | $12,000 | $6,000 | $3,120 | $3,120 |

* Includes $3000 salvage value. The salvage value is added to cash inflow after taxes and depreciation.

Note that the totals are the same for all methods of depreciation, but there are differences in the year-by-year net cash flows.

Time diagrams are quite helpful in presenting net cash flow problems in pictorial form.

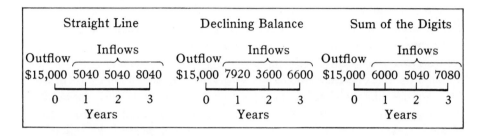

Histograms can be used to give an overall picture of cash flow problems. Sometimes the various inflows and outflows are shaded differently so a busy reader can see at a glance the different expenses and sources of income.

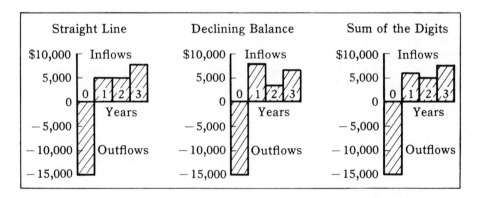

## 8.13 Timing Is Important

In the examples in the preceding section, taxable income was $6000 for all methods of depreciation. Regardless of the method of depreciating an asset, total depreciation allowances will be the same. This means that total income subject to tax will be the same regardless of how an item is depreciated. If tax rates do not change, the government will in the long run collect the same amount of taxes no matter how depreciation is handled. This has led some advocates of fast depreciation to argue that no tax loss will result from accelerated depreciation even if 100% depreciation is allowed the first year. Faster depreciation merely means lower taxes in the early life of an asset and higher taxes in later years.

It is true that the total amount written off on any particular asset will be the same regardless of the number of years. However, companies invest every year and the Treasury collects taxes every year. When depreciation is accelerated, the Treasury collects less revenue year by year than it would otherwise get. In 1971 the Asset Depreciation Range System was introduced. This system permits companies to depreciate assets for tax purposes over a period as much as 20% shorter or 20% longer than guideline lives. It was argued that this would lead to more investment and modernization of plant and equipment.

The Treasury estimated that the proposed changes would result in a $2.7 billion drop in tax revenue in 1972 and a total drop of $37 billion over a decade. Critics of the change claimed that this represented additional money for business that might better be used by Government to alleviate social problems. Ralph Nader's public interest research group argued that a change like this in tax policy should be made only after adequate public hearings. As informed and concerned citizens gain a better understanding of the time value of money, increased attention will be given to the timing of proposed fiscal policies.

## 8.14    Present Value Comparisons

After net cash flows have been determined, compound interest methods can be used in two ways to analyze proposed investments. One way is to use compound discount factors to get the present value of all flows at a specified rate. The other way is to get the rate which makes the inflows and outflows equal. In either case, the solution is obtained using the focal date approach which is so useful throughout the mathematics of finance. The focal date is usually put at the point where the major expenditure of funds will be made. If there are relatively small planning expenditures in the years preceding the installation of an asset, these are brought forward at compound interest. Estimated future net cash flows are discounted to the installation date.

The interest rate (often called the discount rate) to be used in getting present values is commonly called the cost of capital. This is the particular company's best estimate of the return that the firm's creditors and stockholders, its suppliers of long term capital expect on their investment.

To help compensate for the uncertainties involved in estimating future cash flows, interest rates in capital budgeting problems are higher than those used in problems where the return is not in doubt. This is reasonable since a firm that could get 5 or 6 per cent on a bond or mortgage will expect a considerably higher return when putting money into a project that involves greater risks. Present investments must be based on forecasts of a future which can be seen only hazily. No one can be sure how business will be in two or three years, let alone in five or ten years. If there were no premiums for risk-taking and no rewards for foresight and good luck, risk capital would not be available for innovation and expansion. When a reasonable allowance for risk-taking is added to interest costs, a firm may feel that an after-tax return of 10 or 15% or more on invested capital is required to make a project attractive. By invested capital is meant the money supplied by the owners of the company. In the company balance sheet invested capital is usually called stockholders' equity. Invested capital comes partly from the sale of stock. After a company starts making a profit, a part of earnings probably will be paid out in dividends to the stockholders. The remainder will be retained in the business and recorded as an increase in stockholders' equity. Since profits belong to the owners, retained earnings mean in effect that stockholders are investing more money in the business. If the company continues to prosper, retained earnings will contribute to higher profits and increases in the market value of the stock.

It is interesting to see what some of the top corporations do in the way of making money. The data below from the annual *Fortune* surveys of American corporations show after-tax income as a percentage of invested capital.

| | NET INCOME AS PER CENT OF INVESTED CAPITAL | | |
|---|---|---|---|
| *Five largest industrial companies* | 1971 | 1970 | 1969 |
| General Motors | 17.9 | 6.2 | 16.7 |
| Ford | 11.8 | 9.4 | 10.5 |
| Standard Oil of New Jersey | 12.6 | 12.0 | 10.4 |
| General Electric | 16.8 | 12.3 | 10.9 |
| International Business Machines | 16.2 | 17.1 | 17.7 |
| *Five largest merchandising firms* | | | |
| Sears Roebuck | 13.6 | 12.5 | 12.8 |
| Great Atlantic and Pacific Tea | 3.1 | 8.0 | 8.1 |
| Safeway Stores | 14.7 | 13.9 | 11.9 |
| Kroger | 9.2 | 12.0 | 12.5 |
| J. C. Penney | 13.7 | 15.1 | 16.9 |
| *Five largest utilities* | | | |
| American Telephone and Telegraph | 8.5 | 9.0 | 9.3 |
| Consolidated Edison | 8.8 | 6.5 | 6.9 |
| Pacific Gas and Electric | 9.7 | 9.2 | 10.1 |
| Commonwealth Edison | 10.1 | 11.3 | 12.4 |
| Southern California Edison | 8.4 | 9.3 | 8.8 |

Some companies had even more impressive profits. In 1970 Avon had a 36.1% return on invested capital and Coca Cola had 22.4%.

Before accepting a new proposal, the management of a company may insist that the project have an expected rate of return considerably higher than the overall rate for the company. The reason is that the overall rate is after advertising, overhead, and other general expenses. A proportionate share of these costs will probably not be allotted in advance to a proposed new project.

When projects are evaluated on a present value basis, the present value of the inflows must be greater than the present value of the outflows for the project to be attractive.

In discounted cash flow analysis, two discount factors are used: *Present Worth of* 1 for discounting single sums and *Present Worth of* 1 *per Period* for discounting a series of equal cash flows equally spaced. These factors are given in Table 4. Since cash flow analysis is based on estimates, the discount factors are given in Table 4 to 3 decimal places, sufficient for practical work with uncertain data.

EXAMPLE 1: Determine the net present value of the proposal in Section 8.12 using an estimated cost of capital of 8% and the three methods of depreciation.

SOLUTION: We discount each net cash flow to the present using the *Present Worth of* 1 factors. The algebraic sum is the net present value of the project. A tabular arrangement systematizes the work and makes comparisons easy.

| YEAR | DISCOUNT FACTOR AT 8% | STRAIGHT LINE Net Cash Flow | STRAIGHT LINE Present Value | DOUBLE DEC. BALANCE Net Cash Flow | DOUBLE DEC. BALANCE Present Value | SUM OF DIGITS Net Cash Flow | SUM OF DIGITS Present Value |
|---|---|---|---|---|---|---|---|
| 0 | 1.000 | −$15,000 | −$15,000 | −$15,000 | −$15,000 | −$15,000 | −$15,000 |
| 1 | .926 | 5,040 | 4,667 | 7,920 | 7,334 | 6,000 | 5,556 |
| 2 | .857 | 5,040 | 4,319 | 3,600 | 3,085 | 5,040 | 4,319 |
| 3 | .794 | 8,040 | 6,384 | 6,600 | 5,240 | 7,080 | 5,622 |
|  |  |  | $   370 |  | $   659 |  | $   497 |

The positive net present values show that all of the methods of depreciation would result in the project returning better than 8% provided the actual net flows are as high as the estimates. The differences in the net present values show the advantages of a rapid write-off.

EXAMPLE 2: Determine the net present values for the above problem using a cost of capital of 10%.

| YEAR | DISCOUNT FACTOR AT 10% | STRAIGHT LINE Net Cash Flow | STRAIGHT LINE Present Value | DOUBLE DEC. BALANCE Net Cash Flow | DOUBLE DEC. BALANCE Present Value | SUM OF DIGITS Net Cash Flow | SUM OF DIGITS Present Value |
|---|---|---|---|---|---|---|---|
| 0 | 1.000 | −$15,000 | −$15,000 | −$15,000 | −$15,000 | −$15,000 | −$15,000 |
| 1 | .909 | 5,040 | 4,581 | 7,920 | 7,199 | 6,000 | 5,454 |
| 2 | .826 | 5,040 | 4,163 | 3,600 | 2,974 | 5,040 | 4,163 |
| 3 | .751 | 8,040 | 6,038 | 6,600 | 4,957 | 7,080 | 5,317 |
| | | | −$ 218 | | $ 130 | | −$ 66 |

This asset can be expected to produce a 10% return only if the double declining balance method of depreciation is used.

EXAMPLE 3: A company is considering the purchase of a piece of equipment which costs $11,000 and has an estimated scrap value of $1000 at the end of its useful life of 5 years. The equipment is expected to result in operating savings of $5000 a year. Would this investment be attractive to a company that wants a return of 12% a year after taxes? Use straight line depreciation and a tax rate of 48%.

SOLUTION:

$$\text{Annual depreciation allowance} = 10,000/5 = \$2000$$
$$\text{Taxable income} = 5000 - 2000 = 3000$$
$$\text{Income after taxes} = .52 \times 3000 = 1560$$
$$\text{Net cash inflow} = 3560$$
$$\text{(Depreciation allowance + after tax income)}$$

Since the five net cash inflows of $3560 form an ordinary annuity, we get their present value using (13) and the *Present Worth of 1 per Period* factor from Table 4. To this is added the present worth of the scrap value obtained using (11) and the *Present Worth of 1* factor.

$$\text{Present worth of inflows} = 3560a_{\overline{5}|12\%} + 1000(1.12)^{-5}$$
$$= 3560 \times 3.605 + 1000 \times .567$$
$$= 12,834 + 567 = \$13,401$$

This is well above the cost of $11,000. The present value of the asset is $13,401 - 11,000 = \$2041$. Since the equipment can clearly be expected to return more than 12%, it is an acceptable project.

## 8.15 Rate of Return

The internal rate of return is the rate which will make cash inflows equal to outflows. This rate must be found by trial and error unless the cash flows happen to form an ordinary annuity as in the first example.

EXAMPLE 1: A company is considering the purchase of an asset which costs $6000 and has no scrap value at the end of its useful life of 3 years. Annual net income over operating expenses is expected to be $4200. Find the internal rate of return assuming straight line depreciation and a tax rate of 48 %.

SOLUTION:

$$
\begin{aligned}
\text{Annual depreciation allowance} &= 6000/3 = \$2000 \\
\text{Taxable income} = 4200 - 2000 &= 2200 \\
\text{Income after taxes} = .52 \times 2200 &= 1144 \\
\text{Annual net cash inflow} = 2000 + 1144 &= 3144
\end{aligned}
$$

Since the net cash inflows in this problem form an ordinary annuity, we find the rate following the method in Section 4.12. Substituting in (13),

$$3144a_{\overline{3}|} = 6000$$

$$a_{\overline{3}|} = \tfrac{6000}{3144} = 1.908$$

According to the table, the rate is between 25 and 30%. If a more precise answer is required, we interpolate.

| $i$ in % | | $a_{\overline{3}|}$ | |
|---|---|---|---|
| | 25 | 1.952 | |
| 5 | $d \begin{bmatrix} i \end{bmatrix}$ | 1.908 | 44 |
| | 30 | 1.816 | 136 |

$$\frac{d}{5} = \frac{44}{136}$$

$$d = \frac{5 \times 44}{136} = 1.6$$

$$i = 25.0 + 1.6 = 26.6\%$$

Since there are many uncertainties in capital budgeting problems, it is probably well to round this off to the nearest percentage point. We would simply say that the expected internal rate of return on this project is approximately 27%.

EXAMPLE 2: Work the example above using double declining balance for 2 years and straight line for the third year.

SOLUTION: The first year's depreciation is $6000 \times 2/3 = \$4000$. Continuing with the solution in tabular form, we have

| (1) | (2) | (3) | (4) | (5) | (6) |
|-----|-----|-----|-----|-----|-----|
| | NET INCOME BEFORE TAXES AND | DEPRECIATION | TAXABLE INCOME | INCOME AFTER TAXES | NET CASH FLOW |
| YEAR | DEPRECIATION | ALLOWANCE | (2) − (3) | .52 × (4) | (3) + (5) |
| 0 | − $6000 | | | | − $6000 |
| 1 | 4200 | $4000 | $ 200 | $ 104 | 4104 |
| 2 | 4200 | 1333 | 2867 | 1491 | 2824 |
| 3 | 4200 | 667 | 3533 | 1837 | 2504 |
| | | $6000 | $6600 | $3432 | $3432 |

To get the rate of return when the cash inflows are different, we use trial and error until we find a rate which makes the total present value of the inflows equal to the present value of the outflows. By this process we find that the rate is between 25 and 30% because 25% results in a present value greater than $6000 and 30% a value below $6000. The work is summarized below.

| | | PRESENT VALUE AT 25% | | PRESENT VALUE AT 30% | |
|-----|-----|-----|-----|-----|-----|
| YEAR | CASH INFLOW | *of $1* | *of Cash Inflows* | *of $1* | *of Cash Inflows* |
| 1 | $4104 | .800 | $3283 | .769 | $3156 |
| 2 | 2824 | .640 | 1807 | .592 | 1672 |
| 3 | 2504 | .512 | 1282 | .455 | 1139 |
| | | | $6372 | | $5967 |

If a more precise answer is required, we interpolate.

$$
\begin{array}{c}
\textit{Present Value} \\
i\ in\ \% \qquad of\ Inflows
\end{array}
$$

$$
5 \left[\ d \left[ \begin{array}{c} 25 \\ i \\ \end{array} \right. \right.\ \left. \begin{array}{c} 6372 \\ 6000 \end{array} \right] 372\ \right]\ 405
$$

$$
30 \qquad 5967
$$

$$
\frac{d}{5} = \frac{372}{405}
$$

$$
d = \frac{5 \times 372}{405} = 4.6
$$

$$
i = 25.0 + 4.6 = 29.6\%
$$
$$
= \text{approximately } 30\%
$$

Going to a more rapid write-off has increased the internal rate of return by 3 percentage points.

An advantage of the discounted cash flow method is that interest is computed only on the amount of unrecovered capital to date. The rate is not affected by what is done with the recovered capital. This enables us to check a computed rate by finding how long it would take to recover the invested capital if the project were financed at a capital rate equal to the rate of return. If the rate is correct, the period required to recover the investment and the life of the project will be the same.

EXAMPLE 3: A machine which costs $15,925 will produce estimated net cash inflows of $7560 a year for 3 years. Find the rate of return and check.

SOLUTION: Since this is an ordinary annuity with a present value of 15,925 and a periodic payment of 7560, we have

$$a_{\overline{3}|} = \frac{15,925}{7560} = 2.106$$

This *Present Worth of* 1 *per Period* factor corresponds to a rate of 20%. The table below shows that we earn 20% on invested capital and in 3 years recover the investment. The amount of capital recovered equals net cash inflow minus return on unrecovered capital.

| YEAR | UNRECOVERED CAPITAL AT BEGINNING OF THE YEAR | NET CASH INFLOW | RETURN OF 20% ON UNRECOVERED CAPITAL | AMOUNT OF CAPITAL RECOVERED |
|------|------|------|------|------|
| 1 | $15,925 | $7560 | $3185 | $4375 |
| 2 | 11,550 | 7560 | 2310 | 5250 |
| 3 | 6,300 | 7560 | 1260 | 6300 |
| | | | | $15,925 |

## 8.16   Comparison of Alternatives

Discounted cash flow analysis can be used to help management choose among proposed capital expenditures. One method is to get the rate of return for each proposal. Another method is to rank projects on the basis of net present values. If the proposals differ greatly as to costs and income streams, a method that is preferable to net present value comparisons is the use of a **profitability index** which is the ratio of present value of net cash inflows to present value of outlays. This ratio is also called the **benefit cost ratio**. Different methods of comparing alternatives do not always lead to the same ranking, as shown on page 305.

EXAMPLE: A company is considering two projects which have the following net cash flows after allowing for depreciation, taxes, and other expenses. Find the net present values and profitability indexes using a rate of 16%. Find the internal rates of return for the two proposals.

| YEAR | PRESENT WORTH OF 1 AT 16% | PROPOSAL A | | PROPOSAL B | |
|---|---|---|---|---|---|
| | | *Net Cash Inflow* | *Present Value* | *Net Cash Inflow* | *Present Value* |
| 0 | 1.000 | − $30,000 | − $30,000 | − $30,000 | − $30,000 |
| 1 | .862 | 0 | 0 | 0 | 0 |
| 2 | .743 | 25,000 | 18,575 | 0 | 0 |
| 3 | .641 | 25,000 | 16,025 | 0 | 0 |
| 4 | .552 | 0 | 0 | 34,000 | 18,768 |
| 5 | .476 | 0 | 0 | 34,000 | 16,184 |
| | | | $ 4,600 | | $ 4,952 |
| | Profitability Index | | 1.15 | | 1.17 |

$$\text{The profitability index for Proposal } A = \frac{18,575 + 16,025}{30,000}$$

$$= \frac{34,600}{30,000} = 1.15$$

On the basis of either net present value or profitability index, $B$ would be ranked first.

A trial and error determination of the internal rate of return puts $A$ first with a rate of about 23% compared to 20% for $B$. Had the present value comparisons been at a rate close to these true rates of return, $A$ would have also been first on a net present value basis.

Of the methods we have discussed for evaluating alternatives, the net present value and profitability index methods have the advantage of ease of computation as compared to the sometimes tedious calculations required to get the internal rate of return. Another advantage of the present value method is that an allowance for risk can be added to the estimated cost of capital. On the other hand, if the present value analysis is based on an incorrect rate, the ranking of projects may be wrong. When we use the internal rate of return, we can rank proposals in order of yield. Then we can see which will probably be most profitable and how far we can go down the list before reaching a point below the cost of capital where a proposal would be a losing proposition.

It is important to recognize that there is more to decision making than getting a present value or a rate of return for individual proposals. Management is concerned about total return to the firm and takes into account budget constraints. This means seeking the best overall combination of capital projects. There is also the problem of reinvesting money. A project that would yield 25% for a year or two might be less attractive than one that would return 20% for 5 or more years.

There are, of course, situations where nonmonetary considerations, such as employee morale and community relations, result in adopting proposals that are not financially attractive. In some cases expenditures simply have to be made. Management may have no practical alternative to repairing or replacing a defective roof and installing adequate safety devices.

## 8.17  Human Capital

Investment in buildings and equipment is not enough to guarantee economic progress. It is also essential to have adequate investment in the health, education, and training of people.

The economic value of a college education is often given in terms of the increased lifetime earnings of college graduates. This is a crude measure that ignores the time value of money. Much of the increased income is far in the future. In the immediate present there is an opportunity cost in the form of foregone earnings which the student could get if he were working. There are also immediate cash outlays for school expenses.

However, even when the time value of money is taken into account, money spent on education may be the most profitable investment a person can make. With the increasing demand for skilled and educated workers, expenditures by qualified people on education may be a better form of investment than putting the money into savings accounts, bonds, or stocks. In addition to monetary returns, education has advantages which cannot be put into dollars or percentages.

EXAMPLE 1: A young man will soon be graduated from high school. He can get a factory job paying $4000 a year. Or he can go to college at a cost of $2000 a year. His high school counselor estimates that if he goes to college, his lifetime earnings will be about $160,000 more than if his education stops with high school. Estimate the present value of a college education using a rate of 10%.

SOLUTION: To simplify computations, assume that the $160,000 is distributed equally over 40 years for additional income each year of $4000. Since it would not be possible to determine differences in personal tax rates far into the future, comparisons are made on a before-tax basis. No allowance is made for depreciation or scrap value. It is true that some skills become worthless. On the other hand, an employee who continues to learn is one of the few assets that increases in value as the years go by. A time diagram helps to visualize the net cash flows.

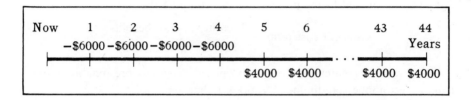

The outflows (loss of $4000 in earnings plus $2000 costs for each 4 years) are an ordinary annuity with a present value of $6000a_{\overline{4}|10\%}$.

The inflows are a deferred annuity with a present value of $4000(a_{\overline{4+40}|} - a_{\overline{4}|})$.

Present value of the education $= -6000 \times 3.170 + 4000(9.849 - 3.170)$
$$= -19,020 + 26,716 = \$7,696$$

EXAMPLE 2: Find the internal rate of return in Problem 1.

SOLUTION: Since the present value is positive at 10%, the internal rate of return is higher than 10%. Trial and error is used to find a rate that results in a negative present value. At 14%, the factors from Table 4 result in:

Present value of the education $= -6000 \times 2.914 + 4000(7.120 - 2.914)$
$$= -17,484 + 16,824 = -\$660$$

Fourteen per cent results in the inflows and outflows being about equal. There are too many uncertainties to justify getting a more precise answer by interpolation. A rate close to 14% indicates that even from a money standpoint alone, more education would be a good investment for this person.

The best investment opportunity open to many young people is in themselves, provided they have the foresight and luck to acquire skills for which there will be a brisk demand.

## 8.18   The Planning-Programming-Budgeting System

In 1961 the Department of Defense introduced a system called Planning-Programming-Budgeting (PPB). This system is now used as a planning tool in many federal agencies and in some state and local governments. PPB emphasizes the analysis of current outlays within the framework of long-range planning. Goals are identified with care. A search is made for alternative means of reaching goals at the least cost. Performance is measured to insure an adequate return on expenditures.

An important part of PPB is benefit cost analysis. Both benefits and costs occur at various points in time so they are not directly comparable. But if all flows are discounted to the present, we can compute the

$$\text{Benefit cost ratio} = \frac{\text{Present value of benefits}}{\text{Present value of costs}}$$

If this ratio is greater than one, a proposed project is presumably desirable from an economic standpoint. A ratio less than one indicates a loser. Because of its apparent simplicity, the benefit cost ratio is an appealing device. What could be nicer than to reduce a complicated problem to a single number which signals "go ahead" if it is greater than one and warns "do something else" if less than one? However, before spending millions on the basis of a favorable benefit cost ratio, answers should be obtained to several questions.

How good are estimates of benefits and costs? Many proposals, a dam or canal, for example, involve inflows and outflows of money far into the future. Putting a dollar value on them now may be largely guesswork. This does not mean that everything should be held up until the results of a project are practically certain. Life is too uncertain for that. It does mean that decision makers should be forced to recognize what they do not know and then search for the best available estimates.

Whose benefits are being measured? There is a difference between whether society as a whole will benefit or whether the returns will go to a small area or to those with special interests.

Was allowance made for external economies and diseconomies? A project may look good on a benefit cost basis if only benefits and costs associated directly with the project are included. But if allowance is made for pollution or other external diseconomies, the proposal may be unacceptable. On the other hand, external economies, such as incidental recreation facilities or jobs for ghetto youth, may improve the chances of a proposal which in itself has a marginal benefit cost ratio.

What discount rate was used? A particular set of benefits and costs might result in a benefit cost ratio well above one if a discount rate of 4% is used. But a more realistic 6 or 8% might result in the same dollar flows having a benefit cost ratio less than one.

The mathematics used in benefit cost analysis is the same that we have used in other discount problems. But the judgment of the person doing the work now can have considerable effect on the data used in the problem and in this way affect the final result. By assuming a long life, limited maintenance, free-spending tourists, and a low discount rate, even pyramid building can be made to look good on a benefit cost basis!

While PPB cannot provide final answers to complex political-economic problems, it can help the decision maker by showing where better information is needed, by organizing data, and by logically comparing alternate proposals for achieving government objectives. The development of PPB means that the mathematics of finance can now be used by government planners to help solve problems that are mathematically similar to those in finance and business.

### EXERCISE 8c

1. A machine costs $20,000. It has an estimated life of 4 years and no scrap value. The machine is expected to increase company revenue by $11,000 a year before maintenance costs which are estimated at $2000 a year. Assume a tax rate of 48% and find the net present value and profitability index at 16% using:
   (a) Straight line depreciation.
   (b) Double declining balance for 2 years and straight line thereafter.
   (c) Sum of the years digits.

   |     | Net Present Value | Profitability Index |
   |-----|-------------------|---------------------|
   | (a) | −$190             | .99                 |
   | (b) | 447               | 1.02                |
   | (c) | 305               | 1.02                |

2. The management of a company has established an internal rate of return of 14% as the cutoff point for capital projects. This means that to be acceptable, a proposal must have an expected rate of return of 14% or more after taxes. A department manager recommends installing a machine which costs $12,000 and has an estimated life of 3 years with no scrap value. He claims that the machine should reduce labor costs by $8000 a year. Estimated maintenance costs on the machine are $1000 a year. Assume a tax rate of 48% and find the net present value and profitability index using:
   (a) Straight line depreciation.
   (b) Double declining balance for 1 year and then straight line.
   (c) Sum of the years digits.

3. A student will soon get his bachelor's degree. He can start earning $7000 a year. Or he can go to graduate school and receive an all-expense grant plus $2000 a year. He thinks that he can get his doctor's degree in 3 years. With the higher degree, he believes that he can average about $3000 more a year for 35 years. Is graduate school a profitable investment if the student wants a return of 8% a year before taxes? (Yes. Present value of foregone

income is $12,885; present value of additional income is $27,756. Net present value of additional education is $14,871.)

4. A high school student can get a job at the end of his sophomore year and earn about $3600 a year. Or he can stay in high school and earn about $1500 a year more for 40 years than if he had become a dropout. What is the present value of the 2 additional years of high school at 8% before taxes?

5. A piece of equipment costs $40,000. It has an estimated life of 10 years and a scrap value of $5000. The equipment is expected to increase company revenue $12,500 a year over operating expenses. Assume straight line depreciation and a tax rate of 48% and find the net present value at 14%.
($4017)

6. Solve Problem 5 using a rate of 16%.

7. A lease on a retail store has 12 more years to run. Fire insurance now costs the store $60,000 a year. If the store installs an automatic sprinkler system at a cost of $180,000, the annual cost for fire insurance will drop to $15,800. Estimated annual maintenance cost of the sprinkler system will be $200. If the system is depreciated to zero on a straight line basis over 12 years and the tax rate is 48%, what after tax return would be earned on this investment? (13%)

8. The lease on a dry cleaning establishment has 10 more years to run. The present cost of fire insurance is $4160 a year. The company can install an automatic sprinkler at a cost of $7600 with estimated annual maintenance costs of $100. The cost of fire insurance will then drop to $900 a year. The sprinkler system can be depreciated to zero over the remaining years of the lease. Assume straight line depreciation and a 48% tax rate and get the internal rate of return.

9. An airport terminal building has an estimated life of 20 years. The annual cost of fire insurance without a sprinkler system would be $2213. With a sprinkler, the cost would drop to $357 a year. Estimated annual maintenance costs are $100. The cost of installing a sprinkler system would be $5120. What would be the approximate rate of return after taxes on this investment if it is depreciated to zero over 20 years on a straight line basis and the tax rate is 48%? (20%)

10. What would be the approximate rate of return in Problem 9 if the building has an estimated life of 10 years and the sprinkler system is depreciated over 10 years on a straight line basis?

11. A company is considering the purchase of materials handling equipment. The initial cost will be $36,000 and the annual outlay for maintenance, power, and other expenses will be an estimated $1000. It is expected that the equipment will reduce labor costs by $10,000 a year for 12 years. The estimated life of the asset is 12 years with no salvage value. Assume a tax

rate of 48 % and straight line depreciation and get the rate of return to the nearest per cent.                                                                     (13%)

12. A tractor costs $14,000. It has an estimated life of 6 years and a salvage value of $2000. The annual outlay for maintenance will run about $500. It is expected that this tractor will result in an annual increase in revenue of $5000. Assume a tax rate of 48 % and straight line depreciation and get the rate of return to the nearest per cent.

13. A company is considering the purchase of an asset which costs $6000 and has no scrap value at the end of its useful life of 4 years. Annual net income over operating expenses but before taxes and depreciation is expected to be $3500 a year. The tax rate is 48 %. For comparison purposes, find the rate of return to the nearest tenth of one per cent assuming (a) straight line depreciation; (b) double declining balance for 2 years and then straight line; (c) sum of the years digits.   [(a) 25.0%; (b) 27.6%; (c) 26.9%]

14. A company is considering the purchase of a machine which costs $8000 and has an estimated scrap value of 10% of cost at the end of 4 years. It is estimated that this machine will increase the net income before taxes and depreciation by $3000 a year. The tax rate is 48 %. For comparison purposes, find the rate of return to the nearest tenth of one per cent using (a) straight line depreciation; (b) double declining balance for 2 years and then straight line; (c) sum of the years digits.

15. A company is considering the purchase of an asset which costs $15,000 and has an estimated scrap value of $3000 at the end of 5 years. It is estimated that this asset will reduce labor costs by $5000 a year. Assume a tax rate of 48 % and find the rate of return assuming (a) straight line depreciation; (b) double declining balance for 3 years and then straight line; (c) sum of the years digits.                [(a) 12.6%; (b) 14.3%; (c) 13.4%]

16. A contractor can purchase a heavy-duty truck with a 12-cubic-yard dump body for $13,000. Its estimated life is 7 years and its estimated salvage value is $2000. Maintenance is estimated at $1100 per year. Daily operating expenses are expected to be $23 including the cost of the driver. The contractor can hire a similar unit and its driver for $53 a day. If the interest rate is taken at 8 %, how many days per year must the services of a dump truck be required to justify the purchase of a truck? Use straight line depreciation. Assume that the daily savings resulting from owning a truck can be lumped together and considered as a single year-end savings. Make no allowance for taxes.

## 8.19  Depletion

Some natural resources, such as mines, oil wells, timber tracts, and sources of natural gas, produce an income for awhile and then become used up. This gradual using up of a resource which will not be replaced is called **depletion**. The income from an asset of this type should not only pay a return on the investment, but should also recover the cost of the asset less any resale value it may have when the natural resources are exhausted. Only in this way can the business operate in accordance with the fundamental principle of keeping the invested capital unimpaired.

EXAMPLE 1: A firm buys a mine for $200,000. An annual return of $30,000 over operating costs is expected for the next 15 years. At the end of this time it is estimated that the land can be sold for $10,000. This means that there will be a decrease in the value of the property of $190,000. In this case we shall assume that the invested capital will be recovered by making periodic deposits to a sinking fund paying 3%. What return can the firm expect on their investment?

SOLUTION: We must first find the size of the annual deposit to the sinking fund.

$$R = 190,000 \times \frac{1}{s_{\overline{15}|3\%}} = 190,000 \times .05376658 = \$10,215.65$$

This should be deducted from the $30,000 to replace the invested capital. This makes the net return

$$\$30,000.00 - 10,215.65 = \$19,784.35$$

The rate of return on the investment then becomes

$$\frac{19,784.35}{200,000} = .0989 \text{ or } 9.9\%$$

If $C$ is the original cost, $S$ the resale value when the natural resource is used up, $i$ the yield rate on the investment, and $r$ the rate earned on the sinking fund, we can write the following general formula:

Annual return = (Cost × the yield rate)
            + (Annual deposit into sinking fund)

Or using symbols:

$$\text{Annual return} = Ci + (C - S) \cdot \frac{1}{s_{\overline{n}|r}}$$

In this formula we have added the subscript $r$ to the $1/s_{\overline{n}|}$ factor to emphasize the fact that the sinking fund rate is to be used when getting the numerical value of this factor.

In some cases the investor knows what rate of return he wants on his investment, so the problem becomes one of determining a purchase price that will result in the desired yield.

EXAMPLE 2: A mining property is expected to yield an annual return of $40,000 over operating costs for the next 20 years when it will be exhausted and have a resale value of about $20,000. What could a firm pay for the mine if they want a return of 8% on their investment and can set up a sinking fund at 3%?

SOLUTION:

$$40,000 = C \times .08 + (C - 20,000) \cdot \frac{1}{s_{\overline{20}|3\%}}$$

$$40,000 = .08C + .03721571C - 744.31$$
$$40,744.31 = .11721571C$$

$$C = \frac{40,744.31}{.11721571} = \$347,601$$

## EXERCISE 8d

1. A sand and gravel company is considering the purchase of a piece of property for sale at $45,000. It is estimated that the property will produce a net annual return over operating costs of $7000 for 10 years at the end of which time the estimated resale value of the property is $5000. If the firm can build up a replacement fund for their capital at 3% converted annually, what is the estimated rate of return they could expect on this investment? Give answer to the nearest .1%. (7.8%)

2. A lumber company leases a tract of timber for 8 years for $60,000. They expect to get an annual return over operating costs of about $10,000. If they set up a sinking fund at 4% to recover their investment, what return can they expect on their investment?

3. A quarry is expected to yield a net income over operating costs of $20,000 a year for 15 years at which time it will have little or no resale value. What could a firm pay for this quarry if they want a yield of 8% on their investment and set up a sinking fund at $2\frac{1}{2}\%$ to replace their capital? Give answer to the nearest $100. ($147,300)

4. A company is considering the purchase of some timber land. Company engineers estimate that the land will produce a net return of $30,000 a year over operating costs for 6 years at which time the land can be sold for about $40,000. How much can the company pay for the land if they want a return of 7% on their investment and they can set up a sinking fund at $3\frac{1}{2}\%$ to replace their capital?

**5.** A mine is expected to yield an annual return of $40,000 over operating costs for the next 20 years when it will be exhausted and have an estimated resale value of $2000. What could a firm pay for the mine if they want an annual return of 8% on their investment and can accumulate a sinking fund at 3%? Answer to the nearest $100.                                             ($341,900)

**6.** A gravel pit is expected to produce an average return over operating costs of $7000 a year for 8 years. If it will have little or no resale value, what can a firm pay for it if they want a 6% return on their investment and can accumulate a sinking fund at 3%?

## 8.20   Capitalized Cost

The **capitalized cost** of an asset is the original cost of an item plus the present value of an unlimited number of renewals. We shall first determine the formulas used for capitalized cost and then discuss their application. The quantities and symbols used in capitalized cost work are

$$K = \text{the capitalized cost}$$
$$C = \text{the original cost}$$
$$S = \text{the scrap or salvage value}$$
$$W = \text{the wearing value. } W = C - S$$
$$n = \text{useful life in interest conversion periods.}$$

To find the present value of the unlimited number of renewals, we use perpetuity formula (21) substituting $W$ for the periodic payment. This is added to the first cost to give us the basic formula for capitalized cost:

$$K = C + \frac{W}{i} \times \frac{1}{s_{\overline{n}|}} \tag{26}$$

In many cases the item has little or no scrap value. In this case the replacement cost equals the first cost and a simpler formula can be derived as follows:

$$K = C + \frac{C}{i} \times \frac{1}{s_{\overline{n}|}}$$

Multiplying $C$ by $i/i$ and factoring $C/i$, we have

$$K = \frac{C}{i}\left(i + \frac{1}{s_{\overline{n}|}}\right)$$

Replacing $1/s_{\overline{n}|}$ by its exponential form,

$$K = \frac{C}{i}\left(i + \frac{i}{(1 + i)^n - 1}\right) = \frac{C}{i}\left(\frac{i(1 + i)^n - i + i}{(1 + i)^n - 1}\right)$$

Combining terms and multiplying numerator and denominator by $(1 + i)^{-n}$,

$$K = \frac{C}{i}\left(\frac{i}{1 - (1 + i)^{-n}}\right)$$

Substituting $1/a_{\overline{n}|}$ for the exponential expression,

$$K = \frac{C}{i} \times \frac{1}{a_{\overline{n}|}} \tag{27}$$

All of the factors in a capitalized cost problem are estimates: the useful life of the asset, its replacement cost, and the value of money in the future. In spite of these limitations capitalized cost can be a very useful tool. It can be used to arrive at an estimate of the endowment required for a specific purpose. A more frequent use is to determine which of two or more items would be more economical for a particular job. The capitalized cost formulas enable us to get two assets with different costs and different useful lives on a common basis. The asset with the lower capitalized cost will be the more economical. No actual fund will be set up in cases such as this.

EXAMPLE 1: What is the estimated endowment for the construction of a mess hall at a boy's camp if the building costs $12,000, and will need to be replaced about every 25 years at approximately the same cost? By how much will the endowment have to be increased to provide $300 at the end of each year for maintenance? Estimated return on the endowment fund is 3%.

SOLUTION: Since the replacement cost is assumed to be the same as the first cost, we can use (27):

$$K = \frac{12,000}{.03} \times \frac{1}{a_{\overline{25}|3\%}}$$

$$= 400,000 \times .05742787 = \$22,971.15$$

The annual maintenance costs form a perpetuity. The present value can be found from (20):

$$A_\infty = \frac{300}{.03} = \$10,000$$

Therefore, to provide for initial construction, replacement every 25 years, and annual maintenance, an endowment of about $33,000 would be needed.

EXAMPLE 2: A machine costs $4500, has an estimated life of 15 years, and an estimated scrap value of $700. Find the capitalized cost at 4%.

SOLUTION: Substituting in (26), we have

$$K = 4500 + \frac{3800}{.04} \times \frac{1}{s_{\overline{15}|4\%}}$$

$$= 4500 + (95,000 \times .0499410) = 4500 + 4744.40$$

$$K = \$9244.40$$

EXAMPLE 3: One grade of floor covering for a store costs $750 installed and has an estimated life of 8 years. A better grade has an estimated life of 12 years. If money is worth 3%, the better grade would be worth how much?

SOLUTION: To solve this problem we shall assume that the two are equally desirable from an economic standpoint if their capitalized costs are equal. In either case an initial installation and an unlimited number of renewals would be provided for. If $C$ is the unknown cost of the better grade we can use (27) and set the two capitalized costs equal to each other.

$$\frac{C}{.03} \times \frac{1}{a_{\overline{12}|3\%}} = \frac{750}{.03} \times \frac{1}{a_{\overline{8}|3\%}}$$

$$C = 750 \times a_{\overline{12}|} \times \frac{1}{a_{\overline{8}|}}$$

$$= 750 \times 9.954004 \times .142456 = \$1063.51$$

Therefore if the better grade can be installed for less than $1063.51 it will be more economical.

### EXERCISE 8e

1. A memorial library for a town will cost $60,000. The estimated annual maintenance cost is $1800 and the estimated life is 60 years. If the replacement cost is assumed to be the same as the first cost, what endowment (to the nearest $1000) will build, replace and maintain this library in perpetuity? Assume that 4% will be earned on the endowment.                    ($111,000)

2. Work Problem 1 if the interest on the endowment will be $3\frac{1}{2}\%$.

3. A philanthropist wants to provide an endowment to construct a community building costing $350,000 and replace it every 50 years. If the estimated return on the endowment is $3\frac{1}{2}\%$, what size endowment will be needed?

                                                                ($426,337)

4. The original cost of a shelter house for a park is $7000. It is estimated that it will have to be replaced every 12 years at the same cost. What donation will be needed to endow this shelter house in perpetuity if the money can be invested at 4%?

5. One type of roof costs $600 and has to be replaced every 10 years. Another type costs $1200 and will last 25 years. If money is worth 4%, which is the more economical? (The $600 roof)

6. A building can be painted for $1200 with a paint that will last 4 years. If a better paint is used, the cost will be $1500 and the job will last 6 years. If money is worth 3%, which job is more economical?

7. A machine costs $15,000, has an estimated life of 12 years, and a scrap value of $2000. Find the capitalized cost at 3%. ($45,533.57)

8. A machine costs $7500, has an estimated life of 6 years and a scrap value of $1200. What is the capitalized cost at 5%?

9. Timbers used in a certain type of construction work cost $700 and last 12 years. A preservative treatment is expected to increase the life to 18 years. If money is worth 4%, how much can be paid for the preservative treatment? ($244.19)

## 8.21 Composite Life

Usually the assets of a business have probable lives that vary widely. When a plant is to be used as security for a bond issue, it may be necessary to determine the **composite life** of the plant. This is the time necessary for the total annual depreciation charge to equal the total wearing value.

EXAMPLE: Find the composite life of the following plant if depreciation is based on the straight line method.

SOLUTION: The following table shows how the total annual charge and the total wearing value are obtained.

| ITEM | LIFE IN YEARS | COST | SCRAP VALUE | WEARING VALUE | ANNUAL CHARGE |
|---|---|---|---|---|---|
| Building | 60 | $120,000 | $ 0 | $120,000 | $2000 |
| Machine tools | 15 | 50,000 | 5000 | 45,000 | 3000 |
| Other machinery | 10 | 30,000 | 2000 | 28,000 | 2800 |
| | | | | $193,000 | $7800 |

Composite life = 193,000 ÷ 7800 = 24.7 years

This example shows that if this plant is to be used as security for a long-term loan or bond issue, the term of the loan should be less than 24 years. To have a reasonable margin of safety the term should probably be considerably less than the composite life.

## EXERCISE 8f

1. A plant consists of the following: (a) a building worth $70,000 with a life of 50 years and no scrap value; (b) machine tools worth $25,000 with a life of 15 years and a scrap value of $3000; (c) equipment worth $20,000 with a life of 12 years and a scrap value of $1000. Find the composite life if depreciation is based on the straight line method.                     (25— years)

2. If depreciation is based on the straight line method, find the composite life of the plant described below:

| ITEM | LIFE IN YEARS | COST | SCRAP VALUE |
|------|------|------|------|
| Building | 40 | $60,000 | $   0 |
| Power plant | 15 | 8,000 | 500 |
| Machine tools | 18 | 22,000 | 1000 |
| Dies, jigs, fixtures, etc. | 7 | 6,500 | 0 |

# 9

# Life
# Annuities

## 9.1 The Mortality Table

Up to now we have been dealing with single payments and with annuities that were certain to be paid. We shall now work problems which are contingent on how long a person lives.

Suppose a group of men who are 18 years old want to set up a fund from which all who are living 20 years from now will receive $1000. How much should each one put into the fund now? To answer this question we need to be able to predict how many of the original group will be living 20 years from now. While no one can tell who will die during the next 20 years, it is possible to use mortality data to predict approximately *how many* will die during a given period. Before we can work the problem, we must understand the basic tool of the life insurance actuary—the mortality table.

Insurance companies have kept records which show the number of people living and dying at each age of life. These statistics of the "march through life" are compiled into a table which is called a mortality table.

As life expectancy changes, a mortality table will become obsolete and must be replaced with more recent data. In this book we use the 1958 Commissioners Standard Ordinary (CSO) Mortality Table. This is Table 5 in the back of the book. This table is being used by many insurance companies and became the mandatory non-forfeiture and valuation standard in most states on January 1, 1966. Note that values for 15-year-old females and up are the same as the values for a male three years younger. Values for females age 0 to 14 are given in the complete tables of the Society of Actuaries. In practical applications, annuity and insurance contracts may be based on different mortality tables. Since the basic principles involved in life annuity and life insurance problems are the same regardless of the mortality table, all problems in this text are based on the 1958 CSO Table.

The CSO Table starts with 10,000,000 people living at age 0. The $l_x$ column gives the number living at age $x$. The $d_x$ column gives the number that can be expected to die before reaching age $x + 1$. Thus 70,800 of the 10,000,000 living at age 0 can be expected to die before reaching age 1. The probability of dying within a year for a person age $x$ is indicated by the symbol $q_x$. It is obtained by dividing the number dying at age $x$ by the number living at age $x$. In symbols, $q_x = d_x/l_x$. An easier figure to work with is the death rate per 1000 which is given in the mortality table under the symbol $1000q_x$.

The Greek letter $\omega$ (omega) is the symbol for the terminal age of a mortality table. It is the lowest age at which there are no survivors. For the 1958 CSO Table, $\omega = 100$ for males and 103 for females. Other mortality tables used by insurance companies have different terminal ages, but the formulas derived in this text are applicable regardless of the interest rate or mortality table.

EXAMPLE 1: What is the probability that a 20-year-old man will live to age 50? Of a group of 1000 20-year-old men, what is the predicted number that will live to age 50?

SOLUTION: The probability that a 20-year-old man will live to age 50 is simply the number still living at age 50 divided by the number living at age 20.

$$\frac{l_{50}}{l_{20}} = \frac{8\ 762\ 306}{9\ 664\ 994} = .9066$$

Out of 1000 20-year-old men, the predicted number that will live to age 50 is $1000 \times .9066 = 907$.

EXAMPLE 2: What is the probability that a 20-year-old man will die before reaching age 50? Of a group of 1000 20-year-old men, what is the predicted number that will die before reaching age 50?

SOLUTION: The probability of a man dying between age 20 and age 50 is the number dying during this period divided by the number living at age 20.

$$\frac{l_{20} - l_{50}}{l_{20}} = \frac{9\,664\,994 - 8\,762\,306}{9\,664\,994} = .0934$$

Note that if we have the probability that a man will live to age 50, we can get the probability that he will die by age 50 by subtracting the probability of living from 1 since he will certainly do one or the other. Probability of dying by age 50 = 1.0000 − .9066 = .0934.

Out of 1000 20-year-old men, the predicted number that will die before reaching age 50 is 1000 × .0934 = 93.

EXAMPLE 3: Get the answers to Examples 1 and 2 for women.

$$\text{Probability of living} = \frac{l_{50}}{l_{20}} = \frac{8\,948\,114}{9\,713\,967} = .9212$$

Predicted number living to age 50 = 1000 × .9212 = 921

$$\text{Probability of dying} = \frac{l_{20} - l_{50}}{l_{20}} = \frac{9\,713\,967 - 8\,948\,114}{9\,713\,967} = .0788$$

Predicted number dying before age 50 = 1000 × .0788 = 79

Note the considerably lower mortality predictions for women.

## 9.2 Expectation of Life

How much longer do you expect to live? While there is no precise answer for you in particular, you can get an estimate using the expectation of life for persons of your age and sex. The expectation of life is a statistic often used as an index for comparing different mortality tables. The actuarial formula for expectation of life is

$$\overset{\circ}{e}_x = .5 + \frac{1}{l_x} \sum_{t=1}^{\omega - x - 1} l_{x+t}$$

where

$\overset{\circ}{e}_x$ = expectation of life of a person aged $x$

$l_x$ = number living at age $x$

$t$ = index or variable of summation

$\omega$ = terminal age of the mortality table

The symbol $\sum$ is the capital Greek letter sigma. This is a standard mathematical symbol used to indicate summation of similar terms.

The index of summation $t$ ranges over the integers $1, 2, 3, \ldots \omega - x - 1$. This means that if we want the expectation of life of a person aged $x$, we start with the number living one year later, add the number living two years later, and continue in this way to the end of the mortality table. This sum gives the full years of future lifetime for the group of persons age $x$. When this sum is divided by $l_x$, the number living at age $x$, we get the full years of future life for each person *on the average*. This summation makes no allowance for fractional years of life. We assume that complete future lifetimes will exceed by half a year the number of complete years so we add .5 year to get the complete future lifetime.

To show how this formula is used, we compute the expectation of life for men aged 90 using the 1958 CSO Table. Calculations for younger people are done in exactly the same way but are more tedious because of the larger number of terms in the summation. We substitute 90 for $x$ in the formula and find from Table 5 that $l_{90} = 468,174$. This is the number of men over whom we will average the full years of future lifetime. For $t = 1$, $l_{91} = 361,365$; for $t = 2$, $l_{92} = 272,522$. We continue in this way to the last term in the summation which is for $t = (100 - 90 - 1) = 9$. For $t = 9$, $l_{99} = 6415$. Arranging the complete problem in tabular form,

| $t$ | $90 + t$ | $l_{90+t}$ |
|---|---|---|
| 1 | 91 | 361 365 |
| 2 | 92 | 272 522 |
| 3 | 93 | 200 072 |
| 4 | 94 | 142 191 |
| 5 | 95 | 97 165 |
| 6 | 96 | 63 037 |
| 7 | 97 | 37 787 |
| 8 | 98 | 19 331 |
| 9 | 99 | 6 415 |
| | | $1\ 199\ 915 = \sum_{t=1}^{9} l_{90+t}$ |

We substitute in the expectation of life formula the 1 199 915 years of future life which are to be averaged over the 468 174 men living at age 90.

$$\mathring{e}_{90} = .5 + \frac{1\ 199\ 915}{468\ 174} = .5 + 2.56 = 3.06$$

This means that the expectation of life for men aged 90 is 3.06 years if based on the 1958 CSO table. Whether a particular person will get more or less than

*Expectation of Life:*
*Males 1958 CSO Mortality Table*

| AGE x | $\overset{\circ}{e}_x$ | AGE x | $\overset{\circ}{e}_x$ | AGE x | $\overset{\circ}{e}_x$ | AGE x | $\overset{\circ}{e}_x$ |
|---|---|---|---|---|---|---|---|
| 0 | 68.30 | 25 | 45.82 | 50 | 23.63 | 75 | 7.81 |
| 1 | 67.78 | 26 | 44.90 | 51 | 22.82 | 76 | 7.39 |
| 2 | 66.90 | 27 | 43.99 | 52 | 22.03 | 77 | 6.98 |
| 3 | 66.00 | 28 | 43.08 | 53 | 21.25 | 78 | 6.59 |
| 4 | 65.10 | 29 | 42.16 | 54 | 20.47 | 79 | 6.21 |
| 5 | 64.19 | 30 | 41.25 | 55 | 19.71 | 80 | 5.85 |
| 6 | 63.27 | 31 | 40.34 | 56 | 18.97 | 81 | 5.51 |
| 7 | 62.35 | 32 | 39.43 | 57 | 18.23 | 82 | 5.19 |
| 8 | 61.43 | 33 | 38.51 | 58 | 17.51 | 83 | 4.89 |
| 9 | 60.51 | 34 | 37.60 | 59 | 16.81 | 84 | 4.60 |
| 10 | 59.58 | 35 | 36.69 | 60 | 16.12 | 85 | 4.32 |
| 11 | 58.65 | 36 | 35.78 | 61 | 15.44 | 86 | 4.06 |
| 12 | 57.72 | 37 | 34.88 | 62 | 14.78 | 87 | 3.80 |
| 13 | 56.80 | 38 | 33.97 | 63 | 14.14 | 88 | 3.55 |
| 14 | 55.87 | 39 | 33.07 | 64 | 13.51 | 89 | 3.31 |
| 15 | 54.95 | 40 | 32.18 | 65 | 12.90 | 90 | 3.06 |
| 16 | 54.03 | 41 | 31.29 | 66 | 12.31 | 91 | 2.82 |
| 17 | 53.11 | 42 | 30.41 | 67 | 11.73 | 92 | 2.58 |
| 18 | 52.19 | 43 | 29.54 | 68 | 11.17 | 93 | 2.33 |
| 19 | 51.28 | 44 | 28.67 | 69 | 10.64 | 94 | 2.07 |
| 20 | 50.37 | 45 | 27.81 | 70 | 10.12 | 95 | 1.80 |
| 21 | 49.46 | 46 | 26.95 | 71 | 9.63 | 96 | 1.51 |
| 22 | 48.55 | 47 | 26.11 | 72 | 9.15 | 97 | 1.18 |
| 23 | 47.64 | 48 | 25.27 | 73 | 8.69 | 98 | .83 |
| 24 | 46.73 | 49 | 24.45 | 74 | 8.24 | 99 | .50 |

Reproduced from Society of Actuaries tables with permission of Charles B. H. Watson, F.S.A., Executive Director.

"his expectation," only time will tell. Expectation of life for men is given above. To get the expectation of life for women aged 15 and above, look up the value for a man three years younger.

For employed persons a statistic analogous to expectation of life is work life expectancy, the average number of remaining years of life in the labor force for persons of a given age and sex. Work life expectancy data are published by the United States Department of Labor. Selected values from the 1960 data are shown on the following page.

|  AGE | WORK LIFE EXPECTANCY IN YEARS |
|------|------------------------------|
| 20   | 42.6 |
| 25   | 37.9 |
| 30   | 33.2 |
| 35   | 28.6 |
| 40   | 24.1 |
| 45   | 19.7 |
| 50   | 15.6 |
| 55   | 11.9 |
| 60   | 8.5 |
| 65   | 6.3 |

### EXERCISE 9a

1. Use the CSO Mortality Table to find the values of: (a) $l_{20}$; (b) $l_{40}$; (c) $l_{60}$ for men and for women.

$$\left[ \begin{array}{l} \text{Men: (a) 9 664 994; (b) 9 241 359; (c) 7 698 698} \\ \text{Women: (a) 9 713 967; (b) 9 325 594; (c) 8 106 161} \end{array} \right]$$

2. Use the CSO Mortality Table to find the values of: (a) $l_{30}$; (b) $l_{50}$; (c) $l_{70}$ for men and for women.

3. Use the CSO Mortality Table to find the values of: (a) $d_{20}$; (b) $d_{40}$; (c) $d_{60}$ for men and for women.

$$\left[ \begin{array}{l} \text{Men: (a) 17 300; (b) 32 622; (c) 156 592} \\ \text{Women: (a) 15 737; (b) 26 112; (c) 125 970} \end{array} \right]$$

4. Use the CSO Mortality Table to find the values of: (a) $d_{30}$; (b) $d_{50}$; (c) $d_{70}$ for men and for women.

5. Find the death rates per 1000 for: (a) 20-year-old; (b) 40-year-old; and (c) 60-year-old men and women.

$$\left[ \begin{array}{l} \text{Men: (a) 1.79; (b) 3.53; (c) 20.34} \\ \text{Women: (a) 1.62; (b) 2.80; (c) 15.54} \end{array} \right]$$

6. Find the death rates per 1000 for (a) 30-year-old; (b) 50-year-old; and (c) 70-year-old men and women.

7. Of a group of 1000 25-year-old men and 1000 25-year-old women, what are the predicted numbers that will die before reaching the age of 45?

(Men 55; women 47)

8. Of a group of 1000 30-year-old men and 1000 30-year-old women, what are the predicted numbers that will die before reaching the age of 65?

9. A college graduating class has 300 21-year-old men in it. What is the

predicted number of living alumni from this group: (a) 25 years; (b) 50 years; and (c) 75 years after graduation? [(a) 280; (b) 165; (c) 2]
**10.** Work Problem 9 assuming a group of 300 21-year-old women.

## 9.3 Interest and Loading

In determining the premium a policyholder should pay, an insurance company will make allowance for the interest that will be earned on the premiums when they are invested by the company. All computations in this book are based on a rate of $2\frac{1}{2}\%$ compounded annually.

Actual insurance premiums consist of two parts—the **net premium** and the **loading**. The net premium takes into account mortality and interest on invested premiums. The loading takes care of the insurance company's cost of doing business. Since each company has its own method of allowing for loading, we shall compute only net premiums. In all cases the present value of the net premiums will equal the present value of all future benefits. This means that, regardless of the type of policy, we derive the formula for net premiums from the basic equation of value:

$$\frac{\text{Net premiums discounted}}{\text{to date of issue}} = \frac{\text{Benefits discounted}}{\text{to date of issue}}$$

Actuarial symbols used in this book correspond to those used by the Society of Actuaries. Since many of the symbols require multiple subscripts, it is suggested that students use the verbal description of each problem when discussing it. Then the right formula can be obtained by simply referring to the discussion of that type of problem.

## 9.4 Pure Endowment

The problem at the beginning of this chapter was what is known as a **pure endowment**, that is, a *single* payment which will go to a person at a certain time *if he is living at that time*. To get a formula for a pure endowment we assume that the size of the payment is 1. Then to solve any problem all we need do is multiply by the size of the payment in the particular problem.

If $l_x$ individuals aged $x$ establish a fund to pay \$1 to each member living at age $x + n$, the number of dollars needed in $n$ years will equal the $l_{x+n}$ entry in the mortality table. Since the money is not needed until $n$ years from now, we need set aside today only the present or discounted value of this amount. If the symbol $_nE_x$ is used to represent each person's contribution to the fund, the total original premiums will equal $l_x \cdot {_nE_x}$, and the problem can be sketched as shown on the following page.

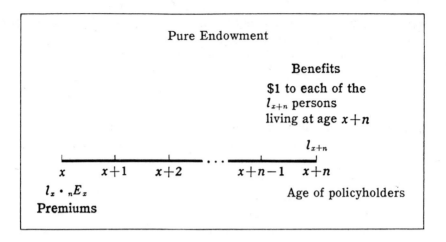

Discounting the benefits and setting up an equation of value, we have

$$l_x \cdot {}_nE_x = (1 + i)^{-n}l_{x+n}$$

Following actuarial practice, we substitute the letter $v$ for $(1 + i)^{-1}$. Then $v^n = [(1 + i)^{-1}]^n = (1 + i)^{-n}$. Substituting in the above formula and solving for ${}_nE_x$, we have the following expression for the net premium for a \$1 endowment in $n$ years issued to a person aged $x$ years:

$$_nE_x = \frac{v^n l_{x+n}}{l_x}$$

To reduce the numerical work required to solve life annuity and insurance problems, we now introduce the **commutation functions** which are used by life insurance actuaries. These functions simplify formulas and eliminate multiple and tedious computations. They are defined below.

$$\begin{aligned}
\text{Commutation} \\
\text{functions;} \\
\text{numerical} \\
\text{values are} \\
\text{in Table 6}
\end{aligned}
\left\{
\begin{aligned}
D_x &= v^x l_x \\
N_x &= D_x + D_{x+1} + \cdots + D_{\omega-1} \\
C_x &= v^{x+1} d_x \\
M_x &= C_x + C_{x+1} + \cdots + C_{\omega-1}
\end{aligned}
\right.$$

Note that all of the commutation functions combine *Present Worth of* 1 factors and values from the mortality table. This means that a different table of commutation functions is required for each combination of interest rate and mortality table. Commutation functions may involve 100 terms or more. They simplify actuarial formulas, and they are indispensable labor savers when calculations are done manually or with desk calculators.

The Commutation Columns in Table 6 were taken from Volume I of the Monetary Tables published by the Society of Actuaries. Examples and answers to problems are based on the complete factors. Because of the numerical work involved if a calculator is not available, some instructors have students substitute complete factors and then permit them to round the values to a specified number of significant figures before completing the problem using logarithms, slide rule, or arithmetic to get the final answer. Answers obtained in this way will usually differ slightly from the more precise answers in the text.

If we multiply the numerator and denominator of the equation for the present value of a pure endowment by $v^x$, we have

$$_nE_x = \frac{v^{x+n}l_{x+n}}{v^x l_x}$$

Substituting commutation functions, this can be written as follows:

$$_nE_x = \frac{D_{x+n}}{D_x} \tag{28}$$

In all formulas in this and the next chapter, $x$ is the age of the person at the time the endowment, annuity, or life insurance is purchased. The meaning of $n$ is defined for each formula. In this formula it means that the person will receive the endowment at the end of $n$ years if he is then living. In some problems we are given the age at which the person is to get the endowment. In such cases, it is not necessary to get $n$ since this age equals $x + n$.

EXAMPLE 1: What is the net single premium for an 18-year-old man for a 20-year pure endowment of $1000?

SOLUTION: (28) gives the cost of a pure endowment of $1. Therefore a $1000 pure endowment due in 20 years would cost an 18-year-old man,

$$1000 \frac{D_{38}}{D_{18}} = 1000 \frac{3\ 638\ 747.1}{6\ 218\ 174.5} = \$585.18$$

EXAMPLE 2: Solve Example 1 for an 18-year-old woman.

SOLUTION:

$$1000 \frac{D_{38}}{D_{18}} = 1000 \frac{3\ 949\ 851.1}{6\ 727\ 326.8} = \$587.14$$

Note the higher cost to a woman because she has a higher expectation than a man of living to the end of the endowment period.

EXAMPLE 3: Find the net single premium for an 18-year-old man for a pure endowment of $1000 at age 60.

SOLUTION:

$$1000\,\frac{D_{60}}{D_{18}} = 1000\,\frac{1\,749\,787.7}{6\,218\,174.5} = \$281.40$$

This is less than the answer to Example 1 because the endowment period is much longer. Pure endowments are rarely sold separately. However, they are often a part of life insurance policies. The endowment feature can make such policies quite expensive unless the endowment period is a long one.

Pure endowments illustrate what it means to accumulate a fund with benefit of survivorship. In Example 3, the share of each individual who survives to age 60 is made up in part of the shares forfeited by those who die before reaching 60. Thus each survivor receives more than he would get from interest alone. At $2\frac{1}{2}\%$ compounded annually, the \$281.40 in Example 3 would amount to $281.40(1.025)^{42} = \$793.83$. With interest and survivorship, those who live to the end of the endowment period get \$1000.

### EXERCISE 9b

1. Find the net cost to a 30-year-old man of a pure endowment of \$1000 in (a) 20 years, (b) 40 years.  [(a) \$564.05; (b) \$219.68]
2. Work Problem 1 for a woman.
3. What would be the cost to a 25-year-old man of an endowment of \$10,000 when he is 65 years of age?  (\$2644.97)
4. Work Problem 3 for a woman.

## 9.5   Whole Life Annuities

Instead of a single payment, people often prefer to receive benefits from insurance policies and other investments in equal periodic payments. If these payments are to continue as long as the designated person or annuitant lives, the annuity is called a **whole life annuity**. While the payments can be made at any interval, we shall limit ourselves to annual payments. Also in all of our derivations the size of each payment will be \$1. Then to solve any particular problem, all we have to do is multiply the appropriate formula by the size of the payment. As was the case with annuities certain, the first payment can be made one year hence, at once, or several years hence.

We first consider the *ordinary* or *immediate life* annuity which provides for annual payments starting in one year, if the annuitant is then living, and continuing throughout his lifetime. Our computations will be based on the assumption that $l_x$ persons age $x$ each deposit $\$a_x$. Thus the original amount in the fund, $l_x a_x$, plus interest must be adequate to pay each person \$1 at the end of each year throughout the rest of his life.

One year after the plan is started there will be $l_{x+1}$ persons living and each of them must be paid out of the fund. Every year from then on each of the survivors will get \$1. This will continue as long as there are survivors, which is age 99 for men and 102 for women when the CSO Table is used.

Since beginning students find derivations easier to follow when numerical values are used, the formulas in this chapter are derived assuming the CSO Table for males with $l_{99}$ as the last entry in the table. Formulas derived in this way are completely general and are the same as we would get using the expression $l_{\omega-1}$ for the final entry.

To get an equation of value, we discount all future payments to the present date. Thus the present value of the payment to be made in one year is $vl_{x+1}$; the present value of the payment to be made in two years is $v^2 l_{x+2}$ and so on. A time diagram of payments and premiums is shown below. The symbol $a_x$ is used to represent the premium of each person.

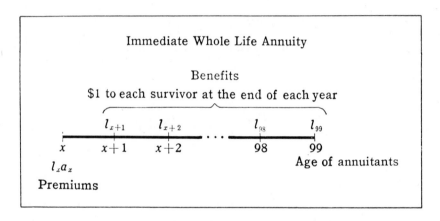

Bringing everything back to the present and setting up an equation of value, we have

$$l_x a_x = v l_{x+1} + v^2 l_{x+2} + \cdots + v^{98-x} l_{98} + v^{99-x} l_{99}$$

Therefore the cost per person is

$$a_x = \frac{v l_{x+1} + v^2 l_{x+2} + \cdots + v^{98-x} l_{98} + v^{99-x} l_{99}}{l_x}$$

To get the cost of this annuity for a man aged 20, we would have to discount all the annual payments from 21 to 99. To avoid this labor we first multiply numerator and denominator by $v^x$.

$$a_x = \frac{v^{x+1} l_{x+1} + v^{x+2} l_{x+2} + \cdots + v^{98} l_{98} + v^{99} l_{99}}{v^x l_x}$$

Then we simplify, using commutation symbols.

$$a_x = \frac{D_{x+1} + D_{x+2} + \cdots + D_{98} + D_{99}}{D_x}$$

$$a_x = \frac{N_{x+1}}{D_x} \qquad (29)$$

## 9.6   Whole Life Annuity Due

If the first payment is made at once and payments are made throughout the lifetime of the annuitant, the annuity is called a **whole life annuity due**. The present value of a whole life annuity due of 1 per year is indicated by the symbol $\ddot{a}_x$. Since the only difference between this annuity and the immediate whole life annuity described in the preceding section is the payments made to the $l_x$ individuals at the start, we can say

$$l_x\ddot{a}_x = l_x + vl_{x+1} + v^2 l_{x+2} + \cdots + v^{98-x} l_{98} + v^{99-x} l_{99}$$

Solving for $\ddot{a}_x$ and multiplying numerator and denominator by $v^x$,

$$\ddot{a}_x = \frac{v^x l_x + v^{x+1} l_{x+1} + v^{x+2} l_{x+2} + \cdots + v^{98} l_{98} + v^{99} l_{99}}{v^x l_x}$$

$$= \frac{D_x + D_{x+1} + D_{x+2} + \cdots + D_{98} + D_{99}}{D_x}$$

$$\ddot{a}_x = \frac{N_x}{D_x} \qquad (30)$$

Because of its frequent use in annuity work, values of $\ddot{a}_x$ are given in Table 6 along with the commutation columns. By simply subtracting 1 from the values of $\ddot{a}_x$ we can get the present value of an ordinary or immediate whole life annuity of 1 per year. Therefore,

$$a_x = \ddot{a}_x - 1$$

EXAMPLE 1: Find the net single premium for a whole life annuity due of $1000 per year issued to a man who is 50 years old.

SOLUTION: (30) gives the net single premium for a whole life annuity due of $1 per year. For annual payments of $1000 the premium is

$$1000\ddot{a}_{50} = 1000 \times 17.614151 = \$17,614.15$$

EXAMPLE 2: How much would an immediate life annuity of $500 a year cost a man who is 18 years old?

SOLUTION: From (29) the value of an immediate life annuity of $500 a year is $500a_{18}$. Since the immediate life annuity is the same as the life annuity due except that the first payment is made in one year, the value of $a_{18}$ can be obtained by subtracting 1 from $\ddot{a}_{18}$. Therefore the cost is

$$500(\ddot{a}_{18} - 1) = 500(28.963722 - 1.0000) = \$13{,}981.86$$

EXAMPLE 3: A man dies and leaves his widow a $20,000 insurance policy. If she is 60 years old and elects to receive annual payments for life with the first payment to be made now, what is the size of each payment?

SOLUTION: In this problem the present value of the life annuity due is known and the size of the annual payment is to be determined. Letting $R$ represent the size of each payment, we have

$$R\ddot{a}_{60} = 20{,}000$$

$$R = \frac{20{,}000}{\ddot{a}_{60}} = \frac{20{,}000}{14.502179} = \$1379.10$$

EXAMPLE 4: Find the size of the payment in Example 3 if the first payment is to be made in 1 year.

SOLUTION: This is an ordinary or immediate whole life annuity.

$$Ra_{60} = R(\ddot{a}_{60} - 1) = 20{,}000$$

$$R = \frac{20{,}000}{13.502179} = \$1481.24$$

EXAMPLE 5: As compensation for injuries, accident victims sometimes receive cash settlements. Money left after legal and other costs can be used to provide the injured person an income for life. A Chicago construction worker was awarded $696,000 for an injury that resulted in his being paralyzed from the neck down. If the worker, who was 28 years old, put two-thirds of this money in a whole life annuity due, what would be his annual income?

SOLUTION:

$$R\ddot{a}_{28} = 464{,}000$$

$$R = \frac{464{,}000}{\ddot{a}_{28}} = \frac{464{,}000}{26.163201} = \$17{,}735$$

While this may seem like a large sum, it should be recognized that it must not only replace lost income but also cover the extra costs which must be borne by a disabled person.

To protect themselves against lawsuits that could result in financial losses, individuals and companies may find it advisable to carry large liability policies.

**EXERCISE 9c**

1. Find the net single premium for a life annuity of $1000 per year for a 30-year-old man if: (a) the first payment is to be made now; (b) the first payment is to be made in 1 year.        [(a) $25,518.94; (b) $24,518.94]

2. A man plans to retire at 65. At that time, a life annuity of $2000 a year would cost how much if: (a) the first payment is made at age 65; (b) the first payment is made at age 66?

3. A 50-year-old widow wants to use part of her estate to purchase an immediate life annuity of $2500 a year. Find the net single premium.

($44,813.60)

4. A 50-year-old man wants to buy an annuity which will pay him $1000 a year for life with the first payment to be made when he is age 51. Find the net single premium.

5. A man will retire at age 65 and start receiving social security benefits of $150 a month. Find the approximate present value of these payments. For this purpose, replace the 12 monthly payments with an approximately equivalent payment of $1800 at the end of each year.        ($18,066)

6. At age 62, a widow is to receive $100 a month in social security benefits. What is the approximate present value of her benefits?

7. A 20-year-old man takes out a life insurance policy on which the premiums are $100 a year at the beginning of each year for life. Find the net present value of these premiums.        ($2845.36)

8. A 35-year-old man takes out a life insurance policy on which the premiums are $250 a year at the beginning of each year for life. Find the net present value of the premiums.

9. A widow, who is the beneficiary of a $20,000 insurance policy, decides to take an annual income for life. If she is 48 years old, find the size of each payment if the first payment is to be made: (a) now; (b) in 1 year.

[(a) $1010.97; (b) $1064.79]

10. A 50-year-old man invests $100,000 in a whole life annuity with the first payment to be made in 1 year. What is the size of each payment?

11. In his will, a man directs that each of his twin children, a boy and a girl, is to receive a life annuity due with a present value of $100,000. At his death, the children are 19 years of age. Find the lifetime income of each.

(Boy $3482.94; Girl $3394.99)

12. A man directs that $\frac{2}{3}$ of his estate is to be used to purchase an ordinary life annuity for his wife and the remaining $\frac{1}{3}$ an ordinary life annuity for his son. The estate amounts to $150,000. When the annuities are purchased, the widow is 62 and the son is 30. Find the annual income of each.

**13.** On March 5, 1966, a jet plane crashed in Japan killing all 135 passengers and crew. A series of record-breaking settlements has resulted in millions of dollars being paid to relatives of the victims. A couple who lost two minor children received $541,000. If one-third of this went for legal expenses, the balance would buy an immediate whole life annuity of how much a year for a woman if she purchased the annuity when she was 37 years old?

($15,587)

**14.** The parents of three adult children killed in the above accident received $172,500. If the mother, at age 57, purchased an immediate whole life annuity with two-thirds of the money, what would be her annual income?

**15.** A housewife was blinded by the explosion of a can of drain cleaner. She received $930,000 in damages. If, at age 48, she used two-thirds of this amount to buy a whole life annuity due, what would be her annual income?

($31,340)

**16.** A pizza baker, skilled at tossing dough high into the air, was injured in an automobile accident. His lawyer claimed that he would no longer be able to throw the dough and please crowds as he had in the past. A jury awarded $335,000 in damages. If the injured 33-year-old pizza tosser used $200,000 of this to buy a whole life annuity due, how much would he receive each year?

## 9.7 Deferred Whole Life Annuity

Another type of annuity is the $n$-year deferred immediate life annuity. This is the same as an immediate life annuity with the first $n$ payments omitted. The first payment is made at age $x + n + 1$. The present value of an annuity of 1 per year is denoted by $_{n|}a_x$. The benefits and premiums are shown on the time diagram below.

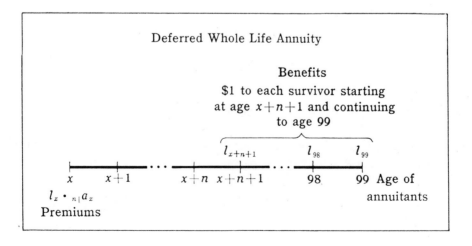

Discounting the benefits and setting up the equation of value, we have

$$l_x \cdot {}_{n|}a_x = v^{n+1}l_{x+n+1} + \cdots + v^{98-x}l_{98} + v^{99-x}l_{99}$$

Solving for the individual premium and multiplying numerator and denominator by $v^x$,

$$_{n|}a_x = \frac{v^{x+n+1}l_{x+n+1} + \cdots + v^{98}l_{98} + v^{99}l_{99}}{v^x l_x}$$

$$= \frac{D_{x+n+1} + \cdots + D_{98} + D_{99}}{D_x}$$

$$_{n|}a_x = \frac{N_{x+n+1}}{D_x} \tag{31}$$

In many deferred life annuity problems, we are given the age at which the first payment is to be made. Since this is equal to $x + n + 1$, we can simply substitute this value in the formula and need not determine $n$.

EXAMPLE 1: A man 40 years of age wants a life income of $2000 a year with the first annual payment to be made when he is 65. What is the net cost of this annuity?

SOLUTION: Since the first payment is to be made at age 65, $x + n + 1 = 65$. Substituting in (31),

$$\text{Net cost} = 2000 \frac{N_{65}}{D_{40}} = 2000 \frac{15\,077\,832.8}{3\,441\,765.1} = \$8761.69$$

EXAMPLE 2: A 15-year-old girl receives an inheritance of $30,000. If she is to get annual payments for life starting on her 21st birthday, what will be the size of each payment?

SOLUTION: If $R$ represents the annual payment, we have

$$30,000 = R \frac{N_{21}}{D_{15}}$$

$$R = 30,000 \frac{D_{15}}{N_{21}} = 30,000 \frac{7\,273\,432.5}{180\,101\,480.3} = \$1211.56$$

All whole life annuity problems can be solved using the following general formula in which $R$ is the periodic payment.

$$\text{Net present value} = R \frac{N_{\text{age at first payment}}}{D_{\text{age when annuity is purchased}}}$$

This verbal form of the whole life annuity formulas simplifies solving deferred whole life annuities. When values of $\ddot{a}_x$ are available, as they are in Table 6 in this text, the easiest way to solve immediate whole life annuities and whole life annuities due is to use the $\ddot{a}_x$ function.

EXAMPLE 3: Find the net cost of a $2000 a year whole life annuity for a 50-year-old woman if the first payment is to be made when she is: (a) 50, (b) 51, (c) 62.

SOLUTION: For parts (a) and (b) we use $\ddot{a}_x$. Part (c) is solved using (31) or the general formula given above.

(a)  Net cost $= 2000\ddot{a}_{50} = 2000 \times 18.92\ 5440 = \$37,850.88$
(b)  Net cost $= 2000(\ddot{a}_{50} - 1) = 2000 \times 17.92\ 5440 = \$35,850.88$

(c)  Net cost $= 2000\,\dfrac{N_{62}}{D_{50}} = 2000\,\dfrac{24\ 883\ 551.1}{2\ 803\ 559.9} = \$17,751.40$

## EXERCISE 9d

1. What is the net cost of a whole life annuity of $1000 a year for a 50-year-old man if the first payment is to be made 15 years hence?  ($5914.44)
2. Find the net single premium for an annuity of $1000 a year issued to a 55-year-old man if the first payment is to be made at the age of 65.
3. Find the answer to Problem 1 if the annuitant is a woman.  ($7003.19)
4. Find the answer to Problem 2 if the annuitant is a woman.
5. A 45-year-old man receives an inheritance of $25,000. He uses this money to buy a whole life annuity the first payment of which is to be made when he is 60. What will be the size of the annual payment?  ($3229.85)
6. When his $10,000 endowment policy matures at age 50, a man decides to use this money to buy a life annuity starting at age 65 when his social security payments will begin. What annual payment will be provided by the proceeds of the insurance policy?
7. A man who is now 48 years old would like to have an annual income of $2400 starting when he is age 60. What is the net cost of this annuity?
  ($20,360.15)
8. A 58-year-old man expects to get about $1500 a year from social security when he reaches age 65. He now has money with which he wants to buy a life annuity which will provide another $1500 a year for life with the first annual payment to be made when he reaches age 65. How much will this annuity cost him now?
9. A widow is 50 years old when her husband dies. One of his insurance policies is for $15,000. This policy is to provide the widow an income for life starting when she is 60. What annual payment will she receive?  ($1461.55)

10. A 45-year-old widow is left $15,000 from an insurance policy. What annual income for life would she get from this policy if the first payment is made: (a) now; (b) in 1 year; (c) when she is age 65?

11. A 44-year-old machinist was also a part-time singer. He was struck by an object protruding from a train and suffered an injury that affected his tenor voice. A jury awarded $150,000 in damages. If the man used $100,000 of this to buy a whole life annuity with the first payment to be made when he is 55, what will be the size of the annual payment?          ($9304)

12. Find the annual payment in Problem 11 if the first payment is to be made when the man is 50.

## 9.8   Temporary Immediate Life Annuity

A temporary life annuity is one which ends after a certain number of years or at the death of the annuitant, whichever occurs first. If the first payment is made one year hence and if the payments are made for $n$ years, we have an **$n$-year temporary immediate life annuity**. Indicating the present value by $a_{x:\overline{n}|}$ and showing benefits and premiums on a time scale, we have

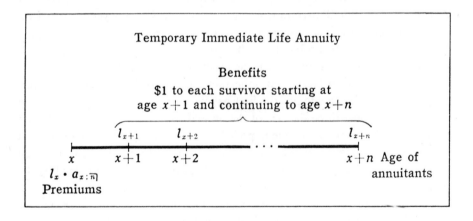

Note that this annuity ceases with the final payments to the $l_{x+n}$ individuals living $n$ years after the start of the program. The equation of value becomes

$$l_x \cdot a_{x:\overline{n}|} = v l_{x+1} + v^2 l_{x+2} + \cdots + v^n l_{x+n}$$

Solving for the individual premium, multiplying numerator and denominator by $v^x$ and substituting commutation symbols, we have

$$a_{x:\overline{n}|} = \frac{D_{x+1} + D_{x+2} + \cdots + D_{x+n}}{D_x}$$

Since

$$N_{x+1} = D_{x+1} + D_{x+2} + \cdots + D_{x+n} + D_{x+n+1} + \cdots + D_{99}$$

And

$$N_{x+n+1} = \qquad\qquad\qquad\quad D_{x+n+1} + \cdots + D_{99}$$

The numerator can be written as $N_{x+1} - N_{x+n+1}$

$$a_{x:\overline{n}|} = \frac{N_{x+1} - N_{x+n+1}}{D_x} \tag{32}$$

EXAMPLE: How much would a man aged 18 have to pay for a 5-year temporary life annuity of \$1000 per year if the first payment is to be made when the man is aged 19?

SOLUTION:

$$1000a_{18:\overline{5}|} = 1000\,\frac{N_{18+1} - N_{18+5+1}}{D_{18}} = 1000\,\frac{N_{19} - N_{24}}{D_{18}}$$

$$= 1000\,\frac{173\ 883\ 305.8 - 145\ 143\ 761.6}{6\ 218\ 174.5} = \$4621.86$$

## 9.9   Temporary Life Annuity Due

If the first payment is made at once, we have a temporary life annuity due, the present value of which is indicated by $\ddot{a}_{x:\overline{n}|}$. Proceeding in the usual manner, we find that the present value is

$$\ddot{a}_{x:n|} = \frac{N_x - N_{x+n}}{D_x} \tag{33}$$

EXAMPLE: How much would a 5-year temporary life annuity due of \$1000 per year cost a man who is 18 years old?

SOLUTION:

$$1000\ddot{a}_{18:\overline{5}|} = 1000\,\frac{N_{18} - N_{18+5}}{D_{18}} = 1000\,\frac{N_{18} - N_{23}}{D_{18}}$$

$$= 1000\,\frac{180\ 101\ 480.3 - 150\ 590\ 927.4}{6\ 218\ 174.5} = \$4745.85$$

## 9.10   Deferred Temporary Life Annuity

A series of annual payments which commences at age $x + n + 1$ and continues for $m$ years if the annuitant survives is called an **$n$-year deferred $m$-year**

**temporary immediate annuity.** The symbol for the present value of $1 per year is denoted by $_{n|m}a_x$. Proceeding in the usual manner, we get the following formula for the present value. Note that in this formula, which is given here as it appears in actuarial publications, $n$ stands for the interval of deferment and $m$ is the number of payments.

$$_{n|m}a_x = \frac{N_{x+n+1} - N_{x+n+m+1}}{D_x} \tag{34}$$

EXAMPLE 1: How much would a 5-year temporary life annuity of $1000 a year cost a man aged 18 if he is to receive the first payment when he is 28?

SOLUTION: In this problem $x$, the age of the annuitant, is 18; $n$, the interval of deferment, is 9; and $m$, the number of payments, is 5. Substituting in (34), we have

$$1000_{9|5}a_{18} = 1000 \frac{N_{28} - N_{33}}{D_{18}}$$

$$= 1000 \frac{124\ 748\ 159.0 - 102\ 134\ 645.1}{6\ 218\ 174.5} = \$3636.68$$

All temporary life annuity problems can be solved using the following general formula in which $R$ is the size of the periodic payment.

$$\text{Net present value} = R \frac{N_{\text{age at first payment}} - N_{\text{age at first payment + number of payments}}}{D_{\text{age when annuity is purchased}}}$$

EXAMPLE 2: Find the net cost of a $2000-a-year temporary life annuity for 10 years for a 50-year-old woman if the first payment is to be made when she is: (a) 50; (b) 51; (c) 62.

SOLUTION:

(a) Net cost $= 2000 \dfrac{N_{50} - N_{60}}{D_{50}}$

$$= 2000 \frac{53\ 058\ 604.2 - 28\ 773\ 199.9}{2\ 803\ 559.9} = \$17,324.69$$

(b) Net cost $= 2000 \dfrac{N_{51} - N_{61}}{D_{50}}$

$$= 2000 \frac{50\ 255\ 044.3 - 26\ 789\ 139.5}{2\ 803\ 559.9} = \$16,740.08$$

(c) Net cost $= 2000 \dfrac{N_{62} - N_{72}}{D_{50}}$

$\qquad\quad = 2000 \dfrac{24\ 883\ 551.1 - 10\ 065\ 398.9}{2\ 803\ 559.9} = \$10{,}570.95$

EXAMPLE 3: A woman purchased a preparation advertised as a fingernail hardener. Instead of hardening her fingernails, it caused the loss of them. A jury awarded her $25,000 damages and her husband $5000 for the loss of her services. If the woman was 40 years old and used $15,000 of the settlement to buy a temporary life annuity of 10 annual payments, what would be the size of each payment if the first payment is made when she is: (a) 40, (b) 41, (c) 50 years old?

SOLUTION: The present value of the annuity is known and $R$ is to be found. We substitute in the general formula and solve for $R$.

(a) $15{,}000 = R \dfrac{N_{40} - N_{50}}{D_{40}}$

$\qquad R = 15{,}000 \dfrac{D_{40}}{N_{40} - N_{50}}$

$\qquad\quad = 15{,}000 \dfrac{3\ 740\ 188.5}{86\ 113\ 147.1 - 53\ 058\ 604.2} = \$1695.78$

(b) $15{,}000 = R \dfrac{N_{41} - N_{51}}{D_{40}}$

$\qquad R = 15{,}000 \dfrac{D_{40}}{N_{41} - N_{51}}$

$\qquad\quad = 15{,}000 \dfrac{3\ 740\ 188.5}{82\ 372\ 958.6 - 50\ 255\ 044.3} = \$1746.78$

(c) $15{,}000 = R \dfrac{N_{50} - N_{60}}{D_{40}}$

$\qquad R = 15{,}000 \dfrac{D_{40}}{N_{50} - N_{60}}$

$\qquad\quad = 15{,}000 \dfrac{3\ 740\ 188.5}{53\ 058\ 604.2 - 28\ 773\ 199.9} = \$2310.14$

## EXERCISE 9e

1. Find the net single premium of a temporary immediate life annuity of $1000 per year for 10 years if the annuitant is an 18-year-old man.  ($8668.66)

**2.** Find the net single premium of a temporary immediate life annuity of $1200 a year for 10 years if the annuitant is a 64-year-old man.

**3.** How much would a 10-year temporary life annuity due of $1200 a year cost a 28-year-old man?                                    ($10,664.73)

**4.** Find the net cost of a 15-year temporary life annuity due of $840 a year for a 65-year-old man.

**5.** At age 55, a man buys an annuity which will provide him 15 annual payments of $800. If the first payment is to be made when the man is age 65, how much will the annuity cost?                                    ($4846.78)

**6.** How much money must be set aside to provide a 12-year-old boy with $2000 a year for 4 years if he is to receive the first payment when he is 18?

**7.** Circus elephants doing a dance caused plaster to loosen and fall in the room below. The falling plaster injured a man who was awarded $18,000 in the United States District Court. If at age 58 he put $10,000 of this settlement in a 5-year temporary life annuity, what would be the size of the annual payment if the first payment is made at age: (a) 58; (b) 59; (c) 65?

[(a) $2177.67; (b) $2278.44; (c) $3134.82]

**8.** A boy suffered burns over 40 percent of his body as a result of a fire started while playing with a camera containing an electric flash attachment. A suit on his behalf resulted in a $315,000 settlement. If $200,000 is used to buy a temporary life annuity of 30 annual payments when the boy is 10 years old, what will be the size of each payment if the first payment is made when he is: (a) 10; (b) 11; (c) 21 years old?

**9.** A 23-year-old woman was awarded $245,000 in a suit against an automobile manufacturer. Her attorney claimed that her permanent injuries were caused by the faulty design of the car. If the woman used $100,000 to buy a temporary life annuity of 40 annual payments, what would be the size of each payment if the first payment is made when she is: (a) 23; (b) 24; (c) 25 years old?

[(a) $4074.20; (b) $4194.40; (c) $4319.47]

### 9.11  Joint Life Annuities

All of the annuities in this chapter were based on a single life. This means that when the annuitant dies the payments cease. Annuities may also be based on more than one life. For example, a joint life annuity continues in existence as long as all the lives survive, and stops upon the occurrence of the first death. A joint-and-survivor annuity continues as long as any member of the group survives. This type of annuity might be attractive to a retired couple who would want their income to continue as long as both or either of them is living. These other types of annuities are based on the principles given in this chapter. However, the mathematics involved is beyond the range of an elementary text.

They are mentioned here to acquaint students with the fact that annuities are available to meet those practical situations that involve combinations of two or more lives.

## 9.12 Summary of Life Annuity Formulas

The six annuity formulas derived in this chapter can be divided into two general classes:

(1) Whole life annuities which provide equal periodic payments as long as the annuitant lives.

(2) Temporary life annuities in which the payments cease after a specified time or when the annuitant dies, depending on which comes first.

Both of the general classes of annuities are divided into three types, depending on when the first payment is made relative to $x$, the age of the annuitant at the time the annuity is purchased. Immediate or ordinary life annuities have the first payment made at age $x + 1$. Life annuities due have the first payment made at age $x$. Deferred immediate life annuities have the first payment made at age $x + n + 1$ where $n$ is the interval of deferment.

The formulas in this book are the same as those used by the Society of Actuaries. This will acquaint students with modern actuarial practice. It will also provide a sound foundation for those students who want to continue to more advanced work in insurance.

The annuity formulas are summarized below as derived in this chapter and in a second form using verbal subscripts. All formulas are for periodic payments of $1. For other periodic payments simply multiply by the size of the payment.

*Whole Life Annuities*

| | | |
|---|---|---|
| Immediate or ordinary<br>(First payment at age $x + 1$) | $a_x = \dfrac{N_{x+1}}{D_x}$ | $(a_x = \ddot{a}_x - 1)$   (29) |
| Due<br>(First payment at age $x$) | $\ddot{a}_x = \dfrac{N_x}{D_x}$ | (30) |
| Deferred<br>(First payment at age $x + n + 1$) | $_{n\mid}a_x = \dfrac{N_{x+n+1}}{D_x}$ | (31) |

All of the whole life annuities can be solved using the following general formula. This is convenient when the time of the first payment is given in terms of the age of the annuitant.

$$\text{Value} = \frac{N_{\text{age at which the first payment is due}}}{D_{\text{age when annuity is purchased}}}$$

## Temporary Life Annuities

---

Immediate or ordinary
(First payment at age $x + 1$. Payments at the end of each year for $n$ years.)

$$a_{x:\overline{n}|} = \frac{N_{x+1} - N_{x+n+1}}{D_x} \qquad (32)$$

---

Due
(First payment at age $x$. Payments at the beginning of each year for $n$ years.)

$$\ddot{a}_{x:\overline{n}|} = \frac{N_x - N_{x+n}}{D_x} \qquad (33)$$

---

Deferred
(First payment at age $x + n + 1$. Payments for $m$ years.)

$$_{n|m}a_x = \frac{N_{x+n+1} - N_{x+n+m+1}}{D_x} \qquad (34)$$

---

All of the temporary life annuities can be solved using the following general formula. This is convenient when the time of the first payment is given in terms of the age of the annuitant.

$$\text{Value} = \frac{N_{\text{age at first payment}} - N_{\text{age at first payment} + \text{number of payments}}}{D_{\text{age when annuity is purchased}}}$$

# 10

# Life
# Insurance

## 10.1 Life Insurance

Life insurance makes it possible for a man of moderate income to provide an income for his family if he should die. The fundamental principle of life insurance can be illustrated by a simple example.

Suppose that a group of 10,000 18-year-old men in good health want to take out an insurance policy that would pay $1000 to the beneficiary of each of the young men who dies before reaching age 19. If we refer to the CSO Mortality Table, we find that the average death rate for 18-year-old men is 1.69 per 1000. Therefore, our group would expect about 17 deaths during the coming year. If each of the 10,000 men pays a premium of $1.70 into a common fund, there would immediately be set up a fund of $17,000 from which the 17 death benefits would be paid.

In practical insurance plans interest is earned on invested funds. An interest rate of $2\frac{1}{2}\%$ will be used in all insurance problems in this book. Gross insurance premiums must be large enough to pay both death benefits and company expenses. We shall compute only net premiums making no allowance for loading for the four most common types of policies: term, straight life, limited payment life, and endowment.

Before we start computing net premiums, it is interesting to see how the cost of commercial insurance varies with the type of policy. While there is some variation in cost from one company to another, the following graphs are typical of costs from a representative company. The rates are annual rates per $1000 for a man taking out a $10,000 or larger policy. In general, the rates would be somewhat higher for smaller policies. A much larger policy, such as $25,000, would probably have a lower rate. Rates for women are likely to be lower because of their higher life expectancy.

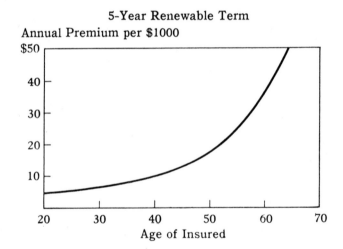

Term insurance has a premium which is based on expected death benefits for a limited period such as 5 or 10 years. Because mortality rates increase as people get older, the premium for a term policy increases with the age of the insured. Term insurance is quite expensive beyond middle age.

A level premium policy costs more initially than term insurance, but the premium does not increase. During the early years of the policy this excess premium is set aside as a reserve to help meet increased death benefits later on. The sketches in this section are for level premium policies issued to a man who is 20 years old.

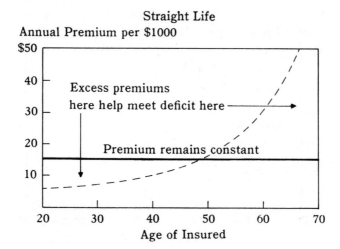

The most common type of level premium policy is straight life, also known as whole life or ordinary life. The cost of this policy is determined by the age of the insured when he first takes out the policy. He can then carry it for the rest of his life at the same premium.

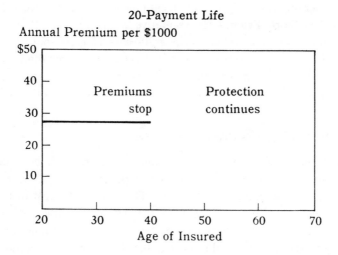

Limited pay life requires payments for a certain number of years at the end of which time the policy becomes fully paid-up for the life of the insured. This means that the premiums must be higher than for ordinary or straight life because the reserve must be built up in a shorter time. How much higher will depend on the payment period.

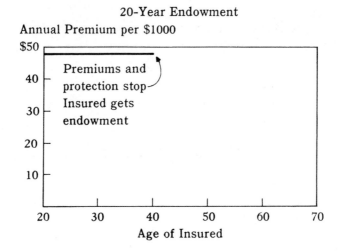

20-Year Endowment

Annual Premium per $1000

Endowment policies provide protection for a stated number of years. At the end of the endowment period protection ceases and, if the insured is still living, the face value of the policy is paid to him. The insurance company must set the premium large enough to take care of the *certainty* that they will have to pay someone, either the beneficiary or the insured, by the end of the endowment period. This makes endowment policies very expensive if the endowment period is short. From a representative company a ten thousand dollar 20-year endowment policy would cost a 20-year-old man about $480 a year. Policies with longer endowment periods will have lower premiums. An endowment policy at age 65 for $10,000 would cost a 20-year-old man about $191 from the same company. This policy has an endowment period of 45 years.

## 10.2    Determining the Premium

As an illustration of how insurance premiums are determined, let us see how we could get the premium for an ordinary life policy for an 18-year-old man. We shall assume that the policy is for $1. Then to get the cost of any policy, all we need do is multiply our result by the size of the policy. Also we shall assume that the policy is to be purchased by a net single premium of $A$.

Referring to the mortality table we see that there are 9,698,230 men alive at age 18. If each of them took out a $1 whole life policy, and paid for it with a single premium, the total premiums plus interest would have to be sufficient to pay the $1 death benefits to the beneficiary of each insured person at the end of the year in which the insured dies. All of the formulas in this book are for payments made at the end of the year in which a person dies. (In practice insurance companies pay benefits upon proof of death rather than waiting until the end of the year. To take care of this practice insurance companies make a small adjustment in the net premiums.) Referring to the mortality table we see that the company would have to pay 16,390 death benefits one year after the policies were issued, 16,846 in two years, and so on to the end of the mortality table as shown below.

Thus the insurance company will need $16,390 in a year, $16,846 in two years, $12,916 in 81 years, $6415 in 82 years, and various other amounts for all of the intervening years. The total present value of all these future payments must now be determined by discounting each year's death benefits. Then dividing this total by 9,698,230 will give us the cost per person.

## 10.3 Straight Life Insurance

To avoid the work involved in discounting many payments, we now derive a formula for getting the premium for an ordinary or straight life policy using the commutation functions. The company issues $1 policies to $l_x$ persons living at age $x$. At the end of the first year the company will have to pay $\$d_x$ in death benefits. Payments at the end of the second year will be $\$d_{x+1}$ and so on out to $\$d_{99}$. Each of the $l_x$ persons will pay a net single premium, $\$A_x$, for his policy. Thus the number living at age $x$ times the net single premium paid by each must equal the present value of all future death benefits.

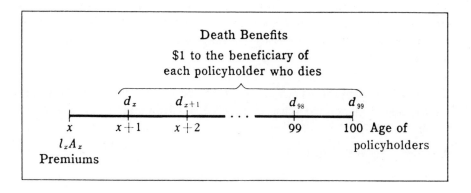

The equation of value is

$$l_x A_x = v d_x + v^2 d_{x+1} + \cdots + v^{99-x} d_{98} + v^{100-x} d_{99}$$

Solving for $A_x$ and multiplying numerator and denominator by $v^x$,

$$A_x = \frac{v^{x+1} d_x + v^{x+2} d_{x+1} + \cdots + v^{99} d_{98} + v^{100} d_{99}}{v^x l_x}$$

We can now substitute the appropriate commutation functions defined on page 326 and simplify.

$$A_x = \frac{C_x + C_{x+1} + \cdots + C_{98} + C_{99}}{D_x}$$

$$A_x = \frac{M_x}{D_x} \qquad (35)$$

Values of $1000 A_x$ are given in Table 6.

EXAMPLE 1: Find the net single premium for a $10,000 whole life policy for an 18-year-old man.

SOLUTION:

$$10{,}000 A_{18} = 10 \times 293.5677 = \$2935.68$$

By paying $2935.68 (plus loading) the person would have a $10,000 policy for the rest of his life.

Because of the large premium, most young people are not able to buy a whole life policy with a single premium. A man who has carried insurance for many years may find it advisable to use the cash value of his policy to buy a paid-up policy that will be in effect for the rest of his life without the payment of additional premiums. At the time a man retires, his children will probably be grown and self supporting, so he will need less insurance. At the same time his income may be less. By converting his insurance to a paid-up policy, he can get the protection he needs without having to use money needed to meet other expenses.

EXAMPLE 2: A man retires at age 65. He has been carrying a $20,000 straight life policy which now has a cash value of $11,400. How much paid-up insurance will this buy?

SOLUTION: According to Table 6,

$$1000 A_{65} = 730.80721$$

This means that the single premium for a $1 straight life policy is .73080 721. Letting $y$ represent the unknown amount of insurance this man can buy with $11,400, we have

$$.73080\ 721y = 11,400$$

$$y = \frac{11,400}{.73080\ 721} = \$15,599.19$$

If this is enough insurance to meet his present needs, it would be foolish to continue to pay premiums out of retirement income that is needed for other purposes.

Since the cost of a single premium policy is too large for most people, most insurance is paid for with annual or more frequent payments. We now determine how to get the annual premium for a straight life policy. The insurance company must take into account the fact that the money received from a policyholder will depend on how long he lives. Even though a policyholder dies after paying only one annual premium, his beneficiary will get the full value of the policy. The expected death benefits will be the same as in the preceding example. The expected total premium for any year will be the number living at that time multiplied by the net annual premium, which we designate by $P_x$. The present value of the death benefits must equal the present value of the expected premiums.

Since the premiums are equal and are paid at the beginning of each year, they form a whole life annuity due. The present value of a whole life annuity due of $1 is $N_x/D_x$ [(30), page 330]. Therefore, the present value of the premiums is $P_x(N_x/D_x)$. This will equal the present value of the death benefits which are the same as for a single premium whole life or $M_x/D_x$ [(35), page 348]. Setting the present value of the premiums equal to the present value of the death benefits, we have

$$P_x \frac{N_x}{D_x} = \frac{M_x}{D_x}$$

$$P_x = \frac{D_x}{N_x} \cdot \frac{M_x}{D_x}$$

$$P_x = \frac{M_x}{N_x} \tag{36}$$

EXAMPLE 3: Find the net annual premium for a $1000 straight life policy for an 18-year-old man.

SOLUTION:

$$1000P_{18} = 1000 \frac{M_{18}}{N_{18}} = 1000 \frac{1\ 825\ 455.4}{180\ 101\ 480.3} = \$10.14$$

**EXERCISE 10a**

1. Find the net single premiums for a $1000 straight life policy issued to: (a) a 22-year-old man; (b) a 27-year-old man; (c) a 32-year-old man; and to a woman of the same ages.

$$\begin{bmatrix} \text{Man: (a) \$318.99; (b) \$354.29; (c) \$394.03} \\ \text{Woman: (a) \$299.72; (b) \$332.60; (c) \$369.64} \end{bmatrix}$$

2. Find the net single premiums for a $1000 straight life policy issued to: (a) a 20-year-old man; (b) a 40-year-old man; (c) a 60-year-old man; and to a woman of the same ages.

3. Find the net single premiums for a straight life policy of $5000 issued to: (a) a 20-year-old man; (b) a 40-year-old man; (c) a 60-year-old man; and to a woman of the same ages.

$$\begin{bmatrix} \text{Man: (a) \$1530.05; (b) \$2335.64; (c) \$3393.11} \\ \text{Woman: (a) \$1437.62; (b) \$2192.23; (c) \$3231.44} \end{bmatrix}$$

4. Find the net single premiums for a straight life policy of $10,000 issued to: (a) an 18-year-old man; (b) a 28-year-old man; (c) a 38-year-old man; and to a woman of the same ages.

5. Find the net annual premiums for the policies in Problem 3.

$$\begin{bmatrix} \text{Man: (a) \$53.77; (b) \$106.91; (c) \$257.51} \\ \text{Woman: (a) \$49.21; (b) \$95.22; (c) \$222.82} \end{bmatrix}$$

6. Find the net annual premiums for the policies in Problem 4.

7. Find the net single premium and the net annual premium for a straight life policy of $2500 issued to a 25-year-old man and woman.

(Man: $849.12, $31.36; Woman: $797.48, $28.56)

8. Get the net single premium and the net annual premium for a straight life policy of $5000 issued to (a) a 12-year-old boy; (b) a 24-year-old man.

9. A father takes out $2000 straight life policies for each of his three boys who are 9, 11, and 14 years of age. Get the net annual premium for each policy. ($15.65; $16.55; $18.04)

10. Get the annual premiums for the policies in Problem 9 if the boys are 19, 21, and 24 years of age.

11. A man who is now 60 years old has a life insurance policy with a cash value of $7000. He decides to convert this to a paid-up life policy. How much paid-up insurance will he get? ($10,315)

12. A man who is 50 years old has $10,000 with which to buy a paid-up policy. How much insurance will he get?

## 10.4 Term Insurance

Term insurance, as we have seen, has an increasing premium as the insured gets older. Usually the premium is not changed every year, but only every 5, 10, or 20 years. Thus term insurance is usually described as 5-year term, 10-year term, and so on. We now derive a general formula for the net single premium, $A^1_{x:\overline{n}|}$, for a \$1, $n$-year term policy, issued to $l_x$ individuals aged $x$. The deaths and premiums for the period from age $x$ to age $x + n$ can be sketched as follows:

**Death Benefits**
**\$1 to the beneficiary of**
**each policyholder who dies**

As in the preceding example, we bring everything back to age $x$ and set up an equation of value:

$$l_x A^1_{x:\overline{n}|} = v d_x + v^2 d_{x+1} + \cdots + v^{n-1} d_{x+n-2} + v^n d_{x+n-1}$$

Multiplying through by $v^x$ and substituting commutation functions, we have

$$A^1_{x:\overline{n}|} = \frac{C_x + C_{x+1} + \cdots + C_{x+n-2} + C_{x+n-1}}{D_x}$$

Since

$$M_x = C_x + C_{x+1} + \cdots + C_{x+n-1} + C_{x+n} + \cdots + C_{99}$$

and

$$M_{x+n} = \qquad\qquad\qquad C_{x+n} + \cdots + C_{99}$$

we can write the numerator as $M_x - M_{x+n}$ so that

$$A^1_{x:\overline{n}|} = \frac{M_x - M_{x+n}}{D_x} \tag{37}$$

If the policy is paid for with net annual premiums, $P^1_{x:\overline{n}|}$, the premiums form an $n$-year, temporary life annuity due. The present value of such an annuity of \$1 is $(N_x - N_{x+n})/D_x$ [(33), page 337]. Therefore, the present value of the premiums is $P^1_{x:\overline{n}|} \cdot (N_x - N_{x+n})/D_x$. This will equal the present value of the death benefits which are the same as for a single premium, $n$-year term policy or $(M_x - M_{x+n})/D_x$ [(37), above]. Setting the present value of the premiums equal to the present value of the death benefits, we have

$$P^1_{x:\overline{n}|} \cdot \frac{N_x - N_{x+n}}{D_x} = \frac{M_x - M_{x+n}}{D_x}$$

$$P^1_{x:\overline{n}|} = \frac{D_x}{N_x - N_{x+n}} \cdot \frac{M_x - M_{x+n}}{D_x}$$

$$P^1_{x:\overline{n}|} = \frac{M_x - M_{x+n}}{N_x - N_{x+n}} \tag{38}$$

EXAMPLE: Find the net single premium and the net annual premium for a 5-year, $1000 term policy for a man aged 18.

SOLUTION:

$$\text{Net single premium} = 1000A^1_{18:\overline{5}|} = 1000 \frac{M_{18} - M_{23}}{D_{18}}$$

$$= 1000 \frac{1\ 825\ 455.4 - 1\ 774\ 216.4}{6\ 218\ 174.5} = \$8.24$$

$$\text{Net annual premium} = 1000P^1_{18:\overline{5}|} = 1000 \frac{M_{18} - M_{23}}{N_{18} - N_{23}}$$

$$= 1000 \frac{1\ 825\ 455.4 - 1\ 774\ 216.4}{180\ 101\ 480.3 - 150\ 590\ 927.4} = \$1.74$$

Note that when the insured reaches age 23, this policy will have a higher premium.

### EXERCISE 10b

1. Find the net single premium and the net annual premium for a 5-year, $5000 term policy issued to a 30-year-old man and woman.

(Man: $52.14, $11.00; Woman: $48.16; $10.15)

2. Find the net single premium and the net annual premium for a 10-year, $5000 term policy issued to a 30-year-old man and woman.

3. Find the net annual premium for a 5-year, $1000 term policy issued to: (a) a 20-year-old man; (b) a 30-year-old man; (c) a 40-year-old man; (d) a 50-year-old man; (e) a 60-year-old man.

[(a) $1.81; (b) $2.20; (c) $4.08; (d) $9.73; (e) $23.70]

4. From a representative company get the actual premiums charged for the policies in Problem 3 and draw a graph to show the changing annual premium for term insurance. The age of the insured should be plotted on the horizontal axis.

5. Find the net single premiums for the following $1000 policies issued to a 22-year-old man; (a) 5-year term; (b) 10-year term; (c) 20-year term.

[(a) $8.84; (b) $17.27; (c) $35.94]

6. Get the net single premiums for the following $1000 policies issued to a 22-year-old woman; (a) 5-year term; (b) 10-year term; (c) 20-year term.

7. Find the net annual premiums for the policies in Problem 5.

[(a) $1.86; (b) $1.94; (c) $2.29]

8. Get the net annual premiums for the policies in Problem 6.

## 10.5   Limited Payment Life Insurance

A $t$-payment life policy is one which provides protection for the lifetime of the insured although premiums are paid for only $t$ years. The present value of the benefits is the same as for an ordinary life policy, $M_x/D_x$. [(35), page 348.] The net single premium for a limited payment life policy is the same as for a straight life policy since in both cases lifetime protection is provided. The net annual premiums form a $t$-year temporary life annuity due which has a present value of $(N_x - N_{x+t})/D_x$ for payments of \$1. [(33), page 337.] If we designate the net annual premium for a $t$-payment life policy as $_tP_x$, the present value of the premiums will be $_tP_x[(N_x - N_{x+t})/D_x]$. Setting the present value of the premiums equal to the present value of the benefits, we have

$$_tP_x \frac{N_x - N_{x+t}}{D_x} = \frac{M_x}{D_x}$$

$$_tP_x = \frac{D_x}{N_x - N_{x+t}} \cdot \frac{M_x}{D_x}$$

$$_tP_x = \frac{M_x}{N_x - N_{x+t}} \tag{39}$$

Limited payment policies are frequently issued on the basis of being paid-up as of a certain age. Paid-up at age 65 means that when the insured reaches age 65, he will have paid-up protection for the rest of his life equal to the face value of the policy. His last premium is paid at age 64. A 20-year-old man buying a paid-up policy at age 65 makes payments from age 20 to age 64 inclusive, a total of 45 payments. This means that $x + t$ in (39) is 65 or the age at which the policy is paid-up. This makes it unnecessary to get $t$ for policies which are paid-up as of a certain age. Simply replace $x + t$ with the age at which the policy is paid-up.

EXAMPLE 1: Find the net annual premium for a \$1000, 20-payment life policy issued to an 18-year-old man.

SOLUTION: The net annual premium is

$$1000 \,_{20}P_{18} = 1000 \frac{M_{18}}{N_{18} - N_{18+20}}$$

$$= 1000 \frac{1\ 825\ 455.4}{180\ 101\ 480.3 - 82\ 372\ 958.6} = \$18.68$$

EXAMPLE 2: Find the net annual premium for a \$1000 paid-up policy at age 65 issued to an 18-year-old man.

SOLUTION: The net annual premium is

$$1000 \frac{M_{18}}{N_{18} - N_{65}} = 1000 \frac{1\ 825\ 455.4}{180\ 101\ 480.3 - 15\ 077\ 832.8} = \$11.06$$

Note that this is not much higher than the annual premium of \$10.14 for a straight life policy determined in Section 10.3.

**EXERCISE 10c**

1. Find the net annual premium for a \$5000, 20-payment life policy issued to a 30-year-old man and woman.          (Man \$121.15; Woman \$113.27)

2. Find the net annual premium for a \$5000, 30-payment life policy issued to an 18-year-old man.

3. Find the net annual premium for a \$1000, 20-payment life policy issued to (a) a 20-year-old man; (b) a 40-year-old man; (c) a 60-year-old man.
                                             [(a) \$19.48; (b) \$30.84; (c) \$56.66]

4. A 32-year-old man takes out a \$10,000 paid-up life policy at age 65. What is the annual premium?

5. Find the net annual premium for a \$1000, 30-payment life policy issued to (a) a 20-year-old man; (b) a 30-year-old man.          [(a) \$14.68; (b) \$18.49]

6. A 24-year-old man takes out a \$5000, 20-payment life policy. What is the annual premium?

7. Find the net annual premium for a \$10,000 paid-up policy at age 65 issued to a 25-year-old man and woman.          (Man \$140.61; Woman \$130.67)

8. Find the net annual premium for a \$10,000 paid-up policy at age 65 issued to a 35-year-old man and woman.

## 10.6   Endowment Insurance

An endowment policy provides protection during the term of the policy and a pure endowment equal to the face value of the policy if the insured is still living when the policy matures. Therefore the net single premium for this policy would be the sum of the net single premium for an $n$-year term policy and a pure endowment due in $n$ years. Using the symbol $A_{x:\overline{n|}}$ for the net single premium and combining (37) and (28), we have

$$A_{x:\overline{n|}} = \frac{M_x - M_{x+n}}{D_x} + \frac{D_{x+n}}{D_x}$$

$$A_{x:\overline{n|}} = \frac{M_x - M_{x+n} + D_{x+n}}{D_x} \tag{40}$$

EXAMPLE 1: Find the net single premium for a \$1000, 20-year endowment policy issued to a man aged 18.

SOLUTION: The net single premium is

$$1000A_{18:\overline{20}|} = 1000 \frac{M_{18} - M_{18+20} + D_{18+20}}{D_{18}}$$

$$= 1000 \frac{1\ 825\ 455.4 - 1\ 629\ 650.6 + 3\ 638\ 747.1}{6\ 218\ 174.5}$$

$$= \$616.67$$

If an $n$-year endowment policy is purchased with net annual premiums, the premiums form an $n$-year temporary life annuity due. Using $P_{x:\overline{n}|}$ to designate the net annual premium and setting the present value of the annual premiums equal to the present value of the benefits, we have

$$P_{x:\overline{n}|} \frac{N_x - N_{x+n}}{D_x} = \frac{M_x - M_{x+n} + D_{x+n}}{D_x}$$

$$P_{x:\overline{n}|} = \frac{D_x}{N_x - N_{x+n}} \cdot \frac{M_x - M_{x+n} + D_{x+n}}{D_x}$$

$$P_{x:\overline{n}|} = \frac{M_x - M_{x+n} + D_{x+n}}{N_x - N_{x+n}} \tag{41}$$

Endowment policies are frequently issued on the basis of the endowment being paid as of a certain age. Endowment at age 65 means that if the insured lives to age 65, he will receive the face amount of the policy. His last premium is paid at age 64. A 20-year-old man buying an endowment at age 65 will make payments from age 20 to 64 inclusive, a total of 45 payments. This means that $x + n$ in (41) is 65 or the age at which the endowment is paid. This makes it unnecessary to get $n$ for endowment policies as of a certain age. Simply replace $x + n$ with the age at which the endowment is paid.

EXAMPLE 2: Find the net annual premium for a $1000, 20-year endowment policy issued to a man aged 18.

SOLUTION:

$$1000P_{18:\overline{20}|} = 1000 \frac{M_{18} - M_{18+20} + D_{18+20}}{N_{18} - N_{18+20}}$$

$$= 1000 \frac{1\ 825\ 455.4 - 1\ 629\ 650.6 + 3\ 638\ 747.1}{180\ 101\ 480.3 - 82\ 372\ 958.6} = \$39.24$$

EXAMPLE 3: Find the net annual premium for a $1000 endowment policy at age 65 issued to an 18-year-old man.

SOLUTION: Substituting in (41), the net annual premium is

$$1000P_{18:\overline{47}|} = 1000 \frac{M_{18} - M_{65} + D_{65}}{N_{18} - N_{65}}$$

$$= 1000 \frac{1\,825\,455.4 - 998\,376.6 + 1\,366\,128.5}{180\,101\,480.3 - 15\,077\,832.8} = \$13.29$$

An interesting type of endowment occurs when a person with a straight life policy outlives the mortality table on which the policy is based. A mortality table has a terminal age $\omega$ as a matter of convenience for mathematical analysis. Actuaries know that some people will live beyond age $\omega$. But to simplify computations and formulas, it is necessary to assume a terminal age at which there will be no survivors. Using the CSO Table for males, straight life premiums are based on the assumption that there will be no survivors at age 100. The person who lives to 100 is then statistically dead. The time has come to pay someone. Since the insured is still living, he becomes the beneficiary of an endowment equal to the value of the policy.

**EXERCISE 10d**

1. Find the net single premium and the net annual premium for a $5000, 20-year endowment policy issued to a 30-year-old man and to a 30-year-old woman.
$$\begin{bmatrix} \text{Man: } \$3099.55, \$198.90 \\ \text{Woman: } \$3092.75, \$197.75 \end{bmatrix}$$

2. Find the net single premium and the net annual premium for a $2500, 20-year endowment policy issued to a 28-year-old man and to a 28-year-old woman.

3. Find the net annual premium for a $1000, 20-year endowment policy issued to: (a) a 20-year-old man; (b) a 40-year-old man; (c) a 60-year-old man.
[(a) $39.28; (b) $41.62; (c) $59.10]

4. Find the net single premium and the net annual premium for a $1000, 15-year endowment policy issued to a 6-year-old boy.

5. A 25-year-old man and a 25-year-old woman take out a $5000 endowment policy at age 65. Find the net single premium and the net annual premium.
$$\begin{bmatrix} \text{Man: } \$2054.25, \$85.04 \\ \text{Woman: } \$2023.01, \$82.87 \end{bmatrix}$$

6. A 23-year-old man takes out a $10,000 endowment policy at age 60. Find the net single premium and the net annual premium.

## 10.7 Insurance Reserves

The net premium for a 1-year term policy is just sufficient to pay the death claims at the end of that year. This is sometimes called the natural premium.

As people get older (beyond age 10) the probability of death increases and the 1-year term premium becomes greater. As was pointed out in the general description of the various insurance policies, it is possible to avoid this increasing premium by writing level premium policies. These policies have a higher premium than the 1-year term premium for the earlier years of the policy. This excess plus accumulated interest is used to build up a **reserve fund** which will be used to help pay death benefits when the level premium is smaller than the 1-year term premium. In this book we shall compute **terminal reserves** which are the reserves at the end of a policy year.

The following table shows the 1-year term premium for a $1000 policy for a person as his age increases from 20 to 70. Also shown is the level premium for a straight life policy issued to a person at age 20, and the difference in premiums between the natural premium and the level premium.

| Age | 1-Year Term Premium | Level Premium for Straight Life | Excess of Level Premium over 1-Year Term |
|---|---|---|---|
| 20 | $ 1.75 | $10.75 | $ 9.00 |
| 25 | 1.88 | | 8.87 |
| 30 | 2.08 | | 8.67 |
| 35 | 2.45 | | 8.30 |
| 40 | 3.44 | | 7.31 |
| 45 | 5.22 | | 5.53 |
| 50 | 8.12 | | 2.63 |
| 55 | 12.68 | | 1.93 ⎫ |
| 60 | 19.84 | | 9.09 ⎬ Deficit |
| 65 | 30.98 | | 20.23 ⎪ |
| 70 | 48.58 | | 37.83 ⎭ |

The sketch on the following page shows how the 1-year term premium and the level premium for straight life compare at different ages.

We shall now see how the reserve fund is built up when a person takes out a level premium policy. The best way to do this is to work out the financial details when a large group of persons of the same age are insured at the same time. So that the table will be complete and not too long, we work with a $1000, 10-year endowment policy issued to men aged 20. The CSO Table shows that $l_{20} = 9\ 664\ 994$. From (41), we get an annual premium of $87.98. We now compute the following for the first policy year.

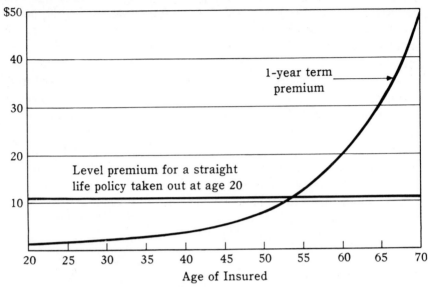

Net Annual Premium for a $1000 Policy

Age of Insured

Total premiums

$$9,664,994 \times 87.98 = \$850,326,172.12$$

Fund with interest at $2\frac{1}{2}\%$
at the end of the year

$$850,326,172.12(1.025) = \$871,584,326.42$$

From the Mortality Table
$d_{20} = 17,300$. Death claims
at the end of the first year
will be

$$17,300 \times 1000 = \$17,300,000$$

Fund at the end of the
year

$$871,584,326.42 - 17,300,000.00 = \$854,284,326.42$$

The survivors at the end of the first year are the same as the number living at the beginning of the second year or $l_{21} = 9,647,694$. This makes the fund per survivor

$$\frac{854,284,326.42}{9,647,694} = \$88.55$$

The premiums at the beginning of the second year equal the number of survivors at the end of the first year times the annual premium:

$$9,647,694 \times 87.98 = \$848,804,118.12$$

The fund at the beginning of the second year is the sum of the fund at the end of the first year and the second year's premiums:

$$854,284,326.42 + 848,804,118.12 = \$1,703,088,444.54$$

Values for the full 10 years of the policy are given below. The Fund per Survivor is given to the nearest cent; other entries are rounded to the dollar.

| POLICY YEAR | PREMIUMS | FUND AT BEGINNING OF YEAR | FUND WITH INTEREST | DEATH BENEFITS | FUND AT END OF YEAR | NUMBER OF SURVIVORS | FUND PER SURVIVOR |
|---|---|---|---|---|---|---|---|
| 1 | $850,326,172 | $ 850,326,172 | $ 871,584,326 | $17,300,000 | $ 854,284,326 | 9,647,694 | $ 88.55 |
| 2 | 848,808,118 | 1,703,088,445 | 1,745,665,657 | 17,655,000 | 1,728,010,656 | 9,630,039 | 179.44 |
| 3 | 847,250,831 | 2,575,261,487 | 2,639,643,024 | 17,912,000 | 2,621,731,024 | 9,612,127 | 272.75 |
| 4 | 845,674,933 | 3,467,405,958 | 3,554,091,106 | 18,167,000 | 3,535,924,106 | 9,593,960 | 368.56 |
| 5 | 844,076,601 | 4,380,000,707 | 4,489,500,725 | 18,324,000 | 4,471,176,725 | 9,575,636 | 466.93 |
| 6 | 842,464,455 | 5,313,641,180 | 5,446,482,210 | 18,481,000 | 5,428,001,210 | 9,557,155 | 567.95 |
| 7 | 840,838,497 | 6,268,839,707 | 6,425,560,699 | 18,732,000 | 6,406,828,699 | 9,538,423 | 671.69 |
| 8 | 839,190,456 | 7,246,019,155 | 7,427,169,634 | 18,981,000 | 7,408,188,634 | 9,519,442 | 778.22 |
| 9 | 837,520,507 | 8,245,709,141 | 8,451,851,869 | 19,324,000 | 8,432,527,869 | 9,500,118 | 887.62 |
| 10 | 835,820,382 | 9,268,348,251 | 9,500,056,957 | 19,760,000 | 9,480,296,957 | 9,480,358 | 1000.00 |

## 10.8 The Prospective Method

In the preceding section the reserve was determined by accumulating premiums and deducting death benefits. This is called the **retrospective method** because it is based on past premiums and past benefits. Formulas can be derived to compute terminal reserves by the retrospective method without constructing a table. Another way to get reserves is to use the **prospective method** which is based on future benefits and premiums. The two methods give the same numerical result when dealing with net level premium policies. Advanced texts on insurance point out principles which will help the actuary to choose the method which will lead to the simpler formula for a particular problem.

The prospective method of computing reserves is based on the general definition of a reserve as the excess of the present value of future benefits over the present value of future premiums. At any time the reserve must be sufficient to make up the difference between the present value of the future benefits and the present value of the premiums. Expressing this as an equation of value, we have

$$\text{Reserve} = \left(\begin{array}{c}\text{Present value} \\ \text{of future benefits}\end{array}\right) - \left(\begin{array}{c}\text{Present value of} \\ \text{future premiums}\end{array}\right)$$

EXAMPLE 1: Get the reserve per survivor at the end of the 5th policy year for a $1000, 10-year endowment policy issued to a person when he is aged 20.

SOLUTION: At the end of the 5th policy year the insured is 25 years old. At that time the value of the future benefits is the net single premium for a 5-year, $1000 endowment policy issued to a person 25 years old. From (40) this is

$$1000A_{25:\overline{5}|} = 1000 \frac{M_{25} - M_{30} + D_{30}}{D_{25}}$$

$$= 1000 \frac{1\ 754\ 288.5 - 1\ 706\ 575.7 + 4\ 519\ 691.4}{5\ 165\ 008.0} = \$884.30$$

From (41) the value for the net annual premium for a 10-year endowment policy for $1000 issued to a person 20 years old is

$$1000P_{20:\overline{10}|} = 1000 \frac{M_{20} - M_{30} + D_{30}}{N_{20} - N_{30}}$$

$$= 1000 \frac{1\ 804\ 922.4 - 1\ 706\ 575.7 + 4\ 519\ 691.4}{167\ 827\ 046.5 - 115\ 337\ 742.5} = \$87.98$$

Note that the net annual premium is based on the age of the insured when he takes out the policy regardless of his age at the time the reserve is to be determined. The 5 remaining payments of $87.98 form a temporary life annuity due. From (33) the present value of this annuity is

$$87.98\ddot{a}_{25:\overline{5}|} = 87.98 \frac{N_{25} - N_{30}}{D_{25}}$$

$$= 87.98 \frac{139\ 839\ 497.6 - 115\ 337\ 742.5}{5\ 165\ 008.0} = \$417.36$$

Using the symbol $V$ for the terminal reserve, we have

$$V = 884.30 - 417.36 = \$466.94$$

The table for the retrospective method in the preceding section shows a terminal reserve of $466.93 at the end of the 5th policy year for the same policy. The difference is due to rounding values to the penny.

**EXERCISE 10e**

1. Complete the first 5 lines of a reserve fund schedule for a $1000 straight life policy issued to a group of 25-year-old men.
2. Complete the first 5 lines of a reserve fund schedule for a $1000, 20-payment life policy issued to a group of 25-year-old men.
3. Complete the first 5 lines of a reserve fund schedule for a $1000, 20-year endowment policy issued to a group of 25-year-old men.
4. Complete the reserve fund schedule for a $1000, 5-year term policy issued to a group of 25-year-old men.
5. Use the prospective method to get the reserve per survivor at the end of the 5th policy year for a $1000, 20-year endowment policy issued to a 30-year-old man.                                                                    ($203.89)

**6.** Get the reserve for the policy in Problem 5 at the end of the 10th policy year.

**7.** Get the reserve per survivor at the end of the 10th policy year for a $10,000 straight life policy issued to a 20-year-old man. ($1031.31)

**8.** Get the reserve for the policy in Problem 7 at the end of the 20th policy year.

## 10.9  Buying Life Insurance

Most students in later life will buy life insurance. Since this insurance will mean a considerable expenditure year after year, a person's insurance program should be planned carefully. The experience gained computing net insurance premiums in a course in mathematics of finance is ideal preparation for recognizing the advantages and disadvantages of various commercial policies.

To begin with, the student should understand that his money can go entirely for protection if he buys term insurance, it can go largely for savings if he buys an annuity, or it can go for a combination of savings and protection if he gets a level premium policy which builds up a reserve as he goes along. With many types of policies to choose from, it is not surprising that people sometimes take out insurance that does not meet their particular needs. This can be tragic when a family finds that an inadequate and poorly planned insurance program does not begin to provide for their material well-being. The same expenditure on a different type of policy might have met family needs reasonably well. We now consider the four basic types of policies from a practical point of view.

Term insurance provides the most protection for the least cost. It may be the only way for a family of limited means to obtain adequate protection. For other families it can be very handy for special situations, such as additional protection when the children are young, or to cover the outstanding debt on a home. The disadvantages of term insurance are the increasing cost as the insured gets older, and the absence of a cash value. If a person gets term insurance with the idea of continuing it or converting it to a level premium plan, he should get a policy which can be renewed to age 60 or older, or converted to another type policy without a new physical examination. The chart on page 362 shows how the premium charged by a representative company for a term policy varies with the age of the insured.

The ordinary or straight life policy has at first a higher premium than term insurance but the cost will never increase. After the payment of a few premiums, there will be a reserve which can be used to keep the insurance in force if the insured is unable to keep up the premiums. Ordinary or straight life is probably the best all-around protection for most families if they can afford enough protection under this plan.

Limited payment policies, if the payment period is as short as 20 years, require high premiums so that the average family can carry such insurance only by reducing the amount of protection. Such policies are well suited to people like professional athletes who may have a relatively short period of high earning power and want to get their insurance paid for while their income is high.

Endowment policies are expensive because the premium must cover both protection and an endowment. Thus an endowment policy is essentially a term insurance policy plus a pure endowment. Very few people buy pure endowments. Many salesmen do not encourage their clients to buy term insurance. Yet when the two are put in one package and sold as an endowment policy, it becomes attractive to some people. Short-term endowment policies are primarily savings. If a family man wants both savings and insurance, he should keep most of his savings separate from his insurance so that his family will get both if he dies. This can be done by carrying the less expensive type of insurance and putting savings into securities, savings accounts, or real estate.

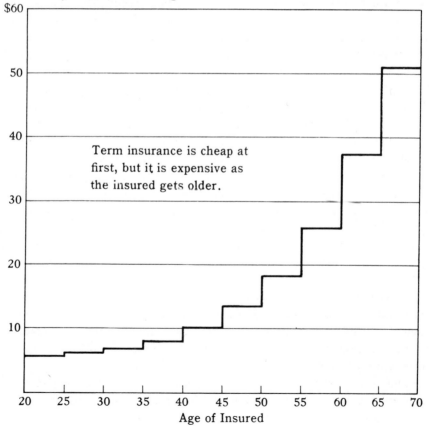

Cost of 5-Year Level Premium Term Insurance

Annual Premium per $1000
for a Policy of $10,000 or Larger.

Term insurance is cheap at first, but it is expensive as the insured gets older.

Age of Insured

Besides the basic policies discussed here, there are many combination policies. The buyer of insurance should analyze such policies carefully to see if a combination policy has any advantage for him over one or more of the four basic types.

## 10.10  Use of the Reserve

Earlier in this chapter we discussed the reserve which is accumulated as premiums are paid on level premium policies. The value of this reserve is not understood by many policyholders. This reserve can be used in several ways. A man can surrender the policy and take the cash. Before getting an expensive endowment policy to put a child through college, a couple should consider getting more straight life insurance on the father. Then the family will have more protection while the children are young. When the children reach college age, this straight life policy will have a substantial cash reserve. This reserve can be used if needed, or the policy can be kept in force to provide continued protection. It may eventually become a part of the couple's retirement income. If moderate income families understood the great flexibility of the straight life policy, there would be less buying of the more expensive plans with their limited protection.

Instead of taking the cash and dropping the policy, a family may borrow on the cash reserve at a rate which is usually far below the rate for small loans from commercial sources. Such loans should be repaid as soon as possible, since the protection is reduced by the amount of the loan. The reserve may also be used as the single premium for a reduced amount of paid-up insurance. Another use of the reserve is extended term insurance which keeps the entire policy in force for a period which depends on the type of policy and the size of the reserve. If a man stops paying premiums on a level premium policy and does not take the cash, the company may automatically put into effect extended term insurance. Many people do not know this. As a result, there are probably policies thrown away or lying around in bureau drawers which are worth thousands of dollars, but which will never be collected because the survivors assume that the policy is worthless since the insured stopped paying premiums many years before his death.

Recently an insurance agent told us of a widow who received $10,000 from her husband's insurance when she had expected $5000. The man had carried two policies of $5000 in the same company. He paid on one until he died; the other he dropped years before. When the widow put in her claim, she did not mention the policy that had been dropped as she assumed that it was worthless. When settling her claim the insurance company found that death had occurred within the extended term period of the other policy, so the widow collected on both. In most cases there is no way for the insurance company to know that death came during the time of the extended term insurance unless a claim is made.

Insurance companies do what they can to prevent loss of benefits by notifying policyholders that extended term insurance is in effect if a policyholder stops paying premiums. Some companies indicate the exact date on which the coverage expires. The policyholder should file all such papers with the policy. Since papers may be lost or the company may lose contact with a policyholder, a check should be made on any policy that could possibly still be in effect.

The guaranteed values provided by the reserve in a particular policy can be found in the policy. To illustrate the great practical value of insurance reserves, the table on page 365 has been reprinted from the Veterans Administration bulletin for National Service Life Insurance. These guaranteed values are based on the American Experience Mortality Table with interest at 3%. Thus the values are somewhat different from those which would be obtained using the CSO Table with interest at $2\frac{1}{2}\%$ which is used in this text. All values are for a $1000 policy issued to a 25-year-old person. Annual premiums for these policies are

| POLICY | ANNUAL PREMIUM |
|---|---|
| Ordinary life | $16.22 |
| 20-payment life | 25.10 |
| 20-year endowment | 41.20 |

## 10.11   Summary of Insurance Formulas

The formulas used to determine life insurance premiums are summarized below for the convenience of the student.

### Insurance Premiums

(All formulas are for a policy of $1)

| TYPE OF POLICY | NET SINGLE PREMIUM | | NET ANNUAL PREMIUM | |
|---|---|---|---|---|
| Straight life | $A_x = \dfrac{M_x}{D_x}$ | (35) | $P_x = \dfrac{M_x}{N_x}$ | (36) |
| Term policy (for $n$ years) | $A^1_{x:\overline{n}|} = \dfrac{M_x - M_{x+n}}{D_x}$ | (37) | $P^1_{x:\overline{n}|} = \dfrac{M_x - M_{x+n}}{N_x - N_{x+n}}$ | (38) |
| Limited payment life (payments for $t$ years) | (Same as straight life) | | $_tP_x = \dfrac{M_x}{N_x - N_{x+t}}$ | (39) |
| Endowment policy (for $n$ years) | $A_{x:\overline{n}|} = \dfrac{M_x - M_{x+n} + D_{x+n}}{D_x}$ | (40) | $P_{x:\overline{n}|} = \dfrac{M_x - M_{x+n} + D_{x+n}}{N_x - N_{x+n}}$ | (41) |

*EXERCISE 10f*

**1.** A 28-year-old man can afford to pay approximately $150 a year for life insurance. This will cover the net annual premium for what size policies of the following types? Give answer to nearest $1000.

| | |
|---|---|
| (a) 5-year term. | ($72,000) |
| (b) Straight life | ($11,000) |
| (c) Paid-up life policy at age 65. | ($10,000) |
| (d) 20-payment life. | ($6000) |
| (e) 20-year endowment. | ($4000) |

*Guaranteed Values at Age 25—$1000*

ORDINARY LIFE (PARTICIPATING)

| End of policy year | Cash value | Paid-up insurance | Years | Days | End of policy year | Cash value | Paid-up insurance | Years | Days |
|---|---|---|---|---|---|---|---|---|---|
| 1 | $8.60 | $23.78 | 1 | 34 | 13 | $134.77 | $304.26 | 15 | 355 |
| 2 | 17.47 | 47.55 | 2 | 87 | 14 | 147.39 | 326.76 | 16 | 297 |
| 3 | 26.61 | 71.28 | 3 | 158 | 15 | 160.36 | 349.05 | 17 | 190 |
| 4 | 36.04 | 94.99 | 4 | 249 | 16 | 173.67 | 371.09 | 18 | 41 |
| 5 | 45.76 | 118.66 | 5 | 354 | 17 | 187.34 | 392.91 | 18 | 215 |
| 6 | 55.77 | 142.24 | 7 | 111 | 18 | 201.37 | 414.49 | 18 | 352 |
| 7 | 66.09 | 165.75 | 8 | 240 | 19 | 215.77 | 435.81 | 19 | 91 |
| 8 | 76.72 | 189.16 | 10 | 6 | 20 | 230.50 | 456.82 | 19 | 165 |
| 9 | 87.67 | 212.47 | 11 | 133 | 25 | 309.14 | 556.79 | 19 | 197 |
| 10 | 98.94 | 235.64 | 12 | 244 | 30 | 394.11 | 646.17 | 18 | 220 |
| 11 | 110.55 | 258.68 | 13 | 325 | 35 | 482.33 | 723.44 | 17 | 52 |
| 12 | 122.49 | 281.56 | 14 | 364 | 40 | 570.12 | 788.29 | 15 | 145 |

20-PAYMENT LIFE (PARTICIPATING)

| End of policy year | Cash value | Paid-up insurance | Years | Days | End of policy year | Cash value | Paid-up insurance | Years | Days |
|---|---|---|---|---|---|---|---|---|---|
| 1 | $17.81 | $49.24 | 2 | 110 | 13 | $287.07 | $648.09 | 31 | 51 |
| 2 | 36.24 | 98.63 | 4 | 294 | 14 | 314.97 | 698.27 | 32 | 126 |
| 3 | 55.31 | 148.16 | 7 | 193 | 15 | 343.86 | 748.47 | 33 | 188 |
| 4 | 75.06 | 197.84 | 10 | 166 | 16 | 373.77 | 798.65 | 34 | 263 |
| 5 | 95.49 | 247.61 | 13 | 195 | 17 | 404.76 | 848.91 | 36 | 27 |
| 6 | 116.64 | 297.48 | 16 | 241 | 18 | 436.85 | 899.18 | 37 | 269 |
| 7 | 138.54 | 347.45 | 19 | 236 | 19 | 470.12 | 949.55 | 40 | 40 |
| 8 | 161.21 | 397.48 | 22 | 121 | 20 | 504.58 | 1,000.00 | — | — |
| 9 | 184.66 | 447.52 | 24 | 237 | 25 | 555.22 | — | — | — |
| 10 | 208.95 | 497.64 | 26 | 232 | 30 | 609.92 | — | — | — |
| 11 | 234.09 | 547.76 | 28 | 124 | 35 | 666.72 | — | — | — |
| 12 | 260.12 | 597.92 | 29 | 300 | 40 | 723.24 | — | — | — |

| | | | | | | | | | | |
|---|---|---|---|---|---|---|---|---|---|---|
| | | | 20-YEAR ENDOWMENT (PARTICIPATING) | | | | | | | |
| End of policy year | Cash value | Paid-up insurance | *Years* | *Days* | Pure endowment | End of policy year | Cash value | Paid-up insurance | *Years* | *Days* | Pure endowment |
| 1 | $34.45 | $57.51 | 4 | 219 | — | 11 | $457.41 | $590.47 | 9 | — | $547.46 |
| 2 | 70.16 | 114.30 | 9 | 345 | — | 12 | 508.90 | 639.28 | 8 | — | 605.94 |
| 3 | 107.19 | 170.35 | 16 | 10 | — | 13 | 562.37 | 687.28 | 7 | — | 662.21 |
| 4 | 145.58 | 225.65 | 16 | — | $68.76 | 14 | 617.88 | 734.43 | 6 | — | 716.35 |
| 5 | 185.39 | 280.18 | 15 | — | 145.19 | 15 | 675.54 | 780.75 | 5 | — | 768.40 |
| 6 | 226.67 | 333.91 | 14 | — | 218.78 | 16 | 735.46 | 826.23 | 4 | — | 818.47 |
| 7 | 269.49 | 386.85 | 13 | — | 289.63 | 17 | 797.73 | 870.88 | 3 | — | 866.59 |
| 8 | 313.91 | 438.99 | 12 | — | 357.82 | 18 | 862.49 | 914.73 | 2 | — | 912.85 |
| 9 | 359.98 | 490.30 | 11 | — | 423.46 | 19 | 929.87 | 957.77 | 1 | — | 957.31 |
| 10 | 407.79 | 540.79 | 10 | — | 486.65 | 20 | 1,000.00 | 1,000.00 | — | — | — |

Students who are interested in getting more information on life insurance can obtain practical and interesting publications from the Institute of Life Insurance, 277 Park Ave., New York, New York, 10017.

2. Work Problem 1 for a 35-year-old man.

3. Assume that the insured dies while the policies in Problem 1 are in force. The benefits are to be paid out in 120 payments certain with the first payment to be made 1 month after the insured dies. If the company allows 3% converted monthly on the proceeds left with them, what will be the size of the monthly payments for the five policies?

[(a) $695.24; (b) $106.22; (c) $96.56; (d) $57.94; (e) $38.62]

4. Get the size of the benefit payments for the policies in Problem 2 if the proceeds are paid out in 120 monthly payments and 3% converted monthly is earned on the balance left with the company.

# 11

# Stocks

## 11.1 The Element of Uncertainty

Mathematically, there are no doubts about the results obtained for simple and compound interest problems and annuities certain. The times and amounts of all payments are specified definitely. While a death or business failure may result in unpredictable changes, no allowance is made for such possibilities when the problem is solved.

In the case of life annuities and life insurance, payments are contingent on a person's age, when he dies, and other factors. These uncertain events can be taken into account with a high degree of accuracy *on the average* if the actuary has reliable mortality data on which to base his calculations. While the company cannot make money on every policy, the actuary probably can set premiums which are low enough to be competitive and high enough for the company to make a profit.

We now consider the application of the mathematics of finance to corporate stocks, even though we can neither make certain calculations for individual problems nor use actuarial data to make predictions that will be true on the average. In spite of the uncertainties, the mathematics of finance can be profitably applied to the buying of stocks.

Most students are interested in stocks, although not always for the right reason. Having heard of someone who made a killing by putting his money in a stock that went up like a rocket, they want to know how to do likewise with their first few paychecks. If we knew how, we would be busily doing it.

## 11.2   Kinds of Stock

In the chapter on bonds, we saw that a person who buys a bond is lending money to a corporation or a government agency and is entitled to interest on his money and the eventual return of his capital. A stockholder is a part owner of the company and must take his chances on the fortunes of the company. His place is at the end of the line after the government, workers, suppliers, and bondholders.

There are two basic types of stocks: *preferred* and *common*. Preferred stock has a stated return which is given on the stock certificate. Holders of preferred stock receive dividends only if declared by the board of directors. Preferred stock has a claim on earnings before payment may be made on the common stock, and preferred is usually entitled to priority over common stock if the company liquidates. However, owners of preferred rank below bondholders and other creditors. Most preferred is *cumulative* which means that if any dividends are omitted, they accumulate and must be paid before the common stockholders get anything. Some preferred stock is *convertible* which means that it may be converted into common. Generally, preferred stock has no voting privileges unless a stated number of dividends have not been declared on the preferred. Preferred stocks are usually redeemable at the company's option at fixed prices. This call feature, of no value to the investor, is important to the corporation because it enables the company to retire stock when the capital market is favorable.

At one time preferred stocks were used extensively by corporations to obtain capital. Today, aside from public utilities, preferred stocks are not much used for new financing. From the investor's standpoint, preferred stocks rank below bonds in safety and below common stocks in opportunities for growth and a share in the increasing profits of a successful corporation.

The venture capital which permits new firms to start and existing ones to expand is often obtained by selling common stock. Common stockholders assume the risks of ownership and, in the event of a failure, may lose all or part

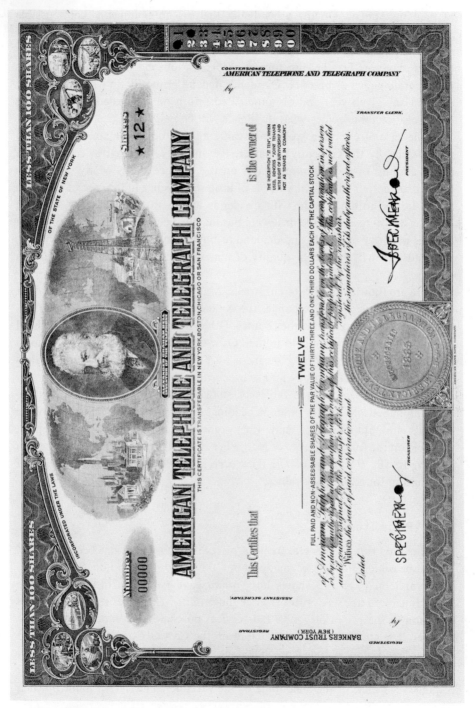

The actual piece of paper which is evidence of ownership of stock in a corporation is called a "stock certificate." Watermarked paper finely engraved with delicate etchings is used to discourage forgery.

of their investment. On the other hand, there is no ceiling on their possible profits. If their firm is successful, they may benefit from both increasing dividends and a rising value in the market price of their stock. As a rule, common stockholders may vote for the directors of a corporation and may suggest changes in corporate policy or practice. Dividends depend primarily on what a company earns in any given year and on anticipated return on reinvested earnings. The board of directors decides what dividends will be paid.

In the case of common stock, par value means the dollar amount assigned to the share by the company's charter. Par may also be used to compute the dollar amount of the common shares on the balance sheet. Many companies today issue no-par stock. Par value is of little significance in the case of common stock. It has nothing to do with dividends and is no indication of what an investor would receive if the firm were liquidated. The market value of common stock is a matter of supply and demand as buyers and sellers consider earnings, dividends, growth prospects, quality of management, and the general business climate.

There are thousands of different stocks. Many of these are traded on the floor of the New York Stock Exchange, the American Stock Exchange, and various other exchanges throughout the country. Other stocks and bonds, called unlisted securities, are bought and sold in the "Over-the-counter" market. This is not a place but a method of doing business by private negotiation among dealers who use the telephone to buy and sell securities.

Many newspapers include tables of stock market information. Stocks are listed alphabetically under column headings that are easy to interpret. While symbols and abbreviations may vary somewhat with different newspapers, the table on the following page of New York Stock Exchange Transactions from the August 16, 1972, issue of *The Wall Street Journal* is a good illustration of information found in stock tables.

## 11.3 Price Trends

Over the long run, the general trend of prices in this country has been upwards. The same statement can be made about the trend in common stock prices. The graph on page 373 shows how prices have varied as measured by the Department of Labor's Consumer Price Index (CPI). This index shows the overall variation in the prices of goods and services purchased by middle-income city families. The stock price graph is based on the Cowles Commission Index and Standard and Poor's Index of 500 Stock Prices. The graphs are plotted on semilog or ratio scales on which equal per cent changes take the same vertical distance regardless of the magnitude of the variables. The steeper a line on such

Highest and lowest prices per share during the indicated period.➤

Abbreviated name of the company. In this case Acme Markets, Inc.——

Number following name shows indicated annual dividend, in this case $1.68. This is an estimate based on recent dividends. Letters following the dividend indicate other information which is usually given in footnotes at the end of the table.

Number of round lots traded. On this day there were 87 lots of 100 shares. This number does not include odd-lot sales, that is, quantities less than 100 shares for most stocks. When a letter "z" appears before this number, the number indicates the actual number of shares traded. When the letter "x" appears, it means ex dividend or without dividend. This is shown on the day the stock goes ex dividend. If a person buys stock when it is selling ex dividend, he will not receive that dividend. It goes to the previous owner.

For this stock the opening price was 15¼, high for the day was 15⅜, low for the day was 15¼, and the stock closed at 15⅜. The closing price was $.125 more than the closing for the previous day as indicated by the net change of +⅛ point.

"pf." following the name indicates a preferred stock.

## A-B-C

| −1972− High | Low | Stocks Div. | Sales in 100s | Open | High | Low | Close | Net Chg. |
|---|---|---|---|---|---|---|---|---|
| 85 | 64⅛ | AbbtLb 1.10 | 94 | 84¾ | 85 | 84⅛ | 85 | + ½ |
| 52¾ | 41½ | ACF Ind 2.40 | 19 | 47 | 47¾ | 47 | 47¾ | + ¾ |
| 18½ | 13½ | AcmeClev .80 | 41 | 18 | 18 | 17⅞ | 18 | + ⅛ |
| 47¾ | 29¾ | Acme Mkt 2b | 8 | 31¾ | 31⅞ | 31⅝ | 31¾ | − ¼ |
| 14⅛ | 12⅜ | AdmsE 1.09e | 45 | 13 | 13 | 12¾ | 12¾ | ..... |
| 13⅜ | 8 | Ad Millls .20 | 8 | 8¾ | 8¾ | 8½ | 8⅝ | ..... |
| 49½ | 33½ | Addresso .60 | 90 | 46⅛ | 46⅞ | 46 | 46⅞ | + ⅝ |
| 27 | 15⅝ | Admiral | 166 | 17 | 17 | 16⅜ | 16¾ | − ¼ |
| 69⅞ | 54½ | AetnaLfe 1.68 | 202 | 63⅛ | 64⅞ | 63 | 64¾ | +1¼ |
| 56 | 47½ | AetnaLf pf 2 | 2 | 50¾ | 51 | 50¾ | 51 | + ½ |
| 17 | 7⅞ | Aguirre Co | 19 | 12½ | 12⅜ | 12½ | 12⅝ | + ⅜ |
| 22⅞ | 9¼ | Aileen Inc | 105 | 10 | 10 | 9⅝ | 9⅝ | − ⅜ |
| 74¼ | 53½ | AirProd .20b | 37 | 72¼ | 72¼ | 71⅞ | 72 | + ⅜ |
| 23¾ | 17 | Airco .80e | 105 | 20½ | 20½ | 20⅛ | 20¼ | − ¼ |
| 5¾ | 3⅞ | AJ Industries | 23 | 4 | 4 | 4 | 4 | + ⅛ |
| 35½ | 25⅛ | Akzona 1a | 36 | 31⅛ | 31⅛ | 30⅝ | 30⅝ | − ½ |
| 18 | 15¼ | Ala Gas 1.10 | 14 | 15¼ | 15½ | 15¼ | 15⅜ | ..... |
| 107½ | 102 | AlaP pf8.28 | z210 | 107 | 107 | 107 | 107 | ..... |
| 54⅛ | 19½ | Alaska Inters | 729 | 42¼ | 45 | 42⅛ | 44¾ | +2¼ |
| 28⅞ | 20½ | AlbertoC .32 | 68 | 26¾ | 27¼ | 26¾ | 27¼ | + ½ |
| 15 | 11¾ | Albertsns .36 | 13 | 12⅝ | 12¾ | 12⅝ | 12⅝ | ..... |
| 22⅞ | 17¾ | AlcanAlu .80 | 87 | 22⅜ | 22½ | 22⅜ | 22½ | + ⅛ |
| 18⅛ | 10 | AlcoStand .34 | 46 | 10⅞ | 10⅞ | 10⅝ | 10¾ | − ¼ |
| 70¼ | 49¼ | Alcon Lab .6 | 35 | 71 | 71 | 69¾ | 70½ | + ¼ |
| 22¾ | 11¾ | Alexndrs .30e | 53 | 12¼ | 12½ | 12⅛ | 12¼ | ..... |
| 14⅞ | 11⅛ | AllALfe .24e | 12 | 12 | 12 | 12 | 12 | ..... |
| 14⅞ | 10 | Alleg Cp .20e | 28 | 10⅜ | 10⅜ | 10¼ | 10¼ | − ⅛ |
| 28⅞ | 18¾ | AllegLudlm 1 | 19 | 27⅝ | 27⅝ | 27½ | 27⅝ | − ⅛ |
| 41¾ | 38 | AllegLud pf 3 | 3 | 41¼ | 41¼ | 41¼ | 41¼ | ..... |
| 23¾ | 19¾ | AllegPw 1.40 | 87 | 20⅞ | 20⅞ | 20⅜ | 20½ | − ⅜ |
| 30½ | 16¼ | AllenGp 1.04t | 36 | 21 | 21¼ | 20¾ | 20⅞ | − ⅜ |
| 36¾ | 27 | Allied Ch 1.20 | 414 | 29½ | 29⅝ | 29¼ | 29⅝ | + ⅛ |
| 45⅝ | 38 | Alld Mnt .45b | 26 | 40¼ | 40½ | 40¼ | 40¼ | + ¼ |
| 23⅞ | 18¼ | AlldMills .75 | 1 | 22¾ | 22¾ | 22¾ | 22¾ | + ½ |
| 25¼ | 16½ | Allied Pd .68 | 6 | 18⅜ | 18⅜ | 18 | 18¼ | − ¼ |
| 37 | 29¼ | AlliedStr 1.40 | 20 | 32⅜ | 33¼ | 32⅜ | 33⅛ | +1⅛ |
| 8⅝ | 4¼ | Allied Super | 29 | 4⅝ | 4¾ | 4⅝ | 4¾ | + ⅛ |
| 15⅝ | 11 | AllisChal .20e | 323 | 12¼ | 12½ | 12 | 12⅛ | − ⅜ |
| 22⅜ | 15 | AllrgtAut .48 | 24 | 15¼ | 15⅜ | 15¼ | 15⅜ | + ⅛ |
| 19¼ | 15⅝ | Alpha Pl .08e | 5 | 17 | 17 | 17 | 17 | ..... |
| 56⅛ | 38⅞ | Alcoa 1.80 | 73 | 54⅛ | 54⅛ | 53⅝ | 53⅝ | − ⅜ |
| 29⅜ | 23⅞ | AmalSug 1.60 | 1 | 24½ | 24½ | 24½ | 24½ | + ½ |
| 18¼ | 12⅞ | AMBAC .50 | 40 | 16⅜ | 16⅜ | 15⅝ | 15⅝ | − ½ |
| 30¾ | 21¼ | Amer Es 1.20 | 11 | 26¾ | 26¾ | 26⅛ | 26⅛ | − ⅞ |
| 51¼ | 41 | Am Es pf2.60 | 17 | 47¼ | 47¼ | 46¾ | 46¾ | − ¼ |
| 54¾ | 40½ | AmHess .15r | 789 | 49¼ | 51 | 49¼ | 50⅜ | +1½ |
| 119¾ | 90¾ | AmeH pf3.50 | 76 | 110 | 110 | 110 | 112 | +3¾ |
| 49 | 35⅞ | A AirFlit .40 | 20 | 48½ | 48½ | 48⅛ | 48¼ | ..... |
| 49⅞ | 27⅞ | Am Airlin | 1073 | 29½ | 30¼ | 29½ | 30 | − ⅛ |
| 16¼ | 11¼ | A Baker .20 | 26 | 12 | 12¼ | 12 | 12 | ..... |
| 49¼ | 41⅞ | ABrnds 2.29 | 144 | 43⅛ | 43¼ | 42⅞ | 42⅞ | ..... |
| 81½ | 51¼ | AmBdcst 1.20 | 283 | 79½ | 79½ | 78¼ | 78¼ | −1¼ |
| 51¼ | 43¼ | AmBldgM .25 | 24 | 46⅞ | 47 | 46¼ | 46¼ | − ⅞ |
| 36¾ | 27 | Am Can 2.20 | 216 | 33 | 33¼ | 32¾ | 32⅞ | ..... |
| 28⅛ | 24⅝ | A Can pf1.75 | 5 | 25¼ | 25¼ | 25¼ | 25¼ | + ⅛ |
| 9⅛ | 6⅝ | AmCem | 37 | 6¾ | 7 | 6¾ | 7 | + ⅛ |
| 28⅞ | 24⅜ | A CenM 2.32e | 45 | 27 | 27 | 26½ | 26¾ | − ¼ |
| 28¼ | 19½ | Am Chain 1 | 26 | 21⅞ | 22 | 21¾ | 22 | + ¼ |
| 34½ | 21 | ACrySug 1.40 | 14 | 33¾ | 33¾ | 33½ | 33½ | + ¼ |
| 89½ | 58 | ACryS pf4.50 | z70 | 85 | 88½ | 85 | 88½ | +4½ |
| 40¼ | 30⅝ | A Cyan 1.25 | 281 | 35¼ | 35¾ | 35¼ | 35½ | − ⅛ |
| 28⅛ | 17⅜ | Am Distill 1 | 4 | 24 | 24 | 24 | 24 | ..... |
| 68¼ | 50 | A DisTel .40e | 68 | 55⅜ | 56¼ | 55¼ | 55⅜ | − ⅛ |
| 10½ | 8⅜ | ADualV .18e | 25 | 9¼ | 9¼ | 9⅛ | 9⅛ | − ⅛ |
| 13¾ | 12⅝ | ADulV pf.84a | 3 | 12⅞ | 13⅛ | 12⅞ | 13⅛ | +⅛ |

a graph, the faster the rate of change. This graph shows that from 1929 to 1932 stock prices dropped much faster than consumer prices. However, over the long trend, particularly from 1942 on, stock prices have, on the average, risen faster than prices of consumer goods. It is these rising long term trends that have made stock buying attractive for the long pull during the last 30 years. Wise investors recognize that money, like wampum, is only a medium of exchange. What really counts economically is maintaining their ability to buy goods. While there is no certainty that trends in either consumer or stock prices will be the same in the future as in the past, the likelihood of further increases should be taken into account when making investment decisions.

These graphs show why a fixed investment, such as a bond, mortgage, or savings account has a risk connected with it, the price-level risk or risk of a loss in purchasing power as a result of price increases. The history of prices in the United States shows that the risk of inflation is a real one. There is a good chance that people who loan money will be repaid in dollars of depreciated purchasing power.

Stocks over the years have provided a long-run hedge against inflation. We emphasize long-run because over shorter periods stock prices have not always kept abreast of consumer prices. There have even been years when stock prices went down while the CPI was rising. But in spite of temporary setbacks, investors with diversified portfolios of quality stocks are not only likely to preserve their purchasing power but to come out ahead in terms of real income over the years. This is what makes stocks attractive to the investor who is interested in the long pull, not a quick profit.

To compare the real value of an investment at one time with its real value at another time, we multiply the number of dollars the investment is worth by the value of the dollar. As explained on page 127, the value of the dollar = 100/CPI. When the CPI = 100 (actually 100%), the value of the dollar is 100/100 = $1.00. If the CPI is 125, the dollar is worth 100/125 = $.80. A CPI of 90 means that the dollar is worth 100/90 = $1.11.

To compare the value of the dollar at one time with its value at another time requires that all values be relative to the same base period. About every 10 years the Bureau of Labor Statistics adopts a new base period for the CPI and past index values are adjusted and spliced to the new series so that a continuous picture of price changes is obtained. Because of their importance for reference purposes and for solving problems in this chapter, the value of the CPI and the corresponding value of the dollar are given on page 374. All values are relative to the latest base period, 1967 = 100.

The graph on page 375 shows the long term trend in the purchasing power of the American dollar. This shows the risk in owning fixed-dollar investments. Since 1940 the value of the dollar has increased in only two years, 1949 and 1955. From 1940 to 1952 the value of the dollar dropped from $2.38 to $1.26, an annual compounded rate of depreciation of 5.2%. During the fifteen years from 1952 to 1967, the annual rate of depreciation was only 1.4%. It was during these years that many people found themselves better off in terms of real income because their dollar incomes increased at a higher rate than prices of consumer goods. Those living on pensions or other fixed incomes were not so fortunate, since even small year-to-year increases in prices can soon mean trouble for those who are barely getting by.

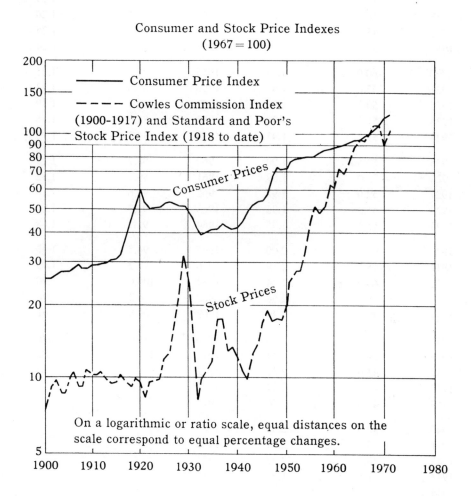

Consumer and Stock Price Indexes
(1967 = 100)

As this is being written, inflation has again become a serious problem. From 1967 to 1971 the dollar depreciated at an annual compounded rate of 4.8 per cent. Room has been left in the table on page 374 and on the graph on page 375 for you to enter the latest results in the nation's efforts to halt runaway prices.

| Year | CPI 1967 = 100 | Value of the Dollar | Year | CPI 1967 = 100 | Value of the Dollar |
|------|------|------|------|------|------|
| 1915 | 30.4 | $3.29 | 1950 | 72.1 | $1.39 |
| 1916 | 32.7 | 3.06 | 1951 | 77.8 | 1.29 |
| 1917 | 38.4 | 2.60 | 1952 | 79.5 | 1.26 |
| 1918 | 45.1 | 2.22 | 1953 | 80.1 | 1.25 |
| 1919 | 51.8 | 1.93 | 1954 | 80.5 | 1.24 |
| 1920 | 60.0 | 1.67 | 1955 | 80.2 | 1.25 |
| 1921 | 53.6 | 1.87 | 1956 | 81.4 | 1.23 |
| 1922 | 50.2 | 1.99 | 1957 | 84.3 | 1.19 |
| 1923 | 51.1 | 1.96 | 1958 | 86.6 | 1.15 |
| 1924 | 51.2 | 1.95 | 1959 | 87.3 | 1.15 |
| 1925 | 52.5 | 1.90 | 1960 | 88.7 | 1.13 |
| 1926 | 53.0 | 1.89 | 1961 | 89.6 | 1.12 |
| 1927 | 52.0 | 1.92 | 1962 | 90.6 | 1.10 |
| 1928 | 51.3 | 1.95 | 1963 | 91.7 | 1.09 |
| 1929 | 51.3 | 1.95 | 1964 | 92.9 | 1.08 |
| 1930 | 50.0 | 2.00 | 1965 | 94.5 | 1.06 |
| 1931 | 45.6 | 2.19 | 1966 | 97.2 | 1.03 |
| 1932 | 40.9 | 2.44 | 1967 | 100.0 | 1.00 |
| 1933 | 38.8 | 2.58 | 1968 | 104.2 | .96 |
| 1934 | 40.1 | 2.49 | 1969 | 109.8 | .91 |
| 1935 | 41.1 | 2.43 | 1970 | 116.3 | .86 |
| 1936 | 41.5 | 2.41 | 1971 | 121.3 | .82 |
| 1937 | 43.0 | 2.33 | 1972 | 124.2* | .81 |
| 1938 | 42.2 | 2.37 | 1973 | | |
| 1939 | 41.6 | 2.40 | 1974 | | |
| 1940 | 42.0 | 2.38 | 1975 | | |
| 1941 | 44.1 | 2.27 | 1976 | | |
| 1942 | 48.8 | 2.05 | 1977 | | |
| 1943 | 51.8 | 1.93 | 1978 | | |
| 1944 | 52.7 | 1.90 | 1979 | | |
| 1945 | 53.9 | 1.86 | 1980 | | |
| 1946 | 58.5 | 1.71 | 1981 | | |
| 1947 | 66.9 | 1.49 | 1982 | | |
| 1948 | 72.1 | 1.39 | 1983 | | |
| 1949 | 71.4 | 1.40 | 1984 | | |

* January – June average

The Shrinking Dollar

## 11.4   Measurement of Growth and Decline

If a quantity has been changing over the years, we can determine the constant annual rate of change that would have produced this change. We simply solve for the rate on a compound interest basis using (9), $S = P(1 + i)^n$. If time series data plot as approximately a straight line on a semilog or ratio graph, a rate based on past trends may be helpful in making predictions.

EXAMPLE 1: The Standard and Poor's Index of Public Utilities Stock Prices (1941–43 = 10) was 31.37 in 1955 and 76.08 in 1965. Find the annual compounded rate of growth.

SOLUTION:

$$31.37(1 + i)^{10} = 76.08$$

$$(1 + i)^{10} = \frac{76.08}{31.37} = 2.425$$

Since a factor this large is not in the *Amount of* 1 column in Table 2, we use logs as in Example 4 on page 126.

$$10 \log (1 + i) = \log 76.08 - \log 31.37$$

$$\log (1 + i) = \frac{1.881271 - 1.496515}{10} = \frac{.384756}{10} = .038476$$

Looking up the antilog of .038476, we find that $1 + i = 1.093$. Therefore $i = .093$ or $9.3\%$.

EXAMPLE 2: The CPI was 88.7 in 1960 and 116.3 in 1970. Compute the annual compounded per cent change.

SOLUTION:

$$88.7(1 + i)^{10} = 116.3$$

$$(1 + i)^{10} = \frac{116.3}{88.7} = 1.3112$$

In line 10 of the compound interest tables, we find that an *Amount of* 1 factor of 1.3112 corresponds to a rate between $2.5\%$ and $3\%$. Interpolation can be used if a more precise answer is needed.

$$\frac{d}{.50} = \frac{311}{638}$$

$$d = .24$$

$$i = 2.50 + .24 = 2.74\%$$

EXAMPLE 3: In 1960 the value of the dollar was $1.13 and in 1970 it was $.86. Get the annual compounded per cent change.

SOLUTION:

$$1.13(1 + i)^{10} = .86$$

Since this will lead to a negative rate, which is not in the compound interest tables, we use logarithms as explained on page 129.

$$\log (1 + i) = \frac{(9.934498 - 10) - .053078}{10} = \frac{9.881420 - 10}{10}$$

$$= .988142 - 1$$

Looking up the antilog of $.988142 - 1$, we find that $1 + i = .9731$. Therefore

$$i = .9731 - 1 = -.0269 = -2.69\%$$

Note that the annual per cent drop in the value of the dollar is not numerically equal to the annual per cent rise in the CPI. A larger change makes it easy to see why this is so. When the CPI goes from 100 to 200, there is a 100% rise in prices. There is a corresponding drop in the value of the dollar from $1.00 to $.50, a decrease of 50%, not 100%. The dollar may be shrinking, but it has not disappeared entirely.

## 11.5   Changes in Stock Value

Some buyers of stocks are interested primarily in receiving a liberal income. Others, who do not need the immediate income, look for stocks which they hope will increase greatly in market value over the years. One way to evaluate past price trends is to get the annual compounded rate of growth by substituting in (9) and solving for $i$.

EXAMPLE 1: On December 31, 1961, Standard Oil of New Jersey common stock was $50\frac{1}{2}$ and on December 31, 1971, it was $73\frac{3}{4}$. What was the annual rate of growth in market value on a compound interest basis?

SOLUTION: Substituting $P = 50.5$, $S = 73.75$, and $n = 10$ in (9),

$$50.5(1 + i)^{10} = 73.75$$

$$(1 + i)^{10} = \frac{73.75}{50.5} = 1.46$$

Reference to line 5 in Table 2 under *Amount of* 1 shows that the annual rate of growth was between 3.5 and 4%. A more precise value obtained by interpolation is 3.9%.

EXAMPLE 2: On December 31, 1958, Procter and Gamble was selling at 57. On December 31, 1971, the stock was quoted at $78\frac{1}{2}$. There were 2 for 1 splits in 1961 and 1970. What was the annual compound rate of growth over this period?

SOLUTION: Allowing for the splits, we have

$$57(1 + i)^{13} = 314$$

Since the rate is beyond the compound interest tables, we use logarithms.

$$\log (1 + i) = \frac{\log 314 - \log 57}{13} = \frac{2.496930 - 1.755875}{13} = .057004$$

Looking up the antilog of .057004, we find that $1 + i = 1.14$. Therefore

$$i = .14 = 14\%$$

As long as an investor holds a security, a gain such as this is a paper profit which may be increased or decreased by changes in the market.

Stock prices can go down. In which case, the owner of a security has the unpleasant experience of watching his investment depreciate in value.

EXAMPLE 3: An investor bought Chesapeake and Ohio in 1959 at 67. Three years later the price was 52. What was the average annual rate of depreciation in the value of this stock?

SOLUTION:

$$67(1 + i)^3 = 52$$

$$\log (1 + i) = \frac{1.716003 - 1.826075}{3}$$

Practical work with logarithms requires that we have positive mantissas and integral characteristics. Therefore, we add 30 to the first log in the numerator and offset this addition by subtracting 30.

$$\log (1 + i) = \frac{(31.716003 - 30) - 1.826075}{3} = \frac{29.889928 - 30}{3}$$

$$= 9.963309 - 10$$

Looking up the antilog of $9.963309 - 10$ we find that $1 + i = .919$. Therefore

$$i = .919 - 1 = -.081 = -8.1\%$$

On the average, the market value of this stock dropped about 8% a year over the 3-year period. If this downward trend is reversed, the stock may in time recover this loss in market value. Careful investors maintain a cash reserve to avoid being forced to sell at a loss stocks which they would like to hold for anticipated future gains.

EXAMPLE 4: In 1940 a man purchased a savings bond for $75. He cashed it in 1950 for $100. Compare the purchasing power of the investment at the two times.

SOLUTION: The purchasing power of an investment depends on the number of dollars and the value of the dollar. Putting this investment at the two times on a comparable basis:

| YEAR | VALUE OF THE DOLLAR (1967 = 100) | VALUE OF INVESTMENT CURRENT DOLLARS | DOLLARS OF CONSTANT PURCHASING POWER |
|------|------|------|------|
| 1940 | $2.38 | $ 75 | $178.50 |
| 1950 | 1.39 | 100 | 139.00 |

In spite of accumulated interest, the buying power of this investment dropped about 22% over the period. Rapidly rising prices are particularly hard on people who have their money in fixed dollar investments.

### EXERCISE 11a

(Get annual compounded rates of change to the tenth of one per cent.)

1. What was the annual compounded per cent change in prices and in the value of the dollar from 1965 to 1970?

     (Prices up 4.2% a year; value of dollar down 4.1% a year.)

2. Compare the annual compounded per cent increase in prices for the period 1915–19 with the period 1941–45. Get the corresponding changes in the value of the dollar.

3. Find the annual compounded rate of change in prices and the value of the dollar from 1930 to 1933.

     (Prices down 8.1% a year; value of dollar up 8.9% a year.)

4. Find the annual compounded rate of change in prices and the value of the dollar from: (a) 1940 to 1950; (b) 1950 to 1960; (c) 1960 to current values.

5. From 1950 to 1960, the Standard and Poor's Index of Industrial Stock Prices (1941–43 = 10) went from 18.33 to 59.43. Find the annual compounded rate of increase.     (12.5%)

6. From 1950 to 1960, the Standard and Poor's Index of Public Utilities Stocks went from 20.59 to 46.86. Find the annual compounded rate of increase.

7. On December 31, 1962, Westinghouse Electric common stock was selling for $32 a share. The stock was split 2 for 1 in 1971. The December 31, 1971, price was $45\frac{7}{8}$. What was the annual compounded rate of growth?

     (12.4%)

8. At the end of 1960, General Motors common was $40\frac{3}{4}$. The closing price in 1971 was $80\frac{1}{2}$. Find the annual compounded rate of increase.

9. Kroger common stock was quoted at $37\frac{7}{8}$ a share on December 31, 1964. On December 30, 1966, the price was $22\frac{1}{8}$. Find the annual compounded rate of change.     $(-23.6\%)$

10. Alcan Aluminum was 34 in December of 1959. In December of 1966, the price had dropped to 28. Find the annual rate of depreciation over this period

11. Standard and Poor's Composite Index of Stock Prices dropped from 26.02 in 1929 to 6.93 in 1932. What was the annual compounded rate of change over this period?     $(-35.7\%)$

12. Standard and Poor's Composite Index of Stock Prices increased from 15.23 in 1949 to 62.38 in 1962. What was the annual compounded rate of increase over this period?

## 11.6  Commission Costs

A broker is paid a commission when he handles the purchase or sale of a stock. Commissions are calculated on the basis of the total money involved. State and federal taxes also add a small amount to the cost of selling stocks.

Stocks are traded in round lots and odd lots. For most stocks a round lot is 100 shares, and an odd lot is a transaction of less than 100 shares. Some preferred stocks are traded on a round lot basis of 10, 25, or 50 shares.

The commission schedules given below are based on current figures from the New York Stock Exchange. The same commissions apply to both purchases and sales.

### COMMISSIONS ON 100 SHARE ORDERS

On each order for 100 shares, commissions are based on the amount of the order and shall not be less than the rates below.

| AMOUNT OF THE ORDER | MINIMUM COMMISSION |
| --- | --- |
| $100 but under $800 | 2% of money involved + $6.40 |
| $800 but under $2500 | 1.3% of money involved + $12.00 |
| $2500 and above | .9% of money involved + $22.00 |

When the amount involved in an order is less than $100, the minimum commission shall be as mutually agreed. The minimum commission on an order for 100 shares shall not exceed $65.00.

### COMMISSIONS ON MULTIPLE ROUND LOT ORDERS

| AMOUNT OF THE ORDER | MINIMUM COMMISSION |
| --- | --- |
| $100 but under $2500 | 1.3% of money involved + $12.00 |
| $2500 but under $20,000 | .9% of money involved + $22.00 |
| $20,000 but under $30,000 | .6% of money involved + $82.00 |
| $30,000 to and including $500,000 | .4% of money involved + $142.00 |

To the above amount there is added a charge for each round lot of 100 shares as follows:

| First to tenth round lot | $6.00 per round lot |
| --- | --- |
| Eleventh round lot and above | $4.00 per round lot |

When the amount involved in an order is less than $100, the minimum commission shall be as mutually agreed. The minimum commission per round lot for multiple round lot orders shall not exceed the single round lot commission as computed using the first of the above commission schedules. Commissions on portions of orders above $500,000 are subject to negotiation.

### COMMISSION ON ODD LOT ORDERS

On purchases of less than 100 shares on the New York Stock Exchange, the customer pays $12\frac{1}{2}$ cents per share above the market price. On sell transactions, the seller of an odd lot has this amount deducted from the market price.

To get the odd lot commission for a sale we add the odd lot differential of $12\frac{1}{2}$ cents to the price of the share and then multiply the adjusted price per share by the number of shares. A figure is then calculated using the rates for a single round lot order. From this figure $2.00 is subtracted to get the commission. The minimum commission on an odd lot order shall not exceed $65.00.

The tables on the following pages show how commissions vary with the price of the stock and the number of shares.

EXAMPLE 1: If Union Carbide is paying an annual dividend of $2.00, what return would an investor get when the market price is 40 if he buys: (a) 50, (b) 100, (c) 200 shares?

SOLUTION: The odd lot differential of $12\frac{1}{2}$ cents is added to the market price. This results in an order for which the single round lot commission as given on page 380 is 1.3% plus $12.00. The $2.00 odd lot deduction is then applied. In summary form the calculations are

(a) Money involved = 50 × 40.125 =        $2006.25
    Commission: 2006.25 × .013 = 26.08
          Plus                    12.00
                            38.08
          Less                     2.00
                                   36.08
          Total Cost               $2042.33

At the current dividend rate the owner will get annual dividends of 50 × 2.00 = $100.00. Rate of return = 100.00/2042.33 = .0490 = 4.90%.

(b) Money involved = 100 × 40.00 =       $4000.00
    Commission: 4000 × .009 = 36.00
          Plus               22.00
                            58.00
          Total Cost               $4058.00

Rate of return = 200/4058 = .0493 = 4.93%.

*Round Lot Commissions*

| SHARES PER ORDER | PRICE OF STOCK | | | | | | | | | |
|---|---|---|---|---|---|---|---|---|---|---|
| | $5 | $10 | $20 | $30 | $40 | $50 | $75 | $100 | $200 | $400 |
| 100 | $ 16.40 | $ 25.00 | $ 38.00 | $ 49.00 | $ 58.00 | $ 65.00 | $ 65.00 | $ 65.00 | $ 65.00 | $ 65.00 |
| 200 | 32.80 | 50.00 | 70.00 | 88.00 | 106.00 | 124.00 | 130.00 | 130.00 | 130.00 | 130.00 |
| 300 | 49.20 | 67.00 | 94.00 | 121.00 | 148.00 | 175.00 | 195.00 | 195.00 | 195.00 | 195.00 |
| 400 | 62.00 | 82.00 | 118.00 | 154.00 | 190.00 | 226.00 | 260.00 | 260.00 | 260.00 | 260.00 |
| 500 | 74.50 | 97.00 | 142.00 | 187.00 | 232.00 | 262.00 | 322.00 | 325.00 | 325.00 | 325.00 |
| 600 | 85.00 | 112.00 | 166.00 | 220.00 | 262.00 | 298.00 | 358.00 | 390.00 | 390.00 | 390.00 |
| 700 | 95.50 | 127.00 | 190.00 | 250.00 | 292.00 | 324.00 | 394.00 | 455.00 | 455.00 | 455.00 |
| 800 | 106.00 | 142.00 | 214.00 | 274.00 | 318.00 | 350.00 | 430.00 | 510.00 | 520.00 | 520.00 |
| 900 | 116.50 | 157.00 | 238.00 | 298.00 | 340.00 | 376.00 | 466.00 | 556.00 | 585.00 | 585.00 |
| 1,000 | 127.00 | 172.00 | 262.00 | 322.00 | 362.00 | 402.00 | 502.00 | 602.00 | 650.00 | 650.00 |
| 2,000 | 212.00 | 302.00 | 402.00 | 482.00 | 562.00 | 642.00 | 842.00 | 1,042.00 | 1,300.00 | * |
| 2,500 | 254.50 | 352.00 | 462.00 | 562.00 | 662.00 | 762.00 | 1,012.00 | 1,262.00 | 1,625.00 | * |
| 5,000 | 452.00 | 562.00 | 762.00 | 962.00 | 1,162.00 | 1,372.00 | 1,862.00 | 2,362.00 | * | * |
| 10,000 | 762.00 | 962.00 | 1,362.00 | 1,762.00 | 2,162.00 | 2,562.00 | * | * | * | * |

* Negotiated rates.

## Odd Lot Commissions

| SHARES PER ORDER | $5 | $10 | $20 | $30 | $40 | $50 | $75 | $100 | $200 | $400 |
|---|---|---|---|---|---|---|---|---|---|---|
| | | | | | | PRICE OF STOCK INCLUDING ODD LOT DIFFERENTIAL | | | | |
| 10 | * | $ 6.40 | $ 8.40 | $10.40 | $12.40 | $14.40 | $19.40 | $23.00 | $36.00 | $56.00 |
| 20 | $ 6.40 | 8.40 | 12.40 | 16.40 | 20.40 | 23.00 | 29.50 | 36.00 | 56.00 | 65.00 |
| 30 | 7.40 | 10.40 | 16.40 | 21.70 | 25.60 | 29.50 | 39.25 | 47.00 | 65.00 | 65.00 |
| 40 | 8.40 | 12.40 | 20.40 | 25.60 | 30.80 | 36.00 | 47.00 | 56.00 | 65.00 | 65.00 |
| 50 | 9.40 | 14.40 | 23.00 | 29.50 | 36.00 | 42.50 | 53.75 | 65.00 | 65.00 | 65.00 |
| 60 | 10.40 | 16.40 | 25.60 | 33.40 | 41.20 | 47.00 | 60.50 | 65.00 | 65.00 | 65.00 |
| 70 | 11.40 | 18.40 | 28.20 | 37.30 | 45.20 | 51.50 | 65.00 | 65.00 | 65.00 | 65.00 |
| 80 | 12.40 | 20.40 | 30.80 | 41.20 | 48.80 | 56.00 | 65.00 | 65.00 | 65.00 | 65.00 |
| 90 | 13.40 | 21.70 | 33.40 | 44.30 | 52.40 | 60.50 | 65.00 | 65.00 | 65.00 | 65.00 |
| 99 | 14.30 | 22.87 | 35.74 | 46.73 | 55.64 | 64.55 | 65.00 | 65.00 | 65.00 | 65.00 |

* Negotiated rates.

(c) Money involved = 200 × 40 =    $8000.00
    Commission: 8000 × .009 = 72.00
             Plus         22.00
    Plus $6 per round lot    12.00
                                 106.00
             Total Cost      $8106.00

Rate of return = 400/8106 = .0493 = 4.93%.

EXAMPLE 2: If Procter and Gamble is paying an annual dividend of $1.50, what return would an investor get when the market price is 75 if he buys: (a) 10, (b) 100, (c) 1000 shares?

SOLUTION: (a) This sale will be executed at $75.125.

Money involved = 10 × 75.125 =    $751.25
    Commission: 751.25 × .02 = 15.03
             Plus         6.40
                      21.43
             Less        2.00
                          19.43
             Total Cost      $770.68

Rate of return = 15/770.68 = .0195 = 1.95%.

(b) Money involved in a 100 share sale = 100 × 75.00 = $7500.00
    Commission: 7500 × .009 = 67.50
             Plus         22.00
             Total      89.50
    Since this exceeds $65, the commission is      65.00
             Total cost      $7565.00

Rate of return = 150/7565 = .0198 = 1.98%.

(c) Money involved in a 1000 share sale = 1000 × 75.00 = $75,000.00
    Commission: 75,000 × .004 = 300.00
             Plus        142.00
    Plus $6 per round lot    60.00
                            502.00
             Total Cost      $75,502.00

Rate of return 1500/75,502 = .0199 = 1.99%.

EXAMPLE 3: If the market price of Penn Central is $5 a share, what would be the cost of (a) 100, (b) 200 shares?

SOLUTION:

(a) Money involved = 100 × 5 =      $500.00
    Commission: 500 × .02 = 10.00
            Plus              6.40
                                     ─────
                                     16.40
            Total Cost               $516.40

(b) Money involved = 200 × 5 =      $1000.00
    Commission: 1000 × .013 =   13.00
            Plus             12.00
    Plus 2 lots at $6        12.00
                             ─────
            Total            $37.00
    Since this exceeds twice the single
    round lot commission of $16.40, the
    commission is
            2 × 16.40 =              32.80
                                     ─────
            Total Cost               $1032.80

## EXERCISE 11b

(For orders of less than 100 shares add $12\frac{1}{2}$ cents per share.)

1. An investor bought Bristol Myers at 60 when the dividend was $1.20. Find the cost including commission and the yield rate for: 10, 100, 200 shares.

$$\begin{bmatrix} Shares & Cost & Yield \\ 10 & \$617.68 & 1.94\% \\ 100 & \$6065.00 & 1.98\% \\ 200 & \$12,130.00 & 1.98\% \end{bmatrix}$$

2. An investor bought Westinghouse Electric at 45 when the dividend was $.94. Find the cost including commission and the yield rate for 50, 100, 1000 shares.

3. An investor bought Kroger when the price was 30 and the dividend $1.30. Find the cost including commission and the yield rate for: 40, 100, 500 shares.

$$\begin{bmatrix} Shares & Cost & Yield \\ 40 & \$1,230.67 & 4.23\% \\ 100 & \$3,049.00 & 4.26\% \\ 500 & \$15,187.00 & 4.28\% \end{bmatrix}$$

4. An investor bought Chesapeake and Ohio Railroad when the price was 55 and the annual dividend $3.00. Find the cost including commission and the yield rate for 25, 50, 100 shares.

5. An investor bought International Business Machines when the price was $370.00 and the dividend $5.40. Find the cost including commission and the yield rate for 10, 40, 100 shares.

$$
\begin{bmatrix}
Shares & Cost & Yield \\
10 & \$3,754.56 & 1.44\% \\
40 & \$14,870.00 & 1.45\% \\
100 & \$37,065.00 & 1.46\%
\end{bmatrix}
$$

6. An investor bought Corning Glass Works at 250 when the dividend was $3.25. Find the cost including commission and the yield rate for 10, 25, 100 shares.

## 11.7  How Much Is a Stock Worth?

The price of a stock on a free market, such as the floor of a stock exchange, is determined by many factors: facts and rumors, hopes and fears, yields expected by investors, general business conditions, outlook for particular industries and companies, and many other things such as tax changes, presidential heart attacks, and what the dictators of distant countries are expected to do next. With so many unpredictable variables influencing stock prices, are there any objective mathematical standards by which the value of a stock can be judged? There are some useful standards of this type which can be used as guidelines in conjunction with other information in arriving at buy or sell decisions.

An important consideration for investors who depend on stocks for income is yield rates and consistent dividends. Many stocks have paid dividends every 3 months for 25 years or more. Some have even had an uninterrupted flow of dividends for a century or more. While this does not guarantee anything for the future, a history of payments over a long period including at times adverse economic conditions is an indication of underlying strength in a company's operations. Even with such stocks, there is an inherent risk in using past results to predict an uncertain future. Present merits must also be considered in evaluating the outlook for future dividends. Will they be maintained, reduced, or increased?

While there is no guarantee that dividends and, therefore, yield rates will continue into the future, a careful consideration of past performance may result in conclusions that are at least quite possible. Suppose that a middle-aged couple would like to invest some money now in a security which will pay them a moderate yield at this time with a good prospect of increased dividends in the future. They decide to invest in an electric utility because they think that in most areas the utility will have an increasing business regardless of general business fluctuations. Their broker suggests the following as representative companies that meet their needs. They have all increased their dividends in each of the last 10 years. Since commission costs cannot be determined until an order is placed, yield rates in material supplied by brokers are determined by simply dividing the dividend by the price. Actual net yields to the investor, determined as in the preceding section, will be slightly lower than these published figures.

| Company | Closing Price Feb. 14, 1972 | Indicated Dividend | Indicated Yield |
|---|---|---|---|
| American Electric Power | $28\frac{1}{2}$ | $1.74 | 6.1% |
| Cleveland Elec. Illum. | 35 | 2.28 | 6.5 |
| Kansas City P. and L. | $32\frac{3}{8}$ | 2.12 | 6.5 |
| Louisville Gas and El. | 35 | 1.74 | 5.0 |
| Oklahoma Gas. and El. | $25\frac{3}{8}$ | 1.28 | 5.0 |
| Toledo Edison | $30\frac{1}{8}$ | 1.84 | 6.1 |

While a fixed investment, such as a savings and loan account or an industrial bond, might pay a somewhat higher return now, the fact that these companies have a past record of increasing dividends is attractive to this couple because returns a few years from now are of greater importance than present yields. This tabulation is, of course, only a preliminary guide for further and more detailed study of these and other companies since past dividend trends may not be continued and may even be reversed.

The *price-earnings ratio*, computed by dividing recent market price by latest 12 months per share earnings, can be a useful guide in making investment decisions. On Wall Street there is considerable support for the idea that a historic norm for this ratio is about 15. However, there is no absolute standard for deciding what the price-earnings ratio should be. It varies from company to company, industry to industry, and as the economic outlook changes. Unusually good or poor 12-months periods should be taken into account in evaluating the significance of the ratio. The price-earnings ratio for a growth company may be high and yet the stock will be quite attractive for certain investment objectives. Thus the price-earnings ratio is a relative matter and is useful only when used for comparison purposes. It is one of the tools which a wise investor uses in conjunction with other information.

For some investors, a liberal income is important. Consider a retired couple who need the income from their investments to meet current living expenses. They will be able to find many stocks which yield 5% or more.

Typical of such stocks are those listed in the following table:

| STOCK | CLOSING PRICE FEB. 14, 1972 | PER SHARE EARNINGS | INDICATED DIVIDEND | INDICATED YIELD | P/E RATIO |
|---|---|---|---|---|---|
| American Tel. and Tel. | $43\frac{5}{8}$ | $4.02 | $2.60 | 6.0% | 10.9 |
| American Natural Gas | $38\frac{1}{8}$ | 3.49 | 2.20 | 5.8 | 10.9 |
| Cincinnati Bell | 23 | 2.10 | 1.30 | 5.7 | 17.7 |
| Norfolk and Western Ry. | 81 | 7.19 | 5.00 | 6.2 | 16.2 |
| Stnd. Oil, Calif. | $57\frac{1}{8}$ | 6.02 | 2.90 | 5.1 | 9.5 |
| Stnd. Oil, N.J. | $76\frac{1}{2}$ | 6.76 | 3.90 | 5.1 | 11.3 |
| American Brands | $42\frac{5}{8}$ | 4.30 | 2.29 | 5.4 | 9.9 |
| American Can | $32\frac{1}{2}$ | 2.66 | 2.20 | 6.8 | 12.2 |

We now consider an investor who is not dependent on present income from his stocks. For him, a price earnings ratio of 20, 30, or more may be acceptable if he thinks that the stock has a large growth potential. The following stocks may be of interest to him:

| STOCK | CLOSING PRICE FEB. 14, 1972 | PER SHARE EARNINGS | INDICATED DIVIDEND | INDICATED YIELD | P/E RATIO |
|---|---|---|---|---|---|
| Avon Products | $107\frac{3}{8}$ | $1.89 | $1.35 | 1.3% | 56.8 |
| Burroughs Corp. | $162\frac{5}{8}$ | 4.03 | .60 | .4 | 32.3 |
| Coca Cola | $124\frac{1}{4}$ | 2.74 | 1.58 | 1.3 | 45.3 |
| Holiday Inns | $51\frac{1}{2}$ | 1.47 | .25 | .5 | 35.0 |
| International Bus. Mach. | 369 | 9.38 | 5.40 | 1.5 | 39.3 |
| Polaroid | $103\frac{1}{8}$ | 2.10 | .32 | .3 | 49.1 |
| Xerox Corp. | $132\frac{1}{2}$ | 2.71 | .84 | .7 | 43.5 |

An idea of whether or not the price-earnings ratio for a growth stock is reasonable might be obtained by using the past growth record of the company to predict the future. Suppose that the earnings of the company are now $10 a share and have been increasing at about 15% a year. This picture fits International Business Machines fairly well in 1972. If the approximately 15%-a-year increase continues for another 5 years, earnings will be about $20. It is on prospects such as these that certain growth stocks are actively traded at high P/E ratios.

**EXERCISE 11c**

1. An investor is interested in buying stock in a drug company. His broker suggests considering the following stocks. Determine the yields and price earnings ratios.

| COMPANY | CLOSING PRICE FEB. 14, 1972 | PER SHARE EARNINGS | INDICATED DIVIDEND | ANSWERS Yield | P/E |
|---|---|---|---|---|---|
| Bristol-Myers Co. | $63\frac{5}{8}$ | $2.45 | $1.20 | 1.9% | 26.0 |
| Merck and Co. | 134 | 3.36 | 2.20 | 1.6 | 39.9 |
| Pfizer, Inc. | 39 | 1.38 | .65 | 1.7 | 28.3 |
| Warner Lambert Co. | $83\frac{1}{2}$ | 2.80 | 1.30 | 1.6 | 29.8 |

2. Compute the yields and price earnings ratio for the following retailers.

| COMPANY | CLOSING PRICE FEB. 14. 1972 | PER SHARE EARNINGS | INDICATED DIVIDEND |
|---|---|---|---|
| Dayton Hudson Corp. | $33\frac{3}{8}$ | $1.35 | $ .50 |
| Federated Dept. Stores | $49\frac{1}{2}$ | 2.08 | 1.00 |
| J. C. Penney | $70\frac{7}{8}$ | 2.28 | 1.04 |
| Sears Roebuck | $101\frac{3}{4}$ | 3.19 | 1.55 |

3. Bring the data in Problem 1 up to date and note any significant changes.
4. Bring the data in Problem 2 up to date and note any significant changes.
5. Compute the yields and price earnings ratios for the following banks.

| BANK | CLOSING PRICE FEB. 14, 1972 | PER SHARE EARNINGS | INDICATED DIVIDEND | ANSWERS Yield | P/E |
|---|---|---|---|---|---|
| Bank of California | 28 | $2.83 | $1.34 | 4.8% | 9.9 |
| Chase Manhattan | 55 | 4.56 | 2.00 | 3.6 | 12.1 |
| First Nat'l. City Corp. | $48\frac{7}{8}$ | 2.91 | 1.32 | 2.7 | 16.8 |
| Manufacturers Hanover | $30\frac{3}{4}$ | 2.90 | 1.56 | 5.1 | 10.6 |

**6.** Compute the yield and price earnings ratio for the following steel companies:

| COMPANY | CLOSING PRICE FEB. 14, 1972 | PER SHARE EARNINGS | INDICATED DIVIDEND |
|---|---|---|---|
| Armco Steel | $20\frac{1}{2}$ | $1.44 | $1.00 |
| Bethlehem Steel | $31\frac{1}{2}$ | 3.14 | 1.20 |
| Inland Steel | $34\frac{1}{2}$ | 2.44 | 2.00 |
| United States Steel | $32\frac{5}{8}$ | 2.85 | 1.60 |

**7.** Bring the data in Problem 5 up to date.

**8.** Bring the data in Problem 6 up to date.

## 11.8 Sound Investment Principles

A sound investment program may include several types of investments, such as real estate, bonds, and stocks. Real estate is likely to require relatively large sums of money and skilled management. High quality bonds have the advantage of safety of principal and, at the present time, good rates of return. There are many fine industrial and utility bonds being sold today at prices which will result in a yield to maturity of over 7 per cent. Some investors put part of their money in bonds for safety of principal and liberal returns. Another part may go into common stocks, some of which are chosen because they pay good dividends and some because of their potential growth.

While stocks can be an attractive investment, a person should be sure that he can afford them. This means more than just having a few dollars on hand. It costs money to buy stocks, and they can go down as well as up. A person should buy stocks only if he feels reasonably sure that he will not be forced to sell at a loss to get cash. He should be able to answer "Yes" to the following questions:

1. Do I have enough to cover living expenses comfortably? For the home buyer this includes a substantial equity in his house.

2. Do I have adequate life insurance to protect my family?

3. Do I have a cash reserve or savings account for emergencies?

How much for living expenses, how much insurance, how large a cash reserve, depend on the circumstances of the particular individual or family. When a person thinks that he has enough for his particular circumstances, he may reasonably start investing in stocks. Note that an honest appraisal of the situation would result in not buying stocks if there are consumer installment loans. We have seen in earlier chapters that these often involve interest charges of 12% or more. Since this is a higher rate than can be expected from most stocks, such debts should be repaid before investing. Having satisfied himself that he can afford to buy stocks, a person should then decide on his investment objectives.

Common stocks may offer one or more of the following: probable safety of principal, liberal income, and growth. Some stocks may meet a couple of these objectives to an attractive degree. Thus a high degree of safety and a liberal dividend rate may be found in the same stock. Or a stock with good growth prospects may pay moderate dividends. However, do not expect to find an all-purpose stock that is very safe, pays large dividends, and is sure to go up.

Before buying, get facts. Do not buy on tips, or rumors, or on the recommendation of a high-pressure telephone salesman. Deal with a reputable broker who can suggest industries and particular companies that will meet your investment objectives. Consider the prospects of the various industries. After deciding on an industry that meets your objectives, ask your broker to supply fact sheets on specific companies. Study these and then make your own decision. The more you know about various companies, the better equipped you will be to make a wise choice. Check on a company's profits, the future for its products, its price-earnings ratio, and the quality of its management. In any industry, some companies will be much better than others. It is management that makes the difference.

When a person is in a position to afford stock in several companies, there are advantages to diversification. Some industries will move ahead faster than others; some may even regress as their products are replaced by new inventions. Diversification protects the investor against the overall loss that would result from having all his money in a failing company. Having stocks in a reasonable number of industries and companies also improves a person's chances of making a profit as a result of one or more of his companies growing at a high rate.

While diversification reduces risk, there are investors who prefer not to diversify. They are willing to accept a higher degree of risk in the hope of having a larger-than-average gain. Even a person who diversifies should not own stocks in so many companies that he is unable to give a reasonable amount of supervision to each. As one authority has said, "Stocks are perishable." Only by keeping abreast of industry trends and the fortunes of particular companies can a person decide whether to buy more stock in a company, sell what he has, or simply hold. Also as a person gets older or his family situation changes, his investment objectives may change, calling for shifts from one type of security to another.

To keep commissions a small percentage of the value of stocks, a person can defer the purchase of stocks until he is able to invest three or four hundred dollars or more.

There is no system which will enable a person to consistently buy when the market is low and sell when it is high. A system which is recommended by some investment counselors is dollar averaging. A person who follows dollar averaging puts a certain number of dollars into the stock of a particular company. At regular intervals, he continues to invest about the same amount in this company. When prices are low, this fixed amount buys more shares than when prices are high. Acquiring more shares when prices are low, and fewer shares when they are high is the theory back of dollar cost averaging. When stock prices rise, a person's profit will be greater because of the larger number of shares purchased when prices were down. Dollar cost averaging means that a person must have the courage and the cash to keep right on buying in line with his plan to buy fixed-dollar amounts at regular intervals. The success of dollar cost averaging depends on the market value of a buyer's stocks having a generally upward trend in spite of inevitable reverses at times.

We have mentioned the advantages of a person diversifying his investment portfolio by getting stocks in different industries and companies. In this way, poor choices are likely to be offset by stocks that do well. Somewhat the same thing can be accomplished by investing in the shares of investment companies. An investment company or investment trust is a concern that uses the capital supplied by individuals to buy a diversified group of securities. There are two principal types: closed-end and open-end. The capitalization of closed-end companies is fixed. Their shares are bought and sold just like other stocks. Some closed-end companies are listed on stock exchanges.

Open-end investment companies, usually called mutual funds, continue to offer new shares of stock for sale. The shares of mutual funds are bought and sold on the basis of their net asset value which is continually changing because the value of the fund's investments is continually changing. Such funds will redeem outstanding shares at any time at the current asset value per share.

The owner of shares of either a closed-end company or a mutual fund gets diversification and professional management. However, he pays for it. The buyer of shares in most mutual funds is required to pay a load which covers commissions and other costs of distribution. The load may be as much as 8%. This is more than the commission rates on common stocks and the shares of closed-end companies. Shares of mutual funds can usually be sold without paying another commission, although there may be a small redemption fee.

In all investment companies, both closed-end and open-end, the owner of shares must pay a management fee. This varies with the size of the fund but a typical figure is $\frac{1}{2}$ of $1\%$ of net assets. This may seem small, but note that it is on assets. As a percentage of earnings, it may be as high as $15\%$ or more. Mutual funds are usually sold by salesmen operating on a commission. Any investment should be *bought* only after the investor has made a thorough study and compared different investment possibilities. Only in this way can a person make a selection that is best from the standpoint of his resources, objectives and temperament. Mutual funds are available for different types of stocks and industries.

Arranging to purchase stocks for cash is a rather simple procedure. After establishing financial responsibility and opening an account with a broker, orders are placed through him. But behind the scenes there is an amazingly complex and efficient system which is described in literature available from the exchanges and brokers. A visit to a broker's office will provide a student or potential investor an interesting overall picture of the operation of the stock market.

The government, the exchanges, and ethical brokers and investment firms help to protect the stock buyer from gyps and swindles. That gyps and swindles still exist is due in part to unwary and greedy buyers. They let themselves be taken by high-pressure salesmen peddling questionable stocks. By direct mail or long-distance calls, suckers learn that they are the lucky ones for whom some kind dealer has set aside a block of two or three hundred shares of low-priced stock at a special bargain price. Unless the buyer acts within a day or two, it will be too late. The chance of a lifetime to make a killing will be gone for good. What is really meant is that it will be gone for the salesman who would make a large commission. "Investigate before you invest" should be the invariable rule of the buyer of stocks. Only in this way will he have a good chance to do well in the interesting and potentially profitable but uncertain stock market.

# 12

## Continuous
## Compounding

### 12.1 *e*

When interest is compounded *m* times a year, the *Amount of* 1 at the end of a year $= (1 + i)^m$, where *i* is the rate per period. This can be written as $[1 + (j/m)]^m$, where *j* is the nominal annual rate. If *j* is 100%, the *Amount of* 1 is $[1 + (1/m)]^m$. While 100% is not a common interest rate, the expression $[1 + (1/m)]^m$ leads to an important constant which has many applications in mathematics and economics. The table below shows that as *m* increases, $[1 + (1/m)]^m$ gets larger and larger but at a decreasing rate.

As long as *m* is finite, no matter how large, the *Amount of* 1 will increase in discrete jumps from one period to the next. Semiannual compounding with jumps every six months and hourly compounding with interest added 8760 times a year are both step functions and therefore discontinuous. However, if

| CONVERSION PERIODS PER YEAR $m$ | RATE PER PERIOD $1/m$ | AMOUNT OF 1 IN ONE YEAR $(1 + 1/m)^m$ |
|---|---|---|
| 1 | 1.00 | 2.000 |
| 2 | .50 | 2.250 |
| 4 | .25 | 2.441 406 |
| 8 | .125 | 2.565 785 |
| 10 | .10 | 2.593 742 |
| 20 | .05 | 2.653 298 |
| 40 | .025 | 2.685 064 |
| 80 | .0125 | 2.701 485 |
| 100 | .01 | 2.704 814 |
| 200 | .005 | 2.711 517 |
| 400 | .0025 | 2.714 892 |
| 800 | .00125 | 2.716 585 |
| 1000 | .001 | 2.716 924 |
| 2000 | .0005 | 2.717 603 |
| 4000 | .00025 | 2.717 942 |
| 8000 | .000125 | 2.718 112 |

$m$ becomes infinite, growth will be steady and continuous and the *Amount of* 1 becomes a continuous function of time. When growth and decay are represented by continuous functions, the calculus can be used as a powerful tool in financial and economic analysis.

In calculus it is shown that as $m$ becomes infinite, the expression $[1 + (1/m)]^m$ approaches a limit. This limit, designated by the symbol $e$, has been calculated to thousands of decimal places. To 10 decimal places, adequate for most purposes, $e = 2.718\ 281\ 8285$.

A graph shows that $[1 + (1/m)]^m$ approaches $e$ rapidly at first as $m$ is increased. In fact, the value of $[1 + (1/m)]^m$ can be made as close to $e$ as we please by making $m$ sufficiently large. However, when the function gets close to $e$, further increases in the frequency of compounding do not have much effect on the numerical value of $[1 + (1/m)]^m$ as shown on page 396.

## 12.2   *e* to Any Power

The *Amount of* 1 at the end of a year for a nominal rate $j$ compounded $m$ times a year is $[1 + (j/m)]^m$. This can be written as

$$\left[\left(1 + \frac{j}{m}\right)^{m/j}\right]^j$$

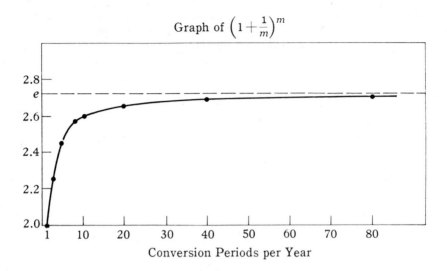

Graph of $\left(1+\dfrac{1}{m}\right)^m$

Since $j$ is constant in any particular problem, we can let $m/j = m'$. As $m$ becomes infinite, so does $m'$. We can now use the limit given in Section 12.1 to find what happens to the *Amount of* 1 for any nominal rate as the frequency of compounding is increased without limit.

$$\lim_{m \to \infty}\left[\left(1 + \frac{j}{m}\right)^{m/j}\right]^j = \lim_{m' \to \infty}\left[\left(1 + \frac{1}{m'}\right)^{m'}\right]^j = e^j$$

Both positive and negative powers of $e$ are needed in economic analysis. Values adequate for the problems in this text are given on page 398–399. The general symbol $x$ is used for the exponent, since tables of $e$ have many applications besides continuous compounding of interest.

Nontabulated values of $e$ can be found using the law of exponents $e^a \times e^b = e^{a+b}$.

EXAMPLE 1: Find $e^{.125}$.

SOLUTION: The exponent is rewritten as the sum of entries found in the table.

$$e^{.125} = e^{.12} \times e^{.005} = 1.127\ 496\ 8516 \times 1.005\ 012\ 5209 = 1.133\ 1484\ 5313$$

EXAMPLE 2: Find $e^{-.833}$.

SOLUTION:

$$e^{-.833} = e^{-.83} \times e^{-.003} = .436\ 049\ 2863 \times .997\ 004\ 4955 = .434\ 743\ 0987$$

Values of $e$ can also be found for any exponent to as many decimal places as desired by using the following series with $n$ sufficiently large.

$$e^x = 1 + x + \frac{x^2}{2!} + \frac{x^3}{3!} + \cdots + \frac{x^n}{n!} + \cdots$$

where $n!$ is read "$n$ factorial" and equals $n(n-1)(n-2)\cdots 2 \times 1$. For example,

$$2! = 2 \times 1 = 2; \quad 3! = 3 \times 2 \times 1 = 6; \quad 4! = 4 \times 3 \times 2 \times 1 = 24.$$

## 12.3 Natural Logarithms

The following systems of logarithms are used in economics and finance:

| System | Base | Principal Use | Symbol |
|---|---|---|---|
| Common logarithms | 10 | Computational work | $\log_{10} N$ or $\log N$ |
| Natural logarithms | $e$ | Theoretical work | $\log_e N$ or $\ln N$ |

Common logarithms are useful for computations because the log of any number, large or small, can be found by simply adding an integer characteristic to a decimal mantissa obtained from a table of mantissas as explained in the appendix.

Tables of logarithms to base $e$ cover a specified set of numbers such as 1.00 to 9.99. Extensive tables of natural logarithms are found in the Standard Mathematical Tables published by the Chemical Rubber Company and in the Handbook of Mathematical Functions, National Bureau of Standards, Applied Mathematics Series 55, available from the United States Government Printing Office. The table of natural logarithms given below is adequate for the problems in this text.

### Natural Logarithms for Numbers from 1.00 to 1.99

| N | 0 | 1 | 2 | 3 | 4 | 5 | 6 | 7 | 8 | 9 |
|---|---|---|---|---|---|---|---|---|---|---|
| 1.0 | .00000 | .00995 | .01980 | .02956 | .03922 | .04879 | .05827 | .06766 | .07696 | .08618 |
| .1 | .09531 | .10436 | .11333 | .12222 | .13103 | .13976 | .14842 | .15700 | .16551 | .17395 |
| .2 | .18232 | .19062 | .19885 | .20701 | .21511 | .22314 | .23111 | .23902 | .24686 | .25464 |
| .3 | .26236 | .27003 | .27763 | .28518 | .29267 | .30010 | .30748 | .31481 | .32208 | .32930 |
| .4 | .33647 | .34359 | .35066 | .35767 | .36464 | .37156 | .37844 | .38526 | .39204 | .39878 |
| .5 | .40547 | .41211 | .41871 | .42527 | .43178 | .43825 | .44469 | .45108 | .45742 | .46373 |
| .6 | .47000 | .47623 | .48243 | .48858 | .49470 | .50078 | .50682 | .51282 | .51879 | .52473 |
| .7 | .53063 | .53649 | .54232 | .54812 | .55389 | .55962 | .56531 | .57098 | .57661 | .58222 |
| .8 | .58779 | .59333 | .59884 | .60432 | .60977 | .61519 | .62058 | .62594 | .63127 | .63658 |
| .9 | .64185 | .64710 | .65233 | .65752 | .66269 | .66783 | .67294 | .67803 | .68310 | .68813 |

## Exponential Function

| $x$ | $e^x$ | $e^{-x}$ | $x$ | $e^x$ | $e^{-x}$ |
|---|---|---|---|---|---|
| .000 | 1.000 000 0000 | 1.000 000 0000 | .21 | 1.233 678 0600 | .810 584 2460 |
| .001 | 1.001 000 5002 | .999 000 4998 | .22 | 1.246 076 7306 | .802 518 7980 |
| .002 | 1.002 002 0013 | .998 001 9987 | .23 | 1.258 600 0099 | .794 533 6025 |
| .003 | 1.003 004 5045 | .997 004 4955 | .24 | 1.271 249 1503 | .786 627 8611 |
| .004 | 1.004 008 0107 | .996 007 9893 | .25 | 1.284 025 4167 | .778 800 7831 |
| .005 | 1.005 012 5209 | .995 012 4792 | .26 | 1.296 930 0867 | .771 051 5858 |
| .006 | 1.006 018 0361 | .994 017 9641 | .27 | 1.309 964 4507 | .763 379 4943 |
| .007 | 1.007 024 5573 | .993 024 4429 | .28 | 1.323 129 8123 | .755 783 7415 |
| .008 | 1.008 032 0855 | .992 031 9148 | .29 | 1.336 427 4880 | .748 263 5676 |
| .009 | 1.009 040 6218 | .991 040 3788 | .30 | 1.349 858 8076 | .740 818 2207 |
| .01 | 1.010 050 1671 | .990 049 8337 | .31 | 1.363 425 1141 | .733 446 9562 |
| .02 | 1.020 201 3400 | .980 198 6733 | .32 | 1.377 127 7643 | .726 149 0371 |
| .03 | 1.030 454 5340 | .970 445 5335 | .33 | 1.390 968 1285 | .718 923 7334 |
| .04 | 1.040 810 7742 | .960 789 4392 | .34 | 1.404 947 5906 | .711 770 3228 |
| .05 | 1.051 271 0964 | .951 229 4245 | .35 | 1.419 067 5486 | .704 688 0897 |
| .06 | 1.061 836 5465 | .941 764 5336 | .36 | 1.433 329 4146 | .697 676 3261 |
| .07 | 1.072 508 1813 | .932 393 8199 | .37 | 1.447 734 6147 | .690 734 3306 |
| .08 | 1.083 287 0677 | .923 116 3464 | .38 | 1.462 284 5894 | .683 861 4092 |
| .09 | 1.094 174 2837 | .913 931 1853 | .39 | 1.476 980 7939 | .677 056 8745 |
| .10 | 1.105 170 9181 | .904 837 4180 | .40 | 1.491 824 6976 | .670 320 0460 |
| .11 | 1.116 278 0705 | .895 834 1353 | .41 | 1.506 817 7851 | .663 650 2501 |
| .12 | 1.127 496 8516 | .886 920 4367 | .42 | 1.521 961 5556 | .657 046 8198 |
| .13 | 1.138 828 3833 | .878 095 4309 | .43 | 1.537 257 5235 | .650 509 0947 |
| .14 | 1.150 273 7989 | .869 358 2354 | .44 | 1.552 707 2185 | .644 036 4211 |
| .15 | 1.161 834 2427 | .860 707 9764 | .45 | 1.568 312 1855 | .637 628 1516 |
| .16 | 1.173 510 8710 | .852 143 7890 | .46 | 1.584 073 9850 | .631 283 6455 |
| .17 | 1.185 304 8513 | .843 664 8166 | .47 | 1.599 994 1932 | .625 002 2683 |
| .18 | 1.197 217 3631 | .835 270 2114 | .48 | 1.616 074 4022 | .618 783 3918 |
| .19 | 1.209 249 5977 | .826 959 1339 | .49 | 1.632 316 2200 | .612 626 3942 |
| .20 | 1.221 402 7582 | .818 730 7531 | .50 | 1.648 721 2707 | .606 530 6597 |

| $x$ | $e^x$ | $e^{-x}$ | $x$ | $e^x$ | $e^{-x}$ |
|---|---|---|---|---|---|
| .51 | 1.665 291 1949 | .600 495 5788 | .76 | 2.138 276 2205 | .467 666 4270 |
| .52 | 1.682 027 6497 | .594 520 5480 | .77 | 2.159 766 2538 | .463 013 0683 |
| .53 | 1.698 932 3086 | .588 604 9697 | .78 | 2.181 472 2655 | .458 406 0113 |
| .54 | 1.716 006 8622 | .582 748 2524 | .79 | 2.203 396 4263 | .453 844 7953 |
| .55 | 1.733 253 0179 | .576 949 8104 | .80 | 2.225 540 9285 | .449 328 9641 |
| .56 | 1.750 672 5003 | .571 209 0638 | .81 | 2.247 907 9867 | .444 858 0662 |
| .57 | 1.768 267 0514 | .565 525 4387 | .82 | 2.270 499 8375 | .440 431 6545 |
| .58 | 1.786 038 4308 | .559 898 3666 | .83 | 2.293 318 7403 | .436 049 2863 |
| .59 | 1.803 988 4154 | .554 327 2847 | .84 | 2.316 366 9768 | .431 710 5234 |
| .60 | 1.822 118 8004 | .548 811 6361 | .85 | 2.339 646 8519 | .427 414 9319 |
| .61 | 1.840 431 3988 | .543 350 8691 | .86 | 2.363 160 6937 | .423 162 0823 |
| .62 | 1.858 928 0418 | .537 944 4376 | .87 | 2.386 910 8535 | .418 951 5492 |
| .63 | 1.877 610 5793 | .532 591 8010 | .88 | 2.410 889 7064 | .414 782 9117 |
| .64 | 1.896 480 8793 | .527 292 4240 | .89 | 2.435 129 6513 | .410 655 7528 |
| .65 | 1.915 540 8290 | .522 045 7768 | .90 | 2.459 603 1112 | .406 569 6597 |
| .66 | 1.934 792 3344 | .516 851 3345 | .91 | 2.484 322 5334 | .402 524 2240 |
| .67 | 1.954 237 3206 | .511 708 5778 | .92 | 2.509 290 3899 | .398 519 0411 |
| .68 | 1.973 877 7322 | .506 616 9924 | .93 | 2.534 509 1776 | .394 553 7104 |
| .69 | 1.993 715 5332 | .501 576 0691 | .94 | 2.559 981 4183 | .390 627 8354 |
| .70 | 2.013 752 7075 | .496 585 3038 | .95 | 2.585 709 6593 | .386 741 0235 |
| .71 | 2.033 991 2586 | .491 644 1975 | .96 | 2.611 696 4734 | .382 892 8860 |
| .72 | 2.054 433 2106 | .486 752 2560 | .97 | 2.637 944 4594 | .379 083 0381 |
| .73 | 2.075 080 6077 | .481 908 9901 | .98 | 2.664 456 2419 | .375 311 0989 |
| .74 | 2.095 935 5145 | .477 113 9155 | .99 | 2.691 234 4723 | .371 576 6910 |
| .75 | 2.117 000 0166 | .472 366 5527 | 1.00 | 2.718 281 8285 | .367 879 4412 |

Natural logarithms can also be obtained by multiplying common logs by a constant as shown below.

By the definition of logarithms,     $10^{\log N} = N$
Taking logarithms to base $e$,        $(\log N) \ln 10 = \ln N$
Substituting the value of $\ln 10$,    $\ln N = 2.302585 \log N$

## 12.4   Single Point Flows and Continuous Compounding

If $\$P$ is invested at a point in time and earns a nominal annual rate $j$ compounded $m$ times a year for $t$ years, the amount after $t$ years is

$$S = P\left(1 + \frac{j}{m}\right)^{mt}$$

This can be written

$$S = P\left[\left(1 + \frac{j}{m}\right)^{m/j}\right]^{jt}$$

If the frequency of compounding is increased without limit, the expression inside the brackets can be replaced by $e$. The amount $S$ of $P$ dollars compounded continuously at a nominal rate $j$ for $t$ years is then

$$S = Pe^{jt} \tag{42}$$

Solving for $P$ results in the present value formula for a single sum discounted for $t$ years at a nominal annual rate $j$ compounded continuously.

$$P = Se^{-jt} \tag{43}$$

In these formulas $t$ can involve a fractional part of a year.

EXAMPLE 1: Find the amount of $\$1000$ at the end of one year at $6\%$ compounded quarterly, monthly, continuously.

SOLUTION:

| FREQUENCY OF COMPOUNDING | AMOUNT |
|---|---|
| Quarterly | $1000(1.015)^4 = 1000 \times 1.061364 = \$1061.36$ |
| Monthly | $1000(1.005)^{12} = 1000 \times 1.061678 = \$1061.68$ |
| Continuously | $1000e^{.06} = 1000 \times 1.061837 = \$1061.84$ |

EXAMPLE 2: A sum of $\$2000$ is due in 2 years. Find the present value at $8\%$ compounded semiannually, quarterly, continuously.

SOLUTION:

| FREQUENCY OF COMPOUNDING | PRESENT VALUE |
|---|---|
| Semiannually | $2000(1.04)^{-4} = 2000 \times .854804 = \$1709.61$ |
| Quarterly | $2000(1.02)^{-8} = 2000 \times .853490 = \$1706.98$ |
| Continuously | $2000e^{-.16} \quad\; = 2000 \times .852144 = \$1704.29$ |

EXAMPLE 3: Find the amount of $200 at the end of 15 months at 8% compounded continuously.

SOLUTION: Substituting $P = 200$, $j = .08$, and $t = 1.25$ in (42),

$$S = 200e^{.10} = 200 \times 1.105\ 17 = \$221.03$$

EXAMPLE 4: An obligation of $500 is due in two and one-half years. Find the present value at 10% compounded continuously.

SOLUTION: Substituting $S = 500$, $j = .10$, and $t = 2.5$ in (43),

$$P = 500e^{-.25} = 500 \times .778\ 80 = \$389.40$$

### EXERCISE 12a

1. One thousand dollars is invested for two and one-half years at a nominal annual rate of 6%. Find the amount if interest is compounded: (a) quarterly; (b) monthly; (c) continuously.      [(a) $1160.54; (b) $1161.40; (c) $1161.83]
2. Solve Problem 1 using a nominal annual rate of 9%.
3. Five thousand dollars is invested for 18 months at a nominal annual rate of 8%. Find the amount if interest is compounded: (a) semiannually; (b) quarterly; (c) continuously.      [(a) $5624.32; (b) $5630.81; (c) $5637.48]
4. Solve Problem 3 using a nominal rate of 6%.
5. An obligation of $10,000 is due in 3 years. Find the present value using a nominal rate of 7% compounded: (a) annually; (b) semiannually; (c) continuously.      [(a) $8162.98; (b) $8135.01; (c) $8105.84]
6. Solve Problem 5 using a nominal rate of 8%.
7. An obligation of $5000 is due in 5 years. Find the present value using a nominal rate of 10% if interest is compounded: (a) semiannually; (b) quarterly; (c) continuously.      [(a) $3069.57; (b) $3051.36; (c) $3032.66]
8. Solve Problem 7 using a nominal rate of 7%.
9. Suppose that the rate of change of a variable at any instant of time is proportional to the amount present at that instant. This is expressed by the differential equation:

$$\frac{dS}{dt} = kS$$

where $k$ is the proportionality constant. If the amount present at time $t = 0$ is $S_o$, show that the solution of this differential equation is $S = S_o e^{kt}$. Note that if we let $S_o = P$ and $k = j$, this is equivalent to equation (42).

## 12.5   Finding the Rate

Taking the natural logarithm of both sides of the amount formula results in a useful formula for getting continuous rates of change.

$$S = Pe^{jt}$$

$$\ln S = \ln P + jt$$

$$j = \frac{\ln S - \ln P}{t}$$

EXAMPLE 1: A sum of money earned 6% simple interest over a year. Find the continuous rate of increase.

SOLUTION: We let $P = \$1.00$, $S = \$1.06$, and $t = 1$.

$$j = \ln 1.06 - \ln 1.00 = .05827 - .00000 = 5.83\%$$

EXAMPLE 2: Gross national product in current dollars increased from $560 billion in 1962 to $794 billion in 1967. Find the continuous rate of increase.

SOLUTION: If available tables do not include the required natural logarithms, the problem can be worked using common logarithms and the relation $\ln N = 2.302585 \log N$.

$$j = \frac{2.302585(\log 794 - \log 560)}{5} = \frac{2.302585(2.899821 - 2.748188)}{5}$$

$$= .06983 = 6.98\%$$

## 12.6   Effective Interest Rate

When interest is compounded at discrete intervals, the effective rate $r$ is the rate converted annually that will produce the same amount of interest per year as the nominal rate converted $m$ times a year. When $m$ becomes infinite we have continuous compounding. Setting the *Amount of* 1 at the effective rate equal to the *Amount of* 1 at the nominal rate $j$ for one year,

$$1 + r = e^j$$
$$r = e^j - 1 \tag{44}$$

To get the nominal rate equivalent to a given effective rate, we take the natural logarithm of both sides of the *Amount of* 1 equality.

$$e^j = 1 + r$$
$$j \ln e = \ln (1 + r)$$
$$j = \ln (1 + r) \tag{45}$$

EXAMPLE 1: Find the effective rate corresponding to 15% compounded continuously.

SOLUTION: Substituting in (44),

$$r = e^{.15} - 1 = 1.1618 - 1 = .1618 = 16.18\%$$

EXAMPLE 2: What nominal rate compounded continuously would produce an effective rate of 10%?

SOLUTION: Substituting in (45),

$$j = \ln (1.10) = .09531 = 9.53\%$$

## 12.7   Annuities and Continuous Compounding

Deposits of $100 each are made four times a year at equal intervals into an ordinary annuity paying 8% compounded continuously. What is the amount at the end of 18 months? Since this is an ordinary annuity, the deposits are made at the end of the payment intervals. A time diagram shows that the last payment does not earn interest, the next to the last payment gets interest for $\frac{1}{4}$ year, the payment before that earns interest for $\frac{2}{4}$ year, and so on down to the first payment, which earns interest for $\frac{5}{4}$ years. Since the problem is given in months while the rate is a nominal annual rate, it is necessary to convert times from months to years as shown on the time diagram.

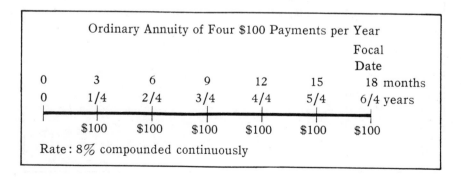

Ordinary Annuity of Four $100 Payments per Year

| | | | | | Focal Date |
|---|---|---|---|---|---|
| 0 | 3 | 6 | 9 | 12 | 15 | 18 months |
| 0 | 1/4 | 2/4 | 3/4 | 4/4 | 5/4 | 6/4 years |
| | $100 | $100 | $100 | $100 | $100 | $100 |

Rate: 8% compounded continuously

Individual payments are taken to a focal date at 18 months using (42).

| PAYMENT NUMBER | YEARS TO FOCAL DATE | AMOUNT AT FOCAL DATE $100^{.08t}$ |
|:---:|:---:|:---:|
| 6 | 0 | $100e^0$ = 100.00 |
| 5 | $\frac{1}{4}$ | $100e^{.02}$ = 102.02 |
| 4 | $\frac{2}{4}$ | $100e^{.04}$ = 104.08 |
| 3 | $\frac{3}{4}$ | $100e^{.06}$ = 106.18 |
| 2 | 1 | $100e^{.08}$ = 108.33 |
| 1 | $\frac{5}{4}$ | $100e^{.10}$ = 110.52 |
| | | $631.13 |

To get a general formula for the amount of an annuity with continuous compounding, we assume that $p$ payments of $1 each are made per year at equal intervals for $t$ years. The total number of payments is $n = pt$. The last payment does not earn interest. Since there are $p$ payments per year, the next to the last payment earns interest for $1/p$ year. Substituting in (42), its amount is $e^{j/p}$. The next payment earns interest for $2/p$ year and has an amount equal to $e^{2j/p}$. At the other end of the annuity, the first payment earns interest for $(n - 1)/p$ years. Its amount is $e^{j[(n-1)/p]}$. A time diagram of this annuity is shown below.

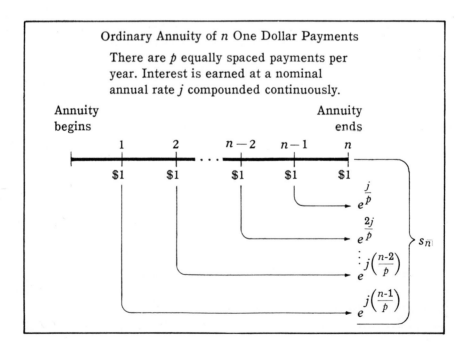

Ordinary Annuity of $n$ One Dollar Payments

There are $p$ equally spaced payments per year. Interest is earned at a nominal annual rate $j$ compounded continuously.

Adding the amounts of the individual payments:

$$S_{\overline{n}|} = 1 + e^{j/p} + e^{2j/p} + \cdots + e^{j[(n-2)/p]} + e^{j[(n-1)/p]}$$

This is a geometric progression with first term 1, common ratio of $e^{j/p}$ and $n$ terms. Substituting in the formula for the sum of a geometric progression:

$$S_{\overline{n}|} = \frac{1[1 - (e^{j/p})^n]}{1 - e^{j/p}} = \frac{1 - e^{jn/p}}{1 - e^{j/p}} = \frac{e^{jn/p} - 1}{e^{j/p} - 1}$$

If the periodic payment is $R$, we multiply by $R$ to get the amount of $n$ payments earning a rate $j$ compounded continuously

$$S_n = R \frac{e^{jn/p} - 1}{e^{j/p} - 1} \tag{46}$$

We now use (43) to discount this equivalent single sum to get the present value of the annuity. Multiply by $e^{-jn/p}$,

$$A_n = R \frac{1 - e^{-jn/p}}{e^{j/p} - 1} \tag{47}$$

EXAMPLE 1: Payments of $100 are made at the end of each 6 months into a fund paying 8% compounded continuously. Find the amount at the end of 4 years.

SOLUTION: Substituting $R = 100$, $j = .08$, $n = 8$, and $p = 2$ in (46),

$$S = 100 \frac{e^{.32} - 1}{e^{.04} - 1} = 100 \frac{1.37713 - 1}{1.04081 - 1} = \$924.11$$

EXAMPLE 2: Payments of $500 are to be made at the end of each quarter for 4 years. Find the present value of these payments at 8% compounded continuously.

SOLUTION: Substituting $R = 500$, $j = .08$, $n = 16$, and $p = 4$ in (47),

$$A_n = 500 \frac{1 - e^{-.32}}{e^{.02} - 1} = 500 \frac{1 - .72615}{1.02020 - 1} = \$6778.47$$

**EXERCISE 12b**

1. Find the amount at the time of the last payment of $100 deposits at the end of each 3 months for 5 years if money is worth 8% compounded: (a) quarterly; (b) continuously.  [(a) $2429.74; (b) $2434.75]
2. Answer Problem 1 for a nominal rate of 6%.
3. Find the amount of an annuity of $1000 every 6 months for 3 years if the rate is 6% compounded: (a) semiannually; (b) continuously.
[(a) $6468.41; (b) $6475.69]

**4.** Answer Problem 3 if the nominal rate is $8\%$.

**5.** A contract calls for payments of \$200 at the end of each 6 months for 4 years. Find the present value at $8\%$ compounded: (a) semiannually; (b) continuously.                                   [(a) \$1346.55; (b) \$1342.07]

**6.** Answer Problem 5 if the nominal rate is $10\%$.

**7.** Find the present value of payments of \$1000 at the end of each year for 8 years if the rate is $7\%$ compounded: (a) annually, (b) continuously.

[(a) \$5971.30; (b) \$5913.71]

**8.** Answer Problem 7 if the nominal rate is $8\%$.

## 12.8   Continuous Flows and Discrete Compounding

Many money flows, particularly those arising from contracts, occur at well-defined points in time. Examples are interest payments on savings accounts, bond interest payments, insurance premiums, payments on home mortgages, and rent payments. Other money flows occur more or less continuously over time. Examples are the day-to-day income of a store, the return from a large manufacturing operation, and the tolls received by a toll road or bridge. While such flows are not absolutely continuous, it may be desirable to approximate them by continuous flows for purposes of economic analysis. When money flows are continuous, interest may be compounded either at discrete intervals or continuously. We now develop formulas for handling a continuous flow of money which earns interest compounded at discrete intervals.

This problem must be handled using the limiting process which is so important in calculus. We start with a total money flow of 1 per year made in $p$ equal payments so each payment is $1/p$. If payments are made quarterly, $p = 4$ and each payment $= \frac{1}{4}$. Interest is earned at a nominal rate $j$, compounded $m$ times a year. We now have a general annuity with payments of $1/p$ at the end of each payment interval earning interest compounded $m$ times a year.

We convert the $p$ payments per year to equivalent payments made on interest conversion dates. Using the method developed for general annuities, the equivalent payment on an interest conversion date is

$$R = \frac{1}{p} \cdot \frac{1}{s_{\overline{m/p}|i}}$$

We now have an ordinary annuity of $n$ payments where $n = tm$, the number of years times the conversion periods per year. The amount of this annuity is

$$S = \frac{1}{p} \cdot \frac{1}{s_{\overline{m/p}|i}} s_{\overline{n}|i}$$

Substituting for the sinking fund function its equivalent value in exponential form,

$$S = \frac{1}{p} \cdot \frac{i}{(1 + i)^{m/p} - 1} \, s_{\overline{n}|i}$$

We let the number of payments increase until in the limit we have a continuous flow with amount

$$S = \lim_{p \to \infty} \left[ \frac{i}{p(1 + i)^{m/p} - p} \right] s_{\overline{n}|i}$$

To simplify this expression we must find

$$\lim_{p \to \infty} [p(1 + i)^{m/p} - p]$$

Getting this limit is simplified if we let $p = 1/q$. We now have

$$\lim_{q \to 0} \frac{(1 + i)^{mq} - 1}{q}$$

This has the indeterminate form 0/0 so we use l'Hôpital's Rule. Differentiating numerator and denominator with respect to $q$,

$$\lim_{q \to 0} \frac{(1 + i)^{mq} m \ln (1 + i)}{1} = m \ln (1 + i)$$

The amount of an annuity of $Y$ dollars per year flowing continuously is then,

$$S = Y \frac{i}{m \ln (1 + i)} \, s_{\overline{n}|i} \tag{48}$$

where $m$ = number of interest conversions per year
$\quad\quad\ i$ = rate per interest conversion period
$\quad\quad\ n$ = number of interest conversion periods = $tm$,
$\quad\quad\quad$ where $t$ is the number of years.

The present value of an annuity of $Y$ dollars per year flowing continuously is found in a similar way,

$$A = Y \frac{i}{m \ln (1 + i)} \, a_{\overline{n}|i} \tag{49}$$

EXAMPLE 1: At 7% compounded annually, what is the amount of a uniform continuous flow of $5000 per year at the end of 6 years?

SOLUTION: Substituting $Y = 5000$, $i = .07$, $m = 1$, and $n = 6$ in (48),

$$S = 5000 \left( \frac{.07}{1 \ln 1.07} \right) s_{\overline{6}|7\%}$$

$$= 5000 \left( \frac{.07}{.06\ 766} \right) 7.153\ 291 = \$37{,}003.44$$

EXAMPLE 2: An investment is expected to yield a continuous net inflow of $1000 a year for 5 years. Find the present value at 8% compounded annually.

SOLUTION: Substituting $Y = 1000$, $i = .08$, $m = 1$, and $n = 5$ in (49).

$$A = 1000 \left( \frac{.08}{1 \ln 1.08} \right) a_{\overline{5}|8\%}$$

$$= 1000 \left( \frac{.08}{.07696} \right) 3.992710 = \$4150.43$$

## 12.9　Continuous Flows and Continuous Compounding

Let the continuous function $f(x)$ represent the rate at which money is flowing per unit of time. If $x$ is in years and $f(x)$ is in dollars per year, the area under $f(x)$ between two points in time gives the total dollar flow over the given time interval.

The function $f(x) = 2000$ represents a uniform money flow of $2000 per year. The graph of this money flow is a horizontal line and the total money flow over a specified time, such as three years, can be found by simple multiplication.

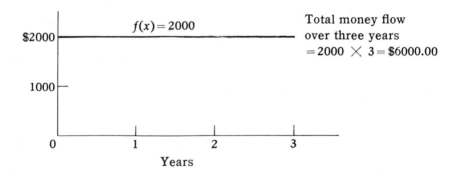

The function $f(x) = 2000e^{.08x}$ is a continuous money flow that is increasing exponentially. The total money flow over a time interval is found by evaluating a definite integral.

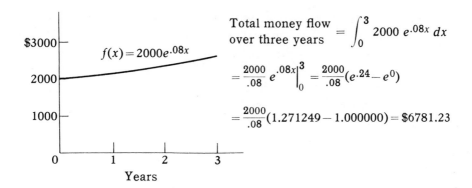

$$\text{Total money flow over three years} = \int_0^3 2000\, e^{.08x}\, dx$$

$$= \frac{2000}{.08}\, e^{.08x}\Big|_0^3 = \frac{2000}{.08}(e^{.24} - e^0)$$

$$= \frac{2000}{.08}(1.271249 - 1.000000) = \$6781.23$$

To find the amount or present value of a continuous money flow with interest compounded continuously, we let $f(x)$ represent the continuous flow. The time axis from 0 to $t$ is divided into $n$ subintervals of width $\Delta x$ where $\Delta x = (t - 0)/n$. When defined in this way, $\Delta x$ is positive. The amount of money that flows over any interval of time is given by the area between the $x$-axis and $f(x)$ over the specified time interval.

The sketch below shows a representative continuous flow with the $x$-axis from 0 to $t$ divided into equal subintervals of width $\Delta x$. A rectangle is drawn over each subinterval with height equal to $f(x_i)$ where $x_i$ is the value of $x$ for the left boundary of the $i$th subinterval. The area of each rectangle is $f(x_i)\, \Delta x_i$. This is approximately equal to the corresponding area under the curve. The rectangular area corresponding to the $i$th subinterval is shaded in the sketch.

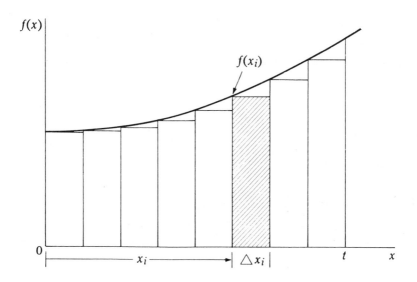

At a nominal rate $j$ compounded continuously, the present value of the money flow over the $i$th subinterval is approximately equal to $f(x_i)\,\Delta x_i e^{-jx_i}$. The total present value is approximately equal to the sum $\sum_{i=1}^{n} f(x_i)\,\Delta x_i e^{-jx_i}$. The approximation can be improved by making $n$ larger so that the rectangular areas are closer to the true areas under the curve. Better yet, the exact present value can be obtained by taking the limit of this sum as $n$ becomes infinite. In the calculus it is shown that this limit is given by the definite integral:

$$\text{Present value} = \int_0^t f(x)e^{-jx}\,dx$$

Multiplying by $e^{jt}$ results in the amount of the flow at time $t$.

$$\text{Amount} = e^{jt}\int_0^t f(x)e^{-jx}\,dx$$

Fortunately most continuous money flows can be expressed in terms of exponential or polynomial functions. Either of these, when multiplied by $e^{-jx}$, results in an expression that can be integrated.

## 12.10   Uniform Flows and Continuous Compounding

If money is flowing continuously at a constant rate of $\$C$ per year for $t$ years we let $f(x) = C$ and get

$$\text{Amount} = e^{jt}\int_0^t Ce^{-jx}\,dx = e^{jt}C\left(\frac{-1}{j}\right)e^{-jx}\Big|_0^t = e^{jt}C\left(\frac{-1}{j}\right)(e^{-jt} - e^0)$$

When simplified, this leads to the amount formula.

$$S = C\frac{e^{jt} - 1}{j} \tag{50}$$

We multiply by $e^{-jt}$ to get the present value formula,

$$A = C\frac{1 - e^{-jt}}{j} \tag{51}$$

EXAMPLE: Find the amount and present value of $100 a year flowing uniformly over a five year period at an interest rate of 8% compounded continuously.

SOLUTION: Substituting $C = 100$, $j = .08$, and $t = 5$ in (50),

$$\text{Amount} = 100\left(\frac{e^{(.08)5} - 1}{.08}\right) = 100\left(\frac{e^{.40} - 1}{.08}\right)$$

$$= 100\left(\frac{1.49182 - 1}{.08}\right)$$

$$= \$614.78$$

Substituting in (51)

$$\text{Present value} = 100 \left( \frac{1 - e^{-(.08)5}}{.08} \right) = 100 \left( \frac{1 - e^{-.40}}{.08} \right)$$

$$= 100 \left( \frac{1 - .67032}{.08} \right)$$

$$= \$412.10$$

These results can be checked by taking the present value forward using (42),

$$S = 412.10 \times e^{.40} = 412.10 \times 1.49182 = \$614.78$$

## 12.11   Exponential Flows

If the money flow is increasing or decreasing exponentially, it can be written $f(x) = Ce^{kx}$ where $C$ is a constant and $k$ is the continuous rate of change which may be positive or negative. The amount of this flow at time $t$ is

$$e^{jt} \int_0^t Ce^{kx}e^{-jx}\,dx = Ce^{jt} \int_0^t e^{(k-j)x}\,dx = \frac{Ce^{jt}}{k-j} \left[ e^{(k-j)x} \right]_0^t$$

Substitution of limits results in the amount formula,

$$S = \frac{Ce^{jt}}{k-j}[e^{(k-j)t} - 1], \qquad\qquad k \neq j \qquad\qquad \textbf{(52)}$$

Multiplying the amount formula by $e^{-jt}$ gives the present value formula,

$$A = \frac{C}{k-j}[e^{(k-j)t} - 1], \qquad\qquad k \neq j \qquad\qquad \textbf{(53)}$$

EXAMPLE 1: A continuous money flow starts at \$1000 and decreases exponentially at 10% a year. Find the amount at the end of 5 years at 8% compounded continuously.

SOLUTION: Substituting $C = 100$, $k = -.10$, $j = .08$, and $t = 5$ in (52),

$$S = \frac{1000e^{.40}}{-.10 - .08}[e^{(-.10-.08)5} - 1] = \frac{1000 \times 1.491825}{-.18}(.406\ 570 - 1)$$

$$= \$4918.30$$

EXAMPLE 2: A continuous money flow starts at \$5000 and increases exponentially at 2% a year for 3 years. Find the present value at 6% compounded continuously.

SOLUTION: Substituting $C = 5000$, $k = .02$, $j = .06$, and $t = 3$ in (53),

$$A = \frac{5000}{.02 - .06}[e^{(.02-.06)3} - 1] = \frac{5000}{-.04}(.886\ 920 - 1) = \$14,135.00$$

## 12.12   Polynomial Flows

Many continuous money flows can be represented by a polynomial:

$$f(x) = a_0 + a_1x + a_2x^2 + \cdots$$

where the $a$'s are constants.

A particular problem may involve only one or two terms of the polynomial function. Formulas (50) and (51) for the amount and present value of a uniform flow earning interest compounded continuously take care of the first term of a polynomial flow. Terms of the first and second degree are given in the exercises. These problems are good illustrations of integration by parts.

### EXERCISE 12c

1. A continuous flow of money is given by the equation $f(x) = Cx$, where $x$ is time in years. Assume that the flow occurs from $x = 0$ to $x = t$. Find the amount and present value at a nominal annual rate $j$ compounded continuously.

$$\text{Amount} = \frac{Ce^{jt}}{j^2}[1 - e^{-jt}(jt + 1)]$$

$$\text{Present value} = \frac{C}{j^2}[1 - e^{-jt}(jt + 1)]$$

2. A continuous flow of money is given by the equation $f(x) = Cx^2$ where $x$ is time in years. Assume that the flow occurs from $x = 0$ to $x = t$. Find the amount and present value at a nominal annual rate $j$ compounded continuously.

$$\text{Amount} = Ce^{jt}\left[\frac{t^2e^{-jt}}{-j} + \frac{2}{j^3}(1 - e^{-jt}(jt + 1))\right]$$

$$\text{Present value} = C\left[\frac{t^2e^{-jt}}{-j} + \frac{2}{j^3}(1 - e^{-jt}(jt + 1))\right]$$

3. A continuous flow of money is given by the expression $f(x) = 1000 - 100x$. It is assumed that the flow will continue until it reaches 0 in 10 years. Find the present value of this flow at 6% compounded continuously. ($4133.66)

4. Solve Problem 3 for 8% compounded continuously.

5. An investment is expected to yield a uniform continuous inflow of $10,000 a year for 4 years. Find the amount at a nominal annual rate of 8% compounded: (a) annually; (b) continuously.     [(a) $46,841.08; (b) $47,140.98]

6. Solve Problem 5 for a nominal rate of 6%.

7. An investment is expected to produce a uniform continuous inflow of $10,000 a year for 4 years. Find the present value at a nominal annual rate of 8% compounded: (a) annually; (b) continuously.

[(a) $34,429.59; (b) $34,231.38]

8. Solve Problem 6 for a nominal rate of 6%.

9. Formulas (52) and (53) specify that $k \neq j$. What would be the amount and present value of an exponential flow if $k = j$?    $(S = Cte^{jt}; A = Ct)$

# Appendix
## Computational Methods

Problems in the mathematics of finance are solved by methods that range from pencil and paper computations to programmed solutions on electronic computers.

An efficient way to solve problems requiring only a few computations is to use a desk calculator. The manual for the particular machine should be consulted for proper operating procedures. Sometimes additional help for common business problems is available in the form of specific instruction sheets with suggested short cuts and checks.

To reduce time spent on routine computations when pencil and paper must be used, most of the problems in this book are based on simple sums. However, when a problem has more than one stage, lengthy computations may be inevitable. Part I describes an abridged method of multiplication.

At one time logarithms were much used for computational work, but they have been superseded for most routine calculations by desk calculators and electronic computers. However, logarithms are still important in business analysis because they are the basis for semilogarithmic or ratio graphs, and because they provide a quick way to get approximate answers when a negative rate of change is involved or when the required positive rate factor is not in available tables. Part II gives examples of logarithmic solutions of practical business problems.

Because of their great speed and high accuracy, electronic computers are very helpful in solving mathematics of finance problems that involve extensive calculations. Programs for problems of this type are given in Part III.

### I. Rapid Multiplication

When problems like $489.13 \times 1.563956$ are worked by pencil and paper methods using ordinary multiplication, the result is obtained to many decimal places and then rounded. Some students prefer to learn a method which produces accurate results with less work. This method is explained in the following examples.

EXAMPLE 1: Multiply 489.13 by 1.563956.

Place the decimal point in the number with the fewer digits behind the first digit from the left. The decimal point in the other number is moved the same number of places in the other direction. These changes offset each other and leave the decimal point in the product unchanged. The problem becomes

$$4.8913 \times 156.3956$$

Reverse the order of digits in the first number and write it under the second. Multiply by the first digit from the right. Draw a line through the 4 as you are finished with it.

156.3956
3198.~~4~~ multiplier reversed
625 5824 first partial product

Multiply by 8, but instead of writing down the first product 48, round it mentally to the nearest number of tens (in this case 5) and add it to the next product making it 40 + 5 = 45. Write the 5 under the last digit, carry 4 as in ordinary multiplication, and complete the second partial product. Draw a line through the 8 and the 6.

156.395~~6~~
319~~8~~.~~4~~
625 5824
125 1165 second partial product

The next line starts by multiplying 9 × 5 = 45. This could be rounded to either 4 or 5 tens. We shall follow the practice of rounding down if the number before the 5 is even and up if it is odd. This will result in rounding errors cancelling each other. The third partial product starts with 81 + 4 = 85. Write down the 5, carry 8, and complete the third partial product. Cross out the next number in each line of the original problem.

156.39~~56~~
31~~98~~.~~4~~
625 5824
125 1165
14 0755 third partial product

The remaining partial products are written to complete the problem. Note that 1 × 9 = 9 is rounded to one ten which makes the first digit in the fourth partial product 3 + 1 = 4. Point off the same number of places in the answer as there are in the top line. The problem is shown below in the short and in the ordinary way. Cross out lines are omitted.

|  |  |
|---|---|
| 156.3956 | 1.563956 |
| 3198.4 | 489.13 |
| 625 5824 | 4691868 |
| 125 1165 | 1563956 |
| 14 0755 | 14 075604 |
| 1564 | 125 11648 |
| 469 | 625 5824 |
| 764.9777 | 764.97779828 |
| = \$764.98 | = \$764.98 |

EXAMPLE 2: Find the product \$23,158.13 × 1.4802443. Try working this on a separate sheet of paper and then check your solution against the one below.

| Short Method | Ordinary Method |
|---|---|
| 14802.443 | 1.4802443 |
| 318513.2 | 23158.13 |
| 29604 886 | 44407329 |
| 4440 733 · | 14802443 |
| 148 024 | 11 8419544 |
| 74 012 | 74 012215 |
| 11 842 | 148 02443 |
| 148 | 4440 7329 |
| 44 | 29604 886 |
| 34279.689 | 34279.689931159 |
| = \$34,279.69 | = \$34,279.69 |

On page 82 in the text it is recommended that factors from the interest tables be taken to the same number of places that there are digits in the sum of money including the cents. When the result is rounded to the penny, this usually results in exactly the same answer as would be obtained by carrying the factor to more decimal places. If you want an extra factor of safety, particularly for an important real life problem, it is easy to use short multiplication and take the factor to an additional place.

EXAMPLE 3: A principal of \$880.11 is invested at $3\frac{1}{2}\%$ compounded annually for 25 years. Find the amount.

SOLUTION: Substituting in (9) $S = 880.11(1.035)^{25} = 880.11 \times 2.363\ 244\ 9843$. If this is worked with the entire factor using a calculator and the answer rounded to the penny we have $2079.92. Short multiplication gives

| 5-place factor | 6-place factor |
|---|---|
| 236.324 | 236.3245 |
| 1108.8 | 1108.8 |
| 1890 592 | 1890 5960 |
| 189 059 | 189 0596 |
| 236 | 2363 |
| 24 | 236 |
| 2079.911 | 2079.9155 |
| = $2079.91 | = $2079.92 |

*Problems*

**1.** $8614.75 × 1.544636.          ($13,306.65)

**2.** $312.81 × 10.702722.          ($3347.92)

**3.** $188.16 × 24.64614.          ($4637.42)

**4.** $27,182.19 × .7703781.          ($20,940.56)

## II. Logarithms

Business problems involving rates of change, that would be difficult or impossible to solve with arithmetic, can be done with ease using logarithms. Graphs with logarithmic scales are valuable tools for business analysis.

A *logarithm* is an exponent, and computations with logarithms are based on the laws of exponents. The exponential expression $10^2 = 100$ becomes in logarithmic form: $\log_{10} 100 = 2$. This is read "log of 100 to the base 10 equals 2." While any positive number other than 1 can be used as the base for a system of logarithms, 10 is the best base for computational work and is the one we use. When the base is not indicated, 10 is understood. In all cases, the log of a number will be the power to which 10 must be raised to equal that number. A few numbers with the corresponding exponential expressions and logs are given below.

| Number N | N as a Power of 10 | Logarithm of N |
|---|---|---|
| .01 | $\frac{1}{100} = 10^{-2}$ | $-2$ |
| .1 | $\frac{1}{10} = 10^{-1}$ | $-1$ |
| 1 | $10^0$ | 0 |
| 10 | $10^1$ | 1 |
| 100 | $10^2$ | 2 |
| 1000 | $10^3$ | 3 |

The table above shows that the logs of numbers which are integral or 0 powers of 10 can be determined by finding the power to which 10 must be raised to equal the number. The logs of other positive numbers are also powers of 10, but their numerical values must be determined by higher mathematics. Fortunately their values have been tabulated in tables which can be used by anyone who has a knowledge of elementary algebra.

The table also gives us an idea of the numerical value to expect for the logs of other numbers. Since 2 is between 1 and 10, log 2 must be between log 1 and log 10. This makes log 2 a decimal between 0 and 1. In a similar way, the logs of numbers like 20 and 200 will lie between integral powers of 10. This is shown in the table below.

| $N$ | $\log N$ |
|---|---|
| 1 | 0 |
| 2 | 0 + a decimal between 0 and 1 |
| 10 | 1 |
| 20 | 1 + a decimal |
| 100 | 2 |
| 200 | 2 + a decimal |
| 1000 | 3 |

Soon we shall show how a log table will give us the numerical value: log 2 = .301030. In exponential form, $2 = 10^{.301030}$. An advantage of logs to the base 10 is that, if we know the log of a number such as 2, we can easily get the log of 20, 200, or any other number which consists of 2 multiplied or divided by some power of 10.

EXAMPLE: If log 2 = .301030, find log 20 and log 200.

SOLUTION: $20 = 2 \times 10 = 10^{.301030} \times 10^1 = 10^{1.301030}$.

Since the exponent to the base 10 is the log of the number, log 20 = 1.301030.

$200 = 2 \times 100 = 10^{.301030} \times 10^2 = 10^{2.301030}$. Thus, log 200 = 2.301030.

The example above emphasized the fact that logs are exponents and follow the laws of exponents. If we keep this in mind, we can omit writing them as exponents and simply say

$$\log\ 20 = \log\ 2 + \log\ 10 = .301030 + 1.000000 = 1.301030$$

$$\log 200 = \log 2 + \log 100 = .301030 + 2.000000 = 2.301030$$

In the same way, we can get the log for any other number which has 2 preceded or followed by zeroes. This means that all we need to get the log of any number is a log table which covers the numbers from 1 to 10, since we can get the log of any number by adding a whole number to the decimal from the table.

Working with logarithms requires the following steps: 1. Getting the *mantissa*; 2. Getting the *characteristic*; and 3. Finding the *antilogarithm*.

The whole number part of a logarithm is the characteristic. The decimal part is the mantissa. For example:

log 20 = 1.301030

The characteristic depends on the size of the number and is determined by the student, as described below.

The mantissa depends on the sequence of significant digits and is obtained from a table.

**Getting the Mantissa.** A section from Table 7 in the back of the book is shown below. In a log table, decimal points are omitted to save space. The column headed *N* is for numbers. The digits 100 under *N* mean 1.00, and so on. To get the mantissa for 1.1, we read down the *N* column to 110, and read next to it the digits 041393, which have a decimal point understood before the

1. Go down the *N*      2. Go across the     3. Locate the mantissa
    column to 117       top row to 6       opposite 117 and under 6

Six-Place Logarithms of Numbers | 100-150

| N | 0 | 1 | 2 | 3 | 4 | 5 | 6 | 7 | 8 | 9 | D |
|---|---|---|---|---|---|---|---|---|---|---|---|
| 100 | 00 0000 | 00 0434 | 00 0868 | 00 1301 | 00 1734 | 00 2166 | 00 2598 | 00 3029 | 00 3461 | 00 3891 | 432 |
| 101 | 4321 | 4751 | 5181 | 5609 | 6038 | 6466 | 6894 | 7321 | 7748 | 8174 | 428 |
| 102 | 8600 | 9026 | 9451 | 9876 | 01 0300 | 01 0724 | 01 1147 | 01 1570 | 01 1993 | 01 2415 | 424 |
| 103 | 01 2837 | 01 3259 | 01 3680 | 01 4100 | 4521 | 4940 | 5360 | 5779 | 6197 | 6616 | 420 |
| 104 | 7033 | 7451 | 7868 | 8284 | 8700 | 9116 | 9532 | 9947 | 02 0361 | 02 0775 | 416 |
| 105 | 02 1189 | 02 1603 | 02 2016 | 02 2428 | 02 2841 | 02 3252 | 02 3664 | 02 4075 | 4486 | 4896 | 412 |
| 106 | 5306 | 5715 | 6125 | 6533 | 6942 | 7350 | 7757 | 8164 | 8571 | 8978 | 408 |
| 107 | 9384 | 9789 | 03 0195 | 03 0600 | 03 1004 | 03 1408 | 03 1812 | 03 2216 | 03 2619 | 03 3021 | 404 |
| 108 | 03 3424 | 03 3826 | 4227 | 4628 | 5029 | 5430 | 5830 | 6230 | 6629 | 7028 | 400 |
| 109 | 7426 | 7825 | 8223 | 8620 | 9017 | 9414 | 9811 | 04 0207 | 04 0602 | 04 0998 | 397 |
| 110 | 04 1393 | 04 1787 | 04 2182 | 04 2576 | 04 2969 | 04 3362 | 04 3755 | 4148 | 4540 | 4932 | 393 |
| 111 | 5323 | 5714 | 6105 | 6495 | 6885 | 7275 | 7664 | 8053 | 8442 | 8830 | 390 |
| 112 | 9218 | 9606 | 9993 | 05 0380 | 05 0766 | 05 1153 | 05 1538 | 05 1924 | 05 2309 | 05 2694 | 386 |
| 113 | 05 3078 | 05 3463 | 05 3846 | 4230 | 4613 | 4996 | 5378 | 5760 | 6142 | 6524 | 383 |
| 114 | 6905 | 7286 | 7666 | 8046 | 8426 | 8805 | 9185 | 9563 | 9942 | 06 0320 | 379 |
| 115 | 06 0698 | 06 1075 | 06 1452 | 06 1829 | 06 2206 | 06 2582 | 06 2958 | 06 3333 | 06 3709 | 4083 | 376 |
| 116 | 4458 | 4832 | 5206 | 5580 | 5953 | 6326 | 6699 | 7071 | 7443 | 7815 | 373 |
| 117 | 8186 | 8557 | 8928 | 9298 | 9668 | 07 0038 | 07 0407 | 07 0776 | 07 1145 | 07 1514 | 370 |
| 118 | 07 1882 | 07 2250 | 07 2617 | 07 2985 | 07 3352 | 3718 | 4085 | 4451 | 4816 | 5182 | 366 |
| 119 | 5547 | 5912 | 6276 | 6640 | 7004 | 7368 | 7731 | 8094 | 8457 | 8819 | 363 |
| 120 | 9182 | 9543 | 9904 | 08 0266 | 08 0626 | 08 0987 | 08 1347 | 08 1707 | 08 2067 | 08 2426 | 360 |

Proportional Parts

| n\d | 435 | 420 | 425 | 420 |
|---|---|---|---|---|
| 1 | 44 | 43 | 43 | 42 |
| 2 | 87 | 86 | 85 | 84 |
| 3 | 131 | 129 | 128 | 126 |
| 4 | 174 | 172 | 170 | 168 |
| 5 | 218 | 215 | 213 | 210 |
| 6 | 261 | 258 | 255 | 252 |
| 7 | 305 | 301 | 298 | 294 |
| 8 | 348 | 344 | 340 | 336 |
| 9 | 392 | 387 | 383 | 378 |

| n\d | 415 | 410 | 405 | 400 |
|---|---|---|---|---|
| 1 | 42 | 41 | 41 | 40 |
| 2 | 83 | 82 | 81 | 80 |
| 3 | 125 | 123 | 122 | 120 |
| 4 | 166 | 164 | 162 | 160 |
| 5 | 208 | 205 | 203 | 200 |
| 6 | 249 | 246 | 243 | 240 |
| 7 | 291 | 287 | 284 | 280 |
| 8 | 332 | 328 | 324 | 320 |
| 9 | 374 | 369 | 365 | 360 |

| n d | 395 | 390 | 385 | 380 |
|---|---|---|---|---|
| 1 | 40 | 39 | 39 | 38 |
| 2 | 79 | 78 | 77 | 76 |
| 3 | 119 | 117 | 116 | 114 |
| 4 | 158 | 156 | 154 | 152 |
| 5 | 198 | 195 | 193 | 190 |
| 6 | 237 | 234 | 231 | 228 |
| 7 | 277 | 273 | 270 | 266 |
| 8 | 316 | 312 | 308 | 304 |
| 9 | 356 | 351 | 347 | 342 |

first digit. The first two digits are sometimes omitted. If only four digits are shown, find the first two digits by looking up the same column until a six-digit mantissa appears.

The numbers across the top of the table permit us to get the mantissas for four-digit numbers. To find the mantissa for 1.176 (or 11.76, 117,600, .001176, or any other number derived from 1176 by multiplying or dividing by a power of 10) we proceed as shown on page 420.

Since 1.176 is between 1 and 10, its log will consist only of the decimal part or mantissa. Therefore, log 1.176 = .070407. The mantissas for other numbers with the same sequence of significant digits, such as 11,760,000 and .001176, would also be .070407, but there would be a nonzero characteristic to be determined as follows.

**Getting the Characteristic.** Put your pencil behind the first nonzero digit from the left. Count the number of places to the decimal point. The characteristic is positive if you move to the right. It is negative if you move to the left. Note that this is the system used to find the exponent of 10 when a number is put in scientific notation.

Always start here

738.6

738.6   Count places to the decimal point.

EXAMPLE 1: If the decimal point is behind the first nonzero digit, the characteristic is 0. Any number that is 1 or more but less than 10 will have a characteristic of 0.

3.67

Decimal point is behind the first digit.
Pencil is not moved. Characteristic is 0.

EXAMPLE 2: If the number is 10 or more, the pencil will be moved to the right and the characteristic is +.

738.6

Two places to the right.
Characteristic is 2.

EXAMPLE 3: If no decimal point is shown, it is understood to be behind the last digit.

86,600,000

Seven places to the right.
Characteristic is 7.

EXAMPLE 4: If the number is less than 1, the pencil will be moved to the left and the characteristic is −.

.000426

Four places to the left. Characteristic is −4. Negative characteristics should be written to the right of the mantissa, since the mantissa from the table is positive. This may be done in various ways, depending on the problem. Some of the ways in which log .000426 could be written are

$$\log .000426 = \begin{cases} .629410 - 4 \\ 6.629410 - 10 \\ 56.629410 - 60 \end{cases}$$

Note that in all of these the *net* value of the characteristic is −4.

**Finding the Antilogarithm.** To find the number corresponding to a logarithm, we go into the body of the table to find the mantissa and then write down the sequence of digits corresponding to this mantissa. To locate the decimal point in the answer, put the pencil behind the first nonzero digit from the left and move it one place to the right for each unit in the characteristic if it is positive, and one place to the left for each unit in the characteristic if it is negative. The final result is the antilogarithm or antilog.

EXAMPLE 1: If log $N = 3.170262$, find $N$.

SOLUTION: The sequence of digits corresponding to a mantissa of .170262 is 148. We put the pencil behind the 1 and count three places to the right, making the answer 1480.

EXAMPLE 2: If log $N = .554731 - 2$ or $8.554731 - 10$, find $N$.

SOLUTION: The sequence of digits corresponding to a mantissa of .554731 is 3587. We put the pencil behind the 3 and count two places to the left, making the answer .03587.

*Interpolated Values*

To get the mantissa of a number which has more significant figures than the table we are using, we interpolate between the two closest tabular values. *Interpolation* means reading between the lines of a table of data and is done frequently in mathematics of finance and other business applications of mathematics.

EXAMPLE 1: Find the log of 2246.3.

SOLUTION: We find the mantissas for the numbers immediately preceding and following 22463 and arrange in tabular form, omitting decimal points:

| NUMBER | MANTISSA |
|--------|----------|
| 22470 | 351603 |
| 22463 | 351410 + d |
| 22460 | 351410 |

10 ⌈ 3 ⌊ ... | 193 ... d

Since 22463 is $\frac{3}{10}$ of the way from 22460 to 22470, the mantissa will be $\frac{3}{10}$ of the way from 351410 to 351603. Letting $d$ represent the unknown difference, we set the two ratios equal to each other. This equality of ratios, or proportion, is solved like any fractional equation.

$$\frac{d}{193} = \frac{3}{10}$$

$$d = \frac{3(193)}{10} = .3(193) = 57.9; \text{ correct to 2 digits, 58.}$$

Therefore the mantissa of 22463 is $351410 + 58 = 351468$. Since the characteristic is 3, log $2246.3 = 3.351468$.

When using Table 7, numbers with more than 5 significant digits should be rounded to 5 before getting the mantissa.

Interpolation is also used to find antilogs.

EXAMPLE 2: Find $N$ if log $N = 8.681650 - 10$.

SOLUTION: We record the numbers corresponding to the mantissas on both sides of .681650.

| NUMBER | MANTISSA |
|--------|----------|
| 48050 | 681693 |
| 48040 + d | 681650 |
| 48040 | 681603 |

10 ⌈ d ⌊ ... | 90 ... 47

$$\frac{d}{10} = \frac{47}{90}; \quad d = \frac{10(47)}{90} = 5, \text{ correct to one digit.}$$

The sequence of digits in the answer is $48040 + 5 = 48045$. Since the characteristic is $-2$, $N = .048045$.

The preceding examples show in detail the basic method of interpolation that is applicable not only to log tables but also to compound interest and other tables used in business. Interpolation with logs can be simplified by using two features of the tables in this book. The difference between successive mantissas can be obtained from the $D$ column. The tenths of a difference can be obtained from the Proportional Parts Tables, where $n\backslash d$ indicates tenths. From the table below, we see that the difference between mantissas in the 450 row is 96. In the Proportional Parts Table, we see that $\frac{1}{10}$ of 96 is 9.6, $\frac{7}{10}$ is 67.2, and so on.

Six-Place Logarithms of Numbers 450-500      Proportional Parts

| N | 0 | 1 | 2 | 3 | 4 | 5 | 6 | 7 | 8 | 9 | D |
|---|---|---|---|---|---|---|---|---|---|---|---|
| 450 | 65 3213 | 65 3309 | 65 3405 | 65 3502 | 65 3598 | 65 3695 | 65 3791 | 65 3888 | 65 3984 | 65 4080 | 96 |
| 451 | 4177 | 4273 | 4369 | 4465 | 4562 | 4658 | 4754 | 4850 | 4946 | 5042 | 96 |
| 452 | 5138 | 5235 | 5331 | 5427 | 5523 | 5619 | 5715 | 5810 | 5906 | 6002 | 96 |
| 453 | 6098 | 6194 | 6290 | 6386 | 6482 | 6577 | 6673 | 6769 | 6864 | 6960 | 96 |
| 454 | 7056 | 7152 | 7247 | 7343 | 7438 | 7534 | 7629 | 7725 | 7820 | 7916 | 96 |
| 455 | 8011 | 8107 | 8202 | 8298 | 8393 | 8488 | 8584 | 8679 | 8774 | 8870 | 95 |
| 456 | 8965 | 9060 | 9155 | 9250 | 9346 | 9441 | 9536 | 9631 | 9726 | 9821 | 95 |
| 457 | 9916 | 66 0011 | 66 0106 | 66 0201 | 66 0296 | 66 0391 | 66 0486 | 66 0581 | 66 0676 | 66 0771 | 95 |
| 458 | 66 0865 | 0960 | 1055 | 1150 | 1245 | 1339 | 1434 | 1529 | 1623 | 1718 | 95 |
| 459 | 1813 | 1907 | 2002 | 2096 | 2191 | 2286 | 2380 | 2475 | 2569 | 2663 | 95 |
| 460 | 2758 | 2852 | 2947 | 3041 | 3135 | 3230 | 3324 | 3418 | 3512 | 3607 | 94 |

| n\d | 97 | 96 |
|---|---|---|
| 1 | 9.7 | 9.6 |
| 2 | 19.4 | 19.2 |
| 3 | 29.1 | 28.8 |
| 4 | 38.8 | 38.4 |
| 5 | 48.5 | 48.0 |
| 6 | 58.2 | 57.6 |
| 7 | 67.9 | 67.2 |
| 8 | 77.6 | 76.8 |
| 9 | 87.3 | 86.4 |

| n\d | 95 | 94 |
|---|---|---|
| 1 | 9.5 | 9.4 |
| 2 | 19.0 | 18.8 |
| 3 | 28.5 | 28.2 |

EXAMPLE 3: Find the log of 450.68.

SOLUTION: The sequence of digits 45068 lies $\frac{8}{10}$ of the way between the tabular values 45060 and 45070. To get the mantissa for 45068 we
1. Find the mantissa for 45060      653791
2. Note that the difference, $D$, is 96
3. Find $\frac{8}{10}$ of 96 under the Proportional Parts and round off      77
4. Add to get the interpolated mantissa      653868
5. Adding the characteristic, log 450.68 = 2.653868.

EXAMPLE 4: Find the antilog of 1.653440.

SOLUTION: To find an antilog, the steps are
1. Find the sequence of digits corresponding to 653405, the mantissa immediately smaller than 653440      45020
2. Subtract to find the difference between mantissas, in this case:
   653440 − 653405 = 35
3. Under Proportional Parts for a $D$ of 96, find the value closest to 35. This is 38.5, which corresponds to $\frac{4}{10}$ in the $n\backslash d$ column      4
4. Add to get the interpolated sequence of digits      45024
5. Point off to get: antilog 1.653440 = 45.024.

With these tables and practice, much of the work involved in interpolation can be done mentally.

For the smaller numbers in a log table, the difference between mantissas in a line is not constant, so the $D$ column gives an average value. This is sufficiently accurate for most practical purposes for the entire line. Also, space does not permit all the $D$'s to be shown under Proportional Parts. If a particular $D$ such as 412 is not included, a close result can be obtained by interpolating mentally between the values for 410 and 415.

### Computations with Logs

Each of the laws of exponents can be applied to problems worked by logarithms. The following types of problems are those met most frequently.

**Products and Quotients.** By the multiplication law for exponents, $a^m \cdot a^n = a^{m+n}$, we are able to multiply numbers by adding their logs, since logs are exponents.

To save time when working with logs, set up the problem before going to the tables. This is illustrated in the first example. In subsequent problems in the text, only the final step is shown.

EXAMPLE 1: Evaluate by logs: $386 \times 71.92$.

| SKELETON SOLUTION WITH REQUIRED LOGS AND STEPS INDICATED | SKELETON SOLUTION FILLED IN WITH ONE REFERENCE TO LOG TABLES |
|---|---|
| $\log 386 = 2.$ | $\log 386 = 2.586587$ |
| $\log 71.92 = 1.$ | $\log 71.92 = 1.856850$ |
| Adding, $\log N =$ | Adding, $\log N = 4.443437$ |
| | $N = 27,761$ |

Note that this is not an exact answer because we can interpolate to only one digit beyond the four given in the table. Interpolation can be omitted if the answer is needed to only 3 or 4 significant figures.

By the division law for exponents, $a^m/a^n = a^{m-n}$, we are able to divide numbers by subtracting the log of the denominator from the log of the numerator.

EXAMPLE 2: Evaluate by logs: $\dfrac{79.6}{28.3}$

SOLUTION:   $\log 79.6 = 1.900913$
$\log 28.3 = 1.451786$
Subtracting, $\log N = .449127$
$N = 2.8127$

Since log tables contain only positive mantissas, it is sometimes necessary to change the form of a log, without changing the numerical value, so that negative mantissas will not appear.

EXAMPLE 3: Evaluate by logs: $\dfrac{3.3}{188}$

SOLUTION: To avoid getting a negative mantissa, we add 10 to the log of 3.3 and then offset this addition by subtracting 10.

$$\log 3.3 = 10.518514 - 10$$
$$\log 188 = \phantom{10.}2.274158$$
$$\text{Subtracting, } \log N = \phantom{1}8.244356 - 10$$
$$N = \phantom{10.}.017553$$

**Powers and Roots.** By the power of a power law for exponents, $(a^m)^n = a^{mn}$. Using this law, we raise a number to a power by multiplying the log of the number by the power.

EXAMPLE 4: Evaluate $(1.095)^{20}$.

SOLUTION: Since $\log 1.095 = .039414$, this problem can be written: $(1.095)^{20} = (10^{.039414})^{20} = 10^{.788280}$. In practice, all we do is multiply the log of the quantity by the exponent, as follows:

Let $N = (1.095)^{20}$. Then $\log N = 20 \log 1.095 = 20(.039414) = .788280$

$$N = 6.1416$$

EXAMPLE 5: Evaluate $\sqrt{18}$ by logs.

SOLUTION: $\quad N = \sqrt{18} = 18^{1/2}$
$$\log N = \tfrac{1}{2} \log 18 = \tfrac{1}{2}(1.255273) = .627637$$
$$N = 4.2426$$

The characteristic must be a whole number. In raising a number to a fractional power, it may be necessary to change the form of a log to avoid a fractional characteristic. In changing the form of a log we must

1. Keep the numerical value unchanged.
2. Finish with a positive mantissa.
3. Finish with a characteristic that is a whole number.

EXAMPLE: Find $(.882)^{1/4}$

SOLUTION: $\quad N = (.882)^{1/4}$
$\quad\quad \log N = \tfrac{1}{4}(\log .882) = \tfrac{1}{4}(.945469 - 1)$. To avoid a fractional characteristic, we rewrite this as $\tfrac{1}{4}(39.945469 - 40) = 9.986367 - 10$

$$N = .9691$$

Negative exponents should be handled as follows:

EXAMPLE 6: Evaluate $(1.05)^{-20}$ by logs.

SOLUTION: Write $(1.05)^{-20}$ as $1/(1.05)^{20}$

$$\begin{array}{rl} \log 1 = & 10.000000 - 10 \\ 20 \log (1.05) = 20(.021189) = & .423780 \\ \text{Subtracting,} \qquad \log N = & 9.576220 - 10 \\ N = & .37690 \end{array}$$

Practical problems often require two or more of the basic operations.

EXAMPLE 7: Evaluate $2500(1.085)^{-5}$.

SOLUTION: The multiplication and raising to a power can be done in a single series of operations as follows:

$$\begin{array}{rl} \log 2500 = & 3.397940 \\ -5 \log 1.085 = -5(.035430) = - & .177150 \\ \log N = & 3.220790 \\ N = & 1662.6 \end{array}$$

## Solving for Bases and Exponents

Logarithms can be used to solve compound interest and other types of problems where a constant rate of change is involved.

EXAMPLE 1: The following equation comes from a compound interest problem. Determine $i$, which represents the interest rate.

$$625(1 + i)^{10} = 3530$$

SOLUTION: We must first solve for the quantity $(1 + i)$.

| *Operation* | *Computations* |
|---|---|
| Divide both sides by 625 | $(1 + i)^{10} = \dfrac{3530}{625}$ |
| Take the logarithm of both sides | $10 \log (1 + i) = \log 3530 - \log 625$ |
| Look up the required logs and divide both sides by 10 | $\log (1 + i) = \dfrac{3.547775 - 2.795880}{10}$ |
| Do the indicated arithmetic | $\log (1 + i) = \dfrac{.751895}{10}$ or .075190 |
| Look up the antilog of .075190 | $(1 + i) = 1.189$ |
| Now we can isolate $i$ by subtracting 1 from both sides | $i = 1.189 - 1 = .189$ |
| Convert $i$ to a per cent if required | $i = 18.9\%$ |

EXAMPLE 2: Over a 6-year period, an investment depreciated in value from $32,000 to $23,500. Determine $r$, the annual compounded rate of depreciation.

SOLUTION: We substitute in (9) replacing $i$ with $-r$.

$$32,000(1 - r)^6 = 23,500$$

As in the preceding example, we first solve for the quantity $(1 - r)$.

| Operation | Computations |
|---|---|
| Divide by 32,000 | $(1 - r)^6 = \dfrac{23,500}{32,000}$ |
| Take the logarithm of both sides. | $6 \log (1 - r) = \log 23,500 - \log 32,000$ |
| Look up the logs and divide both sides by 6. | $\log (1 - r) = \dfrac{4.371068 - 4.505150}{6}$ |
| To avoid getting a negative mantissa in the numerator when we subtract, we add 10 to 4.371068 and subtract 10 from the resulting 14.371068. This changes the form of the first term without changing its value. | $\log (1 - r) = \dfrac{(14.371068 - 10) - 4.505150}{6}$ $= \dfrac{9.865918 - 10}{6}$ |
| To avoid getting a fractional characteristic, we must change the $-10$ to a number divisible by 6. An easy way to do this is to subtract 50 from the $-10$, making it $-60$ and then add 50 to the first part of the log so that its value remains the same. | $\log (1 - r) = \dfrac{59.865918 - 60}{6}$ $= 9.977653 - 10$ |
| Solve for the quantity $(1 - r)$ by finding the antilog of $9.977653 - 10$. | $(1 - r) = .94985$ |
| Solve for $r$. | $r = 1 - .94985 = .05015$ $= $ approximately $5\%$ |

In practice, some of the operations described in detail can be combined as shown in the following example.

EXAMPLE 3: Solve for $r$:

$$15,600(1 - r)^{15} = 1500$$

SOLUTION:

$$(1 - r)^{15} = 1500/15,600$$

$$15 \log (1 - r) = \log 1500 - \log 15,600$$

$$\log (1 - r) = \frac{3.176091 - 4.193125}{15}$$

By adding 150 to the first term and then subtracting 150, we can do the subtraction and division with one change in the form of the logs.

$$\log (1 - r) = \frac{(153.176091 - 150) - 4.193125}{15}$$

$$= \frac{148.982966 - 150}{15}$$

$$= 9.932198 - 10$$

Solve for the quantity $(1 - r)$ by finding the antilog of $9.932198 - 10$.

$$1 - r = .8555$$

Solve for $r$.

$$r = .1445 \text{ or } 14.45\%$$

The following examples show how logarithms can be used to solve for the exponent in rate-of-change problems.

EXAMPLE 4: Solve for $n$:

$$380(1.07)^n = 1100$$

SOLUTION:

| *Operation* | *Computations* |
|---|---|
| Divide both sides by 380. | $(1.07)^n = \dfrac{1100}{380}$ |
| Take the logarithm of both sides. | $n \log (1.07) = \log 1100 - \log 380$ |
| Divide both sides by log (1.07). | $n = \dfrac{\log 1100 - \log 380}{\log (1.07)}$ |
| Look up the logs and do the subtraction in the numerator. We now have a problem in division which, like any such problem, can be done by arithmetic or by logs. If we use arithmetic, we have: | $n = \dfrac{3.041393 - 2.579784}{.029384}$ |
| | $n = \dfrac{.461609}{.029384} = 15.71$ |

If we use logs, we take the log of both sides of the new equation getting:

$$\log n = \log .461609 - \log .029384$$

Arrange the problem for ease of computation and round numbers to five significant figures before getting the logs.

$$\log .46161 = 9.664275 - 10$$
$$\log .029384 = 8.468111 - 10$$

Subtracting,    $\log n = 1.196164$

Look up the antilog of 1.196164.    $n = 15.71$

In many practical problems the exponent needs to be determined to only 3 significant figures. The long division can be done rapidly with a slide rule.

EXAMPLE 5: Find $n$ to 3 significant figures.

$$6500(1.12)^n = 2000$$

SOLUTION:

| *Operation* | *Computations* |
|---|---|
| Divide both sides by 6500. | $(1.12)^n = \dfrac{2000}{6500}$ |
| Take the logarithms of both sides. and solve for $n$. | $n = \dfrac{\log 2000 - \log 6500}{\log (1.12)}$ |
| | $= \dfrac{3.301030 - 3.832509}{.049218}$ |
| To slide rule accuracy. | $n = \dfrac{-.531479}{.049218} = -10.8$ |

EXAMPLE 6: Solve for $n$.    $7380(1 - .25)^n = 1000$

SOLUTION:

| *Operation* | *Computations* |
|---|---|
| Rewrite the problem in a form suitable for taking logarithms. | $(.75)^n = \dfrac{1000}{7380}$ |
| Take the logarithms of both sides and solve for $n$. | $n = \dfrac{\log 1000 - \log 7380}{\log .75}$ |
| | $= \dfrac{3.000000 - 3.868056}{.875061 - 1}$ |
| | $= \dfrac{-.868056}{-.124939}$ |
| | $= 6.95$ |

Note that in the last three examples $n$ is simply a number, not a logarithm. This means that we do the indicated arithmetic on the right of the equal sign without having to be concerned about negative decimals and other details of form which are important when we are solving for the logarithm of the unknown.

## Problems

Find the logarithm of each number.

| | |
|---|---|
| **1.** 8654 | (3.937217) |
| **2.** .0004057 | (6.608205 − 10) |
| **3.** 87 million | (7.939519) |
| **4.** 400.86 | (2.602993) |
| **5.** 53,278 | (4.726549) |
| **6.** .0038765 | (7.588440 − 10) |

Find the numbers corresponding to the following logarithms.

| | |
|---|---|
| **7.** 9.905850 − 10 | (.8051) |
| **8.** 2.286905 | (193.6) |
| **9.** 6.700704 − 10 | (.0005020) |
| **10.** 4.324950 | (21,132) |
| **11.** 2.407148 | (255.36) |
| **12.** 9.845700 − 10 | (.70097) |

Evaluate by logarithms.

| | |
|---|---|
| **13.** $1578.2 \times .8675$ | (1369.1) |
| **14.** $851/47.9$ | (17.766) |
| **15.** $(3.89)^5$ | (890.74) |
| **16.** $(.376)^{.25}$ | (.78306) |
| **17.** $(1.005)^{100}$ | (1.6466) |
| **18.** $(1.04)^{-10}$ | (.67557) |

Solve for the unknown.

| | |
|---|---|
| **19.** $650(1 + i)^{10} = 2430$ | (14.1%) |
| **20.** $88.2(1 + i)^3 = 420.6$ | (68.32%) |
| **21.** $7830.50(1 - r)^5 = 1000$ | (33.74%) |
| **22.** $15,500(1 - r)^{20} = 2500$ | (8.72%) |
| **23.** $(26.2)^x = 1650$ | (2.2685) |
| **24.** $50,000(1.10)^n = 100,000$ | (7.2725) |
| **25.** $47,255(1.095)^n = 130,000$ | (11.151) |
| **26.** $5000(1.08)^n = 2100$ | (−11.272) |

## III. Computer Programs

The advantages of electronic computers are great speed and high accuracy. Before a problem can be solved on a computer, skilled specialists must prepare a program or set of instructions for the machine. This program must be absolutely complete and specific with no details omitted. It usually pays to develop and check a program only if it will be used many times.

Computers are particularly helpful in solving problems that require repeated line-by-line computations and problems that must be solved by an iterative or trial and error process. Amortization schedules and interest tables for non-tabulated rates are examples of the first application. Getting the yield rate on a bond is an example of an application using iteration.

The following pages contain programs prepared by the staff of the Xavier University Computer Center under Mr. John F. Niehaus, Director. The programs are written in Basic Fortran IV with output on the high speed printer. Students can solve practical problems using these programs or a modification of them to utilize local computer facilities and forms of output.

### Program for Amortization Schedule

The following program produces an amortization schedule for two cases. The first uses the balance, rate, payment, and number of conversions per year as input and produces the appropriate schedule. The second uses the balance, rate, number of conversions per year, and the duration and produces a schedule. The program adjusts the size of the last payment to exactly amortize the debt.

```
C THIS PROGRAM PRODUCES AN AMORTIZATION SCHEDULE FOR THE FOLLOWING
C TWO CASES*************
C INPUT BALANCE,RATE,PAYMENT, AND NUMBER OF CONVERSIONS PER YEAR
C INPUT BALANCE,RATE,CONVERSIONS PER YEAR, AND DURATION
      DIMENSION ANAME(20)
      DOUBLE PRECISION PMT,PEROD,XINT,BAL,DUR,RATE,PRIN,ARATE,BRATE
  900 READ (1,1025)  ANAME
      WRITE (3,1026) ANAME
C
C  READ BALANCE, RATE, PAYMENT, AND NUMBER OF PERIODS PER YEAR, DURATION OF LOAN
C
   50 READ (1,101)   BAL, ARATE, PMT, PEROD, DUR
      NPEROD=PEROD
      LCNT=0.0
      IF(BAL) 999, 900, 901
C
C  FIND PERIODIC INTREST RATE
C
  901 RATE=ARATE/PEROD
      IF(PMT) 500,500,902
C
C  CONVERT DECIMAL RATE TO PERCENTAGE RATE
C
```

```
  500 NUMPAY=PEROD*DUR
      PMT=BAL*(RATE/(1.-1./((1.+RATE)**NUMPAY)))
      KPMT=(PMT*100.)+.999999999999
      PMT=KPMT
      PMT=PMT/100.
  902 BRATE = ARATE*100.
C
C   PRINT TITLE INFORMATION
C
      WRITE (3,103) BAL,BRATE,NPEROD
      WRITE (3,107) PMT
      WRITE (3,104)
      WRITE (3,108) BAL
C
C   SET COUNTER FOR PAYMENT NUMBER
C
      N = 0
    2 N = N+1
C
C   COMPUTE INTEREST AS PERIODIC RATE X BALANCE
C
      XINT = RATE*BAL
C
C   ROUND INTEREST UP
C
      INT = (XINT + .005)*100.
      XINT = INT
      XINT = XINT/100.
C
C COMPUTE AMOUNT TO PRINCIPAL
C
      PRIN = PMT-XINT
C
C   CHECK AMOUNT TO PRINCIPAL--IF NEGATIVE OR ZERO, PAYMENT IS TOO SMALL
C
      IF (PRIN) 3,3,4
C
C   INFORM OF TOO SMALL PAYMENT
C
    3 WRITE (3,106)
C
C   READ ANOTHER CASE
C
      GO TO 50
C
C   COMPUTE CURRENT BALANCE AS PREVIOUS BALANCE MINUS AMOUNT TO PRINCIPAL
C.
    4 BAL = BAL-PRIN
C
C   CHECK BALANCE--IF NEGATIVE OR ZERO, LAST PAYMENT HAS BEEN REACHED
C
      KBAL=BAL*100.
      IF(KBAL)5,5,6
C
C   OUTPUT PAYMENT NUMBER, AMOUNT OF PAYMENT TO INTEREST, AMOUNT TO PRINCIPAL
C   AND BALANCE DUE
C
    6 WRITE (3,102) N,XINT,PRIN,BAL
      LCNT=LCNT+1
      IF(LCNT-42)2,700,700
  700 WRITE(3,110)
      LCNT=0
C
C   TRANSFER TO COMPUTE NEXT PAYMENT
C
      GO TO 2
C
C   LAST PAYMENT COMPUTATION
C
```

```
   5 PRIN = PRIN + BAL
     BAL = 0.00
     WRITE (3,102) N,XINT,PRIN,BAL
     WRITE (3,105)
C
C   TRANSFER TO COMPUTE NEXT SCHEDULE
C
     GO TO 50
 999 CALL EXIT
 110 FORMAT(1H1)
 101 FORMAT(2F20.0, 3F10.0)
 102 FORMAT (1H ,15X,I4,7X,F10.2,5X,F10.2,4X,F10.2)
 103 FORMAT (1H ,29X,21HAMORTIZATION SCHEDULE/1H0,25X,F10.2,17H = AMOUN
    1T OF LOAN ,/1H0,9X,F9.4,35H PERCENT YEARLY INTEREST CONVERTED ,I2,
    216H TIMES EACH YEAR )
 104 FORMAT (1H0,15X,7HPAYMENT,12X,10HPAYMENT TO,14X,7HBALANCE/1H ,15X
    1,6HNUMBER,7X,8HINTEREST,6X,9HPRINCIPAL,7X,7HOF LOAN/1H )
 105 FORMAT (1H1)
 106 FORMAT (21H0PAYMENT IS TOO SMALL /1H1)
 107 FORMAT (1H0,25X,F10.2,19H = PERIODIC PAYMENT)
 108 FORMAT (1H ,55X,F10.2)
1025 FORMAT(20A4)
1026 FORMAT(1H1/20A4)
     END
```

EXAMPLE: A debt of $1200 is to be amortized in 12 monthly payments. The interest rate is 12% converted monthly. Prepare an amortization schedule.

SOLUTION:

AMORTIZATION SCHEDULE

1200.00 = AMOUNT OF LOAN

12.0000 PERCENT YEARLY INTEREST CONVERTED 12 TIMES EACH YEAR

106.62 = PERIODIC PAYMENT

| PAYMENT NUMBER | PAYMENT TO INTEREST | PAYMENT TO PRINCIPAL | BALANCE OF LOAN |
|---|---|---|---|
| | | | 1200.00 |
| 1 | 12.00 | 94.62 | 1105.38 |
| 2 | 11.05 | 95.57 | 1009.81 |
| 3 | 10.10 | 96.52 | 913.29 |
| 4 | 9.13 | 97.49 | 815.80 |
| 5 | 8.16 | 98.46 | 717.34 |
| 6 | 7.17 | 99.45 | 617.89 |
| 7 | 6.18 | 100.44 | 517.45 |
| 8 | 5.17 | 101.45 | 416.00 |
| 9 | 4.16 | 102.46 | 313.54 |
| 10 | 3.14 | 103.48 | 210.06 |
| 11 | 2.10 | 104.52 | 105.54 |
| 12 | 1.06 | 105.54 | 0.0 |

## Program for Compound Interest Tables

This program will produce a compound interest and annuity table for a range of rates and periods. This is a useful program when a rate is not included in available tables. *The Amount of* 1, the *Amount of* 1 *per Period*, and the *Present*

*Worth of* 1 *per Period*, are given in modified scientific notation due to the range which these numbers can span. The number following the D is the power to which 10 is raised. For example, D 02 is equivalent to $10^2$. A computer entry of .1862625392D 02 equals 18.62625392 in conventional notation. As input, this program uses a starting rate, an ending rate, a rate increment, a starting period, an ending period, and a period increment.

```
C THIS PROGRAM WILL COMPUTE COMPOUND INTREST AND ANNUITY TABLES
C
C FOR A RANGE OF RATES AND A RANGE OF PERIODS.
C
      DIMENSION NYEAR(49),ANAME(20)
      DOUBLE PRECISION ANS(49,6),RTHIGH,RTSTRT,RTSTOP,A,ANMULT,RTINK,B
  100 READ (1,1025)  ANAME
      WRITE (3,1026)  ANAME
C
C INPUT STARTING RATE, ENDING RATE, RATE INCREMENT, STARTING PERIOD
C
C ENDING PERIOD, AND PERIOD INCREMENT
C
    2 READ (1,1000)  RTSTRT, RTSTOP, RTINK, NSTRT, NSTOP, NINK
      IF(RTSTRT)999,999,600
  600 IF(RTINK)601,601,602
  601 RTINK=1.
  602 IF(NINK)603,603,3
  603 NINK=1
    3 A=NSTOP-NSTRT+NINK
      B=NINK*48
      NUMPGE=(A/B)+.999999999999
      RTHIGH=RTSTRT-RTINK
      M=48
    5 RTHIGH=RTHIGH+RTINK
      ANMULT=(1.+RTHIGH)**NINK
      DO 8 J=1, NUMPGE
      DO 4 I=1, M
      NYEAR(I)=0
      DO 4 K=1, 6
    4 ANS(I, K)=0.
      IF(NSTRT) 27, 27, 28
   27 ANS(1, 1)=1.
      GO TO 29
   28 ANS(1, 1)=(1.+RTHIGH)**((48*(J-1)*NINK)+NSTRT)
   29 ANS(1, 2)=(ANS(1, 1)-1.)/RTHIGH
      IF(ANS(1, 2)) 32, 32, 31
   32 ANS(1, 3)=99.9999999999
      GO TO 33
   31 ANS(1, 3)=1./ANS(1, 2)
   33 ANS(1, 4)=1./ANS(1, 1)
      ANS(1, 5)=(1.-ANS(1, 4))/RTHIGH
      IF(ANS(1, 5)) 35, 35, 34
   35 ANS(1, 6)=99.9999999999
      GO TO 36
   34 ANS(1, 6)=1./ANS(1, 5)
   36 DO 11 M=1, 48
      NYEAR(M)=(NSTRT-NINK)+(48*NINK*(J-1))+(M*NINK)
      IF(NSTOP-NYEAR(M)-NINK+1) 12, 12, 11
   11 CONTINUE
      M=48
   12 DO 13 N=2, M
      ANS(N, 1)=ANS(N-1, 1)*ANMULT
      ANS(N, 2)=(ANS(N, 1)-1.)/RTHIGH
      ANS(N, 3)=1./ANS(N, 2)
      ANS(N, 4)=1./ANS(N, 1)
      ANS(N, 5)=(1.-ANS(N, 4))/RTHIGH
   13 ANS(N, 6)=1./ANS(N, 5)
      WRITE (3,1001)  RTHIGH
```

```
      WRITE (3,1007)
      DO 20 L=1, M
   20 WRITE (3,1002) NYEAR(L), (ANS(L, KK), KK=1, 6)
      WRITE (3,1003)
    8 CONTINUE
      IF(RTSTOP-RTHIGH-RTINK+.000000000001) 2, 2, 5
 1000 FORMAT(2F20.0,F10.0,3I10)
 1001 FORMAT(43X36HCOMPOUND INTEREST AND ANNUITY TABLES/4X2HI=, F15.10/4
     1X115H----------------------------------------------------------
     2--------------------------------------------------------/4X8HIPERIOD
     3I, 5X11HAMOUNT OF 1,4X1HI, 6X9HAMOUNT OF, 5X50HI  SINKING FUND I P
     4RESENT WORTH I  PRESENT WORTH I,4X7HPARTIAL, 4X1HI)
 1002 FORMAT(4X1HI, I5, 2H I, 2(E19.10, 2H I), 2(F14.10, 2H I), E15.10,
     12H I, F14.10, 2H I)
 1003 FORMAT(4X115H--------------------------------------------------
     1---------------------------------------------------------/1H1
     2)
 1007 FORMAT(4X1HI,6X1HI,20X1HI,4X12H1 PER PERIOD,4X1HI,15X1HI,6X4HOF 1,
     115X18HIOF 1 PER PERIOD I,4X7HPAYMENT, 4X1HI/4X115H-----------------
     2-----------------------------------------------------------------
     3-----------------------------)
 1026 FORMAT(1H1,20A4)
 1025 FORMAT(20A4)
  999 CALL EXIT
      END
```

EXAMPLE:  Produce a compound interest and annuity table for .6875%.

SOLUTION:

COMPOUND INTEREST TABLE FOR .6875% FOR TWENTY PERIODS
COMPOUND INTEREST AND ANNUITY TABLES

I = 0.0068750000

| PERIOD | AMOUNT OF 1 | AMOUNT OF 1 PER PERIOD | SINKING FUND | PRESENT WORTH OF 1 | PRESENT WORTH OF 1 PER PERIOD | PARTIAL PAYMENT |
|---|---|---|---|---|---|---|
| 1 | 0.1006875000D 01 | 0.1000000000D 01 | 1.000000000 | 0.9931719429 | 0.9931719429D 00 | 1.006875000 |
| 2 | 0.1013797266D 01 | 0.2006875000D 01 | 0.4982871380 | 0.9863905081 | 0.1979562451D 01 | 0.5051621380 |
| 3 | 0.1020767122D 01 | 0.3020672226D 01 | 0.3310521341 | 0.9796553774 | 0.2959217828D 01 | 0.3379271341 |
| 4 | 0.1027784896D 01 | 0.4041439387D 01 | 0.2474365948 | 0.9729662346 | 0.3932184063D 01 | 0.2543115948 |
| 5 | 0.1034850917D 01 | 0.5069224283D 01 | 0.1972688412 | 0.9663227656 | 0.4898506829D 01 | 0.2041438412 |
| 6 | 0.1041965170D 01 | 0.6104075200D 01 | 0.1638249804 | 0.9597246585 | 0.5858231487D 01 | 0.1706999804 |
| 7 | 0.1049128030D 01 | 0.7146040717D 01 | 0.1399376697 | 0.9531716038 | 0.6811403091D 01 | 0.1468126297 |
| 8 | 0.1056341192D 01 | 0.8195169747D 01 | 0.1220230979 | 0.9466632936 | 0.7758066384D 01 | 0.1288980979 |
| 9 | 0.1063604142D 01 | 0.9251515593D 01 | 0.1080904451 | 0.9401994226 | 0.8698265807D 01 | 0.1149654451 |
| 10 | 0.1070916420D 01 | 0.1031515156D 02 | 0.0969451076 | 0.9337796872 | 0.9632045494D 01 | 0.1038201076 |
| 11 | 0.1078278971D 01 | 0.1138603210D 02 | 0.0878260085 | 0.9274037862 | 0.1055944928D 02 | 0.0947010085 |
| 12 | 0.1085692139D 01 | 0.1246431107D 02 | 0.0802290631 | 0.9210714202 | 0.1148052070D 02 | 0.0871040631 |
| 13 | 0.1093156272D 01 | 0.1355003321D 02 | 0.0737925205 | 0.9147822919 | 0.1239530299D 02 | 0.0806675205 |
| 14 | 0.1100671721D 01 | 0.1464315948D 02 | 0.0682917729 | 0.9085361062 | 0.1330383910D 02 | 0.0751667729 |
| 15 | 0.1108238840D 01 | 0.1574383831D 02 | 0.0635169411 | 0.9023325698 | 0.1420617167D 02 | 0.0703919411 |
| 16 | 0.1115857982D 01 | 0.1685207040D 02 | 0.0593399910 | 0.8961713915 | 0.1510234306D 02 | 0.0662149910 |
| 17 | 0.1123529505D 01 | 0.1796792803D 02 | 0.0556547198 | 0.8900522820 | 0.1599239534D 02 | 0.0625297198 |
| 18 | 0.1131253771D 01 | 0.1909145753D 02 | 0.0523794476 | 0.8839749542 | 0.1687637030D 02 | 0.0592544476 |
| 19 | 0.1139031140D 01 | 0.2022271113D 02 | 0.0494493535 | 0.8779391227 | 0.1775430942D 02 | 0.0563243535 |
| 20 | 0.1146861979D 01 | 0.2136174244D 02 | 0.0468126607 | 0.8719445043 | 0.1862625392D 02 | 0.0536876607 |

## Rate of Return on a Bond

This program uses an iterative scheme to compute the periodic rate of return on a bond given the present value (sale price), number of coupons, the iterative tolerance, the flows, and the times at which the flows occur. This program assumes that the redemption price of the bond is included with the last coupon. The program can also be used to compute the periodic rate of return on a set of inflows and/or outflows at irregular intervals.

```
C PROGRAM TO CALCULATE INTERNAL RATE OF RETURN
      DIMENSION A(30),V(30),ANAME(20)
    1 READ (1,1000) ANAME
      WRITE (3,1001) ANAME
    2 RATE=1.1
C
C READ NUMBER OF FLOWS, PRESENT VALUE, ITERATION TOLERANCE
C
      READ (1,1002) NUMFLO,   PV,TOL
      IF(NUMFLO)999,1,3
    3 IF(NUMFLO-30)5,5,4
    4 WRITE(3,1003)
      GO TO 999
C
C READ PERIOD AND ASSOCIATED FLOW
C
    5 READ (1,1004) (V(I),A(I),I=1,NUMFLO)
      IF(TOL)19,19,20
   19 TOL=.001
   20 TOL=TOL/2.
    6 CNPV=0.
      DO 7 N=1,NUMFLO
    7 CNPV=CNPV+A(N)*RATE**(-V(N))
      IF(ABS(PV-CNPV)-.1E-30)9,30,30
   30 IF(CNPV-PV)10,9,8
    8 ARATE=(2.*(RATE-1.))+1.
      IF(ABS (RATE-ARATE)-TOL)17,17,11
   11 RATE=ARATE
      GO TO 6
   10 ARATE=((RATE-1.)/2.)+1.
   16 ANINT=ABS (RATE-ARATE)
      IF(ANINT-TOL)17,17,12
   12 RATE=ARATE
      CNPV=0.
      DO 13 N=1,NUMFLO
   13 CNPV=CNPV+A(N)*RATE**(-V(N))
      IF(ABS(PV-CNPV)-.1E-30)9,31,31
   31 IF(CNPV-PV)15,9,14
   14 ARATE=RATE+(ANINT/2.)
      GO TO 16
   15 ARATE=RATE-(ANINT/2.)
      GO TO 16
   17 RATE=ARATE
      CNPV=0.
      DO 18 N=1,NUMFLO
   18 CNPV=CNPV+A(N)*RATE**(-V(N))
    9 TOL=2.*TOL
      RATE=RATE-1.
      WRITE (3,1005)    PV,TOL, (V(N),A(N),N=1,NUMFLO)
      WRITE (3,1006) RATE,RATE,CNPV
      GO TO 2
  999 CALL EXIT
 1000 FORMAT(20A4)
 1001 FORMAT(1H1,20A4)
```

```
1002 FORMAT(I2,2F14.2)
1003 FORMAT(29H1MAXIMUM NUMBER OF FLOWS= 30.)
1004 FORMAT(6F12.0)
1005 FORMAT(1H0,26X14HPRESENT VALUE=,    F14.2/1H0,28X10HTOLERANCE=,F14
    1.8/1H0,31X16HPERIOD      FLOW/(32XF4.0,F14.2))
1006 FORMAT(1H0,24X25HRATE OF RETURN PER PERIOD,
   9                        F14.8/1H0,5X40HCALCULATED NET PRESENT
    1 VALUE, USING R OF,F14.8,2H =,F14.2/1H1)
     END
```

EXAMPLE: A \$1000, 4% bond with semiannual coupons is sold for \$980 on June 1, 1973. The bond matures on December 1, 1980. Find the periodic yield rate.

SOLUTION:

```
          PRESENT VALUE=         980.00

            TOLERANCE=     0.00001000

             PERIOD        FLOW
               1.          20.00
               2.          20.00
               3.          20.00
               4.          20.00
               5.          20.00
               6.          20.00
               7.          20.00
               8.          20.00
               9.          20.00
              10.          20.00
              11.          20.00
              12.          20.00
              13.          20.00
              14.          20.00
              15.        1020.00

        RATE OF RETURN PER PERIOD     0.02157402

CALCULATED NET PRESENT VALUE, USING R OF     0.02157402 =        980.01
```

# Index

(Numbers refer to pages)

# Mathematical
# Tables

# Index of Tables

# Table 1

*The Number of Each Day of the Year*

| DAY OF MONTH | Jan. | Feb. | Mar. | April | May | June | July | Aug. | Sept. | Oct. | Nov. | Dec. | DAY OF MONTH |
|---|---|---|---|---|---|---|---|---|---|---|---|---|---|
| 1 | 1 | 32 | 60 | 91 | 121 | 152 | 182 | 213 | 244 | 274 | 305 | 335 | 1 |
| 2 | 2 | 33 | 61 | 92 | 122 | 153 | 183 | 214 | 245 | 275 | 306 | 336 | 2 |
| 3 | 3 | 34 | 62 | 93 | 123 | 154 | 184 | 215 | 246 | 276 | 307 | 337 | 3 |
| 4 | 4 | 35 | 63 | 94 | 124 | 155 | 185 | 216 | 247 | 277 | 308 | 338 | 4 |
| 5 | 5 | 36 | 64 | 95 | 125 | 156 | 186 | 217 | 248 | 278 | 309 | 339 | 5 |
| 6 | 6 | 37 | 65 | 96 | 126 | 157 | 187 | 218 | 249 | 279 | 310 | 340 | 6 |
| 7 | 7 | 38 | 66 | 97 | 127 | 158 | 188 | 219 | 250 | 280 | 311 | 341 | 7 |
| 8 | 8 | 39 | 67 | 98 | 128 | 159 | 189 | 220 | 251 | 281 | 312 | 342 | 8 |
| 9 | 9 | 40 | 68 | 99 | 129 | 160 | 190 | 221 | 252 | 282 | 313 | 343 | 9 |
| 10 | 10 | 41 | 69 | 100 | 130 | 161 | 191 | 222 | 253 | 283 | 314 | 344 | 10 |
| 11 | 11 | 42 | 70 | 101 | 131 | 162 | 192 | 223 | 254 | 284 | 315 | 345 | 11 |
| 12 | 12 | 43 | 71 | 102 | 132 | 163 | 193 | 224 | 255 | 285 | 316 | 346 | 12 |
| 13 | 13 | 44 | 72 | 103 | 133 | 164 | 194 | 225 | 256 | 286 | 317 | 347 | 13 |
| 14 | 14 | 45 | 73 | 104 | 134 | 165 | 195 | 226 | 257 | 287 | 318 | 348 | 14 |
| 15 | 15 | 46 | 74 | 105 | 135 | 166 | 196 | 227 | 258 | 288 | 319 | 349 | 15 |
| 16 | 16 | 47 | 75 | 106 | 136 | 167 | 197 | 228 | 259 | 289 | 320 | 350 | 16 |
| 17 | 17 | 48 | 76 | 107 | 137 | 168 | 198 | 229 | 260 | 290 | 321 | 351 | 17 |
| 18 | 18 | 49 | 77 | 108 | 138 | 169 | 199 | 230 | 261 | 291 | 322 | 352 | 18 |
| 19 | 19 | 50 | 78 | 109 | 139 | 170 | 200 | 231 | 262 | 292 | 323 | 353 | 19 |
| 20 | 20 | 51 | 79 | 110 | 140 | 171 | 201 | 232 | 263 | 293 | 324 | 354 | 20 |
| 21 | 21 | 52 | 80 | 111 | 141 | 172 | 202 | 233 | 264 | 294 | 325 | 355 | 21 |
| 22 | 22 | 53 | 81 | 112 | 142 | 173 | 203 | 234 | 265 | 295 | 326 | 356 | 22 |
| 23 | 23 | 54 | 82 | 113 | 143 | 174 | 204 | 235 | 266 | 296 | 327 | 357 | 23 |
| 24 | 24 | 55 | 83 | 114 | 144 | 175 | 205 | 236 | 267 | 297 | 328 | 358 | 24 |
| 25 | 25 | 56 | 84 | 115 | 145 | 176 | 206 | 237 | 268 | 298 | 329 | 359 | 25 |
| 26 | 26 | 57 | 85 | 116 | 146 | 177 | 207 | 238 | 269 | 299 | 330 | 360 | 26 |
| 27 | 27 | 58 | 86 | 117 | 147 | 178 | 208 | 239 | 270 | 300 | 331 | 361 | 27 |
| 28 | 28 | 59 | 87 | 118 | 148 | 179 | 209 | 240 | 271 | 301 | 332 | 362 | 28 |
| 29 | 29 | | 88 | 119 | 149 | 180 | 210 | 241 | 272 | 302 | 333 | 363 | 29 |
| 30 | 30 | | 89 | 120 | 150 | 181 | 211 | 242 | 273 | 303 | 334 | 364 | 30 |
| 31 | 31 | | 90 | | 151 | | 212 | 243 | | 304 | | 365 | 31 |

For leap years the number of the day after
February 28 is one greater than that given in the table.

## Table 2

*Compound Interest and Annuity Tables*

A WORD ABOUT THE MARGINAL INDEX

Down the side margin of each page runs an index designed to save much of the adjustment of rates which makes the ordinary table so confusing to the novice. It will help you.

All figures in the tables are calculated at some *rate per period*. This period may be anything from a day to 5 years or more, depending on how often the interest is calculated. You, however, usually have the *annual* rate quoted and that is what you can look up in the marginal index. Suppose a bank pays 2% per annum compounded *semiannually* (*i.e.*, adds interest each half year). Use the marginal index in the part where "SEMIANNUALLY" appears in capital letters, and find "2%" in that part. You have the table you want. Actually you realize that 2% per annum compounded semiannually means 1% per period where each period is a half year—but you do not need to make this adjustment in advance, simply use the index.

Caution: the number of periods in the table is not necessarily the number of years. It is the number of whatever unit you are using. When you use the "SEMIANNUALLY" index it is the number of half years. If you use the "MONTHLY" index it is the number of months.

*The marginal index is there to help you. Use it.*

WHAT THE TABLES ARE

IN A FEW SIMPLE WORDS

(Not how to use them, but what they are)

*1. Amount of 1.* If you put a dollar in the bank and leave it there it grows, and this table (left-hand column on left-hand page) shows to what sum it does grow. If the rate is 2% to be figured each year, then at the end of 1 year you have $1.02 in the bank. The second year this grows to 1.02 × 1.02 or 1.0404. The third year this 1.0404 becomes 1.0404 × 1.02 or 1.061208. Observe that each result at the 2% rate can be obtained by multiplying the preceding result by 1.02 which is the ratio of increase at 2%. The table at any interest rate can be constructed by successive multiplication by its ratio of increase. There is nothing complicated to that.

*2. Amount of 1 per Period.* If you do not just put a dollar in the bank and leave it there, but at periodic intervals you go back and deposit another dollar each time, this table (middle column on left-hand page) shows what happens and how your money grows. Note that this table assumes that the deposit is made at the *end* of each period: the figure for 1 period is 1, meaning that 1 has

5

just been deposited at the end of the period and has not had a chance to grow. At the end of the second period this first dollar has grown (at 2%) to $1.02 and the second $1 has just been deposited, so the table shows $2.02.

Observe that this is just like the table for compound amount (left-hand column) in that the deposit of $1 is the basic event, and each $1 deposited starts to grow as shown in that table; but here we have a whole series of $1 deposits all growing at the same time, and each successively has been in the bank for one more period than the next deposit, right down to the latest deposit which has just been deposited. Therefore this table consists merely of adding all the items in the first table (left-hand column) down to the point desired. That feature of payment at the *end* of the period must be watched because it throws us out by one period: if you want to check the entry for 5 periods you could add up the first 4 entries in the left-hand column, then add 1 for the final deposit that has just been made, and you have the tabulated result.

This explanation is only here to show you that this table is just the combined total of a lot of $1 deposits, each growing for a different length of time in the manner shown in the left-hand column. Perhaps this is a little complicated, but there certainly is no dark mystery involved.

*3. Sinking Fund.* This table (right-hand column on left-hand page) shows how much money you must deposit each period in order to have $1 when you need it in the future. Each result is obtained merely by dividing 1 by the entry in the middle column beside it. For if $1 per period will grow to $25, then how much will be needed to grow to $1? Obviously $1 divided by $25, or 4¢. You will not find any such simple unit figures in the tables but the reasoning is the same. It is entirely a matter of simple proportion. To put it concisely, each entry in this table is the *reciprocal* of the corresponding entry in the column to its left.

*4. Present Worth of 1.* If you want to have $1 in the bank at some time in the future this table (left-hand column of right-hand page) shows you how much you must deposit today. Obviously since the table for *Amount of 1* shows how money grows when left in the bank, this table is directly related to it. In other words, if $1 left in the bank will grow to $5, how much money will be needed to grow to $1? Obviously one-fifth of $1, or 20¢. Again, you will not find such simple figures in even units in the table, but it is just a matter of simple proportion. To put it concisely, each entry in this table is the *reciprocal* of the corresponding entry in the table for the *Amount of 1.*

*5. Present Worth of 1 per Period.* We just saw that the preceding table showed us how much money we must put in the bank today in order to be able to draw out $1 at some specified date in the future. Now suppose we want to draw out $1, not on some one single occasion in the future, but $1 for each periodic interval for some length of time into the future. That is what is shown in this table.

Obviously since we are going to draw $1 at each date, we could use the preceding table for each of them, and add the entries. In fact, that is what the table is.  If you will add the first five entries in the *Present Worth of 1* column you will get the result shown for 5 periods in the *Present Worth of 1 per Period* column.  To express it concisely, each entry is the cumulative total of the figures in the column to the left of it.

6. *Partial Payment Table.*  The preceding table shows what amount you must have today in order to get periodic payments of $1 in the future; but if you have $1 today, what size periodic payments will it get you in the future?  Again, it is a matter of simple proportion.  To put it concisely, each entry is the *reciprocal* of the corresponding entry in the column to the left of it.  Usually, as the title indicates, this table will be used to show what you will have to pay at each period in the future if you borrow $1 today, but the explanation still stands.

Another basic relationship should be understood.  In the *Sinking Fund* table we are concerned with the sum which must be set aside to grow to $1; but in this *Partial Payment* table we are concerned with paying off a loan of $1, which is the same thing as building up a sinking fund to pay the loan except that it includes the interest on the loan of $1.  Therefore if you have the entry in the *Sinking Fund* table and add interest (always the *i* at the top of the page) you will get the corresponding entry in the *Partial Payment* table.

| P E R I O D S | AMOUNT OF 1<br>How $1 left at compound interest will grow. | AMOUNT OF 1 PER PERIOD<br>How $1 deposited periodically will grow. | SINKING FUND<br>Periodic deposit that will grow to $1 at future date. |
|---|---|---|---|
| 1 | 1.002 500 0000 | 1.000 000 0000 | 1.000 000 0000 |
| 2 | 1.005 006 2500 | 2.002 500 0000 | .499 375 7803 |
| 3 | 1.007 518 7656 | 3.007 506 2500 | .332 501 3872 |
| 4 | 1.010 037 5625 | 4.015 025 0156 | .249 064 4507 |
| 5 | 1.012 562 6564 | 5.025 062 5782 | .199 002 4969 |
| 6 | 1.015 094 0631 | 6.037 625 2346 | .165 628 0344 |
| 7 | 1.017 631 7982 | 7.052 719 2977 | .141 789 2812 |
| 8 | 1.020 175 8777 | 8.070 351 0959 | .123 910 3464 |
| 9 | 1.022 726 3174 | 9.090 526 9737 | .110 004 6238 |
| 10 | 1.025 283 1332 | 10.113 253 2911 | .098 880 1498 |
| 11 | 1.027 846 3411 | 11.138 536 4243 | .089 778 4019 |
| 12 | 1.030 415 9569 | 12.166 382 7654 | .082 193 6988 |
| 13 | 1.032 991 9968 | 13.196 798 7223 | .075 775 9530 |
| 14 | 1.035 574 4768 | 14.229 790 7191 | .070 275 1024 |
| 15 | 1.038 163 4130 | 15.265 365 1959 | .065 507 7679 |
| 16 | 1.040 758 8215 | 16.303 528 6089 | .061 336 4152 |
| 17 | 1.043 360 7186 | 17.344 287 4304 | .057 655 8711 |
| 18 | 1.045 969 1204 | 18.387 648 1490 | .054 384 3341 |
| 19 | 1.048 584 0432 | 19.433 617 2694 | .051 457 2242 |
| 20 | 1.051 205 5033 | 20.482 201 3126 | .048 822 8772 |
| 21 | 1.053 833 5170 | 21.533 406 8158 | .046 439 4700 |
| 22 | 1.056 468 1008 | 22.587 240 3329 | .044 272 7835 |
| 23 | 1.059 109 2711 | 23.643 708 4337 | .042 294 5496 |
| 24 | 1.061 757 0443 | 24.702 817 7048 | .040 481 2120 |
| 25 | 1.064 411 4369 | 25.764 574 7491 | .038 812 9829 |
| 26 | 1.067 072 4655 | 26.828 986 1859 | .037 273 1192 |
| 27 | 1.069 740 1466 | 27.896 058 6514 | .035 847 3580 |
| 28 | 1.072 414 4970 | 28.965 798 7980 | .034 523 4739 |
| 29 | 1.075 095 5332 | 30.038 213 2950 | .033 290 9281 |
| 30 | 1.077 783 2721 | 31.113 308 8283 | .032 140 5867 |
| 31 | 1.080 477 7303 | 32.191 092 1003 | .031 064 4944 |
| 32 | 1.083 178 9246 | 33.271 569 8306 | .030 055 6903 |
| 33 | 1.085 886 8719 | 34.354 748 7551 | .029 108 0574 |
| 34 | 1.088 601 5891 | 35.440 635 6270 | .028 216 1982 |
| 35 | 1.091 323 0930 | 36.529 237 2161 | .027 375 3321 |
| 36 | 1.094 051 4008 | 37.620 560 3091 | .026 581 2096 |
| 37 | 1.096 786 5293 | 38.714 611 7099 | .025 830 0408 |
| 38 | 1.099 528 4956 | 39.811 398 2392 | .025 118 4345 |
| 39 | 1.102 277 3168 | 40.910 926 7348 | .024 443 3475 |
| 40 | 1.105 033 0101 | 42.013 204 0516 | .023 802 0409 |
| 41 | 1.107 795 5927 | 43.118 237 0618 | .023 192 0428 |
| 42 | 1.110 565 0816 | 44.226 032 6544 | .022 611 1170 |
| 43 | 1.113 341 4943 | 45.336 597 7360 | .022 057 2352 |
| 44 | 1.116 124 8481 | 46.449 939 2304 | .021 528 5535 |
| 45 | 1.118 915 1602 | 47.566 064 0785 | .021 023 3918 |
| 46 | 1.121 712 4481 | 48.684 979 2387 | .020 540 2162 |
| 47 | 1.124 516 7292 | 49.806 691 6868 | .020 077 6234 |
| 48 | 1.127 328 0210 | 50.931 208 4160 | .019 634 3270 |
| 49 | 1.130 146 3411 | 52.058 536 4370 | .019 209 1455 |
| 50 | 1.132 971 7069 | 53.188 682 7781 | .018 800 9920 |
| 51 | 1.135 804 1362 | 54.321 654 4851 | .018 408 8649 |
| 52 | 1.138 643 6466 | 55.457 458 6213 | .018 031 8396 |
| 53 | 1.141 490 2557 | 56.596 102 2678 | .017 669 0613 |
| 54 | 1.144 343 9813 | 57.737 592 5235 | .017 319 7384 |
| 55 | 1.147 204 8413 | 58.881 936 5048 | .016 983 1371 |
| 56 | 1.150 072 8534 | 60.029 141 3461 | .016 658 5758 |
| 57 | 1.152 948 0355 | 61.179 214 1994 | .016 345 4208 |
| 58 | 1.155 830 4056 | 62.332 162 2349 | .016 043 0822 |
| 59 | 1.158 719 9816 | 63.487 992 6405 | .015 751 0099 |
| 60 | 1.161 616 7816 | 64.646 712 6221 | .015 468 6907 |
| n | $s=(1+i)^n$ | $s_{\overline{n}|} = \dfrac{(1+i)^n - 1}{i}$ | $\dfrac{1}{s_{\overline{n}|}} = \dfrac{i}{(1+i)^n - 1}$ |

.0025
per period

ANNUALLY
If compounded annually nominal annual rate is
1/4%

SEMIANNUALLY
If compounded semiannually nominal annual rate is
1/2%

QUARTERLY
If compounded quarterly nominal annual rate is
1%

MONTHLY
If compounded monthly nominal annual rate is
3%

$i$ = .0025
$j_{(2)}$ = .005
$j_{(4)}$ = .01
$j_{(12)}$ = .03

| PRESENT WORTH OF 1 — *What $1 due in the future is worth today.* | PRESENT WORTH OF 1 PER PERIOD — *What $1 payable periodically is worth today.* | PARTIAL PAYMENT — *Annuity worth $1 today. Periodic payment necessary to pay off a loan of $1.* | PERIODS | RATE |
|---|---|---|---|---|
| | | | | **¼%** |
| .997 506 2344 | .997 506 2344 | 1.002 500 0000 | 1 | |
| .995 018 6877 | 1.992 524 9221 | .501 875 7803 | 2 | |
| .992 537 3443 | 2.985 062 2664 | .335 001 3872 | 3 | .0025 |
| .990 062 1889 | 3.975 124 4553 | .251 564 4507 | 4 | |
| .987 593 2058 | 4.962 717 6612 | .201 502 4969 | 5 | *per period* |
| .985 130 3799 | 5.947 848 0410 | .168 128 0344 | 6 | |
| .982 673 6957 | 6.930 521 7367 | .144 289 2812 | 7 | |
| .980 223 1378 | 7.910 744 8745 | .126 410 3464 | 8 | |
| .977 778 6911 | 8.888 523 5656 | .112 504 6238 | 9 | |
| .975 340 3402 | 9.863 863 9058 | .101 380 1498 | 10 | |
| .972 908 0701 | 10.836 771 9759 | .092 278 4019 | 11 | |
| .970 481 8654 | 11.807 253 8413 | .084 693 6988 | 12 | |
| .968 061 7111 | 12.775 315 5524 | .078 275 9530 | 13 | |
| .965 647 5921 | 13.740 963 1446 | .072 775 1024 | 14 | |
| .963 239 4934 | 14.704 202 6380 | .068 007 7679 | 15 | |
| .960 837 3999 | 15.665 040 0379 | .063 836 4152 | 16 | |
| .958 441 2967 | 16.623 481 3345 | .060 155 8711 | 17 | |
| .956 051 1687 | 17.579 532 5033 | .056 884 3341 | 18 | |
| .953 667 0012 | 18.533 199 5045 | .053 957 2242 | 19 | |
| .951 288 7793 | 19.484 488 2838 | .051 322 8772 | 20 | |
| .948 916 4881 | 20.433 404 7719 | .048 939 4700 | 21 | ANNUALLY |
| .946 550 1128 | 21.379 954 8847 | .046 772 7835 | 22 | If compounded *annually* |
| .944 189 6387 | 22.324 144 5234 | .044 794 5496 | 23 | nominal annual rate is |
| .941 835 0511 | 23.265 979 5744 | .042 981 2120 | 24 | |
| .939 486 3352 | 24.205 465 9096 | .041 312 9829 | 25 | **¼%** |
| .937 143 4765 | 25.142 609 3862 | .039 773 1192 | 26 | |
| .934 806 4604 | 26.077 415 8466 | .038 347 3580 | 27 | |
| .932 475 2722 | 27.009 891 1188 | .037 023 4739 | 28 | |
| .930 149 8975 | 27.940 041 0162 | .035 790 9281 | 29 | |
| .927 830 3217 | 28.867 871 3379 | .034 640 5867 | 30 | |
| .925 516 5303 | 29.793 387 8682 | .033 564 4944 | 31 | SEMIANNUALLY |
| .923 208 5091 | 30.716 596 3773 | .032 555 6903 | 32 | If compounded *semiannually* |
| .920 906 2434 | 31.637 502 6207 | .031 608 0574 | 33 | nominal annual rate is |
| .918 609 7192 | 32.556 112 3399 | .030 716 1982 | 34 | |
| .916 318 9218 | 33.472 431 2617 | .029 875 3321 | 35 | **½%** |
| .914 033 8373 | 34.386 465 0990 | .029 081 2096 | 36 | |
| .911 754 4511 | 35.298 219 5501 | .028 330 0408 | 37 | |
| .909 480 7493 | 36.207 700 2993 | .027 618 4345 | 38 | |
| .907 212 7175 | 37.114 913 0168 | .026 943 3475 | 39 | |
| .904 950 3416 | 38.019 863 3584 | .026 302 0409 | 40 | |
| .902 693 6076 | 38.922 556 9660 | .025 692 0428 | 41 | QUARTERLY |
| .900 442 5013 | 39.822 999 4673 | .025 111 1170 | 42 | If compounded *quarterly* |
| .898 197 0088 | 40.721 196 4761 | .024 557 2352 | 43 | nominal annual rate is |
| .895 957 1160 | 41.617 153 5921 | .024 028 5535 | 44 | |
| .893 722 8090 | 42.510 876 4011 | .023 523 3918 | 45 | **1%** |
| .891 494 0738 | 43.402 370 4750 | .023 040 2162 | 46 | |
| .889 270 8966 | 44.291 641 3715 | .022 577 6234 | 47 | |
| .887 053 2634 | 45.178 694 6349 | .022 134 3270 | 48 | |
| .884 841 1605 | 46.063 535 7955 | .021 709 1455 | 49 | |
| .882 634 5741 | 46.946 170 3695 | .021 300 9920 | 50 | |
| .880 433 4904 | 47.826 603 8599 | .020 908 8649 | 51 | MONTHLY |
| .878 237 8956 | 48.704 841 7555 | .020 531 8396 | 52 | If compounded *monthly* |
| .876 047 7762 | 49.580 889 5317 | .020 169 0613 | 53 | nominal annual.rate is |
| .873 863 1184 | 50.454 752 6500 | .019 819 7384 | 54 | |
| .871 683 9086 | 51.326 436 5586 | .019 483 1371 | 55 | **3%** |
| .869 510 1333 | 52.195 946 6919 | .019 158 5758 | 56 | |
| .867 341 7788 | 53.063 288 4707 | .018 845 4208 | 57 | |
| .865 178 8317 | 53.928 467 3025 | .018 543 0822 | 58 | $i = .0025$ |
| .863 021 2785 | 54.791 488 5810 | .018 251 0099 | 59 | $j_{(2)} = .005$ |
| .860 869 1058 | 55.652 357 6868 | .017 968 6907 | 60 | $j_{(4)} = .01$ |
| | | | | $j_{(12)} = .03$ |
| $v^n = \dfrac{1}{(1+i)^n}$ | $a_{\overline{n}|} = \dfrac{1-v^n}{i}$ | $\dfrac{1}{a_{\overline{n}|}} = \dfrac{i}{1-v^n}$ | n | |

| P E R I O D S | AMOUNT OF 1<br>*How $1 left at compound interest will grow.* | AMOUNT OF 1 PER PERIOD<br>*How $1 deposited periodically will grow.* | SINKING FUND<br>*Periodic deposit that will grow to $1 at future date.* |
|---|---|---|---|
| 61 | 1.164 520 8235 | 65.808 329 4037 | .015 195 6448 |
| 62 | 1.167 432 1256 | 66.972 850 2272 | .014 931 4237 |
| 63 | 1.170 350 7059 | 68.140 282 3527 | .014 675 6069 |
| 64 | 1.173 276 5826 | 69.310 633 0586 | .014 427 8007 |
| 65 | 1.176 209 7741 | 70.483 909 6413 | .014 187 6352 |
| 66 | 1.179 150 2985 | 71.660 119 4154 | .013 954 7632 |
| 67 | 1.182 098 1743 | 72.839 269 7139 | .013 728 8581 |
| 68 | 1.185 053 4197 | 74.021 367 8882 | .013 509 6125 |
| 69 | 1.188 016 0533 | 75.206 421 3079 | .013 296 7369 |
| 70 | 1.190 986 0934 | 76.394 437 3612 | .013 089 9583 |
| 71 | 1.193 963 5586 | 77.585 423 4546 | .012 889 0190 |
| 72 | 1.196 948 4675 | 78.779 387 0132 | .012 693 6758 |
| 73 | 1.199 940 8387 | 79.976 335 4808 | .012 503 6987 |
| 74 | 1.202 940 6908 | 81.176 276 3195 | .012 318 8701 |
| 75 | 1.205 948 0425 | 82.379 217 0103 | .012 138 9840 |
| 76 | 1.208 962 9126 | 83.585 165 0528 | .011 963 8455 |
| 77 | 1.211 985 3199 | 84.794 127 9654 | .011 793 2695 |
| 78 | 1.215 015 2832 | 86.006 113 2853 | .011 627 0805 |
| 79 | 1.218 052 8214 | 87.221 128 5685 | .011 465 1119 |
| 80 | 1.221 097 9535 | 88.439 181 3900 | .011 307 2055 |
| 81 | 1.224 150 6984 | 89.660 279 3434 | .011 153 2108 |
| 82 | 1.227 211 0751 | 90.884 430 0418 | .011 002 9848 |
| 83 | 1.230 279 1028 | 92.111 641 1169 | .010 856 3911 |
| 84 | 1.233 354 8005 | 93.341 920 2197 | .010 713 3001 |
| 85 | 1.236 438 1876 | 94.575 275 0202 | .010 573 5881 |
| 86 | 1.239 529 2830 | 95.811 713 2078 | .010 437 1372 |
| 87 | 1.242 628 1062 | 97.051 242 4908 | .010 303 8351 |
| 88 | 1.245 734 6765 | 98.293 870 5970 | .010 173 5743 |
| 89 | 1.248 849 0132 | 99.539 605 2735 | .010 046 2524 |
| 90 | 1.251 971 1357 | 100.788 454 2867 | .009 921 7714 |
| 91 | 1.255 101 0636 | 102.040 425 4224 | .009 800 0375 |
| 92 | 1.258 238 8162 | 103.295 526 4860 | .009 680 9614 |
| 93 | 1.261 384 4133 | 104.553 765 3022 | .009 564 4571 |
| 94 | 1.264 537 8743 | 105.815 149 7155 | .009 450 4426 |
| 95 | 1.267 699 2190 | 107.079 687 5898 | .009 338 8393 |
| 96 | 1.270 868 4670 | 108.347 386 8087 | .009 229 5719 |
| 97 | 1.274 045 6382 | 109.618 255 2757 | .009 122 5681 |
| 98 | 1.277 230 7523 | 110.892 300 9139 | .009 017 7586 |
| 99 | 1.280 423 8292 | 112.169 531 6662 | .008 915 0769 |
| 100 | 1.283 624 8887 | 113.449 955 4954 | .008 814 4592 |
| 101 | 1.286 833 9510 | 114.733 580 3841 | .008 715 8441 |
| 102 | 1.290 051 0358 | 116.020 414 3351 | .008 619 1728 |
| 103 | 1.293 276 1634 | 117.310 465 3709 | .008 524 3887 |
| 104 | 1.296 509 3538 | 118.603 741 5344 | .008 431 4372 |
| 105 | 1.299 750 6272 | 119.900 250 8882 | .008 340 2661 |
| 106 | 1.303 000 0038 | 121.200 001 5154 | .008 250 8250 |
| 107 | 1.306 257 5038 | 122.503 001 5192 | .008 163 0653 |
| 108 | 1.309 523 1476 | 123.809 259 0230 | .008 076 9404 |
| 109 | 1.312 796 9554 | 125.118 782 1706 | .007 992 4052 |
| 110 | 1.316 078 9478 | 126.431 579 1260 | .007 909 4164 |
| 111 | 1.319 369 1452 | 127.747 658 0738 | .007 827 9322 |
| 112 | 1.322 667 5680 | 129.067 027 2190 | .007 747 9122 |
| 113 | 1.325 974 2370 | 130.389 694 7870 | .007 669 3177 |
| 114 | 1.329 289 1726 | 131.715 669 0240 | .007 592 1112 |
| 115 | 1.332 612 3955 | 133.044 958 1966 | .007 516 2563 |
| 116 | 1.335 943 9265 | 134.377 570 5920 | .007 441 7181 |
| 117 | 1.339 283 7863 | 135.713 514 5185 | .007 368 4629 |
| 118 | 1.342 631 9958 | 137.052 798 3048 | .007 296 4581 |
| 119 | 1.345 988 5758 | 138.395 430 3006 | .007 225 6721 |
| 120 | 1.349 353 5472 | 139.741 418 8763 | .007 156 0745 |
| **n** | $s=(1+i)^n$ | $s_{\overline{n}|}=\dfrac{(1+i)^n-1}{i}$ | $\dfrac{1}{s_{\overline{n}|}}=\dfrac{i}{(1+i)^n-1}$ |

.0025
*per period*

ANNUALLY
If compounded *annually* nominal annual rate is

**1/4%**

SEMIANNUALLY
If compounded *semiannually* nominal annual rate is

**1/2%**

QUARTERLY
If compounded *quarterly* nominal annual rate is

**1%**

MONTHLY
If compounded *monthly* nominal annual rate is

**3%**

$i$ = .0025
$j_{(2)}$ = .005
$j_{(4)}$ = .01
$j_{(12)}$ = .03

10

| PRESENT WORTH OF 1 | PRESENT WORTH OF 1 PER PERIOD | PARTIAL PAYMENT | P E R I O D S | RATE |
|---|---|---|---|---|
| *What $1 due in the future is worth today.* | *What $1 payable periodically is worth today.* | *Annuity worth $1 today.* *Periodic payment necessary to pay off a loan of $1.* | | $\frac{1}{4}\%$ |

| PRESENT WORTH OF 1 | PRESENT WORTH OF 1 PER PERIOD | PARTIAL PAYMENT | PERIODS | RATE |
|---|---|---|---|---|
| .858 722 3000 | 56.511 079 9868 | .017 695 6448 | 61 | |
| .856 580 8479 | 57.367 660 8348 | .017 431 4237 | 62 | .0025 |
| .854 444 7361 | 58.222 105 5708 | .017 175 6069 | 63 | *per period* |
| .852 313 9512 | 59.074 419 5220 | .016 927 8007 | 64 | |
| .850 188 4800 | 59.924 608 0020 | .016 687 6352 | 65 | |
| .848 068 3092 | 60.772 676 3112 | .016 454 7632 | 66 | |
| .845 953 4257 | 61.618 629 7369 | .016 228 8581 | 67 | |
| .843 843 8161 | 62.462 473 5530 | .016 009 6125 | 68 | |
| .841 739 4674 | 63.304 213 0205 | .015 796 7369 | 69 | |
| .839 640 3665 | 64.143 853 3870 | .015 589 9583 | 70 | |
| .837 546 5003 | 64.981 399 8873 | .015 389 0190 | 71 | |
| .835 457 8556 | 65.816 857 7429 | .015 193 6758 | 72 | |
| .833 374 4196 | 66.650 232 1625 | .015 003 6987 | 73 | |
| .831 296 1791 | 67.481 528 3417 | .014 818 8701 | 74 | |
| .829 223 1213 | 68.310 751 4630 | .014 638 9840 | 75 | |
| .827 155 2333 | 69.137 906 6963 | .014 463 8455 | 76 | |
| .825 092 5020 | 69.962 999 1983 | .014 293 2695 | 77 | |
| .823 034 9147 | 70.786 034 1130 | .014 127 0805 | 78 | |
| .820 982 4586 | 71.607 016 5716 | .013 965 1119 | 79 | |
| .818 935 1208 | 72.425 951 6923 | .013 807 2055· | 80 | **ANNUALLY** |
| .816 892 8885 | 73.242 844 5809 | .013 653 2108 | 81 | If compounded *annually* nominal annual rate is |
| .814 855 7492 | 74.057 700 3300 | .013 502 9848 | 82 | |
| .812 823 6900 | 74.870 524 0200 | .013 356 3911 | 83 | |
| .810 796 6982 | 75.681 320 7182 | .013 213 3001 | 84 | $\frac{1}{4}\%$ |
| .808 774 7613 | 76.490 095 4795 | .013 073 5881 | 85 | |
| .806 757 8666 | 77.296 853 3461 | .012 937 1372 | 86 | |
| .804 746 0016 | 78.101 599 3478 | .012 803 8351 | 87 | |
| .802 739 1537 | 78.904 338 5015 | .012 673 5743 | 88 | |
| .800 737 3105 | 79.705 075 8120 | .012 546 2524 | 89 | |
| .798 740 4593 | 80.503 816 2713 | .012 421 7714 | 90 | **SEMIANNUALLY** |
| .796 748 5879 | 81.300 564 8592 | .012 300 0375 | 91 | If compounded *semiannually* nominal annual rate is |
| .794 761 6836 | 82.095 326 5428 | .012 180 9614 | 92 | |
| .792 779 7343 | 82.888 106 2771 | .012 064 4571 | 93 | |
| .790 802 7275 | 83.678 909 0046 | .011 950 4426 | 94 | $\frac{1}{2}\%$ |
| .788 830 6509 | 84.467 739 6555 | .011 838 8393 | 95 | |
| .786 863 4921 | 85.254 603 1476 | .011 729 5719 | 96 | |
| .784 901 2390 | 86.039 504 3866 | .011 622 5681 | 97 | |
| .782 943 8793 | 86.822 448 2660 | .011 517 7586 | 98 | |
| .780 991 4008 | 87.603 439 6668 | .011 415 0769 | 99 | |
| .779 043 7914 | 88.382 483 4581 | .011 314 4592 | 100 | **QUARTERLY** |
| .777 101 0388 | 89.159 584 4969 | .011 215 8441 | 101 | If compounded *quarterly* nominal annual rate is |
| .775 163 1309 | 89.934 747 6278 | .011 119 1728 | 102 | |
| .773 230 0558 | 90.707 977 6836 | .011 024 3887 | 103 | |
| .771 301 8013 | 91.479 279 4849 | .010 931 4372 | 104 | **1%** |
| .769 378 3554 | 92.248 657 8403 | .010 840 2661 | 105 | |
| .767 459 7061 | 93.016 117 5464 | .010 750 8250 | 106 | |
| .765 545 8415 | 93.781 663 3880 | .010 663 0653 | 107 | |
| .763 636 7497 | 94.545 300 1376 | .010 576 9404 | 108 | |
| .761 732 4186 | 95.307 032 5562 | .010 492 4052 | 109 | |
| .759 832 8365 | 96.066 865 3928 | .010 409 4164 | 110 | **MONTHLY** |
| .757 937 9915 | 96.824 803 3843 | .010 327 9322 | 111 | If compounded *monthly* nominal annual rate is |
| .756 047 8719 | 97.580 851 2562 | .010 247 9122 | 112 | |
| .754 162 4657 | 98.335 013 7218 | .010 169 3177 | 113 | |
| .752 281 7613 | 99.087 295 4831 | .010 092 1112 | 114 | **3%** |
| .750 405 7469 | 99.837 701 2301 | .010 016 2563 | 115 | |
| .748 534 4109 | 100.586 235 6410 | .009 941 7181 | 116 | |
| .746 667 7415 | 101.332 903 3825 | .009 868 4629 | 117 | |
| .744 805 7272 | 102.077 709 1097 | .009 796 4581 | 118 | $i$ = .0025 |
| .742 948 3563 | 102.820 657 4661 | .009 725 6721 | 119 | $j_{(2)}$ = .005 |
| .741 095 6173 | 103.561 753 0834 | .009 656 0745 | 120 | $j_{(4)}$ = .01 |
| $v^n = \dfrac{1}{(1+i)^n}$ | $a_{\overline{n}|} = \dfrac{1-v^n}{i}$ | $\dfrac{1}{a_{\overline{n}|}} = \dfrac{i}{1-v^n}$ | n | $j_{(12)}$ = .03 |

11

| P E R I O D S | AMOUNT OF 1 *How $1 left at compound interest will grow.* | AMOUNT OF 1 PER PERIOD *How $1 deposited periodically will grow.* | SINKING FUND *Periodic deposit that will grow to $1 at future date.* |
|---|---|---|---|
| 121 | 1.352 726 9311 | 141.090 772 4235 | .007 087 6357 |
| 122 | 1.356 108 7484 | 142.443 499 3546 | .007 020 3274 |
| 123 | 1.359 499 0203 | 143.799 608 1030 | .006 954 1219 |
| 124 | 1.362 897 7678 | 145.159 107 1232 | .006 888 9925 |
| 125 | 1.366 305 0122 | 146.522 004 8910 | .006 824 9134 |
| 126 | 1.369 720 7748 | 147.888 309 9033 | .006 761 8597 |
| 127 | 1.373 145 0767 | 149.258 030 6780 | .006 699 8070 |
| 128 | 1.376 577 9394 | 150.631 175 7547 | .006 638 7320 |
| 129 | 1.380 019 3842 | 152.007 753 6941 | .006 578 6118 |
| 130 | 1.383 469 4327 | 153.387 773 0783 | .006 519 4245 |
| 131 | 1.386 928 1063 | 154.771 242 5110 | .006 461 1486 |
| 132 | 1.390 395 4265 | 156.158 170 6173 | .006 403 7635 |
| 133 | 1.393 871 4151 | 157.548 566 0439 | .006 347 2491 |
| 134 | 1.397 356 0936 | 158.942 437 4590 | .006 291 5859 |
| 135 | 1.400 849 4839 | 160.339 793 5526 | .006 236 7549 |
| 136 | 1.404 351 6076 | 161.740 643 0365 | .006 182 7379 |
| 137 | 1.407 862 4866 | 163.144 994 6441 | .006 129 5169 |
| 138 | 1.411 382 1428 | 164.552 857 1307 | .006 077 0747 |
| 139 | 1.414 910 5982 | 165.964 239 2735 | .006 025 3944 |
| 140 | 1.418 447 8747 | 167.379 149 8717 | .005 974 4598 |
| 141 | 1.421 993 9944 | 168.797 597 7464 | .005 924 2549 |
| 142 | 1.425 548 9794 | 170.219 591 7408 | .005 874 7644 |
| 143 | 1.429 112 8518 | 171.645 140 7201 | .005 825 9733 |
| 144 | 1.432 685 6339 | 173.074 253 5719 | .005 777 8669 |
| 145 | 1.436 267 3480 | 174.506 939 2058 | .005 730 4311 |
| 146 | 1.439 858 0164 | 175.943 206 5538 | .005 683 6522 |
| 147 | 1.443 457 6614 | 177.383 064 5702 | .005 637 5168 |
| 148 | 1.447 066 3056 | 178.826 522 2317 | .005 592 0117 |
| 149 | 1.450 683 9713 | 180.273 588 5372 | .005 547 1243 |
| 150 | 1.454 310 6813 | 181.724 272 5086 | .005 502 8422 |
| 151 | 1.457 946 4580 | 183.178 583 1899 | .005 459 1535 |
| 152 | 1.461 591 3241 | 184.636 529 6478 | .005 416 0463 |
| 153 | 1.465 245 3024 | 186.098 120 9719 | .005 373 5094 |
| 154 | 1.468 908 4157 | 187.563 366 2744 | .005 331 5315 |
| 155 | 1.472 580 6867 | 189.032 274 6901 | .005 290 1019 |
| 156 | 1.476 262 1384 | 190.504 855 3768 | .005 249 2100 |
| 157 | 1.479 952 7938 | 191.981 117 5152 | .005 208 8456 |
| 158 | 1.483 652 6758 | 193.461 070 3090 | .005 168 9986 |
| 159 | 1.487 361 8075 | 194.944 722 9848 | .005 129 6592 |
| 160 | 1.491 080 2120 | 196.432 084 7923 | .005 090 8180 |
| 161 | 1.494 807 9125 | 197.923 165 0042 | .005 052 4657 |
| 162 | 1.498 544 9323 | 199.417 972 9167 | .005 014 5931 |
| 163 | 1.502 291 2946 | 200.916 517 8490 | .004 977 1916 |
| 164 | 1.506 047 0229 | 202.418 809 1437 | .004 940 2524 |
| 165 | 1.509 812 1404 | 203.924 856 1665 | .004 903 7671 |
| 166 | 1.513 586 6708 | 205.434 668 3069 | .004 867 7276 |
| 167 | 1.517 370 6374 | 206.948 254 9777 | .004 832 1258 |
| 168 | 1.521 164 0640 | 208.465 625 6151 | .004 796 9539 |
| 169 | 1.524 966 9742 | 209.986 789 6792 | .004 762 2043 |
| 170 | 1.528 779 3916 | 211.511 756 6534 | .004 727 8696 |
| 171 | 1.532 601 3401 | 213.040 536 0450 | .004 693 9424 |
| 172 | 1.536 432 8435 | 214.573 137 3851 | .004 660 4156 |
| 173 | 1.540 273 9256 | 216.109 570 2286 | .004 627 2824 |
| 174 | 1.544 124 6104 | 217.649 844 1542 | .004 594 5358 |
| 175 | 1.547 984 9219 | 219.193 968 7645 | .004 562 1693 |
| 176 | 1.551 854 8842 | 220.741 953 6865 | .004 530 1764 |
| 177 | 1.555 734 5214 | 222.293 808 5707 | .004 498 5508 |
| 178 | 1.559 623 8577 | 223.849 543 0921 | .004 467 2863 |
| 179 | 1.563 522 9174 | 225.409 166 9498 | .004 436 3768 |
| 180 | 1.567 431 7247 | 226.972 689 8672 | .004 405 8164 |
| n | $s=(1+i)^n$ | $s_{\overline{n}|}=\dfrac{(1+i)^n-1}{i}$ | $\dfrac{1}{s_{\overline{n}|}}=\dfrac{i}{(1+i)^n-1}$ |

.0025

*per period*

**ANNUALLY**
If compounded
*annually*
nominal annual rate is

1/4%

**SEMIANNUALLY**
If compounded
*semiannually*
nominal annual rate is

1/2%

**QUARTERLY**
If compounded
*quarterly*
nominal annual rate is

1%

**MONTHLY**
If compounded
*monthly*
nominal annual rate is

3%

$i$ = .0025
$j_{(2)}$ = .005
$j_{(4)}$ = .01
$j_{(12)}$ = .03

12

| PRESENT WORTH OF 1<br>*What $1 due in the future is worth today.* | PRESENT WORTH OF 1 PER PERIOD<br>*What $1 payable periodically is worth today.* | PARTIAL PAYMENT<br>*Annuity worth $1 today.*<br>*Periodic payment necessary to pay off a loan of $1.* | PERIODS | RATE<br>1/4% |
|---|---|---|---|---|
| .739 247 4985 | 104.301 000 5819 | .009 587 6357 | 121 | |
| .737 403 9886 | 105.038 404 5705 | .009 520 3274 | 122 | .0025 |
| .735 565 0759 | 105.773 969 6464 | .009 454 1219 | 123 | *per period* |
| .733 730 7490 | 106.507 700 3954 | .009 388 9925 | 124 | |
| .731 900 9965 | 107.239 601 3919 | .009 324 9134 | 125 | |
| .730 075 8070 | 107.969 677 1989 | .009 261 8597 | 126 | |
| .728 255 1691 | 108.697 932 3680 | .009 199 8070 | 127 | |
| .726 439 0714 | 109.424 371 4394 | .009 138 7320 | 128 | |
| .724 627 5026 | 110.148 998 9420 | .009 078 6118 | 129 | |
| .722 820 4515 | 110.871 819 3935 | .009 019 4245 | 130 | |
| .721 017 9067 | 111.592 837 3003 | .008 961 1486 | 131 | |
| .719 219 8571 | 112.312 057 1574 | .008 903 7635 | 132 | |
| .717 426 2914 | 113.029 483 4488 | .008 847 2491 | 133 | |
| .715 637 1984 | 113.745 120 6472 | .008 791 5859 | 134 | |
| .713 852 5670 | 114.458 973 2141 | .008 736 7549 | 135 | |
| .712 072 3860 | 115.171 045 6001 | .008 682 7379 | 136 | |
| .710 296 6444 | 115.881 342 2445 | .008 629 5169 | 137 | |
| .708 525 3311 | 116.589 867 5756 | .008 577 0747 | 138 | |
| .706 758 4350 | 117.296 626 0105 | .008 525 3944 | 139 | |
| .704 995 9451 | 118.001 621 9557 | .008 474 4598 | 140 | |
| .703 237 8505 | 118.704 859 8061 | .008 424 2549 | 141 | ANNUALLY<br>*If compounded*<br>*annually*<br>nominal annual rate is<br>1/4% |
| .701 484 1401 | 119.406 343 9463 | .008 374 7644 | 142 | |
| .699 734 8031 | 120.106 078 7494 | .008 325 9733 | 143 | |
| .697 989 8286 | 120.804 068 5780 | .008 277 8669 | 144 | |
| .696 249 2055 | 121.500 317 7835 | .008 230 4311 | 145 | |
| .694 512 9232 | 122.194 830 7067 | .008 183 6522 | 146 | |
| .692 780 9708 | 122.887 611 6775 | .008 137 5168 | 147 | |
| .691 053 3375 | 123.578 665 0150 | .008 092 0117 | 148 | |
| .689 330 0124 | 124.267 995 0274 | .008 047 1243 | 149 | |
| .687 610 9850 | 124.955 606 0124 | .008 002 8422 | 150 | SEMIANNUALLY<br>*If compounded*<br>*semiannually*<br>nominal annual rate is<br>1/2% |
| .685 896 2444 | 125.641 502 2568 | .007 959 1535 | 151 | |
| .684 185 7799 | 126.325 688 0367 | .007 916 0463 | 152 | |
| .682 479 5810 | 127.008 167 6176 | .007 873 5094 | 153 | |
| .680 777 6369 | 127.688 945 2545 | .007 831 5315 | 154 | |
| .679 079 9370 | 128.368 025 1915 | .007 790 1019 | 155 | |
| .677 386 4708 | 129.045 411 6624 | .007 749 2100 | 156 | |
| .675 697 2278 | 129.721 108 8901 | .007 708 8456 | 157 | |
| .674 012 1973 | 130.395 121 0874 | .007 668 9986 | 158 | |
| .672 331 3689 | 131.067 452 4563 | .007 629 6592 | 159 | |
| .670 654 7320 | 131.738 107 1883 | .007 590 8180 | 160 | QUARTERLY<br>*If compounded*<br>*quarterly*<br>nominal annual rate is<br>1% |
| .668 982 2763 | 132.407 089 4646 | .007 552 4657 | 161 | |
| .667 313 9914 | 133.074 403 4560 | .007 514 5931 | 162 | |
| .665 649 8667 | 133.740 053 3227 | .007 477 1916 | 163 | |
| .663 989 8920 | 134.404 043 2147 | .007 440 2524 | 164 | |
| .662 334 0568 | 135.066 377 2715 | .007 403 7671 | 165 | |
| .660 682 3509 | 135.727 059 6224 | .007 367 7276 | 166 | |
| .659 034 7640 | 136.386 094 3864 | .007 332 1258 | 167 | |
| .657 391 2858 | 137.043 485 6723 | .007 296 9539 | 168 | |
| .655 751 9061 | 137.699 237 5783 | .007 262 2043 | 169 | |
| .654 116 6145 | 138.353 354 1928 | .007 227 8696 | 170 | MONTHLY<br>*If compounded*<br>*monthly*<br>nominal annual rate is<br>3% |
| .652 485 4010 | 139.005 839 5939 | .007 193 9424 | 171 | |
| .650 858 2554 | 139.656 697 8492 | .007 160 4156 | 172 | |
| .649 235 1675 | 140.305 933 0167 | .007 127 2824 | 173 | |
| .647 616 1271 | 140.953 549 1438 | .007 094 5358 | 174 | |
| .646 001 1243 | 141.599 550 2682 | .007 062 1693 | 175 | |
| .644 390 1490 | 142.243 940 4171 | .007 030 1764 | 176 | |
| .642 783 1910 | 142.886 723 6081 | .006 998 5508 | 177 | |
| .641 180 2404 | 143.527 903 8485 | .006 967 2863 | 178 | $i$ = .0025 |
| .639 581 2872 | 144.167 485 1356 | .006 936 3768 | 179 | $j_{(2)}$ = .005 |
| .637 986 3214 | 144.805 471 4570 | .006 905 8164 | 180 | $j_{(4)}$ = .01<br>$j_{(12)}$ = .03 |
| $v^n = \dfrac{1}{(1+i)^n}$ | $a_{\overline{n}} = \dfrac{1-v^n}{i}$ | $\dfrac{1}{a_{\overline{n}}} = \dfrac{i}{1-v^n}$ | **n** | |

13

## 1/3%

| P E R I O D S | AMOUNT OF 1<br>*How $1 left at<br>compound interest<br>will grow.* | AMOUNT OF<br>1 PER PERIOD<br>*How $1 deposited<br>periodically will<br>grow.* | SINKING FUND<br>*Periodic deposit<br>that will grow to $1<br>at future date.* |
|---|---|---|---|
| 1 | 1.003 333 3333 | 1.000 000 0000 | 1.000 000 0000 |
| 2 | 1.006 677 7778 | 2.003 333 3333 | .499 168 0532 |
| 3 | 1.010 033 3704 | 3.010 011 1111 | .332 224 6872 |
| 4 | 1.013 400 1483 | 4.020 044 4815 | .248 753 4664 |
| 5 | 1.016 778 1488 | 5.033 444 6298 | .198 671 1037 |
| 6 | 1.020 167 4093 | 6.050 222 7785 | .165 283 1700 |
| 7 | 1.023 567 9673 | 7.070 390 1878 | .141 434 9100 |
| 8 | 1.026 979 8605 | 8.093 958 1551 | .123 548 9461 |
| 9 | 1.030 403 1267 | 9.120 938 0156 | .109 637 8463 |
| 10 | 1.033 837 8038 | 10.151 341 1423 | .098 509 1513 |
| 11 | 1.037 283 9298 | 11.185 178 9461 | .089 404 0234 |
| 12 | 1.040 741 5429 | 12.222 462 8759 | .081 816 5709 |
| 13 | 1.044 210 6814 | 13.263 204 4189 | .075 396 5609 |
| 14 | 1.047 691 3837 | 14.307 415 1003 | .069 893 8273 |
| 15 | 1.051 183 6883 | 15.355 106 4839 | .065 124 9147 |
| 16 | 1.054 687 6339 | 16.406 290 1722 | .060 952 2317 |
| 17 | 1.058 203 2594 | 17.460 977 8061 | .057 270 5613 |
| 18 | 1.061 730 6036 | 18.519 181 0655 | .053 998 0681 |
| 19 | 1.065 269 7056 | 19.580 911 6690 | .051 070 1451 |
| 20 | 1.068 820 6046 | 20.646 181 3746 | .048 435 1068 |
| 21 | 1.072 383 3399 | 21.715 001 9792 | .046 051 1125 |
| 22 | 1.075 957 9511 | 22.787 385 3191 | .043 883 9290 |
| 23 | 1.079 544 4776 | 23.863 343 2702 | .041 905 2766 |
| 24 | 1.083 142 9592 | 24.942 887 7477 | .040 091 5888 |
| 25 | 1.086 753 4357 | 26.026 030 7069 | .038 423 0700 |
| 26 | 1.090 375 9471 | 27.112 784 1426 | .036 882 9698 |
| 27 | 1.094 010 5336 | 28.203 160 0897 | .035 457 0196 |
| 28 | 1.097 657 2354 | 29.297 170 6233 | .034 132 9889 |
| 29 | 1.101 316 0929 | 30.394 827 8588 | .032 900 3344 |
| 30 | 1.104 987 1465 | 31.496 143 9516 | .031 749 9184 |
| 31 | 1.108 670 4370 | 32.601 131 0981 | .030 673 7824 |
| 32 | 1.112 366 0051 | 33.709 801 5351 | .029 664 9625 |
| 33 | 1.116 073 8918 | 34.822 167 5402 | .028 717 3393 |
| 34 | 1.119 794 1381 | 35.938 241 4320 | .027 825 5129 |
| 35 | 1.123 526 7852 | 37.058 035 5701 | .026 984 7007 |
| 36 | 1.127 271 8745 | 38.181 562 3554 | .026 190 6517 |
| 37 | 1.131 029 4474 | 39.308 834 2299 | .025 439 5741 |
| 38 | 1.134 799 5456 | 40.439 863 6773 | .024 728 0754 |
| 39 | 1.138 582 2107 | 41.574 663 2229 | .024 053 1113 |
| 40 | 1.142 377 4848 | 42.713 245 4337 | .023 411 9414 |
| 41 | 1.146 185 4097 | 43.855 622 9184 | .022 802 0932 |
| 42 | 1.150 006 0278 | 45.001 808 3282 | .022 221 3293 |
| 43 | 1.153 839 3812 | 46.151 814 3559 | .021 667 6205 |
| 44 | 1.157 685 5125 | 47.305 653 7371 | .021 139 1223 |
| 45 | 1.161 544 4642 | 48.463 339 2496 | .020 634 1539 |
| 46 | 1.165 416 2790 | 49.624 883 7137 | .020 151 1807 |
| 47 | 1.169 301 0000 | 50.790 299 9928 | .019 688 7988 |
| 48 | 1.173 198 6700 | 51.959 600 9928 | .019 245 7213 |
| 49 | 1.177 109 3322 | 53.132 799 6627 | .018 820 7662 |
| 50 | 1.181 033 0300 | 54.309 908 9949 | .018 412 8462 |
| 51 | 1.184 969 8067 | 55.490 942 0249 | .018 020 9592 |
| 52 | 1.188 919 7061 | 56.675 911 8317 | .017 644 1802 |
| 53 | 1.192 882 7718 | 57.864 831 5378 | .017 281 6540 |
| 54 | 1.196 859 0477 | 59.057 714 3096 | .016 932 5889 |
| 55 | 1.200 848 5779 | 60.254 573 3573 | .016 596 2506 |
| 56 | 1.204 851 4065 | 61.455 421 9351 | .016 271 9573 |
| 57 | 1.208 867 5778 | 62.660 273 3416 | .015 959 0750 |
| 58 | 1.212 897 1364 | 63.869 140 9194 | .015 657 0135 |
| 59 | 1.216 940 1269 | 65.082 038 0558 | .015 365 2226 |
| 60 | 1.220 996 5939 | 66.298 978 1826 | .015 083 1887 |
| **n** | $s=(1+i)^n$ | $s_{\overline{n}\rceil}=\dfrac{(1+i)^n-1}{i}$ | $\dfrac{1}{s_{\overline{n}\rceil}}=\dfrac{i}{(1+i)^n-1}$ |

.00333333

*per period*

ANNUALLY
If compounded
*annually*
nominal annual rate is

1/3%

SEMIANNUALLY
If compounded
*semiannually*
nominal annual rate is

2/3%

QUARTERLY
If compounded
*quarterly*
nominal annual rate is

1 1/3%

MONTHLY
If compounded
*monthly*
nominal annual rate is

4%

$i \quad = .0033333\dot{3}$
$j_{(2)} = .00666666$
$j_{(4)} = .01333333$
$j_{(12)} = .04$

| PRESENT WORTH OF 1<br>*What $1 due in the future is worth today.* | PRESENT WORTH OF 1 PER PERIOD<br>*What $1 payable periodically is worth today.* | PARTIAL PAYMENT<br>*Annuity worth $1 today.*<br>*Periodic payment necessary to pay off a loan of $1.* | PERIODS | RATE<br>$\frac{1}{3}\%$ |
|---|---|---|---|---|
| .996 677 7409 | .996 677 7409 | 1.003 333 3333 | 1 | |
| .993 366 5191 | 1.990 044 2600 | .502 501 3866 | 2 | |
| .990 066 2981 | 2.980 110 5581 | .335 558 0206 | 3 | .00333333 |
| .986 777 0413 | 3.966 887 5995 | .252 086 7998 | 4 | *per period* |
| .983 498 7123 | 4.950 386 3118 | .202 004 4370 | 5 | |
| .980 231 2747 | 5.930 617 5865 | .168 616 5033 | 6 | |
| .976 974 6924 | 6.907 592 2789 | .144 768 2434 | 7 | |
| .973 728 9293 | 7.881 321 2082 | .126 882 2795 | 8 | |
| .970 493 9495 | 8.851 815 1577 | .112 971 1796 | 9 | |
| .967 269 7171 | 9.819 084 8747 | .101 842 4846 | 10 | |
| .964 056 1964 | 10.783 141 0712 | .092 737 3567 | 11 | |
| .960 853 3519 | 11.743 994 4231 | .085 149 9042 | 12 | |
| .957 661 1481 | 12.701 655 5712 | .078 729 8943 | 13 | |
| .954 479 5496 | 13.656 135 1208 | .073 227 1606 | 14 | |
| .951 308 5212 | 14.607 443 6420 | .068 458 2480 | 15 | |
| .948 148 0278 | 15.555 591 6698 | .064 285 5650 | 16 | |
| .944 998 0343 | 16.500 589 7041 | .060 603 8946 | 17 | |
| .941 858 5060 | 17.442 448 2100 | .057 331 4014 | 18 | |
| .938 729 4079 | 18.381 177 6180 | .054 403 4784 | 19 | |
| .935 610 7056 | 19.316 788 3236 | .051 768 4401 | 20 | |
| .932 502 3644 | 20.249 290 6879 | .049 384 4459 | 21 | ANNUALLY<br>If compounded *annually* nominal annual rate is |
| .929 404 3499 | 21.178 695 0378 | .047 217 2624 | 22 | |
| .926 316 6278 | 22.105 011 6656 | .045 238 6099 | 23 | |
| .923 239 1639 | 23.028 250 8295 | .043 424 9222 | 24 | |
| .920 171 9242 | 23.948 422 7537 | .041 756 4033 | 25 | $\frac{1}{3}\%$ |
| .917 114 8746 | 24.865 537 6282 | .040 216 3032 | 26 | |
| .914 067 9813 | 25.779 605 6095 | .038 790 3529 | 27 | |
| .911 031 2106 | 26.690 636 8201 | .037 466 3222 | 28 | |
| .908 004 5288 | 27.598 641 3490 | .036 233 6677 | 29 | |
| .904 987 9025 | 28.503 629 2515 | .035 083 2517 | 30 | SEMIANNUALLY<br>If compounded *semiannually* nominal annual rate is |
| .901 981 2982 | 29.405 610 5496 | .034 007 1157 | 31 | |
| .898 984 6826 | 30.304 595 2322 | .032 998 2959 | 32 | |
| .895 998 0225 | 31.200 593 2547 | .032 050 6726 | 33 | |
| .893 021 2849 | 32.093 614 5395 | .031 158 8462 | 34 | |
| .890 054 4367 | 32.983 668 9763 | .030 318 0341 | 35 | $\frac{2}{3}\%$ |
| .887 097 4453 | 33.870 766 4215 | .029 523 9850 | 36 | |
| .884 150 2777 | 34.754 916 6992 | .028 772 9074 | 37 | |
| .881 212 9013 | 35.636 129 6005 | .028 061 4088 | 38 | |
| .878 285 2837 | 36.514 414 8843 | .027 386 4446 | 39 | |
| .875 367 3924 | 37.389 782 2767 | .026 745 2748 | 40 | QUARTERLY<br>If compounded *quarterly* nominal annual rate is |
| .872 459 1951 | 38.262 241 4718 | .026 135 4265 | 41 | |
| .869 560 6596 | 39.131 802 1313 | .025 554 6626 | 42 | |
| .866 671 7537 | 39.998 473 8850 | .025 000 9539 | 43 | |
| .863 792 4456 | 40.862 266 3306 | .024 472 4556 | 44 | |
| .860 922 7032 | 41.723 189 0338 | .023 967 4872 | 45 | $1\frac{1}{3}\%$ |
| .858 062 4949 | 42.581 251 5287 | .023 484 5141 | 46 | |
| .855 211 7889 | 43.436 463 3177 | .023 022 1322 | 47 | |
| .852 370 5538 | 44.288 833 8714 | .022 579 0546 | 48 | |
| .849 538 7579 | 45.138 372 6293 | .022 154 0995 | 49 | |
| .846 716 3700 | 45.985 088 9993 | .021 746 1795 | 50 | MONTHLY<br>If compounded *monthly* nominal annual rate is |
| .843 903 3588 | 46.828 992 3582 | .021 354 2925 | 51 | |
| .841 099 6932 | 47.670 092 0513 | .020 977 5135 | 52 | |
| .838 305 3420 | 48.508 397 3933 | .020 614 9874 | 53 | |
| .835 520 2744 | 49.343 917 6678 | .020 265 9223 | 54 | |
| .832 744 4596 | 50.176 662 1274 | .019 929 5839 | 55 | $4\%$ |
| .829 977 8667 | 51.006 639 9940 | .019 605 2906 | 56 | |
| .827 220 4651 | 51.833 860 4592 | .019 292 4083 | 57 | |
| .824 472 2244 | 52.658 332 6836 | .018 990 3468 | 58 | $i\ \ =.00333333$ |
| .821 733 1140 | 53.480 065 7976 | .018 698 5559 | 59 | $j_{(2)}\ =.00666666$ |
| .819 003 1037 | 54.299 068 9012 | .018 416 5221 | 60 | $j_{(4)}\ =.01333333$<br>$j_{(12)}=.04$ |
| $v^n=\dfrac{1}{(1+i)^n}$ | $a_{\overline{n}\rvert}=\dfrac{1-v^n}{i}$ | $\dfrac{1}{a_{\overline{n}\rvert}}=\dfrac{i}{1-v^n}$ | n | |

15

.00333333

*per period*

| P E R I O D S | AMOUNT OF 1<br>*How $1 left at compound interest will grow.* | AMOUNT OF 1 PER PERIOD<br>*How $1 deposited periodically will grow.* | SINKING FUND<br>*Periodic deposit that will grow to $1 at future date.* |
|---|---|---|---|
| 61 | 1.225 066 5826 | 67.519 974 7766 | .014 810 4321 |
| 62 | 1.229 150 1379 | 68.745 041 3592 | .014 546 5037 |
| 63 | 1.233 247 3050 | 69.974 191 4970 | .014 290 9833 |
| 64 | 1.237 358 1293 | 71.207 438 8020 | .014 043 4766 |
| 65 | 1.241 482 6564 | 72.444 796 9314 | .013 803 6138 |
| 66 | 1.245 620 9320 | 73.686 279 5878 | .013 571 0475 |
| 67 | 1.249 773 0017 | 74.931 900 5198 | .013 345 4509 |
| 68 | 1.253 938 9117 | 76.181 673 5215 | .013 126 5166 |
| 69 | 1.258 118 7081 | 77.435 612 4332 | .012 913 9548 |
| 70 | 1.262 312 4371 | 78.693 731 1413 | .012 707 4925 |
| 71 | 1.266 520 1453 | 79.956 043 5785 | .012 506 8720 |
| 72 | 1.270 741 8791 | 81.222 563 7237 | .012 311 8497 |
| 73 | 1.274 977 6853 | 82.493 305 6028 | .012 122 1958 |
| 74 | 1.279 227 6110 | 83.768 283 2882 | .011 937 6924 |
| 75 | 1.283 491 7030 | 85.047 510 8991 | .011 758 1337 |
| 76 | 1.287 770 0087 | 86.331 002 6021 | .011 583 3243 |
| 77 | 1.292 062 5754 | 87.618 772 6108 | .011 413 0793 |
| 78 | 1.296 369 4506 | 88.910 835 1862 | .011 247 2231 |
| 79 | 1.300 690 6821 | 90.207 204 6368 | .011 085 5891 |
| 80 | 1.305 026 3177 | 91.507 895 3189 | .010 928 0188 |
| 81 | 1.309 376 4055 | 92.812 921 6366 | .010 774 3618 |
| 82 | 1.313 740 9935 | 94.122 298 0421 | .010 624 4750 |
| 83 | 1.318 120 1301 | 95.436 039 0356 | .010 478 2220 |
| 84 | 1.322 513 8639 | 96.754 159 1657 | .010 335 4730 |
| 85 | 1.326 922 2434 | 98.076 673 0296 | .010 196 1044 |
| 86 | 1.331 345 3176 | 99.403 595 2730 | .010 059 9983 |
| 87 | 1.335 783 1353 | 100.734 940 5906 | .009 927 0421 |
| 88 | 1.340 235 7458 | 102.070 723 7259 | .009 797 1285 |
| 89 | 1.344 703 1982 | 103.410 959 4716 | .009 670 1549 |
| 90 | 1.349 185 5422 | 104.755 662 6699 | .009 546 0233 |
| 91 | 1.353 682 8274 | 106.104 848 2121 | .009 424 6400 |
| 92 | 1.358 195 1035 | 107.458 531 0395 | .009 305 9154 |
| 93 | 1.362 722 4205 | 108.816 726 1429 | .009 189 7637 |
| 94 | 1.367 264 8285 | 110.179 448 5634 | .009 076 1028 |
| 95 | 1.371 822 3780 | 111.546 713 3920 | .008 964 8540 |
| 96 | 1.376 395 1192 | 112.918 535 7699 | .008 855 9420 |
| 97 | 1.380 983 1030 | 114.294 930 8892 | .008 749 2944 |
| 98 | 1.385 586 3800 | 115.675 913 9921 | .008 644 8420 |
| 99 | 1.390 205 0012 | 117.061 500 3721 | .008 542 5182 |
| 100 | 1.394 839 0179 | 118.451 705 3733 | .008 442 2592 |
| 101 | 1.399 488 4813 | 119.846 544 3913 | .008 344 0036 |
| 102 | 1.404 153 4429 | 121.246 032 8726 | .008 247 6925 |
| 103 | 1.408 833 9544 | 122.650 186 3155 | .008 153 2693 |
| 104 | 1.413 530 0676 | 124.059 020 2699 | .008 060 6795 |
| 105 | 1.418 241 8345 | 125.472 550 3374 | .007 969 8707 |
| 106 | 1.422 969 3072 | 126.890 792 1719 | .007 880 7925 |
| 107 | 1.427 712 5383 | 128.313 761 4791 | .007 793 3963 |
| 108 | 1.432 471 5801 | 129.741 474 0174 | .007 707 6356 |
| 109 | 1.437 246 4853 | 131.173 945 5974 | .007 623 4651 |
| 110 | 1.442 037 3069 | 132.611 192 0828 | .007 540 8416 |
| 111 | 1.446 844 0980 | 134.053 229 3897 | .007 459 7233 |
| 112 | 1.451 666 9116 | 135.500 073 4877 | .007 380 0698 |
| 113 | 1.456 505 8013 | 136.951 740 3993 | .007 301 8422 |
| 114 | 1.461 360 8207 | 138.408 246 2006 | .007 225 0030 |
| 115 | 1.466 232 0234 | 139.869 607 0213 | .007 149 5160 |
| 116 | 1.471 119 4635 | 141.335 839 0447 | .007 075 3463 |
| 117 | 1.476 023 1950 | 142.806 958 5082 | .007 002 4599 |
| 118 | 1.480 943 2723 | 144.282 981 7032 | .006 930 8243 |
| 119 | 1.485 879 7499 | 145.763 924 9756 | .006 860 4080 |
| 120 | 1.490 832 6824 | 147.249 804 7255 | .006 791 1805 |
| **n** | $s=(1+i)^n$ | $s_{\overline{n}\|}=\dfrac{(1+i)^n-1}{i}$ | $\dfrac{1}{s_{\overline{n}\|}}=\dfrac{i}{(1+i)^n-1}$ |

ANNUALLY
If compounded
*annually*
nominal annual rate is

**1/3%**

SEMIANNUALLY
If compounded
*semiannually*
nominal annual rate is

**2/3%**

QUARTERLY
If compounded
*quarterly*
nominal annual rate is

**1 1/3%**

MONTHLY
If compounded
*monthly*
nominal annual rate is

**4%**

$i$ = .00333333
$j_{(2)}$ = .00666666
$j_{(4)}$ = .01333333
$j_{(12)}$ = .04

| PRESENT WORTH OF 1 *What $1 due in the future is worth today.* | PRESENT WORTH OF 1 PER PERIOD *What $1 payable periodically is worth today.* | PARTIAL PAYMENT *Annuity worth $1 today.* *Periodic payment necessary to pay off a loan of $1.* | PERIODS | RATE |
|---|---|---|---|---|
| | | | | |
| .816 282 1631 | 55.115 351 0644 | .018 143 7654 | 61 | |
| .813 570 2622 | 55.928 921 3266 | .017 879 8371 | 62 | |
| .810 867 3710 | 56.739 788 6976 | .017 624 3166 | 63 | .00333333 |
| .808 173 4595 | 57.547 962 1571 | .017 376 8099 | 64 | |
| .805 488 4978 | 58.353 450 6549 | .017 136 9472 | 65 | *per period* |
| .802 812 4563 | 59.156 263 1112 | .016 904 3808 | 66 | |
| .800 145 3053 | 59.956 408 4165 | .016 678 7842 | 67 | |
| .797 487 0152 | 60.753 895 4317 | .016 459 8499 | 68 | |
| .794 837 5567 | 61.548 732 9884 | .016 247 2881 | 69 | |
| .792 196 9004 | 62.340 929 8888 | .016 040 8259 | 70 | |
| .789 565 0170 | 63.130 494 9058 | .015 840 2053 | 71 | |
| .786 941 8774 | 63.917 436 7831 | .015 645 1831 | 72 | |
| .784 327 4525 | 64.701 764 2357 | .015 455 5291 | 73 | |
| .781 721 7135 | 65.483 485 9492 | .015 271 0257 | 74 | |
| .779 124 6314 | 66.262 610 5806 | .015 091 4670 | 75 | |
| .776 536 1775 | 67.039 146 7581 | .014 916 6576 | 76 | |
| .773 956 3231 | 67.813 103 0811 | .014 746 4126 | 77 | |
| .771 385 0396 | 68.584 488 1207 | .014 580 5564 | 78 | |
| .768 822 2986 | 69.353 310 4193 | .014 418 9224 | 79 | |
| .766 268 0717 | 70.119 578 4910 | .014 261 3521 | 80 | |
| .763 722 3306 | 70.883 300 8216 | .014 107 6952 | 81 | ANNUALLY *If compounded annually* nominal annual rate is |
| .761 185 0471 | 71.644 485 8687 | .013 957 8083 | 82 | |
| .758 656 1931 | 72.403 142 0619 | .013 811 5553 | 83 | |
| .756 135 7407 | 73.159 277 8025 | .013 668 8063 | 84 | |
| .753 623 6618 | 73.912 901 4643 | .013 529 4378 | 85 | **1/3%** |
| .751 119 9287 | 74.664 021 3930 | .013 393 3316 | 86 | |
| .748 624 5136 | 75.412 645 9066 | .013 260 3755 | 87 | |
| .746 137 3890 | 76.158 783 2956 | .013 130 4619 | 88 | |
| .743 658 5273 | 76.902 441 8229 | .013 003 4883 | 89 | |
| .741 187 9009 | 77.643 629 7238 | .012 879 3567 | 90 | |
| .738 725 4826 | 78.382 355 2065 | .012 757 9734 | 91 | SEMIANNUALLY *If compounded semiannually* nominal annual rate is |
| .736 271 2452 | 79.118 626 4516 | .012 639 2487 | 92 | |
| .733 825 1613 | 79.852 451 6129 | .012 523 0970 | 93 | |
| .731 387 2039 | 80.583 838 8169 | .012 409 4361 | 94 | |
| .728 957 3461 | 81.312 796 1630 | .012 298 1873 | 95 | **2/3%** |
| .726 535 5609 | 82.039 331 7239 | .012 189 2753 | 96 | |
| .724 121 8215 | 82.763 453 5454 | .012 082 6277 | 97 | |
| .721 716 1012 | 83.485 169 6466 | .011 978 1753 | 98 | |
| .719 318 3733 | 84.204 488 0199 | .011 875 8516 | 99 | |
| .716 928 6112 | 84.921 416 6311 | .011 775 5925 | 100 | |
| .714 546 7886 | 85.635 963 4197 | .011 677 3370 | 101 | QUARTERLY *If compounded quarterly* nominal annual rate is |
| .712 172 8790 | 86.348 136 2987 | .011 581 0259 | 102 | |
| .709 806 8562 | 87.057 943 1549 | .011 486 6026 | 103 | |
| .707 448 6938 | 87.765 391 8487 | .011 394 0128 | 104 | |
| .705 098 3660 | 88.470 490 2146 | .011 303 2040 | 105 | **1 1/3%** |
| .702 755 8465 | 89.173 246 0611 | .011 214 1258 | 106 | |
| .700 421 1094 | 89.873 667 1705 | .011 126 7297 | 107 | |
| .698 094 1290 | 90.571 761 2995 | .011 040 9689 | 108 | |
| .695 774 8794 | 91.267 536 1789 | .010 956 7985 | 109 | |
| .693 463 3350 | 91.960 999 5139 | .010 874 1750 | 110 | |
| .691 159 4701 | 92.652 158 9840 | .010 793 0566 | 111 | MONTHLY *If compounded monthly* nominal annual rate is |
| .688 863 2592 | 93.341 022 2431 | .010 713 4031 | 112 | |
| .686 574 6769 | 94.027 596 9201 | .010 635 1756 | 113 | |
| .684 293 6979 | 94.711 890 6180 | .010 558 3364 | 114 | |
| .682 020 2970 | 95.393 910 9150 | .010 482 8494 | 115 | **4%** |
| .679 754 4488 | 96.073 665 3638 | .010 408 6796 | 116 | |
| .677 496 1284 | 96.751 161 4921 | .010 335 7932 | 117 | |
| .675 245 3107 | 97.426 406 8028 | .010 264 1577 | 118 | $i$ = .00333333 |
| .673 001 9708 | 98.099 408 7735 | .010 193 7414 | 119 | $j_{(2)}$ = .00666666 $j_{(4)}$ = .01333333 |
| .670 766 0838 | 98.770 174 8573 | .010 124 5138 | 120 | $j_{(12)}$ = .04 |
| $v^n = \dfrac{1}{(1+i)^n}$ | $a_{\overline{n}\rvert} = \dfrac{1-v^n}{i}$ | $\dfrac{1}{a_{\overline{n}\rvert}} = \dfrac{i}{1-v^n}$ | n | |

17

**RATE**

**1/3%**

.00333333

*per period*

| P E R I O D S | AMOUNT OF 1 *How $1 left at compound interest will grow.* | AMOUNT OF 1 PER PERIOD *How $1 deposited periodically will grow.* | SINKING FUND *Periodic deposit that will grow to $1 at future date.* |
|---|---|---|---|
| 121 | 1.495 802 1247 | 148.740 637 4079 | .006 723 1122 |
| 122 | 1.500 788 1318 | 150.236 439 5326 | .006 656 1748 |
| 123 | 1.505 790 7589 | 151.737 227 6644 | .006 590 3405 |
| 124 | 1.510 810 0614 | 153.243 018 4232 | .006 525 5828 |
| 125 | 1.515 846 0949 | 154.753 828 4847 | .006 461 8757 |
| 126 | 1.520 898 9153 | 156.269 674 5796 | .006 399 1942 |
| 127 | 1.525 968 5783 | 157.790 573 4949 | .006 337 5142 |
| 128 | 1.531 055 1402 | 159.316 542 0732 | .006 276 8121 |
| 129 | 1.536 158 6574 | 160.847 597 2134 | .006 217 0652 |
| 130 | 1.541 279 1862 | 162.383 755 8708 | .006 158 2514 |
| 131 | 1.546 416 7835 | 163.925 035 0570 | .006 100 3495 |
| 132 | 1.551 571 5061 | 165.471 451 8406 | .006 043 3385 |
| 133 | 1.556 743 4112 | 167.023 023 3467 | .005 987 1985 |
| 134 | 1.561 932 5559 | 168.579 766 7579 | .005 931 9100 |
| 135 | 1.567 138 9977 | 170.141 699 3137 | .005 877 4539 |
| 136 | 1.572 362 7944 | 171.708 838 3114 | .005 823 8120 |
| 137 | 1.577 604 0037 | 173.281 201 1058 | .005 770 9665 |
| 138 | 1.582 862 6837 | 174.858 805 1095 | .005 718 8999 |
| 139 | 1.588 138 8926 | 176.441 667 7932 | .005 667 5955 |
| 140 | 1.593 432 6890 | 178.029 806 6858 | .005 617 0369 |
| 141 | 1.598 744 1312 | 179.623 239 3748 | .005 567 2084 |
| 142 | 1.604 073 2784 | 181.221 983 5060 | .005 518 0943 |
| 143 | 1.609 420 1893 | 182.826 056 7844 | .005 469 6799 |
| 144 | 1.614 784 9232 | 184.435 476 9737 | .005 421 9504 |
| 145 | 1.620 167 5397 | 186.050 261 8969 | .005 374 8917 |
| 146 | 1.625 568 0981 | 187.670 429 4366 | .005 328 4900 |
| 147 | 1.630 986 6584 | 189.295 997 5347 | .005 282 7319 |
| 148 | 1.636 423 2806 | 190.926 984 1931 | .005 237 6043 |
| 149 | 1.641 878 0249 | 192.563 407 4738 | .005 193 0946 |
| 150 | 1.647 350 9517 | 194.205 285 4987 | .005 149 1904 |
| 151 | 1.652 842 1215 | 195.852 636 4504 | .005 105 8797 |
| 152 | 1.658 351 5952 | 197.505 478 5719 | .005 063 1507 |
| 153 | 1.663 879 4339 | 199.163 830 1671 | .005 020 9920 |
| 154 | 1.669 425 6987 | 200.827 709 6010 | .004 979 3925 |
| 155 | 1.674 990 4510 | 202.497 135 2997 | .004 938 3415 |
| 156 | 1.680 573 7525 | 204.172 125 7507 | .004 897 8282 |
| 157 | 1.686 175 6650 | 205.852 699 5032 | .004 857 8425 |
| 158 | 1.691 796 2506 | 207.538 875 1682 | .004 818 3744 |
| 159 | 1.697 435 5714 | 209.230 671 4187 | .004 779 4140 |
| 160 | 1.703 093 6900 | 210.928 106 9901 | .004 740 9519 |
| 161 | 1.708 770 6689 | 212.631 200 6801 | .004 702 9787 |
| 162 | 1.714 466 5712 | 214.339 971 3490 | .004 665 4854 |
| 163 | 1.720 181 4597 | 216.054 437 9202 | .004 628 4631 |
| 164 | 1.725 915 3979 | 217.774 619 3799 | .004 591 9033 |
| 165 | 1.731 668 4493 | 219.500 534 7779 | .004 555 7976 |
| 166 | 1.737 440 6774 | 221.232 203 2271 | .004 520 1376 |
| 167 | 1.743 232 1463 | 222.969 643 9045 | .004 484 9154 |
| 168 | 1.749 042 9202 | 224.712 876 0509 | .004 450 1233 |
| 169 | 1.754 873 0632 | 226.461 918 9711 | .004 415 7535 |
| 170 | 1.760 722 6401 | 228.216 792 0343 | .004 381 7985 |
| 171 | 1.766 591 7156 | 229.977 514 6744 | .004 348 2512 |
| 172 | 1.772 480 3546 | 231.744 106 3900 | .004 315 1043 |
| 173 | 1.778 388 6225 | 233.516 586 7446 | .004 282 3510 |
| 174 | 1.784 316 5846 | 235.294 975 3671 | .004 249 9845 |
| 175 | 1.790 264 3065 | 237.079 291 9517 | .004 217 9981 |
| 176 | 1.796 231 8542 | 238.869 556 2582 | .004 186 3853 |
| 177 | 1.802 219 2937 | 240.665 788 1124 | .004 155 1398 |
| 178 | 1.808 226 6914 | 242.468 007 4061 | .004 124 2554 |
| 179 | 1.814 254 1137 | 244.276 234 0974 | .004 093 7261 |
| 180 | 1.820 301 6274 | 246.090 488 2111 | .004 063 5459 |
| **n** | $s=(1+i)^n$ | $s_{\overline{n}|}=\dfrac{(1+i)^n-1}{i}$ | $\dfrac{1}{s_{\overline{n}|}}=\dfrac{i}{(1+i)^n-1}$ |

**ANNUALLY**
If compounded
*annually*
nominal annual rate is

**1/3%**

**SEMIANNUALLY**
If compounded
*semiannually*
nominal annual rate is

**2/3%**

**QUARTERLY**
If compounded
*quarterly*
nominal annual rate is

**1 1/3%**

**MONTHLY**
If compounded
*monthly*
nominal annual rate is

**4%**

$i\ \ = .00333333$
$j_{(2)} = .00666666$
$j_{(4)} = .01333333$
$j_{(12)} = .04$

18

| PRESENT WORTH OF 1 | PRESENT WORTH OF 1 PER PERIOD | PARTIAL PAYMENT | P E R I O D S | RATE |
|---|---|---|---|---|
| *What $1 due in the future is worth today.* | *What $1 payable periodically is worth today.* | *Annuity worth $1 today.* *Periodic payment necessary to pay off a loan of $1.* | | **1/3%** |
| .668 537 6251 | 99.438 712 4824 | .010 056 4456 | 121 | |
| .666 316 5698 | 100.105 029 0522 | .009 989 5081 | 122 | |
| .664 102 8935 | 100.769 131 9457 | .009 923 6739 | 123 | .00333333 |
| .661 896 5716 | 101.431 028 5173 | .009 858 9161 | 124 | |
| .659 697 5797 | 102.090 726 0970 | .009 795 2090 | 125 | *per period* |
| .657 505 8934 | 102.748 231 9904 | .009 732 5276 | 126 | |
| .655 321 4884 | 103.403 553 4788 | .009 670 8475 | 127 | |
| .653 144 3406 | 104.056 697 8194 | .009 610 1454 | 128 | |
| .650 974 4258 | 104.707 672 2452 | .009 550 3985 | 129 | |
| .648 811 7201 | 105.356 483 9654 | .009 491 5848 | 130 | |
| .646 656 1995 | 106.003 140 1648 | .009 433 6828 | 131 | |
| .644 507 8400 | 106.647 648 0048 | .009 376 6719 | 132 | |
| .642 366 6179 | 107.290 014 6227 | .009 320 5319 | 133 | |
| .640 232 5096 | 107.930 247 1323 | .009 265 2433 | 134 | |
| .638 105 4913 | 108.568 352 6235 | .009 210 7873 | 135 | |
| .635 985 5395 | 109.204 338 1630 | .009 157 1454 | 136 | |
| .633 872 6307 | 109.838 210 7937 | .009 104 2998 | 137 | |
| .631 766 7415 | 110.469 977 5352 | .009 052 2332 | 138 | |
| .629 667 8487 | 111.099 645 3839 | .009 000 9288 | 139 | |
| .627 575 9290 | 111.727 221 3129 | .008 950 3703 | 140 | |
| .625 490 9591 | 112.352 712 2720 | .008 900 5417 | 141 | ANNUALLY |
| .623 412 9160 | 112.976 125 1880 | .008 851 4277 | 142 | If compounded *annually* nominal annual rate is |
| .621 341 7768 | 113.597 466 9648 | .008 803 0132 | 143 | |
| .619 277 5184 | 114.216 744 4832 | .008 755 2837 | 144 | |
| .617 220 1180 | 114.833 964 6012 | .008 708 2250 | 145 | **1/3%** |
| .615 169 5528 | 115.449 134 1540 | .008 661 8233 | 146 | |
| .613 125 8002 | 116.062 259 9542 | .008 616 0652 | 147 | |
| .611 088 8374 | 116.673 348 7915 | .008 570 9377 | 148 | |
| .609 058 6419 | 117.282 407 4334 | .008 526 4280 | 149 | |
| .607 035 1913 | 117.889 442 6247 | .008 482 5238 | 150 | |
| .605 018 4630 | 118.494 461 0877 | .008 439 2130 | 151 | SEMIANNUALLY |
| .603 008 4349 | 119.097 469 5226 | .008 396 4840 | 152 | If compounded *semiannually* nominal annual rate is |
| .601 005 0846 | 119.698 474 6073 | .008 354 3253 | 153 | |
| .599 008 3900 | 120.297 482 9973 | .008 312 7259 | 154 | |
| .597 018 3289 | 120.894 501 3262 | .008 271 6748 | 155 | **2/3%** |
| .595 034 8793 | 121.489 536 2055 | .008 231 1616 | 156 | |
| .593 058 0193 | 122.082 594 2248 | .008 191 1759 | 157 | |
| .591 087 7268 | 122.673 681 9516 | .008 151 7077 | 158 | |
| .589 123 9802 | 123.262 805 9318 | .008 112 7473 | 159 | |
| .587 166 7577 | 123.849 972 6895 | .008 074 2852 | 160 | |
| .585 216 0376 | 124.435 188 7271 | .008 036 3120 | 161 | QUARTERLY |
| .583 271 7982 | 125.018 460 5253 | .007 998 8187 | 162 | If compounded *quarterly* nominal annual rate is |
| .581 334 0182 | 125.599 794 5435 | .007 961 7965 | 163 | |
| .579 402 6759 | 126.179 197 2195 | .007 925 2367 | 164 | |
| .577 477 7501 | 126.756 674 9696 | .007 889 1309 | 165 | **1 1/3%** |
| .575 559 2194 | 127.332 234 1889 | .007 853 4709 | 166 | |
| .573 647 0625 | 127.905 881 2514 | .007 818 2488 | 167 | |
| .571 741 2583 | 128.477 622 5097 | .007 783 4566 | 168 | |
| .569 841 7857 | 129.047 464 2954 | .007 749 0868 | 169 | |
| .567 948 6236 | 129.615 412 9190 | .007 715 1318 | 170 | |
| .566 061 7511 | 130.181 474 6701 | .007 681 5845 | 171 | MONTHLY |
| .564 181 1473 | 130.745 655 8174 | .007 648 4377 | 172 | If compounded *monthly* nominal annual rate is |
| .562 306 7913 | 131.307 962 6087 | .007 615 6844 | 173 | |
| .560 438 6624 | 131.868 401 2711 | .007 583 3178 | 174 | |
| .558 576 7400 | 132.426 978 0111 | .007 551 3314 | 175 | **4%** |
| .556 721 0033 | 132.983 699 0144 | .007 519 7186 | 176 | |
| .554 871 4318 | 133.538 570 4462 | .007 488 4732 | 177 | |
| .553 028 0052 | 134.091 598 4514 | .007 457 5888 | 178 | $i \;\; = .00333333$ |
| .551 190 7028 | 134.642 789 1542 | .007 427 0595 | 179 | $j_{(2)} = .00666666$ |
| .549 359 5045 | 135.192 148 6587 | .007 396 8793 | 180 | $j_{(4)} = .01333333$ $j_{(12)} = .04$ |
| $v^n = \dfrac{1}{(1+i)^n}$ | $a_{\overline{n}|} = \dfrac{1-v^n}{i}$ | $\dfrac{1}{a_{\overline{n}|}} = \dfrac{i}{1-v^n}$ | **n** | |

19

| P E R I O D S | AMOUNT OF 1<br>*How $1 left at compound interest will grow.* | AMOUNT OF 1 PER PERIOD<br>*How $1 deposited periodically will grow.* | SINKING FUND<br>*Periodic deposit that will grow to $1 at future date.* |
|---|---|---|---|
| 1 | 1.004 166 6667 | 1.000 000 0000 | 1.000 000 0000 |
| 2 | 1.008 350 6944 | 2.004 166 6667 | .498 960 4990 |
| 3 | 1.012 552 1557 | 3.012 517 3611 | .331 948 2944 |
| 4 | 1.016 771 1230 | 4.025 069 5168 | .248 442 9140 |
| 5 | 1.021 007 6693 | 5.041 840 6398 | .198 340 2633 |
| 6 | 1.025 261 8680 | 6.062 848 3091 | .164 938 9774 |
| 7 | 1.029 533 7924 | 7.088 110 1771 | .141 081 3285 |
| 8 | 1.033 823 5165 | 8.117 643 9695 | .123 188 4527 |
| 9 | 1.038 131 1145 | 9.151 467 4860 | .109 272 0923 |
| 10 | 1.042 456 6608 | 10.189 598 6005 | .098 139 2927 |
| 11 | 1.046 800 2303 | 11.232 055 2614 | .089 030 9010 |
| 12 | 1.051 161 8979 | 12.278 855 4916 | .081 440 8151 |
| 13 | 1.055 541 7391 | 13.330 017 3895 | .075 018 6568 |
| 14 | 1.059 939 8297 | 14.385 559 1286 | .069 514 1559 |
| 15 | 1.064 356 2457 | 15.445 498 9583 | .064 743 7809 |
| 16 | 1.068 791 0633 | 16.509 855 2040 | .060 569 8831 |
| 17 | 1.073 244 3594 | 17.578 646 2673 | .056 887 2019 |
| 18 | 1.077 716 2109 | 18.651 890 6268 | .053 613 8679 |
| 19 | 1.082 206 6952 | 19.729 606 8377 | .050 685 2472 |
| 20 | 1.086 715 8897 | 20.811 813 5329 | .048 049 6329 |
| 21 | 1.091 243 8726 | 21.898 529 4226 | .045 665 1669 |
| 22 | 1.095 790 7221 | 22.989 773 2952 | .043 497 6016 |
| 23 | 1.100 356 5167 | 24.085 564 0173 | .041 518 6457 |
| 24 | 1.104 941 3356 | 25.185 920 5340 | .039 704 7231 |
| 25 | 1.109 545 2578 | 26.290 861 8696 | .038 036 0296 |
| 26 | 1.114 168 3630 | 27.400 407 1273 | .036 495 8081 |
| 27 | 1.118 810 7312 | 28.514 575 4904 | .035 069 7839 |
| 28 | 1.123 472 4426 | 29.633 386 2216 | .033 745 7215 |
| 29 | 1.128 153 5778 | 30.756 858 6642 | .032 513 0733 |
| 30 | 1.132 854 2177 | 31.885 012 2419 | .031 362 6977 |
| 31 | 1.137 574 4436 | 33.017 866 4596 | .030 286 6329 |
| 32 | 1.142 314 3371 | 34.155 440 9032 | .029 277 9122 |
| 33 | 1.147 073 9802 | 35.297 755 2403 | .028 330 4135 |
| 34 | 1.151 853 4551 | 36.444 829 2205 | .027 438 7347 |
| 35 | 1.156 652 8445 | 37.596 682 6756 | .026 598 0913 |
| 36 | 1.161 472 2313 | 38.753 335 5200 | .025 804 2304 |
| 37 | 1.166 311 6990 | 39.914 807 7514 | .025 053 3588 |
| 38 | 1.171 171 3310 | 41.081 119 4503 | .024 342 0825 |
| 39 | 1.176 051 2116 | 42.252 290 7814 | .023 667 3558 |
| 40 | 1.180 951 4250 | 43.428 341 9930 | .023 026 4374 |
| 41 | 1.185 872 0559 | 44.609 293 4179 | .022 416 8536 |
| 42 | 1.190 813 1895 | 45.795 165 4738 | .021 836 3661 |
| 43 | 1.195 774 9111 | 46.985 978 6633 | .021 282 9450 |
| 44 | 1.200 757 3066 | 48.181 753 5744 | .020 754 7448 |
| 45 | 1.205 760 4620 | 49.382 510 8810 | .020 250 0841 |
| 46 | 1.210 784 4639 | 50.588 271 3430 | .019 767 4278 |
| 47 | 1.215 829 3992 | 51.799 055 8069 | .019 305 3712 |
| 48 | 1.220 895 3550 | 53.014 885 2061 | .018 862 6269 |
| 49 | 1.225 982 4190 | 54.235 780 5611 | .018 438 0125 |
| 50 | 1.231 090 6791 | 55.461 762 9801 | .018 030 4402 |
| 51 | 1.236 220 2236 | 56.692 853 6592 | .017 638 9075 |
| 52 | 1.241 371 1412 | 57.929 073 8828 | .017 262 4890 |
| 53 | 1.246 543 5209 | 59.170 445 0240 | .016 900 3292 |
| 54 | 1.251 737 4523 | 60.416 988 5449 | .016 551 6360 |
| 55 | 1.256 953 0250 | 61.668 725 9972 | .016 215 6747 |
| 56 | 1.262 190 3293 | 62.925 679 0222 | .015 891 7634 |
| 57 | 1.267 449 4556 | 64.187 869 3514 | .015 579 2677 |
| 58 | 1.272 730 4950 | 65.455 318 8071 | .015 277 5973 |
| 59 | 1.278 033 5388 | 66.728 049 3021 | .014 986 2016 |
| 60 | 1.283 358 6785 | 68.006 082 8408 | .014 704 5670 |
| n | $s=(1+i)^n$ | $s_{\overline{n}|}=\dfrac{(1+i)^n-1}{i}$ | $\dfrac{1}{s_{\overline{n}|}}=\dfrac{i}{(1+i)^n-1}$ |

.00416666̇

*per period*

ANNUALLY
If compounded
*annually*
nominal annual rate is

$5/12\%$

SEMIANNUALLY
If compounded
*semiannually*
nominal annual rate is

$5/6\%$

QUARTERLY
If compounded
*quarterly*
nominal annual rate is

$1\tfrac{2}{3}\%$

MONTHLY
If compounded
*monthly*
nominal annual rate is

$5\%$

$i\ =\ .00416666$
$j_{(2)}\ =\ .00833333$
$j_{(4)}\ =\ .01666666$
$j_{(12)}\ =\ .05$

| PRESENT WORTH OF 1<br>*What $1 due in the future is worth today.* | PRESENT WORTH OF 1 PER PERIOD<br>*What $1 payable periodically is worth today.* | PARTIAL PAYMENT<br>*Annuity worth $1 today.*<br>*Periodic payment necessary to pay off a loan of $1.* | PERIODS | RATE<br>5/12% |
|---|---|---|---|---|
| .995 850 6224 | .995 850 6224 | 1.004 166 6667 | 1 | |
| .991 718 4621 | 1.987 569 0846 | .503 127 1656 | 2 | |
| .987 603 4478 | 2.975 172 5323 | .336 114 9611 | 3 | .00416666 |
| .983 505 5082 | 3.958 678 0405 | .252 609 5807 | 4 | *per period* |
| .979 424 5724 | 4.938 102 6129 | .202 506 9300 | 5 | |
| .975 360 5701 | 5.913 463 1830 | .169 105 6440 | 6 | |
| .971 313 4308 | 6.884 776 6138 | .145 247 9951 | 7 | |
| .967 283 0846 | 7.852 059 6984 | .127 355 1193 | 8 | |
| .963 269 4618 | 8.815 329 1602 | .113 438 7590 | 9 | |
| .959 272 4931 | 9.774 601 6533 | .102 305 9594 | 10 | |
| .955 292 1093 | 10.729 893 7626 | .093 197 5677 | 11 | |
| .951 328 2416 | 11.681 222 0043 | .085 607 4818 | 12 | |
| .947 380 8216 | 12.628 602 8259 | .079 185 3235 | 13 | |
| .943 449 7808 | 13.572 052 6067 | .073 680 8226 | 14 | |
| .939 535 0514 | 14.511 587 6581 | .068 910 4475 | 15 | |
| .935 636 5657 | 15.447 224 2238 | .064 736 5498 | 16 | |
| .931 754 2563 | 16.378 978 4802 | .061 053 8686 | 17 | |
| .927 888 0561 | 17.306 866 5363 | .057 780 5346 | 18 | |
| .924 037 8982 | 18.230 904 4344 | .054 851 9139 | 19 | |
| .920 203 7160 | 19.151 108 1505 | .052 216 2996 | 20 | |
| .916 385 4434 | 20.067 493 5938 | .049 831 8335 | 21 | ANNUALLY<br>If compounded *annually* nominal annual rate is |
| .912 583 0141 | 20.980 076 6080 | .047 664 2683 | 22 | |
| .908 796 3626 | 21.888 872 9706 | .045 685 3124 | 23 | |
| .905 025 4234 | 22.793 898 3940 | .043 871 3897 | 24 | 5/12% |
| .901 270 1311 | 23.695 168 5251 | .042 202 6963 | 25 | |
| .897 530 4211 | 24.592 698 9462 | .040 662 4748 | 26 | |
| .893 806 2284 | 25.486 505 1746 | .039 236 4506 | 27 | |
| .890 097 4889 | 26.376 602 6635 | .037 912 3882 | 28 | |
| .886 404 1383 | 27.263 006 8018 | .036 679 7400 | 29 | |
| .882 726 1129 | 28.145 732 9147 | .035 529 3644 | 30 | SEMIANNUALLY<br>If compounded *semiannually* nominal annual rate is |
| .879 063 3489 | 29.024 796 2636 | .034 453 2995 | 31 | |
| .875 415 7831 | 29.900 212 0467 | .033 444 5789 | 32 | |
| .871 783 3525 | 30.771 995 3992 | .032 497 0801 | 33 | |
| .868 165 9942 | 31.640 161 3934 | .031 605 4014 | 34 | 5/6% |
| .864 563 6457 | 32.504 725 0391 | .030 764 7580 | 35 | |
| .860 976 2447 | 33.365 701 2837 | .029 970 8971 | 36 | |
| .857 403 7291 | 34.223 105 0129 | .029 220 0255 | 37 | |
| .853 846 0373 | 35.076 951 0501 | .028 508 7492 | 38 | |
| .850 303 1077 | 35.927 254 1578 | .027 834 0225 | 39 | |
| .846 774 8790 | 36.774 029 0368 | .027 193 1041 | 40 | QUARTERLY<br>If compounded *quarterly* nominal annual rate is |
| .843 261 2903 | 37.617 290 3271 | .026 583 5203 | 41 | |
| .839 762 2808 | 38.457 052 6079 | .026 003 0328 | 42 | |
| .836 277 7900 | 39.293 330 3979 | .025 449 6117 | 43 | |
| .832 807 7577 | 40.126 138 1556 | .024 921 4115 | 44 | 1 2/3% |
| .829 352 1238 | 40.955 490 2795 | .024 416 7508 | 45 | |
| .825 910 8287 | 41.781 401 1082 | .023 934 0944 | 46 | |
| .822 483 8128 | 42.603 884 9210 | .023 472 0379 | 47 | |
| .819 071 0169 | 43.422 955 9379 | .023 029 2936 | 48 | |
| .815 672 3820 | 44.238 628 3199 | .022 604 6792 | 49 | |
| .812 287 8493 | 45.050 916 1692 | .022 197 1069 | 50 | MONTHLY<br>If compounded *monthly* nominal annual rate is |
| .808 917 3603 | 45.859 833 5295 | .021 805 5741 | 51 | |
| .805 560 8567 | 46.665 394 3862 | .021 429 1557 | 52 | |
| .802 218 2806 | 47.467 612 6668 | .021 066 9959 | 53 | |
| .798 889 5740 | 48.266 502 2408 | .020 718 3026 | 54 | 5% |
| .795 574 6795 | 49.062 076 9203 | .020 382 3414 | 55 | |
| .792 273 5397 | 49.854 350 4600 | .020 058 4300 | 56 | |
| .788 986 0977 | 50.643 336 5577 | .019 745 9344 | 57 | $i$ = .00416666 |
| .785 712 2964 | 51.429 048 8542 | .019 444 2639 | 58 | $j_{(2)}$ = .00833333 |
| .782 452 0794 | 52.211 500 9336 | .019 152 8683 | 59 | $j_{(4)}$ = .01666666 |
| .779 205 3903 | 52.990 706 3239 | .018 871 2336 | 60 | $j_{(12)}$ = .05 |
| $v^n = \dfrac{1}{(1+i)^n}$ | $a_{\overline{n}|} = \dfrac{1-v^n}{i}$ | $\dfrac{1}{a_{\overline{n}|}} = \dfrac{i}{1-v^n}$ | n | |

| P E R I O D S | AMOUNT OF 1<br>*How $1 left at compound interest will grow.* | AMOUNT OF 1 PER PERIOD<br>*How $1 deposited periodically will grow.* | SINKING FUND<br>*Periodic deposit that will grow to $1 at future date.* |
|---|---|---|---|
| 61 | 1.288 706 0063 | 69.289 441 5193 | .014 432 2133 |
| 62 | 1.294 075 6147 | 70.578 147 5257 | .014 168 6915 |
| 63 | 1.299 467 5964 | 71.872 223 1404 | .013 913 5810 |
| 64 | 1.304 882 0447 | 73.171 690 7368 | .013 666 4875 |
| 65 | 1.310 319 0533 | 74.476 572 7815 | .013 427 0410 |
| 66 | 1.315 778 7160 | 75.786 891 8348 | .013 194 8939 |
| 67 | 1.321 261 1273 | 77.102 670 5508 | .012 969 7194 |
| 68 | 1.326 766 3820 | 78.423 931 6781 | .012 751 2097 |
| 69 | 1.332 294 5753 | 79.750 698 0600 | .012 539 0752 |
| 70 | 1.337 845 8026 | 81.082 992 6353 | .012 333 0426 |
| 71 | 1.343 420 1602 | 82.420 838 4379 | .012 132 8540 |
| 72 | 1.349 017 7442 | 83.764 258 5981 | .011 938 2660 |
| 73 | 1.354 638 6514 | 85.113 276 3423 | .011 749 0484 |
| 74 | 1.360 282 9791 | 86.467 914 9937 | .011 564 9834 |
| 75 | 1.365 950 8249 | 87.828 197 9728 | .011 385 8649 |
| 76 | 1.371 642 2867 | 89.194 148 7977 | .011 211 4978 |
| 77 | 1.377 357 4629 | 90.565 791 0844 | .011 041 6967 |
| 78 | 1.383 096 4523 | 91.943 148 5472 | .010 876 2862 |
| 79 | 1.388 859 3542 | 93.326 244 9995 | .010 715 0995 |
| 80 | 1.394 646 2681 | 94.715 104 3537 | .010 557 9781 |
| 81 | 1.400 457 2943 | 96.109 750 6218 | .010 404 7716 |
| 82 | 1.406 292 5330 | 97.510 207 9161 | .010 255 3366 |
| 83 | 1.412 152 0852 | 98.916 500 4490 | .010 109 5368 |
| 84 | 1.418 036 0522 | 100.328 652 5342 | .009 967 2424 |
| 85 | 1.423 944 5358 | 101.746 688 5865 | .009 828 3297 |
| 86 | 1.429 877 6380 | 103.170 633 1223 | .009 692 6807 |
| 87 | 1.435 835 4615 | 104.600 510 7603 | .009 560 1828 |
| 88 | 1.441 818 1093 | 106.036 346 2218 | .009 430 7286 |
| 89 | 1.447 825 6847 | 107.478 164 3310 | .009 304 2155 |
| 90 | 1.453 858 2917 | 108.925 990 0157 | .009 180 5454 |
| 91 | 1.459 916 0346 | 110.379 848 3075 | .009 059 6247 |
| 92 | 1.465 999 0181 | 111.839 764 3421 | .008 941 3636 |
| 93 | 1.472 107 3473 | 113.305 763 3602 | .008 825 6764 |
| 94 | 1.478 241 1279 | 114.777 870 7075 | .008 712 4808 |
| 95 | 1.484 400 4660 | 116.256 111 8355 | .008 601 6983 |
| 96 | 1.490 585 4679 | 117.740 512 3014 | .008 493 2533 |
| 97 | 1.496 796 2407 | 119.231 097 7694 | .008 387 0737 |
| 98 | 1.503 032 8917 | 120.727 894 0101 | .008 283 0899 |
| 99 | 1.509 295 5288 | 122.230 926 9018 | .008 181 2355 |
| 100 | 1.515 584 2601 | 123.740 222 4305 | .008 081 4466 |
| 101 | 1.521 899 1945 | 125.255 806 6907 | .007 983 6618 |
| 102 | 1.528 240 4412 | 126.777 705 8852 | .007 887 8222 |
| 103 | 1.534 608 1097 | 128.305 946 3264 | .007 793 8710 |
| 104 | 1.541 002 3102 | 129.840 554 4361 | .007 701 7539 |
| 105 | 1.547 423 1531 | 131.381 556 7462 | .007 611 4184 |
| 106 | 1.553 870 7496 | 132.928 979 8993 | .007 522 8141 |
| 107 | 1.560 345 2110 | 134.482 850 6489 | .007 435 8923 |
| 108 | 1.566 846 6494 | 136.043 195 8600 | .007 350 6065 |
| 109 | 1.573 375 1771 | 137.610 042 5094 | .007 266 9115 |
| 110 | 1.579 930 9070 | 139.183 417 6865 | .007 184 7639 |
| 111 | 1.586 513 9525 | 140.763 348 5935 | .007 104 1220 |
| 112 | 1.593 124 4273 | 142.349 862 5460 | .007 024 9453 |
| 113 | 1.599 762 4457 | 143.942 986 9733 | .006 947 1950 |
| 114 | 1.606 428 1226 | 145.542 749 4190 | .006 870 8335 |
| 115 | 1.613 121 5731 | 147.149 177 5416 | .006 795 8246 |
| 116 | 1.619 842 9130 | 148.762 299 1147 | .006 722 1333 |
| 117 | 1.626 592 2584 | 150.382 142 0276 | .006 649 7257 |
| 118 | 1.633 369 7262 | 152.008 734 2861 | .006 578 5693 |
| 119 | 1.640 175 4334 | 153.642 104 0123 | .006 508 6326 |
| 120 | 1.647 009 4977 | 155.282 279 4457 | .006 439 8849 |
| **n** | $s = (1+i)^n$ | $s_{\overline{n}|} = \dfrac{(1+i)^n - 1}{i}$ | $\dfrac{1}{s_{\overline{n}|}} = \dfrac{i}{(1+i)^n - 1}$ |

.00416666
*per period*

ANNUALLY
If compounded *annually* nominal annual rate is
5/12%

SEMIANNUALLY
If compounded *semiannually* nominal annual rate is
5/6%

QUARTERLY
If compounded *quarterly* nominal annual rate is
1 2/3%

MONTHLY
If compounded *monthly* nominal annual rate is
5%

$i$ = .00416666
$j_{(2)}$ = .00833333
$j_{(4)}$ = .01666666
$j_{(12)}$ = .05

22

| PRESENT WORTH OF 1<br>*What $1 due in the future is worth today.* | PRESENT WORTH OF 1 PER PERIOD<br>*What $1 payable periodically is worth today.* | PARTIAL PAYMENT<br>*Annuity worth $1 today.*<br>*Periodic payment necessary to pay off a loan of $1.* | PERIODS | RATE<br>5/12% |
|---|---|---|---|---|
| .775 972 1729 | 53.766 678 4969 | .018 598 8800 | 61 | |
| .772 752 3714 | 54.539 430 8682 | .018 335 3582 | 62 | |
| .769 545 9300 | 55.308 976 7982 | .018 080 2477 | 63 | .00416666 |
| .766 352 7934 | 56.075 329 5916 | .017 833 1542 | 64 | |
| .763 172 9063 | 56.838 502 4979 | .017 593 7077 | 65 | *per period* |
| .760 006 2137 | 57.598 508 7116 | .017 361 5606 | 66 | |
| .756 852 6609 | 58.355 361 3725 | .017 136 3860 | 67 | |
| .753 712 1935 | 59.109 073 5660 | .016 917 8764 | 68 | |
| .750 584 7570 | 59.859 658 3230 | .016 705 7419 | 69 | |
| .747 470 2974 | 60.607 128 6204 | .016 499 7092 | 70 | |
| .744 368 7609 | 61.351 497 3813 | .016 299 5207 | 71 | |
| .741 280 0939 | 62.092 777 4752 | .016 104 9327 | 72 | |
| .738 204 2428 | 62.830 981 7180 | .015 915 7150 | 73 | |
| .735 141 1547 | 63.566 122 8727 | .015 731 6500 | 74 | |
| .732 090 7765 | 64.298 213 6492 | .015 552 5316 | 75 | |
| .729 053 0554 | 65.027 266 7046 | .015 378 1644 | 76 | |
| .726 027 9390 | 65.753 294 6435 | .015 208 3634 | 77 | |
| .723 015 3749 | 66.476 310 0185 | .015 042 9529 | 78 | |
| .720 015 3111 | 67.196 325 3296 | .014 881 7662 | 79 | |
| .717 027 6957 | 67.913 353 0253 | .014 724 6448 | 80 | |
| .714 052 4771 | 68.627 405 5024 | .014 571 4382 | 81 | ANNUALLY<br>If compounded<br>*annually*<br>nominal annual rate is |
| .711 089 6037 | 69.338 495 1061 | .014 422 0032 | 82 | |
| .708 139 0245 | 70.046 634 1306 | .014 276 2035 | 83 | |
| .705 200 6883 | 70.751 834 8188 | .014 133 9091 | 84 | |
| .702 274 5443 | 71.454 109 3632 | .013 994 9964 | 85 | 5/12% |
| .699 360 5421 | 72.153 469 9052 | .013 859 3473 | 86 | |
| .696 458 6311 | 72.849 928 5363 | .013 726 8494 | 87 | |
| .693 568 7613 | 73.543 497 2976 | .013 597 3952 | 88 | |
| .690 690 8826 | 74.234 188 1802 | .013 470 8821 | 89 | |
| .687 824 9453 | 74.922 013 1255 | .013 347 2121 | 90 | SEMIANNUALLY<br>If compounded<br>*semiannually*<br>nominal annual rate is |
| .684 970 8999 | 75.606 984 0254 | .013 226 2914 | 91 | |
| .682 128 6970 | 76.289 112 7224 | .013 108 0303 | 92 | |
| .679 298 2875 | 76.968 411 0098 | .012 992 3431 | 93 | |
| .676 479 6224 | 77.644 890 6322 | .012 879 1475 | 94 | |
| .673 672 6530 | 78.318 563 2852 | .012 768 3650 | 95 | 5/6% |
| .670 877 3308 | 78.989 440 6159 | .012 659 9200 | 96 | |
| .668 093 6074 | 79.657 534 2233 | .012 553 7403 | 97 | |
| .665 321 4348 | 80.322 855 6581 | .012 449 7566 | 98 | |
| .662 560 7649 | 80.985 416 4230 | .012 347 9022 | 99 | |
| .659 811 5501 | 81.645 227 9731 | .012 248 1133 | 100 | QUARTERLY<br>If compounded<br>*quarterly*<br>nominal annual rate is |
| .657 073 7429 | 82.302 301 7160 | .012 150 3285 | 101 | |
| .654 347 2958 | 82.956 649 0117 | .012 054 4888 | 102 | |
| .651 632 1618 | 83.608 281 1735 | .011 960 5377 | 103 | |
| .648 928 2939 | 84.257 209 4674 | .011 868 4206 | 104 | |
| .646 235 6454 | 84.903 445 1128 | .011 778 0851 | 105 | 1⅔% |
| .643 554 1697 | 85.546 999 2824 | .011 689 4807 | 106 | |
| .640 883 8204 | 86.187 883 1028 | .011 602 5590 | 107 | |
| .638 224 5514 | 86.826 107 6543 | .011 517 2732 | 108 | |
| .635 576 3168 | 87.461 683 9711 | .011 433 5782 | 109 | |
| .632 939 0707 | 88.094 623 0417 | .011 351 4306 | 110 | MONTHLY<br>If compounded<br>*monthly*<br>nominal annual rate is |
| .630 312 7675 | 88.724 935 8092 | .011 270 7887 | 111 | |
| .627 697 3618 | 89.352 633 1710 | .011 191 6120 | 112 | |
| .625 092 8084 | 89.977 725 9794 | .011 113 8617 | 113 | |
| .622 499 0623 | 90.600 225 0417 | .011 037 5002 | 114 | |
| .619 916 0787 | 91.220 141 1204 | .010 962 4913 | 115 | 5% |
| .617 343 8128 | 91.837 484 9331 | .010 888 7999 | 116 | |
| .614 782 2202 | 92.452 267 1533 | .010 816 3924 | 117 | |
| .612 231 2566 | 93.064 498 4100 | .010 745 2360 | 118 | $i = .00416666$ |
| .609 690 8780 | 93.674 189 2879 | .010 675 2992 | 119 | $j_{(2)} = .00833333$ |
| .607 161 0403 | 94.281 350 3282 | .010 606 5515 | 120 | $j_{(4)} = .01666666$<br>$j_{(12)} = .05$ |
| $v^n = \dfrac{1}{(1+i)^n}$ | $a_{\overline{n}} = \dfrac{1-v^n}{i}$ | $\dfrac{1}{a_{\overline{n}}} = \dfrac{i}{1-v^n}$ | n | |

23

## 5/12%

| | P E R I O D S | AMOUNT OF 1 *How $1 left at compound interest will grow.* | AMOUNT OF 1 PER PERIOD *How $1 deposited periodically will grow.* | SINKING FUND *Periodic deposit that will grow to $1 at future date.* |
|---|---|---|---|---|
| | 121 | 1.653 872 0373 | 156.929 288 9434 | .006 372 2968 |
| | 122 | 1.660 763 1708 | 158.583 160 9806 | .006 305 8397 |
| .00416666 | 123 | 1.667 683 0173 | 160.243 924 1514 | .006 240 4862 |
| | 124 | 1.674 631 6965 | 161.911 607 1687 | .006 176 2095 |
| *per period* | 125 | 1.681 609 3286 | 163.586 238 8652 | .006 112 9836 |
| | 126 | 1.688 616 0341 | 165.267 848 1938 | .006 050 7837 |
| | 127 | 1.695 651 9343 | 166.956 464 2280 | .005 989 5854 |
| | 128 | 1.702 717 1507 | 168.652 116 1622 | .005 929 3653 |
| | 129 | 1.709 811 8055 | 170.354 833 3129 | .005 870 1005 |
| | 130 | 1.716 936 0213 | 172.064 645 1184 | .005 811 7692 |
| | 131 | 1.724 089 9214 | 173.781 581 1397 | .005 754 3498 |
| | 132 | 1.731 273 6294 | 175.505 671 0611 | .005 697 8216 |
| | 133 | 1.738 487 2695 | 177.236 944 6905 | .005 642 1645 |
| | 134 | 1.745 730 9665 | 178.975 431 9601 | .005 587 3591 |
| | 135 | 1.753 004 8455 | 180.721 162 9266 | .005 533 3863 |
| | 136 | 1.760 309 0324 | 182.474 167 7721 | .005 480 2278 |
| | 137 | 1.767 643 6534 | 184.234 476 8045 | .005 427 8657 |
| | 138 | 1.775 008 8352 | 186.002 120 4579 | .005 376 2828 |
| | 139 | 1.782 404 7054 | 187.777 129 2931 | .005 325 4622 |
| | 140 | 1.789 831 3917 | 189.559 533 9985 | .005 275 3875 |
| ANNUALLY *If compounded annually nominal annual rate is* | 141 | 1.797 289 0225 | 191.349 365 3901 | .005 226 0429 |
| | 142 | 1.804 777 7267 | 193.146 654 4126 | .005 177 4130 |
| | 143 | 1.812 297 6339 | 194.951 432 1393 | .005 129 4827 |
| 5/12% | 144 | 1.819 848 8741 | 196.763 729 7732 | .005 082 2375 |
| | 145 | 1.827 431 5777 | 198.583 578 6473 | .005 035 6631 |
| | 146 | 1.835 045 8759 | 200.411 010 2250 | .004 989 7458 |
| | 147 | 1.842 691 9004 | 202.246 056 1009 | .004 944 4722 |
| | 148 | 1.850 369 7833 | 204.088 748 0013 | .004 899 8292 |
| | 149 | 1.858 079 6574 | 205.939 117 7847 | .004 855 8040 |
| SEMIANNUALLY *If compounded semiannually nominal annual rate is* | 150 | 1.865 821 6560 | 207.797 197 4421 | .004 812 3844 |
| | 151 | 1.873 595 9129 | 209.663 019 0981 | .004 769 5583 |
| | 152 | 1.881 402 5625 | 211.536 615 0110 | .004 727 3140 |
| | 153 | 1.889 241 7399 | 213.418 017 5736 | .004 685 6400 |
| 5/6% | 154 | 1.897 113 5805 | 215.307 259 3135 | .004 644 5252 |
| | 155 | 1.905 018 2204 | 217.204 372 8939 | .004 603 9589 |
| | 156 | 1.912 955 7963 | 219.109 391 1143 | .004 563 9303 |
| | 157 | 1.920 926 4455 | 221.022 346 9106 | .004 524 4294 |
| | 158 | 1.928 930 3057 | 222.943 273 3561 | .004 485 4459 |
| | 159 | 1.936 967 5153 | 224.872 203 6618 | .004 446 9703 |
| QUARTERLY *If compounded quarterly nominal annual rate is* | 160 | 1.945 038 2132 | 226.809 171 1770 | .004 408 9928 |
| | 161 | 1.953 142 5391 | 228.754 209 3903 | .004 371 5043 |
| | 162 | 1.961 280 6330 | 230.707 351 9294 | .004 334 4956 |
| | 163 | 1.969 452 6357 | 232.668 632 5624 | .004 297 9580 |
| 1⅔% | 164 | 1.977 658 6883 | 234.638 085 1981 | .004 261 8827 |
| | 165 | 1.985 898 9329 | 236.615 743 8864 | .004 226 2615 |
| | 166 | 1.994 173 5117 | 238.601 642 8193 | .004 191 0860 |
| | 167 | 2.002 482 5680 | 240.595 816 3310 | .004 156 3482 |
| | 168 | 2.010 826 2454 | 242.598 298 8991 | .004 122 0404 |
| | 169 | 2.019 204 6881 | 244.609 125 1445 | .004 088 1549 |
| MONTHLY *If compounded monthly nominal annual rate is* | 170 | 2.027 618 0410 | 246.628 329 8326 | .004 054 6842 |
| | 171 | 2.036 066 4495 | 248.655 947 8736 | .004 021 6211 |
| | 172 | 2.044 550 0597 | 250.692 014 3230 | .003 988 9583 |
| | 173 | 2.053 069 0183 | 252.736 564 3827 | .003 956 6891 |
| 5% | 174 | 2.061 623 4725 | 254.789 633 4010 | .003 924 8065 |
| | 175 | 2.070 213 5703 | 256.851 256 8735 | .003 893 3039 |
| | 176 | 2.078 839 4602 | 258.921 470 4438 | .003 862 1749 |
| $i$ = .00416666 | 177 | 2.087 501 2913 | 261.000 309 9040 | .003 831 4131 |
| $j_{(2)}$ = .00833333 | 178 | 2.096 199 2133 | 263.087 811 1952 | .003 801 0123 |
| $j_{(4)}$ = .01666666 | 179 | 2.104 933 3767 | 265.184 010 4085 | .003 770 9664 |
| $j_{(12)}$ = .05 | 180 | 2.113 703 9324 | 267.288 943 7852 | .003 741 2696 |
| | **n** | $s=(1+i)^n$ | $s_{\overline{n}\|}=\dfrac{(1+i)^n-1}{i}$ | $\dfrac{1}{s_{\overline{n}\|}}=\dfrac{i}{(1+i)^n-1}$ |

| PRESENT WORTH OF 1 | PRESENT WORTH OF 1 PER PERIOD | PARTIAL PAYMENT | P E R I O D S | RATE |
|---|---|---|---|---|
| *What $1 due in the future is worth today.* | *What $1 payable periodically is worth today.* | *Annuity worth $1 today.* *Periodic payment necessary to pay off a loan of $1.* | | $5/12\%$ |
| .604 641 6999 | 94.885 992 0281 | .010 538 9634 | 121 | |
| .602 132 8132 | 95.488 124 8413 | .010 472 5064 | 122 | |
| .599 634 3368 | 96.087 759 1780 | .010 407 1529 | 123 | .00416666 |
| .597 146 2275 | 96.684 905 4055 | .010 342 8761 | 124 | *per period* |
| .594 668 4423 | 97.279 573 8478 | .010 279 6503 | 125 | |
| .592 200 9384 | 97.871 774 7862 | .010 217 4504 | 126 | |
| .589 743 6731 | 98.461 518 4593 | .010 156 2521 | 127 | |
| .587 296 6039 | 99.048 815 0632 | .010 096 0319 | 128 | |
| .584 859 6885 | 99.633 674 7517 | .010 036 7672 | 129 | |
| .582 432 8848 | 100.216 107 6366 | .009 978 4358 | 130 | |
| .580 016 1509 | 100.796 123 7875 | .009 921 0164 | 131 | |
| .577 609 4449 | 101.373 733 2323 | .009 864 4882 | 132 | |
| .575 212 7252 | 101.948 945 9575 | .009 808 8312 | 133 | |
| .572 825 9504 | 102.521 771 9079 | .009 754 0257 | 134 | |
| .570 449 0792 | 103.092 220 9871 | .009 700 0529 | 135 | |
| .568 082 0706 | 103.660 303 0577 | .009 646 8944 | 136 | |
| .565 724 8836 | 104.226 027 9413 | .009 594 5324 | 137 | |
| .563 377 4774 | 104.789 405 4187 | .009 542 9495 | 138 | |
| .561 039 8115 | 105.350 445 2302 | .009 492 1288 | 139 | |
| .558 711 8455 | 105.909 157 0758 | .009 442 0542 | 140 | |
| .556 393 5391 | 106.465 550 6149 | .009 392 7096 | 141 | ANNUALLY |
| .554 084 8522 | 107.019 635 4671 | .009 344 0797 | 142 | If compounded *annually* nominal annual rate is |
| .551 785 7449 | 107.571 421 2120 | .009 296 1494 | 143 | |
| .549 496 1775 | 108.120 917 3896 | .009 248 9041 | 144 | |
| .547 216 1104 | 108.668 133 5000 | .009 202 3298 | 145 | $5/12\%$ |
| .544 945 5041 | 109.213 079 0041 | .009 156 4125 | 146 | |
| .542 684 3195 | 109.755 763 3236 | .009 111 1389 | 147 | |
| .540 432 5173 | 110.296 195 8410 | .009 066 4958 | 148 | |
| .538 190 0588 | 110.834 385 8997 | .009 022 4707 | 149 | |
| .535 956 9050 | 111.370 342 8047 | .008 979 0511 | 150 | SEMIANNUALLY |
| .533 733 0174 | 111.904 075 8221 | .008 936 2250 | 151 | If compounded *semiannually* nominal annual rate is |
| .531 518 3576 | 112.435 594 1797 | .008 893 9807 | 152 | |
| .529 312 8872 | 112.964 907 0669 | .008 852 3067 | 153 | |
| .527 116 5682 | 113.492 023 6351 | .008 811 1919 | 154 | |
| .524 929 3625 | 114.016 952 9976 | .008 770 6255 | 155 | $5/6\%$ |
| .522 751 2324 | 114.539 704 2300 | .008 730 5970 | 156 | |
| .520 582 1401 | 115.060 286 3701 | .008 691 0960 | 157 | |
| .518 422 0483 | 115.578 708 4184 | .008 652 1126 | 158 | |
| .516 270 9194 | 116.094 979 3378 | .008 613 6369 | 159 | |
| .514 128 7164 | 116.609 108 0542 | .008 575 6595 | 160 | QUARTERLY |
| .511 995 4023 | 117.121 103 4565 | .008 538 1709 | 161 | If compounded *quarterly* nominal annual rate is |
| .509 870 9400 | 117.630 974 3965 | .008 501 1623 | 162 | |
| .507 755 2930 | 118.138 729 6895 | .008 464 6246 | 163 | |
| .505 648 4245 | 118.644 378 1140 | .008 428 5494 | 164 | |
| .503 550 2983 | 119.147 928 4123 | .008 392 9281 | 165 | $1\tfrac{2}{3}\%$ |
| .501 460 8780 | 119.649 389 2902 | .008 357 7526 | 166 | |
| .499 380 1274 | 120.148 769 4177 | .008 323 0149 | 167 | |
| .497 308 0107 | 120.646 077 4284 | .008 288 7071 | 168 | |
| .495 244 4920 | 121.141 321 9204 | .008 254 8216 | 169 | |
| .493 189 5356 | 121.634 511 4560 | .008 221 3509 | 170 | MONTHLY |
| .491 143 1060 | 122.125 654 5620 | .008 188 2877 | 171 | If compounded *monthly* nominal annual rate is |
| .489 105 1678 | 122.614 759 7298 | .008 155 6250 | 172 | |
| .487 075 6858 | 123.101 835 4155 | .008 123 3557 | 173 | |
| .485 054 6248 | 123.586 890 0404 | .008 091 4731 | 174 | |
| .483 041 9500 | 124.069 931 9904 | .008 059 9706 | 175 | $5\%$ |
| .481 037 6266 | 124.550 969 6170 | .008 028 8416 | 176 | |
| .479 041 6198 | 125.030 011 2368 | .007 998 0797 | 177 | |
| .477 053 8953 | 125.507 065 1321 | .007 967 6789 | 178 | $i\ =\ .00416666$ |
| .475 074 4185 | 125.982 139 5507 | .007 937 6331 | 179 | $j_{(2)}\ =\ .00833333$ |
| .473 103 1554 | 126.455 242 7061 | .007 907 9363 | 180 | $j_{(4)}\ =\ .01666666$ |
| $v^n=\dfrac{1}{(1+i)^n}$ | $a_{\overline{n}|}=\dfrac{1-v^n}{i}$ | $\dfrac{1}{a_{\overline{n}|}}=\dfrac{i}{1-v^n}$ | **n** | $j_{(12)}\ =\ .05$ |

25

| RATE **½%** | P E R I O D S | AMOUNT OF 1 *How $1 left at compound interest will grow.* | AMOUNT OF 1 PER PERIOD *How $1 deposited periodically will grow.* | SINKING FUND *Periodic deposit that will grow to $1 at future date.* |
|---|---|---|---|---|
| **.005** *per period* | 1 | 1.005 000 0000 | 1.000 000 0000 | 1.000 000 0000 |
|  | 2 | 1.010 025 0000 | 2.005 000 0000 | .498 753 1172 |
|  | 3 | 1.015 075 1250 | 3.015 025 0000 | .331 672 2084 |
|  | 4 | 1.020 150 5006 | 4.030 100 1250 | .248 132 7930 |
|  | 5 | 1.025 251 2531 | 5.050 250 6256 | .198 009 9750 |
|  | 6 | 1.030 377 5094 | 6.075 501 8788 | .164 595 4556 |
|  | 7 | 1.035 529 3969 | 7.105 879 3881 | :140 728 5355 |
|  | 8 | 1.040 707 0439 | 8.141 408 7851 | .122 828 8649 |
|  | 9 | 1.045 910 5791 | 9.182. 115 8290 | .108 907 3606 |
|  | 10 | 1.051 140 1320 | 10.228 026 4082 | .097 770 5727 |
|  | 11 | 1.056 395 8327 | 11.279 166 5402 | .088 659 0331 |
|  | 12 | 1.061 677 8119 | 12.335 562 3729 | .081 066 4297 |
|  | 13 | 1.066 986 2009 | 13.397 240 1848 | .074 642 2387 |
|  | 14 | 1.072 321 1319 | 14.464 226 3857 | .069 136 0860 |
|  | 15 | 1.077 682 7376 | 15.536 547 5176 | .064 364 3640 |
|  | 16 | 1.083 071 1513 | 16.614 230 2552 | .060 189 3669 |
|  | 17 | 1.088 486 5070 | 17.697 301 4065 | .056 505 7902 |
|  | 18 | 1.093 928 9396 | 18.785 787 9135 | .053 231 7305 |
|  | 19 | 1.099 398 5843 | 19.879 716 8531 | .050 302 5273 |
| **ANNUALLY** If compounded *annually* nominal annual rate is **½%** | 20 | 1.104 895 5772 | 20.979 115 4373 | .047 666 4520 |
|  | 21 | 1.110 420 0551 | 22.084 011 0145 | .045 281 6293 |
|  | 22 | 1.115 972 1553 | 23.194 431 0696 | .043 113 7973 |
|  | 23 | 1.121 552 0161 | 24.310 403 2250 | .041 134 6530 |
|  | 24 | 1.127 159 7762 | 25.431 955 2411 | .039 320 6103 |
|  | 25 | 1.132 795 5751 | 26.559 115 0173 | .037 651 8570 |
|  | 26 | 1.138 459 5530 | 27.691 910 5924 | .036 111 6289 |
|  | 27 | 1.144 151 8507 | 28.830 370 1453 | .034 685 6456 |
|  | 28 | 1.149 872 6100 | 29.974 521 9961 | .033 361 6663 |
|  | 29 | 1.155 621 9730 | 31.124 394 6060 | .032 129 1390 |
| **SEMIANNUALLY** If compounded *semiannually* nominal annual rate is **1%** | 30 | 1.161 400 0829 | 32.280 016 5791 | .030 978 9184 |
|  | 31 | 1.167 207 0833 | 33.441 416 6620 | .029 903 0394 |
|  | 32 | 1.173 043 1187 | 34.608 623 7453 | .028 894 5324 |
|  | 33 | 1.178 908 3343 | 35.781 666 8640 | .027 947 2727 |
|  | 34 | 1.184 802 8760 | 36.960 575 1983 | .027 055 8560 |
|  | 35 | 1.190 726 8904 | 38.145 378 0743 | .026 215 4958 |
|  | 36 | 1.196 680 5248 | 39.336 104 9647 | .025 421 9375 |
|  | 37 | 1.202 663 9274 | 40.532 785 4895 | .024 671 3861 |
|  | 38 | 1.208 677 2471 | 41.735 449 4170 | .023 960 4464 |
|  | 39 | 1.214 720 6333 | 42.944 126 6640 | .023 286 0714 |
| **QUARTERLY** If compounded *quarterly* nominal annual rate is **2%** | 40 | 1.220 794 2365 | 44.158 847 2974 | .022 645 5186 |
|  | 41 | 1.226 898 2077 | 45.379 641 5338 | .022 036 3133 |
|  | 42 | 1.233 032 6987 | 46.606 539 7415 | .021 456 2163 |
|  | 43 | 1.239 197 8622 | 47.839 572 4402 | .020 903 1969 |
|  | 44 | 1.245 393 8515 | 49.078 770 3024 | .020 375 4086 |
|  | 45 | 1.251 620 8208 | 50.324 164 1539 | .019 871 1696 |
|  | 46 | 1.257 878 9249 | 51.575 784 9747 | .019 388 9439 |
|  | 47 | 1.264 168 3195 | 52.833 663 8996 | .018 927 3264 |
|  | 48 | 1.270 489 1611 | 54.097 832 2191 | .018 485 0290 |
|  | 49 | 1.276 841 6069 | 55.368 321 3802 | .018 060 8690 |
| **MONTHLY** If compounded *monthly* nominal annual rate is **6%** | 50 | 1.283 225 8149 | 56.645 162 9871 | .017 653 7580 |
|  | 51 | 1.289 641 9440 | 57.928 388 8020 | .017 262 6931 |
|  | 52 | 1.296 090 1537 | 59.218 030 7460 | .016 886 7486 |
|  | 53 | 1.302 570 6045 | 60.514 120 8997 | .016 525 0686 |
|  | 54 | 1.309 083 4575 | 61.816 691 5042 | .016 176 8606 |
|  | 55 | 1.315 628 8748 | 63.125 774 9618 | .015 841 3897 |
|  | 56 | 1.322 207 0192 | 64.441 403 8366 | .015 517 9735 |
|  | 57 | 1.328 818 0543 | 65.763 610 8558 | .015 205 9777 |
| $i = .005$ $j_{(2)} = .01$ $j_{(4)} = .02$ $j_{(12)} = .06$ | 58 | 1.335 462 1446 | 67.092 428 9100 | .014 904 8114 |
|  | 59 | 1.342 139 4553 | 68.427 891 0546 | .014 613 9240 |
|  | 60 | 1.348 850 1525 | 69.770 030 5099 | .014 332 8015 |
| | n | $s=(1+i)^n$ | $s_{\overline{n}|}=\dfrac{(1+i)^n-1}{i}$ | $\dfrac{1}{s_{\overline{n}|}}=\dfrac{i}{(1+i)^n-1}$ |

26

26

| PRESENT WORTH OF 1 | PRESENT WORTH OF 1 PER PERIOD | PARTIAL PAYMENT | P E R I O D S | RATE |
|---|---|---|---|---|
| *What $1 due in the future is worth today.* | *What $1 payable periodically is worth today.* | *Annuity worth $1 today.* <br> *Periodic payment necessary to pay off a loan of $1.* | | **1/2%** |
| .995 024 8756 | .995 024 8756 | 1.005 000 0000 | 1 | |
| .990 074 5031 | 1.985 099 3787 | .503 753 1172 | 2 | |
| .985 148 7593 | 2.970 248 1380 | .336 672 2084 | 3 | .005 |
| .980 247 5217 | 3.950 495 6597 | .253 132 7930 | 4 | *per period* |
| .975 370 6684 | 4.925 866 3281 | .203 009 9750 | 5 | |
| .970 518 0780 | 5.896 384 4061 | .169 595 4556 | 6 | |
| .965 689 6298 | 6.862 074 0359 | .145 728 5355 | 7 | |
| .960 885 2038 | 7.822 959 2397 | .127 828 8649 | 8 | |
| .956 104 6804 | 8.779 063 9201 | .113 907 3606 | 9 | |
| .951 347 9407 | 9.730 411 8608 | .102 770 5727 | 10 | |
| .946 614 8664 | 10.677 026 7272 | .093 659 0331 | 11 | |
| .941 905 3397 | 11.618 932 0668 | .086 066 4297 | 12 | |
| .937 219 2434 | 12.556 151 3103 | .079 642 2387 | 13 | |
| .932 556 4611 | 13.488 707 7714 | .074 136 0860 | 14 | |
| .927 916 8768 | 14.416 624 6482 | .069 364 3640 | 15 | |
| .923 300 3749 | 15.339 925 0231 | .065 189 3669 | 16 | |
| .918 706 8407 | 16.258 631 8637 | .061 505 7902 | 17 | |
| .914 136 1599 | 17.172 768 0236 | .058 231 7305 | 18 | |
| .909 588 2188 | 18.082 356 2424 | .055 302 5273 | 19 | |
| .905 062 9043 | 18.987 419 1467 | .052 666 4520 | 20 | |
| .900 560 1037 | 19.887 979 2504 | .050 281 6293 | 21 | ANNUALLY |
| .896 079 7052 | 20.784 058 9556 | .048 113 7973 | 22 | If compounded *annually* nominal annual rate is |
| .891 621 5972 | 21.675 680 5529 | .046 134 6530 | 23 | |
| .887 185 6689 | 22.562 866 2218 | .044 320 6103 | 24 | |
| .882 771 8098 | 23.445 638 0316 | .042 651 8570 | 25 | **1/2%** |
| .878 379 9103 | 24.324 017 9419 | .041 111 6289 | 26 | |
| .874 009 8610 | 25.198 027 8029 | .039 685 6456 | 27 | |
| .869 661 5532 | 26.067 689 3561 | .038 361 6663 | 28 | |
| .865 334 8788 | 26.933 024 2349 | .037 129 1390 | 29 | |
| .861 029 7302 | 27.794 053 9651 | .035 978 9184 | 30 | |
| .856 746 0002 | 28.650 799 9653 | .034 903 0394 | 31 | SEMIANNUALLY |
| .852 483 5823 | 29.503 283 5475 | .033 894 5324 | 32 | If compounded *semiannually* nominal annual rate is |
| .848 242 3704 | 30.351 525 9179 | .032 947 2727 | 33 | |
| .844 022 2591 | 31.195 548 1771 | .032 055 8560 | 34 | |
| .839 823 1434 | 32.035 371 3205 | .031 215 4958 | 35 | **1%** |
| .835 644 9188 | 32.871 016 2393 | .030 421 9375 | 36 | |
| .831 487 4814 | 33.702 503 7207 | .029 671 3861 | 37 | |
| .827 350 7278 | 34.529 854 4484 | .028 960 4464 | 38 | |
| .823 234 5550 | 35.353 089 0034 | .028 286 0714 | 39 | |
| .819 138 8607 | 36.172 227 8641 | .027 645 5186 | 40 | QUARTERLY |
| .815 063 5430 | 36.987 291 4070 | .027 036 3133 | 41 | If compounded *quarterly* nominal annual rate is |
| .811 008 5005 | 37.798 299 9075 | .026 456 2163 | 42 | |
| .806 973 6323 | 38.605 273 5398 | .025 903 1969 | 43 | |
| .802 958 8381 | 39.408 232 3779 | .025 375 4086 | 44 | |
| .798 964 0180 | 40.207 196 3959 | .024 871 1696 | 45 | **2%** |
| .794 989 0727 | 41.002 185 4686 | .024 388 9439 | 46 | |
| .791 033 9031 | 41.793 219 3717 | .023 927 3264 | 47 | |
| .787 098 4111 | 42.580 317 7828 | .023 485 0290 | 48 | |
| .783 182 4986 | 43.363 500 2814 | .023 060 8690 | 49 | |
| .779 286 0683 | 44.142 786 3497 | .022 653 7580 | 50 | MONTHLY |
| .775 409 0231 | 44.918 195 3728 | .022 262 6931 | 51 | If compounded *monthly* nominal annual rate is |
| .771 551 2668 | 45.689 746 6396 | .021 886 7486 | 52 | |
| .767 712 7033 | 46.457 459 3429 | .021 525 0686 | 53 | |
| .763 893 2371 | 47.221 352 5800 | .021 176 8606 | 54 | |
| .760 092 7732 | 47.981 445 3532 | .020 841 3897 | 55 | **6%** |
| .756 311 2171 | 48.737 756 5704 | .020 517 9735 | 56 | |
| .752 548 4748 | 49.490 305 0452 | .020 205 9777 | 57 | |
| .748 804 4525 | 50.239 109 4977 | .019 904 8114 | 58 | $i = .005$ |
| .745 079 0572 | 50.984 188 5549 | .019 613 9240 | 59 | $j_{(2)} = .01$ |
| .741 372 1962 | 51.725 560 7511 | .019 332 8015 | 60 | $j_{(4)} = .02$ <br> $j_{(12)} = .06$ |
| $v^n = \dfrac{1}{(1+i)^n}$ | $a_{\overline{n}|} = \dfrac{1-v^n}{i}$ | $\dfrac{1}{a_{\overline{n}|}} = \dfrac{i}{1-v^n}$ | n | |

| P E R I O D S | AMOUNT OF 1<br>*How $1 left at compound interest will grow.* | AMOUNT OF 1 PER PERIOD<br>*How $1 deposited periodically will grow.* | SINKING FUND<br>*Periodic deposit that will grow to $1 at future date.* |
|---|---|---|---|
| 61 | 1.355 594 4033 | 71.118 880 6624 | .014 060 9637 |
| 62 | 1.362 372 3753 | 72.474 475 0657 | .013 797 9613 |
| 63 | 1.369 184 2372 | 73.836 847 4411 | .013 543 3735 |
| 64 | 1.376 030 1584 | 75.206 031 6783 | .013 296 8058 |
| 65 | 1.382 910 3092 | 76.582 061 8366 | .013 057 8882 |
| 66 | 1.389 824 8607 | 77.964 972 1458 | .012 826 2728 |
| 67 | 1.396 773 9850 | 79.354 797 0066 | .012 601 6326 |
| 68 | 1.403 757 8550 | 80.751 570 9916 | .012 383 6600 |
| 69 | 1.410 776 6442 | 82.155 328 8466 | .012 172 0650 |
| 70 | 1.417 830 5275 | 83.566 105 4908 | .011 966 5742 |
| 71 | 1.424 919 6801 | 84.983 936 0182 | .011 766 9297 |
| 72 | 1.432 044 2785 | 86.408 855 6983 | .011 572 8879 |
| 73 | 1.439 204 4999 | 87.840 899 9768 | .011 384 2185 |
| 74 | 1.446 400 5224 | 89.280 104 4767 | .011 200 7037 |
| 75 | 1.453 632 5250 | 90.726 504 9991 | .011 022 1374 |
| 76 | 1.460 900 6876 | 92.180 137 5241 | .010 848 3240 |
| 77 | 1.468 205 1911 | 93.641 038 2117 | .010 679 0785 |
| 78 | 1.475 546 2170 | 95.109 243 4028 | .010 514 2252 |
| 79 | 1.482 923 9481 | 96.584 789 6198 | .010 353 5971 |
| 80 | 1.490 338 5678 | 98.067 713 5679 | .010 197 0359 |
| 81 | 1.497 790 2607 | 99.558 052 1357 | .010 044 3910 |
| 82 | 1.505 279 2120 | 101.055 842 3964 | .009 895 5189 |
| 83 | 1.512 805 6080 | 102.561 121 6084 | .009 750 2834 |
| 84 | 1.520 369 6361 | 104.073 927 2164 | .009 608 5545 |
| 85 | 1.527 971 4843 | 105.594 296 8525 | .009 470 2084 |
| 86 | 1.535 611 3417 | 107.122 268 3368 | .009 335 1272 |
| 87 | 1.543 289 3984 | 108.657 879 6784 | .009 203 1982 |
| 88 | 1.551 005 8454 | 110.201 169 0768 | .009 074 3139 |
| 89 | 1.558 760 8746 | 111.752 174 9222 | .008 948 3717 |
| 90 | 1.566 554 6790 | 113.310 935 7968 | .008 825 2735 |
| 91 | 1.574 387 4524 | 114.877 490 4758 | .008 704 9255 |
| 92 | 1.582 259 3896 | 116.451 877 9282 | .008 587 2381 |
| 93 | 1.590 170 6866 | 118.034 137 3178 | .008 472 1253 |
| 94 | 1.598 121 5400 | 119.624 308 0044 | .008 359 5050 |
| 95 | 1.606 112 1477 | 121.222 429 5445 | .008 249 2984 |
| 96 | 1.614 142 7085 | 122.828 541 6922 | .008 141 4302 |
| 97 | 1.622 213 4220 | 124.442 684 4006 | .008 035 8279 |
| 98 | 1.630 324 4891 | 126.064 897 8226 | .007 932 4222 |
| 99 | 1.638 476 1116 | 127.695 222 3118 | .007 831 1466 |
| 100 | 1.646 668 4921 | 129.333 698 4233 | .007 731 9369 |
| 101 | 1.654 901 8346 | 130.980 366 9154 | .007 634 7320 |
| 102 | 1.663 176 3438 | 132.635 268 7500 | .007 539 4728 |
| 103 | 1.671 492 2255 | 134.298 445 0938 | .007 446 1026 |
| 104 | 1.679 849 6866 | 135.969 937 3192 | .007 354 5669 |
| 105 | 1.688 248 9350 | 137.649 787 0058 | .007 264 8133 |
| 106 | 1.696 690 1797 | 139.338 035 9408 | .007 176 7913 |
| 107 | 1.705 173 6306 | 141.034 726 1206 | .007 090 4523 |
| 108 | 1.713 699 4988 | 142.739 899 7512 | .007 005 7496 |
| 109 | 1.722 267 9962 | 144.453 599 2499 | .006 922 6382 |
| 110 | 1.730 879 3362 | 146.175 867 2462 | .006 841 0745 |
| 111 | 1.739 533 7329 | 147.906 746 5824 | .006 761 0168 |
| 112 | 1.748 231 4016 | 149.646 280 3153 | .006 682 4247 |
| 113 | 1.756 972 5586 | 151.394 511 7169 | .006 605 2593 |
| 114 | 1.765 757 4214 | 153.151 484 2755 | .006 529 4829 |
| 115 | 1.774 586 2085 | 154.917 241 6968 | .006 455 0594 |
| 116 | 1.783 459 1395 | 156.691 827 9053 | .006 381 9538 |
| 117 | 1.792 376 4352 | 158.475 287 0449 | .006 310 1321 |
| 118 | 1.801 338 3174 | 160.267 663 4801 | .006 239 5619 |
| 119 | 1.810 345 0090 | 162.069 001 7975 | .006 170 2114 |
| 120 | 1.819 396 7340 | 163.879 346 8065 | .006 102 0502 |
| n | $s=(1+i)^n$ | $s_{\overline{n}|}=\dfrac{(1+i)^n-1}{i}$ | $\dfrac{1}{s_{\overline{n}|}}=\dfrac{i}{(1+i)^n-1}$ |

.005

*per period*

ANNUALLY
If compounded
*annually*
nominal annual rate is

½%

SEMIANNUALLY
If compounded
*semiannually*
nominal annual rate is

1%

QUARTERLY
If compounded
*quarterly*
nominal annual rate is

2%

MONTHLY
If compounded
*monthly*
nominal annual rate is

6%

$i = .005$
$j_{(2)} = .01$
$j_{(4)} = .02$
$j_{(12)} = .06$

28

| PRESENT WORTH OF 1<br>*What $1 due in the future is worth today.* | PRESENT WORTH OF 1 PER PERIOD<br>*What $1 payable periodically is worth today.* | PARTIAL PAYMENT<br>*Annuity worth $1 today.*<br>*Periodic payment necessary to pay off a loan of $1.* | PERIODS | RATE<br>$\frac{1}{2}\%$ |
|---|---|---|---|---|
| .737 683 7774 | 52.463 244 5285 | .019 060 9637 | 61 | |
| .734 013 7088 | 53.197 258 2373 | .018 797 9613 | 62 | |
| .730 361 8993 | 53.927 620 1366 | .018 543 3735 | 63 | .005 |
| .726 728 2580 | 54.654 348 3946 | .018 296 8058 | 64 | *per period* |
| .723 112 6946 | 55.377 461 0892 | .018 057 8882 | 65 | |
| .719 515 1190 | 56.096 976 2082 | .017 826 2728 | 66 | |
| .715 935 4418 | 56.812 911 6499 | .017 601 6326 | 67 | |
| .712 373 5739 | 57.525 285 2238 | .017 383 6600 | 68 | |
| .708 829 4267 | 58.234 114 6505 | .017 172 0650 | 69 | |
| .705 302 9122 | 58.939 417 5627 | .016 966 5742 | 70 | |
| .701 793 9425 | 59.641 211 5052 | .016 766 9297 | 71 | |
| .698 302 4303 | 60.339 513 9355 | .016 572 8879 | 72 | |
| .694 828 2889 | 61.034 342 2244 | .016 384 2185 | 73 | |
| .691 371 4317 | 61.725 713 6561 | .016 200 7037 | 74 | |
| .687 931 7729 | 62.413 645 4290 | .016 022 1374 | 75 | |
| .684 509 2267 | 63.098 154 6557 | .015 848 3240 | 76 | |
| .681 103 7082 | 63.779 258 3639 | .015 679 0785 | 77 | |
| .677 715 1325 | 64.456 973 4964 | .015 514 2252 | 78 | |
| .674 343 4154 | 65.131 316 9118 | .015 353 5971 | 79 | |
| .670 988 4731 | 65.802 305 3849 | .015 197 0359 | 80 | ANNUALLY |
| .667 650 2220 | 66.469 955 6069 | .015 044 3910 | 81 | If compounded *annually* nominal annual rate is |
| .664 328 5791 | 67.134 284 1859 | .014 895 5189 | 82 | |
| .661 023 4618 | 67.795 307 6477 | .014 750 2834 | 83 | |
| .657 734 7878 | 68.453 042 4355 | .014 608 5545 | 84 | |
| .654 462 4754 | 69.107 504 9110 | .014 470 2084 | 85 | $\frac{1}{2}\%$ |
| .651 206 4432 | 69.758 711 3542 | .014 335 1272 | 86 | |
| .647 966 6102 | 70.406 677 9644 | .014 203 1982 | 87 | |
| .644 742 8957 | 71.051 420 8601 | .014 074 3139 | 88 | |
| .641 535 2196 | 71.692 956 0797 | .013 948 3717 | 89 | |
| .638 343 5021 | 72.331 299 5818 | .013 825 2735 | 90 | SEMIANNUALLY |
| .635 167 6638 | 72.966 467 2455 | .013 704 9255 | 91 | If compounded *semiannually* nominal annual rate is |
| .632 007 6256 | 73.598 474 8712 | .013 587 2381 | 92 | |
| .628 863 3091 | 74.227 338 1803 | .013 472 1253 | 93 | |
| .625 734 6359 | 74.853 072 8162 | .013 359 5050 | 94 | |
| .622 621 5283 | 75.475 694 3445 | .013 249 2984 | 95 | 1% |
| .619 523 9087 | 76.095 218 2532 | .013 141 4302 | 96 | |
| .616 441 7002 | 76.711 659 9535 | .013 035 8279 | 97 | |
| .613 374 8261 | 77.325 034 7796 | .012 932 4222 | 98 | |
| .610 323 2101 | 77.935 357 9896 | .012 831 1466 | 99 | |
| .607 286 7762 | 78.542 644 7658 | .012 731 9369 | 100 | QUARTERLY |
| .604 265 4489 | 79.146 910 2147 | .012 634 7320 | 101 | If compounded *quarterly* nominal annual rate is |
| .601 259 1532 | 79.748 169 3679 | .012 539 4728 | 102 | |
| .598 267 8141 | 80.346 437 1820 | .012 446 1026 | 103 | |
| .595 291 3573 | 80.941 728 5393 | .012 354 5669 | 104 | |
| .592 329 7088 | 81.534 058 2480 | .012 264 8133 | 105 | 2% |
| .589 382 7948 | 82.123 441 0428 | .012 176 7913 | 106 | |
| .586 450 5421 | 82.709 891 5849 | .012 090 4523 | 107 | |
| .583 532 8777 | 83.293 424 4626 | .012 005 7496 | 108 | |
| .580 629 7290 | 83.874 054 1916 | .011 922 6382 | 109 | |
| .577 741 0239 | 84.451 795 2155 | .011 841 0745 | 110 | MONTHLY |
| .574 866 6905 | 85.026 661 9060 | .011 761 0168 | 111 | If compounded *monthly* nominal annual rate is |
| .572 006 6572 | 85.598 668 5632 | .011 682 4247 | 112 | |
| .569 160 8529 | 86.167 829 4161 | .011 605 2593 | 113 | |
| .566 329 2069 | 86.734 158 6230 | .011 529 4829 | 114 | |
| .563 511 6486 | 87.297 670 2716 | .011 455 0594 | 115 | 6% |
| .560 708 1081 | 87.858 378 3797 | .011 381 9538 | 116 | |
| .557 918 5155 | 88.416 296 8953 | .011 310 1321 | 117 | |
| .555 142 8015 | 88.971 439 6968 | .011 239 5619 | 118 | $i = .005$ |
| .552 380 8970 | 89.523 820 5938 | .011 170 2114 | 119 | $j_{(2)} = .01$ |
| .549 632 7334 | 90.073 453 3272 | .011 102 0502 | 120 | $j_{(4)} = .02$<br>$j_{(12)} = .06$ |
| $v^n = \dfrac{1}{(1+i)^n}$ | $a_{\overline{n}|} = \dfrac{1-v^n}{i}$ | $\dfrac{1}{a_{\overline{n}|}} = \dfrac{i}{1-v^n}$ | n | |

29

## 1/2%

.005

*per period*

ANNUALLY
If compounded
*annually*
nominal annual rate is

1/2%

SEMIANNUALLY
If compounded
*semiannually*
nominal annual rate is

1%

QUARTERLY
If compounded
*quarterly*
nominal annual rate is

2%

MONTHLY
If compounded
*monthly*
nominal annual rate is

6%

$i = .005$
$j_{(2)} = .01$
$j_{(4)} = .02$
$j_{(12)} = .06$

| P E R I O D S | AMOUNT OF 1 How \$1 left at compound interest will grow. | AMOUNT OF 1 PER PERIOD How \$1 deposited periodically will grow. | SINKING FUND Periodic deposit that will grow to \$1 at future date. |
|---|---|---|---|
| 121 | 1.828 493 7177 | 165.698 743 5405 | .006 035 0488 |
| 122 | 1.837 636 1863 | 167.527 237 2582 | .005 969 1786 |
| 123 | 1.846 824 3672 | 169.364 873 4445 | .005 904 4121 |
| 124 | 1.856 058 4891 | 171.211 697 8117 | .005 840 7224 |
| 125 | 1.865 338 7815 | 173.067 756 3008 | .005 778 0838 |
| 126 | 1.874 665 4754 | 174.933 095 0823 | .005 716 4712 |
| 127 | 1.884 038 8028 | 176.807 760 5577 | .005 655 8603 |
| 128 | 1.893 458 9968 | 178.691 799 3605 | .005 596 2277 |
| 129 | 1.902 926 2918 | 180.585 258 3573 | .005 537 5506 |
| 130 | 1.912 440 9232 | 182.488 184 6491 | .005 479 8068 |
| 131 | 1.922 003 1279 | 184.400 625 5723 | .005 422 9751 |
| 132 | 1.931 613 1435 | 186.322 628 7002 | .005 367 0346 |
| 133 | 1.941 271 2092 | 188.254 241 8437 | .005 311 9653 |
| 134 | 1.950 977 5653 | 190.195 513 0529 | .005 257 7476 |
| 135 | 1.960 732 4531 | 192.146 490 6182 | .005 204 3626 |
| 136 | 1.970 536 1154 | 194.107 223 0712 | .005 151 7918 |
| 137 | 1.980 388 7959 | 196.077 759 1866 | .005 100 0175 |
| 138 | 1.990 290 7399 | 198.058 147 9825 | .005 049 0223 |
| 139 | 2.000 242 1936 | 200.048 438 7224 | .004 998 7893 |
| 140 | 2.010 243 4046 | 202.048 680 9161 | .004 949 3023 |
| 141 | 2.020 294 6216 | 204.058 924 3206 | .004 900 5453 |
| 142 | 2.030 396 0947 | 206.079 218 9422 | .004 852 5029 |
| 143 | 2.040 548 0752 | 208.109 615 0370 | .004 805 1600 |
| 144 | 2.050 750 8156 | 210.150 163 1121 | .004 758 5021 |
| 145 | 2.061 004 5696 | 212.200 913 9277 | .004 712 5150 |
| 146 | 2.071 309 5925 | 214.261 918 4973 | .004 667 1849 |
| 147 | 2.081 666 1404 | 216.333 228 0898 | .004 622 4984 |
| 148 | 2.092 074 4712 | 218.414 894 2303 | .004 578 4423 |
| 149 | 2.102 534 8435 | 220.506 968 7014 | .004 535 0041 |
| 150 | 2.113 047 5177 | 222.609 503 5449 | .004 492 1712 |
| 151 | 2.123 612 7553 | 224.722 551 0627 | .004 449 9317 |
| 152 | 2.134 230 8191 | 226.846 163 8180 | .004 408 2738 |
| 153 | 2.144 901 9732 | 228.980 394 6371 | .004 367 1861 |
| 154 | 2.155 626 4831 | 231.125 296 6102 | .004 326 6575 |
| 155 | 2.166 404 6155 | 233.280 923 0933 | .004 286 6771 |
| 156 | 2.177 236 6385 | 235.447 327 7088 | .004 247 2344 |
| 157 | 2.188 122 8217 | 237.624 564 3473 | .004 208 3191 |
| 158 | 2.199 063 4358 | 239.812 687 1690 | .004 169 9212 |
| 159 | 2.210 058 7530 | 242.011 750 6049 | .004 132 0308 |
| 160 | 2.221 109 0468 | 244.221 809 3579 | .004 094 6384 |
| 161 | 2.232 214 5920 | 246.442 918 4047 | .004 057 7348 |
| 162 | 2.243 375 6650 | 248.675 132 9967 | .004 021 3108 |
| 163 | 2.254 592 5433 | 250.918 508 6617 | .003 985 3577 |
| 164 | 2.265 865 5060 | 253.173 101 2050 | .003 949 8667 |
| 165 | 2.277 194 8336 | 255.438 966 7110 | .003 914 8295 |
| 166 | 2.288 580 8077 | 257.716 161 5446 | .003 880 2378 |
| 167 | 2.300 023 7118 | 260.004 742 3523 | .003 846 0837 |
| 168 | 2.311 523 8303 | 262.304 766 0641 | .003 812 3592 |
| 169 | 2.323 081 4495 | 264.616 289 8944 | .003 779 0568 |
| 170 | 2.334 696 8567 | 266.939 371 3439 | .003 746 1690 |
| 171 | 2.346 370 3410 | 269.274 068 2006 | .003 713 6885 |
| 172 | 2.358 102 1927 | 271.620 438 5416 | .003 681 6081 |
| 173 | 2.369 892 7037 | 273.978 540 7343 | .003 649 9209 |
| 174 | 2.381 742 1672 | 276.348 433 4380 | .003 618 6201 |
| 175 | 2.393 650 8780 | 278.730 175 6052 | .003 587 6991 |
| 176 | 2.405 619 1324 | 281.123 826 4832 | .003 557 1514 |
| 177 | 2.417 647 2281 | 283.529 445 6156 | .003 526 9705 |
| 178 | 2.429 735 4642 | 285.947 092 8437 | .003 497 1504 |
| 179 | 2.441 884 1415 | 288.376 828 3079 | .003 467 6850 |
| 180 | 2.454 093 5622 | 290.818 712 4494 | .003 438 5683 |
| n | $s=(1+i)^n$ | $s_{\overline{n}|}=\dfrac{(1+i)^n-1}{i}$ | $\dfrac{1}{s_{\overline{n}|}}=\dfrac{i}{(1+i)^n-1}$ |

| PRESENT WORTH OF 1 | PRESENT WORTH OF 1 PER PERIOD | PARTIAL PAYMENT | P E R I O D S | RATE |
|---|---|---|---|---|
| *What $1 due in the future is worth today.* | *What $1 payable periodically is worth today.* | *Annuity worth $1 today.* *Periodic payment necessary to pay off a loan of $1.* | | **1/2%** |
| .546 898 2422 | 90.620 351 5693 | .011 035 0488 | 121 | |
| .544 177 3554 | 91.164 528 9247 | .010 969 1786 | 122 | |
| .541 470 0053 | 91.705 998 9300 | .010 904 4121 | 123 | .005 |
| .538 776 1247 | 92.244 775 0548 | .010 840 7224 | 124 | *per period* |
| .536 095 6465 | 92.780 870 7013 | .010 778 0838 | 125 | |
| .533 428 5040 | 93.314 299 2052 | .010 716 4712 | 126 | |
| .530 774 6308 | 93.845 073 8361 | .010 655 8603 | 127 | |
| .528 133 9610 | 94.373 207 7971 | .010 596 2277 | 128 | |
| .525 506 4289 | 94.898 714 2259 | .010 537 5506 | 129 | |
| .522 891 9690 | 95.421 606 1950 | .010 479 8068 | 130 | |
| .520 290 5164 | 95.941 896 7114 | .010 422 9751 | 131 | |
| .517 702 0064 | 96.459 598 7178 | .010 367 0346 | 132 | |
| .515 126 3745 | 96.974 725 0924 | .010 311 9653 | 133 | |
| .512 563 5568 | 97.487 288 6491 | .010 257 7476 | 134 | |
| .510 013 4893 | 97.997 302 1384 | .010 204 3626 | 135 | |
| .507 476 1088 | 98.504 778 2472 | .010 151 7918 | 136 | |
| .504 951 3520 | 99.009 729 5992 | .010 100 0175 | 137 | |
| .502 439 1562 | 99.512 168 7554 | .010 049 0223 | 133 | |
| .499 939 4589 | 100.012 108 2143 | .009 998 7893 | 139 | |
| .497 452 1979 | 100.509 560 4123 | .009 949 3023 | 140 | |
| .494 977 3114 | 101.004 537 7237 | .009 900 5453 | 141 | ANNUALLY |
| .492 514 7377 | 101.497 052 4614 | .009 852 5029 | 142 | If compounded |
| .490 064 4156 | 101.987 116 8770 | .009 805 1600 | 143 | *annually* |
| .487 626 2842 | 102.474 743 1612 | .009 758 5021 | 144 | nominal annual rate is |
| .485 200 2828 | 102.959 943 4439 | .009 712 5150 | 145 | **1/2%** |
| .482 786 3510 | 103.442 729 7950 | .009 667 1849 | 146 | |
| .480 384 4289 | 103.923 114 2239 | .009 622 4984 | 147 | |
| .477 994 4566 | 104.401 108 6805 | .009 578 4423 | 148 | |
| .475 616 3747 | 104.876 725 0552 | .009 535 0041 | 149 | |
| .473 250 1241 | 105.349 975 1793 | .009 492 1712 | 150 | |
| .470 895 6459 | 105.820 870 8252 | .009 449 9317 | 151 | SEMIANNUALLY |
| .468 552 8815 | 106.289 423 7066 | .009 408 2738 | 152 | If compounded |
| .466 221 7726 | 106.755 645 4792 | .009 367 1861 | 153 | *semiannually* |
| .463 902 2613 | 107.219 547 7405 | .009 326 6575 | 154 | nominal annual rate is |
| .461 594 2898 | 107.681 142 0304 | .009 286 6771 | 155 | **1%** |
| .459 297 8008 | 108.140 439 8312 | .009 247 2344 | 156 | |
| .457 012 7372 | 108.597 452 5684 | .009 208 3191 | 157 | |
| .454 739 0419 | 109.052 191 6103 | .009 169 9212 | 158 | |
| .452 476 6587 | 109.504 668 2690 | .009 132 0308 | 159 | |
| .450 225 5310 | 109.954 893 8000 | .009 094 6384 | 160 | |
| .447 985 6030 | 110.402 879 4030 | .009 057 7348 | 161 | QUARTERLY |
| .445 756 8189 | 110.848 636 2219 | .009 021 3108 | 162 | If compounded |
| .443 539 1233 | 111.292 175 3451 | .008 985 3577 | 163 | *quarterly* |
| .441 332 4610 | 111.733 507 8061 | .008 949 8667 | 164 | nominal annual rate is |
| .439 136 7771 | 112.172 644 5832 | .008 914 8295 | 165 | **2%** |
| .436 952 0170 | 112.609 596 6002 | .008 880 2378 | 166 | |
| .434 778 1264 | 113.044 374 7265 | .008 846 0837 | 167 | |
| .432 615 0511 | 113.476 989 7777 | .008 812 3592 | 168 | |
| .430 462 7374 | 113.907 452 5151 | .008 779 0568 | 169 | |
| .428 321 1318 | 114.335 773 6468 | .008 746 1690 | 170 | |
| .426 190 1809 | 114.761 963 8277 | .008 713 6885 | 171 | MONTHLY |
| .424 069 8317 | 115.186 033 6594 | .008 681 6081 | 172 | If compounded |
| .421 960 0315 | 115.607 993 6910 | .008 649 9209 | 173 | *monthly* |
| .419 860 7279 | 116.027 854 4189 | .008 618 6201 | 174 | nominal annual rate is |
| .417 771 8686 | 116.445 626 2874 | .008 587 6991 | 175 | **6%** |
| .415 693 4016 | 116.861 319 6890 | .008 557 1514 | 176 | |
| .413 625 2752 | 117.274 944 9642 | .008 526 9705 | 177 | |
| .411 567 4380 | 117.686 512 4021 | .008 497 1504 | 178 | $i = .005$ |
| .409 519 8388 | 118.096 032 2409 | .008 467 6850 | 179 | $j_{(2)} = .01$ |
| .407 482 4267 | 118.503 514 6676 | .008 438 5683 | 180 | $j_{(4)} = .02$ $j_{(12)} = .06$ |
| $v^n = \dfrac{1}{(1+i)^n}$ | $a_{\overline{n}|} = \dfrac{1-v^n}{i}$ | $\dfrac{1}{a_{\overline{n}|}} = \dfrac{i}{1-v^n}$ | n | |

.00583333

*per period*

ANNUALLY
If compounded
*annually*
nominal annual rate is

### 7/12%

SEMIANNUALLY
If compounded
*semiannually*
nominal annual rate is

### 1 1/6%

QUARTERLY
If compounded
*quarterly*
nominal annual rate is

### 2 1/3%

MONTHLY
If compounded
*monthly*
nominal annual rate is

### 7%

$i \quad = .00583333$
$j_{(2)} = .01166666$
$j_{(4)} = .02333333$
$j_{(12)} = .07$

| P E R I O D S | AMOUNT OF 1 How $1 left at compound interest will grow. | AMOUNT OF 1 PER PERIOD How $1 deposited periodically will grow. | SINKING FUND Periodic deposit that will grow to $1 at future date. |
|---|---|---|---|
| 1 | 1.005 833 3333 | 1.000 000 0000 | 1.000 000 0000 |
| 2 | 1.011 700 6944 | 2.005 833 3333 | .498 545 9078 |
| 3 | 1.017 602 2818 | 3.017 534 0278 | .331 396 4286 |
| 4 | 1.023 538 2951 | 4.035 136 3096 | .247 823 1027 |
| 5 | 1.029 508 9352 | 5.058 674 6047 | .197 680 2380 |
| 6 | 1.035 514 4040 | 6.088 183 5399 | .164 252 6040 |
| 7 | 1.041 554 9047 | 7.123 697 9439 | .140 376 5303 |
| 8 | 1.047 630 6416 | 8.165 252 8486 | .122 470 1817 |
| 9 | 1.053 741 8204 | 9.212 883 4902 | .108 543 6499 |
| 10 | 1.059 888 6476 | 10.266 625 3106 | .097 402 9898 |
| 11 | 1.066 071 3314 | 11.326 513 9582 | .088 288 4181 |
| 12 | 1.072 290 0809 | 12.392 585 2896 | .080 693 4128 |
| 13 | 1.078 545 1063 | 13.464 875 3705 | .074 267 3046 |
| 14 | 1.084 836 6194 | 14.543 420 4768 | .068 759 6155 |
| 15 | 1.091 164 8331 | 15.628 257 0963 | .063 986 6617 |
| 16 | 1.097 529 9613 | 16.719 421 9293 | .059 810 6803 |
| 17 | 1.103 932 2194 | 17.816 951 8906 | .056 126 3232 |
| 18 | 1.110 371 8240 | 18.920 884 1100 | .052 851 6529 |
| 19 | 1.116 848 9929 | 20.031 255 9339 | .049 921 9821 |
| 20 | 1.123 363 9454 | 21.148 104 9269 | .047 285 5607 |
| 21 | 1.129 916 9018 | 22.271 468 8723 | .044 900 4960 |
| 22 | 1.136 508 0837 | 23.401 385 7740 | .042 732 5121 |
| 23 | 1.143 137 7142 | 24.537 893 8577 | .040 753 2939 |
| 24 | 1.149 806 0175 | 25.681 031 5719 | .038 939 2458 |
| 25 | 1.156 513 2193 | 26.830 837 5894 | .037 270 5472 |
| 26 | 1.163 259 5464 | 27.987 350 8087 | .035 730 4272 |
| 27 | 1.170 045 2271 | 29.150 610 3550 | .034 304 5990 |
| 28 | 1.176 870 4909 | 30.320 655 5821 | .032 980 8172 |
| 29 | 1.183 735 5688 | 31.497 526 0730 | .031 748 5252 |
| 30 | 1.190 640 6929 | 32.681 261 6418 | .030 598 5739 |
| 31 | 1.197 586 0970 | 33.871 902 3347 | .029 522 9949 |
| 32 | 1.204 572 0159 | 35.069 488 4316 | .028 514 8157 |
| 33 | 1.211 598 6859 | 36.274 060 4475 | .027 567 9091 |
| 34 | 1.218 666 3449 | 37.485 659 1334 | .026 676 8685 |
| 35 | 1.225 775 2320 | 38.704 325 4784 | .025 836 9055 |
| 36 | 1.232 925 5875 | 39.930 100 7103 | .025 043 7635 |
| 37 | 1.240 117 6534 | 41.163 026 2978 | .024 293 6463 |
| 38 | 1.247 351 6730 | 42.403 143 9512 | .023 583 1570 |
| 39 | 1.254 627 8911 | 43.650 495 6243 | .022 909 2473 |
| 40 | 1.261 946 5538 | 44.905 123 5154 | .022 269 1738 |
| 41 | 1.269 307 9087 | 46.167 070 0692 | .021 660 4606 |
| 42 | 1.276 712 2049 | 47.436 377 9780 | .021 080 8675 |
| 43 | 1.284 159 6927 | 48.713 090 1829 | .020 528 3630 |
| 44 | 1.291 650 6243 | 49.997 249 8756 | .020 001 1001 |
| 45 | 1.299 185 2529 | 51.288 900 4999 | .019 497 3959 |
| 46 | 1.306 763 8336 | 52.588 085 7528 | .019 015 7140 |
| 47 | 1.314 386 6226 | 53.894 849 5863 | .018 554 6487 |
| 48 | 1.322 053 8779 | 55.209 236 2089 | .018 112 9113 |
| 49 | 1.329 765 8588 | 56.531 290 0868 | .017 689 3186 |
| 50 | 1.337 522 8263 | 57.861 055 9456 | .017 282 7817 |
| 51 | 1.345 325 0428 | 59.198 578 7720 | .016 892 2974 |
| 52 | 1.353 172 7723 | 60.543 903 8148 | .016 516 9396 |
| 53 | 1.361 066 2801 | 61.897 076 5871 | .016 155 8519 |
| 54 | 1.369 005 8334 | 63.258 142 8672 | .015 808 2415 |
| 55 | 1.376 991 7008 | 64.627 148 7006 | .015 473 3733 |
| 56 | 1.385 024 1523 | 66.004 140 4013 | .015 150 5647 |
| 57 | 1.393 103 4599 | 67.389 164 5537 | .014 839 1808 |
| 58 | 1.401 229 8967 | 68.782 268 0136 | .014 538 6308 |
| 59 | 1.409 403 7378 | 70.183 497 9103 | .014 248 3636 |
| 60 | 1.417 625 2596 | 71.592 901 6481 | .013 967 8652 |
| $n$ | $s=(1+i)^n$ | $s_{\overline{n}|}=\dfrac{(1+i)^n-1}{i}$ | $\dfrac{1}{s_{\overline{n}|}}=\dfrac{i}{(1+i)^n-1}$ |

| PRESENT WORTH OF 1 | PRESENT WORTH OF 1 PER PERIOD | PARTIAL PAYMENT | PERIODS | RATE |
|---|---|---|---|---|
| What $1 due in the future is worth today. | What $1 payable periodically is worth today. | Annuity worth $1 today. Periodic payment necessary to pay off a loan of $1. | | $7/12\%$ |
| .994 200 4971 | .994 200 4971 | 1.005 833 3333 | 1 | |
| .988 434 6284 | 1.982 635 1255 | .504 379 2411 | 2 | |
| .982 702 1989 | 2.965 337 3245 | .337 229 7619 | 3 | .00583333 |
| .977 003 0147 | 3.942 340 3392 | .253 656 4360 | 4 | |
| .971 336 8829 | 4.913 677 2220 | .203 513 5714 | 5 | per period |
| .965 703 6118 | 5.879 380 8338 | .170 085 9373 | 6 | |
| .960 103 0109 | 6.839 483 8447 | .146 209 8636 | 7 | |
| .954 534 8907 | 7.794 018 7355 | .128 303 5150 | 8 | |
| .948 999 0628 | 8.743 017 7983 | .114 376 9832 | 9 | |
| .943 495 3400 | 9.686 513 1383 | .103 236 3231 | 10 | |
| .938 023 5361 | 10.624 536 6744 | .094 121 7514 | 11 | |
| .932 583 4658 | 11.557 120 1402 | .086 526 7461 | 12 | |
| .927 174 9453 | 12.484 295 0856 | .080 100 6379 | 13 | |
| .921 797 7916 | 13.406 092 8771 | .074 592 9488 | 14 | |
| .916 451 8226 | 14.322 544 6997 | .069 819 9950 | 15 | |
| .911 136 8576 | 15.233 681 5573 | .065 644 0136 | 16 | |
| .905 852 7167 | 16.139 534 2740 | .061 959 6565 | 17 | |
| .900 599 2213 | 17.040 133 4953 | .058 684 9863 | 18 | |
| .895 376 1935 | 17.935 509 6888 | .055 755 3154 | 19 | |
| .890 183 4567 | 18.825 693 1454 | .053 118 8941 | 20 | |
| .885 020 8351 | 19.710 713 9805 | .050 733 8294 | 21 | ANNUALLY |
| .879 888 1542 | 20.590 602 1348 | .048 565 8454 | 22 | If compounded annually nominal annual rate is |
| .874 785 2403 | 21.465 387 3751 | .046 586 6272 | 23 | |
| .869 711 9208 | 22.335 099 2958 | .044 772 5791 | 24 | $7/12\%$ |
| .864 668 0240 | 23.199 767 3198 | .043 103 8806 | 25 | |
| .859 653 3793 | 24.059 420 6991 | .041 563 7605 | 26 | |
| .854 667 8170 | 24.914 088 5161 | .040 137 9324 | 27 | |
| .849 711 1685 | 25.763 799 6846 | .038 814 1506 | 28 | |
| .844 783 2661 | 26.608 582 9507 | .037 581 8585 | 29 | |
| .839 883 9431 | 27.448 466 8938 | .036 431 9072 | 30 | |
| .835 013 0338 | 28.283 479 9276 | .035 356 3282 | 31 | SEMIANNUALLY |
| .830 170 3732 | 29.113 650 3008 | .034 348 1491 | 32 | If compounded semiannually nominal annual rate is |
| .825 355 7978 | 29.939 006 0986 | .033 401 2424 | 33 | |
| .820 569 1444 | 30.759 575 2430 | .032 510 2019 | 34 | $1\frac{1}{6}\%$ |
| .815 810 2513 | 31.575 385 4943 | .031 670 2388 | 35 | |
| .811 078 9574 | 32.386 464 4516 | .030 877 0969 | 36 | |
| .806 375 1026 | 33.192 839 5542 | .030 126 9796 | 37 | |
| .801 698 5279 | 33.994 538 0821 | .029 416 4903 | 38 | |
| .797 049 0749 | 34.791 587 1570 | .028 742 5807 | 39 | |
| .792 426 5865 | 35.584 013 7435 | .028 102 5071 | 40 | QUARTERLY |
| .787 830 9062 | 36.371 844 6497 | .027 493 7939 | 41 | If compounded quarterly nominal annual rate is |
| .783 261 8786 | 37.155 106 5283 | .026 914 2009 | 42 | |
| .778 719 3490 | 37.933 825 8773 | .026 361 6964 | 43 | |
| .774 203 1639 | 38.708 029 0413 | .025 834 4334 | 44 | $2\frac{1}{3}\%$ |
| .769 713 1704 | 39.477 742 2117 | .025 330 7293 | 45 | |
| .765 249 2167 | 40.242 991 4284 | .024 849 0474 | 46 | |
| .760 811 1516 | 41.003 802 5800 | .024 387 9820 | 47 | |
| .756 398 8251 | 41.760 201 4051 | .023 946 2447 | 48 | |
| .752 012 0880 | 42.512 213 4931 | .023 522 6519 | 49 | |
| .747 650 7917 | 43.259 864 2848 | .023 116 1151 | 50 | MONTHLY |
| .743 314 7887 | 44.003 179 0735 | .022 725 6308 | 51 | If compounded monthly nominal annual rate is |
| .739 003 9325 | 44.742 183 0060 | .022 350 2729 | 52 | |
| .734 718 0770 | 45.476 901 0830 | .021 989 1852 | 53 | |
| .730 457 0774 | 46.207 358 1604 | .021 641 5748 | 54 | $7\%$ |
| .726 220 7895 | 46.933 578 9498 | .021 306 7067 | 55 | |
| .722 009 0699 | 47.655 588 0197 | .020 983 8980 | 56 | |
| .717 821 7762 | 48.373 409 7959 | .020 672 5142 | 57 | $i = .00583333$ |
| .713 658 7667 | 49.087 068 5626 | .020 371 9641 | 58 | $j_{(2)} = .01166666$ |
| .709 519 9006 | 49.796 588 4633 | .020 081 6970 | 59 | $j_{(4)} = .02333333$ |
| .705 405 0379 | 50.501 993 5012 | .019 801 1985 | 60 | $j_{(12)} = .07$ |
| $v^n = \dfrac{1}{(1+i)^n}$ | $a_{\overline{n}|} = \dfrac{1-v^n}{i}$ | $\dfrac{1}{a_{\overline{n}|}} = \dfrac{i}{1-v^n}$ | n | |

.00583333

*per period*

ANNUALLY
If compounded
*annually*
nominal annual rate is

$\frac{7}{12}\%$

SEMIANNUALLY
If compounded
*semiannually*
nominal annual rate is

$1\frac{1}{6}\%$

QUARTERLY
If compounded
*quarterly*
nominal annual rate is

$2\frac{1}{3}\%$

MONTHLY
If compounded
*monthly*
nominal annual rate is

$7\%$

$i \quad = .00583333$
$j_{(2)} = .01166666$
$j_{(4)} = .02333333$
$j_{(12)} = .07$

| P E R I O D S | AMOUNT OF 1 How $1 left at compound interest will grow. | AMOUNT OF 1 PER PERIOD How $1 deposited periodically will grow. | SINKING FUND Periodic deposit that will grow to $1 at future date. |
|---|---|---|---|
| 61 | 1.425 894 7403 | 73.010 526 9077 | .013 696 6550 |
| 62 | 1.434 212 4596 | 74.436 421 6480 | .013 434 2836 |
| 63 | 1.442 578 6990 | 75.870 634 1076 | .013 180 3301 |
| 64 | 1.450 993 7414 | 77.313 212 8066 | .012 934 3997 |
| 65 | 1.459 457 8715 | 78.764 206 5480 | .012 696 1223 |
| 66 | 1.467 971 3758 | 80.223 664 4195 | .012 465 1499 |
| 67 | 1.476 534 5421 | 81.691 635 7953 | .012 241 1553 |
| 68 | 1.485 147 6603 | 83.168 170 3374 | .012 023 8307 |
| 69 | 1.493 811 0217 | 84.653 317 9977 | .011 812 8861 |
| 70 | 1.502 524 9193 | 86.147 129 0194 | .011 608 0479 |
| 71 | 1.511 289 6480 | 87.649 653 9387 | .011 409 0582 |
| 72 | 1.520 105 5043 | 89.160 943 5866 | .011 215 6731 |
| 73 | 1.528 972 7864 | 90.681 049 0909 | .011 027 6625 |
| 74 | 1.537 891 7943 | 92.210 021 8772 | .010 844 8082 |
| 75 | 1.546 862 8298 | 93.747 913 6715 | .010 666 9040 |
| 76 | 1.555 886 1963 | 95.294 776 5013 | .010 493 7546 |
| 77 | 1.564 962 1991 | 96.850 662 6975 | .010 325 1746 |
| 78 | 1.574 091 1452 | 98.415 624 8966 | .010 160 9882 |
| 79 | 1.583 273 3436 | 99.989 716 0418 | .010 001 0285 |
| 80 | 1.592 509 1047 | 101.572 989 3854 | .009 845 1370 |
| 81 | 1.601 798 7412 | 103.165 498 4902 | .009 693 1631 |
| 82 | 1.611 142 5672 | 104.767 297 2314 | .009 544 9632 |
| 83 | 1.620 540 8988 | 106.378 439 7985 | .009 400 4011 |
| 84 | 1.629 994 0541 | 107.998 980 6974 | .009 259 3466 |
| 85 | 1.639 502 3527 | 109.628 974 7514 | .009 121 6761 |
| 86 | 1.649 066 1164 | 111.268 477 1041 | .008 987 2714 |
| 87 | 1.658 685 6688 | 112.917 543 2206 | .008 856 0198 |
| 88 | 1.668 361 3352 | 114.576 228 8894 | .008 727 8139 |
| 89 | 1.678 093 4430 | 116.244 590 2246 | .008 602 5509 |
| 90 | 1.687 882 3214 | 117.922 683 6675 | .008 480 1327 |
| 91 | 1.697 728 3016 | 119.610 565 9889 | .008 360 4654 |
| 92 | 1.707 631 7167 | 121.308 294 2905 | .008 243 4594 |
| 93 | 1.717 592 9017 | 123.015 926 0072 | .008 129 0288 |
| 94 | 1.727 612 1936 | 124.733 518 9089 | .008 017 0912 |
| 95 | 1.737 689 9314 | 126.461 131 1026 | .007 907 5681 |
| 96 | 1.747 826 4560 | 128.198 821 0340 | .007 800 3837 |
| 97 | 1.758 022 1104 | 129.946 647 4900 | .007 695 4659 |
| 98 | 1.768 277 2393 | 131.704 669 6004 | .007 592 7452 |
| 99 | 1.778 592 1899 | 133.472 946 8397 | .007 492 1550 |
| 100 | 1.788 967 3110 | 135.251 539 0296 | .007 393 6312 |
| 101 | 1.799 402 9537 | 137.040 506 3406 | .007 297 1126 |
| 102 | 1.809 899 4709 | 138.839 909 2943 | .007 202 5400 |
| 103 | 1.820 457 2178 | 140.649 808 7652 | .007 109 8568 |
| 104 | 1.831 076 5516 | 142.470 265 9830 | .007 019 0084 |
| 105 | 1.841 757 8315 | 144.301 342 5345 | .006 929 9425 |
| 106 | 1.852 501 4188 | 146.143 100 3660 | .006 842 6084 |
| 107 | 1.863 307 6771 | 147.995 601 7848 | .006 756 9576 |
| 108 | 1.874 176 9719 | 149.858 909 4619 | .006 672 9433 |
| 109 | 1.885 109 6709 | 151.733 086 4337 | .006 590 5204 |
| 110 | 1.896 106 1439 | 153.618 196 1046 | .006 509 6455 |
| 111 | 1.907 166 7631 | 155.514 302 2485 | .006 430 2767 |
| 112 | 1.918 291 9026 | 157.421 469 0117 | .006 352 3737 |
| 113 | 1.929 481 9387 | 159.339 760 9142 | .006 275 8975 |
| 114 | 1.940 737 2500 | 161.269 242 8529 | .006 200 8104 |
| 115 | 1.952 058 2173 | 163.209 980 1029 | .006 127 0763 |
| 116 | 1.963 445 2235 | 165.162 038 3201 | .006 054 6601 |
| 117 | 1.974 898 6540 | 167.125 483 5437 | .005 983 5279 |
| 118 | 1.986 418 8962 | 169.100 382 1977 | .005 913 6472 |
| 119 | 1.998 006 3397 | 171.086 801 0938 | .005 844 9863 |
| 120 | 2.009 661 3767 | 173.084 807 4335 | .005 777 5146 |
| **n** | $s=(1+i)^n$ | $s_{\overline{n}\rceil}=\dfrac{(1+i)^n-1}{i}$ | $\dfrac{1}{s_{\overline{n}\rceil}}=\dfrac{i}{(1+i)^n-1}$ |

| PRESENT WORTH OF 1 *What $1 due in the future is worth today.* | PRESENT WORTH OF 1 PER PERIOD *What $1 payable periodically is worth today.* | PARTIAL PAYMENT *Annuity worth $1 today.* *Periodic payment necessary to pay off a loan of $1.* | PERIODS | RATE 7/12% |
|---|---|---|---|---|
| .701 314 0393 | 51.203 307 5405 | .019 529 9884 | 61 | |
| .697 246 7665 | 51.900 554 3071 | .019 267 6170 | 62 | |
| .693 203 0819 | 52.593 757 3890 | .019 013 6634 | 63 | .00583333 |
| .689 182 8486 | 53.282 940 2376 | .018 767 7331 | 64 | *per period* |
| .685 185 9307 | 53.968 126 1683 | .018 529 4556 | 65 | |
| .681 212 1929 | 54.649 338 3611 | .018 298 4832 | 66 | |
| .677 261 5008 | 55.326 599 8619 | .018 074 4886 | 67 | |
| .673 333 7208 | 55.999 933 5827 | .017 857 1640 | 68 | |
| .669 428 7199 | 56.669 362 3026 | .017 646 2194 | 69 | |
| .665 546 3661 | 57.334 908 6687 | .017 441 3812 | 70 | |
| .661 686 5280 | 57.996 595 1967 | .017 242 3915 | 71 | |
| .657 849 0751 | 58.654 444 2718 | .017 049 0065 | 72 | |
| .654 033 8775 | 59.308 478 1493 | .016 860 9958 | 73 | |
| .650 240 8061 | 59.958 718 9554 | .016 678 1415 | 74 | |
| .646 469 7327 | 60.605 188 6880 | .016 500 2374 | 75 | |
| .642 720 5296 | 61.247 909 2176 | .016 327 0879 | 76 | |
| .638 993 0700 | 61.886 902 2876 | .016 158 5079 | 77 | |
| .635 287 2278 | 62.522 189 5154 | .015 994 3215 | 78 | |
| .631 602 8777 | 63.153 792 3931 | .015 834 3618 | 79 | |
| .627 939 8950 | 63.781 732 2881 | .015 678 4704 | 80 | |
| .624 298 1557 | 64.406 030 4438 | .015 526 4964 | 81 | ANNUALLY If compounded *annually* nominal annual rate is |
| .620 677 5368 | 65.026 707 9806 | .015 378 2966 | 82 | |
| .617 077 9156 | 65.643 785 8962 | .015 233 7344 | 83 | |
| .613 499 1704 | 66.257 285 0667 | .015 092 6800 | 84 | |
| .609 941 1802 | 66.867 226 2469 | .014 955 0094 | 85 | 7/12% |
| .606 403 8246 | 67.473 630 0715 | .014 820 6047 | 86 | |
| .602 886 9838 | 68.076 517 0553 | .014 689 3531 | 87 | |
| .599 390 5390 | 68.675 907 5944 | .014 561 1472 | 88 | |
| .595 914 3719 | 69.271 821 9662 | .014 435 8842 | 89 | |
| .592 458 3647 | 69.864 280 3310 | .014 313 4660 | 90 | SEMIANNUALLY If compounded *semiannually* nominal annual rate is |
| .589 022 4007 | 70.453 302 7317 | .014 193 7987 | 91 | |
| .585 606 3636 | 71.038 909 0953 | .014 076 7927 | 92 | |
| .582 210 1378 | 71.621 119 2331 | .013 962 3621 | 93 | |
| .578 833 6084 | 72.199 952 8415 | .013 850 4246 | 94 | |
| .575 476 6612 | 72.775 429 5028 | .013 740 9014 | 95 | 1 1/6% |
| .572 139 1827 | 73.347 568 6854 | .013 633 7171 | 96 | |
| .568 821 0598 | 73.916 389 7453 | .013 528 7993 | 97 | |
| .565 522 1804 | 74.481 911 9257 | .013 426 0785 | 98 | |
| .562 242 4329 | 75.044 154 3586 | .013 325 4883 | 99 | |
| .558 981 7063 | 75.603 136 0649 | .013 226 9645 | 100 | QUARTERLY If compounded *quarterly* nominal annual rate is |
| .555 739 8903 | 76.158 875 9551 | .013 130 4459 | 101 | |
| .552 516 8752 | 76.711 392 8303 | .013 035 8733 | 102 | |
| .549 312 5519 | 77.260 705 3822 | .012 943 1901 | 103 | |
| .546 126 8122 | 77.806 832 1944 | .012 852 3418 | 104 | |
| .542 959 5482 | 78.349 791 7426 | .012 763 2758 | 105 | 2 1/3% |
| .539 810 6527 | 78.889 602 3953 | .012 675 9417 | 106 | |
| .536 680 0192 | 79.426 282 4145 | .012 590 2909 | 107 | |
| .533 567 5419 | 79.959 849 9565 | .012 506 2766 | 108 | |
| .530 473 1154 | 80.490 323 0719 | .012 423 8537 | 109 | |
| .527 396 6350 | 81.017 719 7069 | .012 342 9788 | 110 | MONTHLY If compounded *monthly* nominal annual rate is |
| .524 337 9967 | 81.542 057 7037 | .012 263 6101 | 111 | |
| .521 297 0970 | 82.063 354 8007 | .012 185 7070 | 112 | |
| .518 273 8330 | 82.581 628 6336 | .012 109 2308 | 113 | |
| .515 268 1024 | 83.096 896 7360 | .012 034 1437 | 114 | |
| .512 279 8035 | 83.609 176 5395 | .011 960 4096 | 115 | 7% |
| .509 308 8353 | 84.118 485 3748 | .011 887 9934 | 116 | |
| .506 355 0972 | 84.624 840 4721 | .011 816 8613 | 117 | |
| .503 418 4894 | 85.128 258 9615 | .011 746 9805 | 118 | $i\ =\ .00583333$ |
| .500 498 9124 | 85.628 757 8739 | .011 678 3196 | 119 | $j_{(2)}\ =\ .01166666$ |
| .497 596 2675 | 86.126 354 1414 | .011 610 8479 | 120 | $j_{(4)}\ =\ .02333333$ |
| $v^n = \dfrac{1}{(1+i)^n}$ | $a_{\overline{n}|} = \dfrac{1-v^n}{i}$ | $\dfrac{1}{a_{\overline{n}|}} = \dfrac{i}{1-v^n}$ | n | $j_{(12)}\ =\ .07$ |

35

| P E R I O D S | AMOUNT OF 1<br>*How $1 left at compound interest will grow.* | AMOUNT OF 1 PER PERIOD<br>*How $1 deposited periodically will grow.* | SINKING FUND<br>*Periodic deposit that will grow to $1 at future date.* |
|---|---|---|---|
| 121 | 2.021 384 4014 | 175.094 468 8102 | .005 711 2027 |
| 122 | 2.033 175 8104 | 177.115 853 2116 | .005 646 0220 |
| 123 | 2.045 036 0026 | 179.149 029 0220 | .005 581 9449 |
| 124 | 2.056 965 3793 | 181.194 065 0247 | .005 518 9446 |
| 125 | 2.068 964 3440 | 183.251 030 4040 | .005 456 9952 |
| 126 | 2.081 033 3027 | 185.319 994 7480 | .005 396 0718 |
| 127 | 2.093 172 6636 | 187.401 028 0507 | .005 336 1500 |
| 128 | 2.105 382 8375 | 189.494 200 7143 | .005 277 2064 |
| 129 | 2.117 664 2374 | 191.599 583 5518 | .005 219 2180 |
| 130 | 2.130 017 2788 | 193.717 247 7892 | .005 162 1630 |
| 131 | 2.142 442 3796 | 195.847 265 0680 | .005 106 0197 |
| 132 | 2.154 939 9601 | 197.989 707 4475 | .005 050 7676 |
| 133 | 2.167 510 4432 | 200.144 647 4076 | .004 996 3864 |
| 134 | 2.180 154 2541 | 202.312 157 8509 | .004 942 8567 |
| 135 | 2.192 871 8206 | 204.492 312 1050 | .004 890 1594 |
| 136 | 2.205 663 5729 | 206.685 183 9256 | .004 838 2762 |
| 137 | 2.218 529 9437 | 208.890 847 4985 | .004 787 1892 |
| 138 | 2.231 471 3684 | 211.109 377 4422 | .004 736 8810 |
| 139 | 2.244 488 2847 | 213.340 848 8107 | .004 687 3349 |
| 140 | 2.257 581 1331 | 215.585 337 0954 | .004 638 5344 |
| 141 | 2.270 750 3563 | 217.842 918 2284 | .004 590 4637 |
| 142 | 2.283 996 4001 | 220.113 668 5848 | .004 543 1072 |
| 143 | 2.297 319 7124 | 222.397 664 9848 | .004 496 4501 |
| 144 | 2.310 720 7441 | 224.694 984 6973 | .004 450 4776 |
| 145 | 2.324 199 9484 | 227.005 705 4413 | .004 405 1756 |
| 146 | 2.337 757 7814 | 229.329 905 3897 | .004 360 5303 |
| 147 | 2.351 394 7018 | 231.667 663 1712 | .004 316 5282 |
| 148 | 2.365 111 1709 | 234.019 057 8730 | .004 273 1563 |
| 149 | 2.378 907 6528 | 236.384 169 0439 | .004 230 4017 |
| 150 | 2.392 784 6141 | 238.763 076 6967 | .004 188 2523 |
| 151 | 2.406 742 5243 | 241.155 861 3108 | .004 146 6958 |
| 152 | 2.420 781 8557 | 243.562 603 8351 | .004 105 7206 |
| 153 | 2.434 903 0832 | 245.983 385 6908 | .004 065 3152 |
| 154 | 2.449 106 6845 | 248.418 288 7740 | .004 025 4685 |
| 155 | 2.463 393 1402 | 250.867 395 4585 | .003 986 1697 |
| 156 | 2.477 762 9335 | 253.330 788 5987 | .003 947 4081 |
| 157 | 2.492 216 5506 | 255.808 551 5321 | .003 909 1735 |
| 158 | 2.506 754 4805 | 258.300 768 0827 | .003 871 4558 |
| 159 | 2.521 377 2150 | 260.807 522 5632 | .003 834 2452 |
| 160 | 2.536 085 2487 | 263.328 899 7782 | .003 797 5323 |
| 161 | 2.550 879 0793 | 265.864 985 0269 | .003 761 3076 |
| 162 | 2.565 759 2073 | 268.415 864 1062 | .003 725 5622 |
| 163 | 2.580 726 1360 | 270.981 623 3135 | .003 690 2871 |
| 164 | 2.595 780 3718 | 273.562 349 4495 | .003 655 4738 |
| 165 | 2.610 922 4240 | 276.158 129 8213 | .003 621 1137 |
| 166 | 2.626 152 8048 | 278.769 052 2452 | .003 587 1988 |
| 167 | 2.641 472 0295 | 281.395 205 0500 | .003 553 7208 |
| 168 | 2.656 880 6163 | 284.036 677 0795 | .003 520 6721 |
| 169 | 2.672 379 0866 | 286.693 557 6958 | .003 488 0449 |
| 170 | 2.687 967 9646 | 289.365 936 7823 | .003 455 8318 |
| 171 | 2.703 647 7777 | 292.053 904 7469 | .003 424 0254 |
| 172 | 2.719 419 0564 | 294.757 552 5246 | .003 392 6188 |
| 173 | 2.735 282 3342 | 297.476 971 5810 | .003 361 6047 |
| 174 | 2.751 238 1478 | 300.212 253 9152 | .003 330 9766 |
| 175 | 2.767 287 0370 | 302.963 492 0630 | .003 300 7277 |
| 176 | 2.783 429 5448 | 305.730 779 1001 | .003 270 8516 |
| 177 | 2.799 666 2171 | 308.514 208 6448 | .003 241 3418 |
| 178 | 2.815 997 6034 | 311.313 874 8619 | .003 212 1922 |
| 179 | 2.832 424 2560 | 314.129 872 4653 | .003 183 3967 |
| 180 | 2.848 946 7309 | 316.962 296 7213 | .003 154 9494 |
| **n** | $s=(1+i)^n$ | $s_{\overline{n}|} = \dfrac{(1+i)^n-1}{i}$ | $\dfrac{1}{s_{\overline{n}|}} = \dfrac{i}{(1+i)^n-1}$ |

.00583333
*per period*

ANNUALLY
If compounded
*annually*
nominal annual rate is

7/12%

SEMIANNUALLY
If compounded
*semiannually*
nominal annual rate is

1 1/6%

QUARTERLY
If compounded
*quarterly*
nominal annual rate is

2 1/3%

MONTHLY
If compounded
*monthly*
nominal annual rate is

7%

$i$ = .00583333
$j_{(2)}$ = .01166666
$j_{(4)}$ = .02333333
$j_{(12)}$ = .07

| PRESENT WORTH OF 1<br>*What $1 due in the future is worth today.* | PRESENT WORTH OF 1 PER PERIOD<br>*What $1 payable periodically is worth today.* | PARTIAL PAYMENT<br>*Annuity worth $1 today.*<br>*Periodic payment necessary to pay off a loan of $1.* | P E R I O D S | RATE<br>$7/12\%$ |
|---|---|---|---|---|
| .494 710 4565 | 86.621 064 5979 | .011 544 5360 | 121 | |
| .491 841 3818 | 87.112 905 9797 | .011 479 3553 | 122 | |
| .488 988 9463 | 87.601 894 9259 | .011 415 2782 | 123 | .00583333 |
| .486 153 0535 | 88.088 047 9794 | .011 352 2779 | 124 | *per period* |
| .483 333 6074 | 88.571 381 5868 | .011 290 3286 | 125 | |
| .480 530 5128 | 89.051 912 0996 | .011 229 4051 | 126 | |
| .477 743 6747 | 89.529 655 7742 | .011 169 4834 | 127 | |
| .474 972 9988 | 90.004 628 7730 | .011 110 5397 | 128 | |
| .472 218 3915 | 90.476 847 1646 | .011 052 5514 | 129 | |
| .469 479 7596 | 90.946 326 9242 | .010 995 4963 | 130 | |
| .466 757 0104 | 91.413 083 9346 | .010 939 3531 | 131 | |
| .464 050 0517 | 91.877 133 9863 | .010 884 1009 | 132 | |
| .461 358 7921 | 92.338 492 7784 | .010 829 7198 | 133 | |
| .458 683 1405 | 92.797 175 9189 | .010 776 1900 | 134 | |
| .456 023 0063 | 93.253 198 9252 | .010 723 4927 | 135 | |
| .453 378 2995 | 93.706 577 2247 | .010 671 6095 | 136 | |
| .450 748 9308 | 94.157 326 1555 | .010 620 5225 | 137 | |
| .448 134 8110 | 94.605 460 9665 | .010 570 2143 | 138 | |
| .445 535 8519 | 95.050 996 8184 | .010 520 6682 | 139 | |
| .442 951 9654 | 95.493 948 7838 | .010 471 8677 | 140 | |
| .440 383 0642 | 95.934 331 8480 | .010 423 7970 | 141 | ANNUALLY<br>If compounded<br>*annually*<br>nominal annual rate is |
| .437 829 0614 | 96.372 160 9094 | .010 376 4406 | 142 | |
| .435 289 8705 | 96.807 450 7798 | .010 329 7834 | 143 | |
| .432 765 4056 | 97.240 216 1854 | .010 283 8110 | 144 | |
| .430 255 5814 | 97.670 471 7668 | .010 238 5090 | 145 | $7/12\%$ |
| .427 760 3129 | 98.098 232 0797 | .010 193 8636 | 146 | |
| .425 279 5157 | 98.523 511 5953 | .010 149 8615 | 147 | |
| .422 813 1059 | 98.946 324 7013 | .010 106 4896 | 148 | |
| .420 361 0001 | 99.366 685 7013 | .010 063 7351 | 149 | |
| .417 923 1152 | 99.784 608 8166 | .010 021 5856 | 150 | |
| .415 499 3689 | 100.200 108 1855 | .009 980 0291 | 151 | SEMIANNUALLY<br>If compounded<br>*semiannually*<br>nominal annual rate is |
| .413 089 6791 | 100.613 197 8646 | .009 939 0539 | 152 | |
| .410 693 9643 | 101.023 891 8289 | .009 898 6485 | 153 | |
| .408 312 1435 | 101.432 203 9724 | .009 858 8018 | 154 | |
| .405 944 1360 | 101.838 148 1085 | .009 819 5030 | 155 | $1\,1/6\%$ |
| .403 589 8618 | 102.241 737 9703 | .009 780 7414 | 156 | |
| .401 249 2413 | 102.642 987 2116 | .009 742 5068 | 157 | |
| .398 922 1951 | 103.041 909 4067 | .009 704 7891 | 158 | |
| .396 608 6447 | 103.438 518 0514 | .009 667 5786 | 159 | |
| .394 308 5117 | 103.832 826 5631 | .009 630 8656 | 160 | |
| .392 021 7184 | 104.224 848 2815 | .009 594 6410 | 161 | QUARTERLY<br>If compounded<br>*quarterly*<br>nominal annual rate is |
| .389 748 1873 | 104.614 596 4687 | .009 558 8955 | 162 | |
| .387 487 8415 | 105.002 084 3103 | .009 523 6205 | 163 | |
| .385 240 6047 | 105.387 324 9149 | .009 488 8071 | 164 | |
| .383 006 4007 | 105.770 331 3156 | .009 454 4471 | 165 | $2\,1/3\%$ |
| .380 785 1539 | 106.151 116 4695 | .009 420 5321 | 166 | |
| .378 576 7893 | 106.529 693 2588 | .009 387 0542 | 167 | |
| .376 381 2321 | 106.906 074 4910 | .009 354 0054 | 168 | |
| .374 198 4081 | 107.280 272 8991 | .009 321 3782 | 169 | |
| .372 028 2433 | 107.652 301 1424 | .009 289 1651 | 170 | |
| .369 870 6645 | 108.022 171 8069 | .009 257 3588 | 171 | MONTHLY<br>If compounded<br>*monthly*<br>nominal annual rate is |
| .367 725 5985 | 108.389 897 4053 | .009 225 9521 | 172 | |
| .365 592 9728 | 108.755 490 3781 | .009 194 9381 | 173 | |
| .363 472 7153 | 109.118 963 0934 | .009 164 3100 | 174 | |
| .361 364 7542 | 109.480 327 8476 | .009 134 0611 | 175 | $7\%$ |
| .359 269 0183 | 109.839 596 8659 | .009 104 1849 | 176 | |
| .357 185 4366 | 110.196 782 3025 | .009 074 6751 | 177 | |
| .355 113 9386 | 110.551 896 2411 | .009 045 5255 | 178 | $i\ =\ .00583333$ |
| .353 054 4543 | 110.904 950 6954 | .009 016 7300 | 179 | $j_{(2)}\ =\ .01166666$ |
| .351 006 9139 | 111.255 957 6093 | .008 988 2827 | 180 | $j_{(4)}\ =\ .02333333$<br>$j_{(12)}\ =\ .07$ |
| $v^n=\dfrac{1}{(1+i)^n}$ | $a_{\overline{n}\|}=\dfrac{1-v^n}{i}$ | $\dfrac{1}{a_{\overline{n}\|}}=\dfrac{i}{1-v^n}$ | **n** | |

37

| P E R I O D S | AMOUNT OF 1<br>*How $1 left at compound interest will grow.* | AMOUNT OF 1 PER PERIOD<br>*How $1 deposited periodically will grow.* | SINKING FUND<br>*Periodic deposit that will grow to $1 at future date.* |
|---|---|---|---|
| 1 | 1.006 666 6667 | 1.000 000 0000 | 1.000 000 0000 |
| 2 | 1.013 377 7778 | 2.006 666 6667 | .498 338 8704 |
| 3 | 1.020 133 6296 | 3.020 044 4444 | .331 120 9548 |
| 4 | 1.026 934 5205 | 4.040 178 0741 | .247 513 8426 |
| 5 | 1.033 780 7506 | 5.067 112 5946 | .197 351 0618 |
| 6 | 1.040 672 6223 | 6.100 893 3452 | .163 910 4215 |
| 7 | 1.047 610 4398 | 7.141 565 9675 | .140 025 3116 |
| 8 | 1.054 594 5094 | 8.189 176 4073 | .122 112 4018 |
| 9 | 1.061 625 1394 | 9.243 770 9167 | .108 180 9587 |
| 10 | 1.068 702 6404 | 10.305 396 0561 | .097 036 5423 |
| 11 | 1.075 827 3246 | 11.374 098 6965 | .087 919 0542 |
| 12 | 1.082 999 5068 | 12.449 926 0211 | .080 321 7624 |
| 13 | 1.090 219 5035 | 13.532 925 5279 | .073 893 8523 |
| 14 | 1.097 487 6335 | 14.623 145 0315 | .068 384 7420 |
| 15 | 1.104 804 2178 | 15.720 632 6650 | .063 610 6715 |
| 16 | 1.112 169 5792 | 16.825 436 8828 | .059 433 8208 |
| 17 | 1.119 584 0431 | 17.937 606 4620 | .055 748 7980 |
| 18 | 1.127 047 9367 | 19.057 190 5051 | .052 473 6319 |
| 19 | 1.134 561 5896 | 20.184 238 4418 | .049 543 6081 |
| 20 | 1.142 125 3335 | 21.318 800 0314 | .046 906 9553 |
| 21 | 1.149 739 5024 | 22.460 925 3649 | .044 521 7632 |
| 22 | 1.157 404 4324 | 23.610 664 8673 | .042 953 7417 |
| 23 | 1.165 120 4620 | 24.768 069 2998 | .040 374 5640 |
| 24 | 1.172 887 9317 | 25.933 189 7618 | .038 560 6248 |
| 25 | 1.180 707 1846 | 27.106 077 6935 | .036 892 0952 |
| 26 | 1.188 578 5659 | 28.286 784 8782 | .035 352 1973 |
| 27 | 1.196 502 4230 | 29.475 363 4440 | .033 926 6385 |
| 28 | 1.204 479 1058 | 30.671 865 8670 | .032 603 1681 |
| 29 | 1.212 508 9665 | 31.876 344 9728 | .031 371 2253 |
| 30 | 1.220 592 3596 | 33.088 853 9392 | .030 221 6572 |
| 31 | 1.228 729 6420 | 34.309 446 2988 | .029 146 4919 |
| 32 | 1.236 921 1729 | 35.538 175 9408 | .028 138 7543 |
| 33 | 1.245 167 3141 | 36.775 097 1138 | .027 192 3143 |
| 34 | 1.253 468 4295 | 38.020 264 4279 | .026 301 7634 |
| 35 | 1.261 824 8857 | 39.273 732 8574 | .025 462 3110 |
| 36 | 1.270 237 0516 | 40.535 557 7431 | .024 669 6988 |
| 37 | 1.278 705 2986 | 41.805 794 7947 | .023 920 1289 |
| 38 | 1.287 230 0006 | 43.084 500 0934 | .023 210 2032 |
| 39 | 1.295 811 5340 | 44.371 730 0940 | .022 536 8720 |
| 40 | 1.304 450 2775 | 45.667 541 6279 | .021 897 3907 |
| 41 | 1.313 146 6127 | 46.971 991 9055 | .021 289 2824 |
| 42 | 1.321 900 9235 | 48.285 138 5182 | .020 710 3061 |
| 43 | 1.330 713 5963 | 49.607 039 4416 | .020 158 4294 |
| 44 | 1.339 585 0203 | 50.937 753 0379 | .019 631 8043 |
| 45 | 1.348 515 5871 | 52.277 338 0581 | .019 128 7475 |
| 46 | 1.357 505 6910 | 53.625 853 6452 | .018 647 7218 |
| 47 | 1.366 555 7289 | 54.983 359 3362 | .018 187 3209 |
| 48 | 1.375 666 1004 | 56.349 915 0651 | .017 746 2557 |
| 49 | 1.384 837 2078 | 57.725 581 1655 | .017 323 3423 |
| 50 | 1.394 069 4558 | 59.110 418 3733 | .016 917 4915 |
| 51 | 1.403 363 2522 | 60.504 487 8291 | .016 527 6996 |
| 52 | 1.412 719 0072 | 61.907 851 0813 | .016 153 0401 |
| 53 | 1.422 137 1339 | 63.320 570 0885 | .015 792 6563 |
| 54 | 1.431 618 0481 | 64.742 707 2224 | .015 445 7551 |
| 55 | 1.441 162 1685 | 66.174 325 2706 | .015 111 6010 |
| 56 | 1.450 769 9163 | 67.615 487 4390 | .014 789 5111 |
| 57 | 1.460 441 7157 | 69.066 257 3553 | .014 478 8503 |
| 58 | 1.470 177 9938 | 70.526 699 0710 | .014 179 0274 |
| 59 | 1.479 979 1804 | 71.996 877 0648 | .013 889 4913 |
| 60 | 1.489 845 7083 | 73.476 856 2452 | .013 609 7276 |
| **n** | $s=(1+i)^n$ | $s_{\overline{n}|} = \dfrac{(1+i)^n - 1}{i}$ | $\dfrac{1}{s_{\overline{n}|}} = \dfrac{i}{(1+i)^n - 1}$ |

.00666666

*per period*

ANNUALLY
If compounded
*annually*
nominal annual rate is

**2/3%**

SEMIANNUALLY
If compounded
*semiannually*
nominal annual rate is

**1 1/3%**

QUARTERLY
If compounded
*quarterly*
nominal annual rate is

**2 2/3%**

MONTHLY
If compounded
*monthly*
nominal annual rate is

**8%**

$i$ = .00666666
$j_{(2)}$ = .01333333
$j_{(4)}$ = .02666666
$j_{(12)}$ = .08

| PRESENT WORTH OF 1<br>*What $1 due in the future is worth today.* | PRESENT WORTH OF 1 PER PERIOD<br>*What $1 payable periodically is worth today.* | PARTIAL PAYMENT<br>*Annuity worth $1 today.*<br>*Periodic payment necessary to pay off a loan of $1.* | P E R I O D S | RATE<br>2/3% |
|---|---|---|---|---|
| .993 377 4834 | .993 377 4834 | 1.006 666 6667 | 1 | |
| .986 798 8246 | 1.980 176 3081 | .505 005 5371 | 2 | |
| .980 263 7331 | 2.960 440 0411 | .337 787 6215 | 3 | .00666666 |
| .973 771 9203 | 3.934 211 9614 | .254 180 5093 | 4 | *per period* |
| .967 323 0996 | 4.901 535 0610 | .204 017 7184 | 5 | |
| .960 916 9864 | 5.862 452 0473 | .170 577 0882 | 6 | |
| .954 553 2977 | 6.817 005 3450 | .146 691 9783 | 7 | |
| .948 231 7527 | 7.765 237 0977 | .128 779 0685 | 8 | |
| .941 952 0722 | 8.707 189 1699 | .114 847 6254 | 9 | |
| .935 713 9790 | 9.642 903 1489 | .103 703 2089 | 10 | |
| .929 517 1977 | 10.572 420 3466 | .094 585 7209 | 11 | |
| .923 361 4547 | 11.495 781 8013 | .086 988 4291 | 12 | |
| .917 246 4781 | 12.413 028 2794 | .080 560 5190 | 13 | |
| .911 171 9981 | 13.324 200 2775 | .075 051 4087 | 14 | |
| .905 137 7465 | 14.229 338 0240 | .070 277 3382 | 15 | |
| .899 143 4568 | 15.128 481 4808 | .066 100 4874 | 16 | |
| .893 188 8644 | 16.021 670 3452 | .062 415 4647 | 17 | |
| .887 273 7063 | 16.908 944 0515 | .059 140 2986 | 18 | |
| .881 397 7215 | 17.790 341 7730 | .056 210 2748 | 19 | |
| .875 560 6505 | 18.665 902 4236 | .053 573 6220 | 20 | ANNUALLY<br>If compounded *annually* nominal annual rate is |
| .869 762 2356 | 19.535 664 6592 | .051 188 4299 | 21 | |
| .864 002 2208 | 20.399 666 8800 | .049 020 4083 | 22 | |
| .858 280 3518 | 21.257 947 2317 | .047 041 2307 | 23 | |
| .852 596 3759 | 22.110 543 6077 | .045 227 2915 | 24 | 2/3% |
| .846 950 0423 | 22.957 493 6500 | .043 558 7619 | 25 | |
| .841 341 1017 | 23.798 834 7517 | .042 018 8640 | 26 | |
| .835 769 3063 | 24.634 604 0580 | .040 593 3052 | 27 | |
| .830 234 4102 | 25.464 838 4682 | .039 269 8348 | 28 | |
| .824 736 1691 | 26.289 574 6373 | .038 037 8920 | 29 | |
| .819 274 3402 | 27.108 848 9774 | .036 888 3238 | 30 | SEMIANNUALLY<br>If compounded *semiannually* nominal annual rate is |
| .813 848 6823 | 27.922 697 6597 | .035 813 1586 | 31 | |
| .808 458 9559 | 28.731 156 6156 | .034 805 4209 | 32 | |
| .803 104 9231 | 29.534 261 5387 | .033 858 9810 | 33 | |
| .797 786 3474 | 30.332 047 8861 | .032 968 4301 | 34 | 1 1/3% |
| .792 502 9941 | 31.124 550 8802 | .032 128 9777 | 35 | |
| .787 254 6299 | 31.911 805 5101 | .031 336 3655 | 36 | |
| .782 041 0231 | 32.693 846 5333 | .030 586 7956 | 37 | |
| .776 861 9435 | 33.470 708 4767 | .029 876 8698 | 38 | |
| .771 717 1624 | 34.242 425 6392 | .029 203 5386 | 39 | |
| .766 606 4527 | 35.009 032 0919 | .028 564 0573 | 40 | QUARTERLY<br>If compounded *quarterly* nominal annual rate is |
| .761 529 5888 | 35.770 561 6807 | .027 955 9491 | 41 | |
| .756 486 9465 | 36.527 048 0272 | .027 376 9728 | 42 | |
| .751 476 5031 | 37.278 524 5303 | .026 825 0960 | 43 | |
| .746 499 8375 | 38.025 024 3678 | .026 298 4710 | 44 | 2 2/3% |
| .741 556 1300 | 38.766 580 4978 | .025 795 4142 | 45 | |
| .736 645 1623 | 39.503 225 6601 | .025 314 3885 | 46 | |
| .731 766 7175 | 40.234 992 3776 | .024 853 9876 | 47 | |
| .726 920 5803 | 40.961 912 9579 | .024 412 9223 | 48 | |
| .722 106 5367 | 41.684 019 4946 | .023 990 0089 | 49 | |
| .717 324 3742 | 42.401 343 8688 | .023 584 1582 | 50 | MONTHLY<br>If compounded *monthly* nominal annual rate is |
| .712 573 8817 | 43.113 917 7505 | .023 194 3663 | 51 | |
| .707 854 8493 | 43.821 772 5998 | .022 819 7068 | 52 | |
| .703 167 0689 | 44.524 939 6687 | .022 459 3230 | 53 | |
| .698 510 3333 | 45.223 450 0020 | .022 112 4218 | 54 | 8% |
| .693 884 4371 | 45.917 334 4391 | .021 778 2677 | 55 | |
| .689 289 1759 | 46.606 623 6150 | .021 456 1777 | 56 | |
| .684 724 3469 | 47.291 347 9619 | .021 145 5170 | 57 | |
| .680 189 7486 | 47.971 537 7105 | .020 845 6941 | 58 | i = .00666666 |
| .675 685 1807 | 48.647 222 8912 | .020 556 1580 | 59 | j(2) = .01333333 |
| .671 210 4444 | 49.318 433 3356 | .020 276 3943 | 60 | j(4) = .02666666<br>j(12) = .08 |
| $v^n = \dfrac{1}{(1+i)^n}$ | $a_{\overline{n}|} = \dfrac{1-v^n}{i}$ | $\dfrac{1}{a_{\overline{n}|}} = \dfrac{i}{1-v^n}$ | n | |

.00666666

*per period*

$i\ =.00666666$
$j_{(2)}=.01333333$
$j_{(4)}=.02666666$
$j_{(12)}=.08$

| P E R I O D S | AMOUNT OF 1<br>*How $1 left at compound interest will grow.* | AMOUNT OF 1 PER PERIOD<br>*How $1 deposited periodically will grow.* | SINKING FUND<br>*Periodic deposit that will grow to $1 at future date.* |
|---|---|---|---|
| 61 | 1.499 778 0130 | 74.966 701 9535 | .013 339 2556 |
| 62 | 1.509 776 5331 | 76.466 479 9666 | .013 077 6257 |
| 63 | 1.519 841 7100 | 77.976 256 4997 | .012 824 4166 |
| 64 | 1.529 973 9881 | 79.496 098 2097 | .012 579 2337 |
| 65 | 1.540 173 8147 | 81.026 072 1977 | .012 341 7065 |
| 66 | 1.550 441 6401 | 82.566 246 0124 | .012 111 4868 |
| 67 | 1.560 777 9177 | 84.116 687 6525 | .011 888 2475 |
| 68 | 1.571 183 1038 | 85.677 465 5702 | .011 671 6805 |
| 69 | 1.581 657 6578 | 87.248 648 6740 | .011 461 4956 |
| 70 | 1.592 202 0422 | 88.830 306 3318 | .011 257 4192 |
| 71 | 1.602 816 7225 | 90.422 508 3740 | .011 059 1933 |
| 72 | 1.613 502 1673 | 92.025 325 0965 | .010 866 5739 |
| 73 | 1.624 258 8484 | 93.638 827 2638 | .010 679 3307 |
| 74 | 1.635 087 2407 | 95.263 086 1122 | .010 497 2455 |
| 75 | 1.645 987 8224 | 96.898 173 3530 | .010 320 1120 |
| 76 | 1.656 961 0745 | 98.544 161 1753 | .010 147 7347 |
| 77 | 1.668 007 4817 | 100.201 122 2498 | .009 979 9281 |
| 78 | 1.679 127 5315 | 101.869 129 7315 | .009 816 5166 |
| 79 | 1.690 321 7151 | 103.548 257 2630 | .009 657 3330 |
| 80 | 1.701 590 5265 | 105.238 578 9781 | .009 502 2188 |
| 81 | 1.712 934 4634 | 106.940 169 5046 | .009 351 0231 |
| 82 | 1.724 354 0265 | 108.653 103 9680 | .009 203 6027 |
| 83 | 1.735 849 7200 | 110.377 457 9945 | .009 059 8209 |
| 84 | 1.747 422 0514 | 112.113 307 7144 | .008 919 5477 |
| 85 | 1.759 071 5318 | 113.860 729 7659 | .008 782 6593 |
| 86 | 1.770 798 6753 | 115.619 801 2976 | .008 649 0375 |
| 87 | 1.782 603 9998 | 117.390 599 9729 | .008 518 5696 |
| 88 | 1.794 488 0265 | 119.173 203 9728 | .008 391 1481 |
| 89 | 1.806 451 2800 | 120.967 691 9992 | .008 266 6701 |
| 90 | 1.818 494 2885 | 122.774 143 2792 | .008 145 0375 |
| 91 | 1.830 617 5838 | 124.592 637 5678 | .008 026 1564 |
| 92 | 1.842 821 7010 | 126.423 255 1516 | .007 909 9371 |
| 93 | 1.855 107 1790 | 128.266 076 8526 | .007 796 2936 |
| 94 | 1.867 474 5602 | 130.121 184 0316 | .007 685 1437 |
| 95 | 1.879 924 3906 | 131.988 658 5918 | .007 576 4085 |
| 96 | 1.892 457 2199 | 133.868 582 9824 | .007 470 0126 |
| 97 | 1.905 073 6013 | 135.761 040 2023 | .007 365 8835 |
| 98 | 1.917 774 0920 | 137.666 113 8036 | .007 263 9517 |
| 99 | 1.930 559 2526 | 139.583 887 8957 | .007 164 1506 |
| 100 | 1.943 429 6477 | 141.514 447 1483 | .007 066 4163 |
| 101 | 1.956 385 8453 | 143.457 876 7960 | .006 970 6873 |
| 102 | 1.969 428 4176 | 145.414 262 6413 | .006 876 9045 |
| 103 | 1.982 557 9404 | 147.383 691 0589 | .006 785 0112 |
| 104 | 1.995 774 9933 | 149.366 248 9993 | .006 694 9529 |
| 105 | 2.009 080 1600 | 151.362 023 9926 | .006 606 6770 |
| 106 | 2.022 474 0277 | 153.371 104 1525 | .006 520 1330 |
| 107 | 2.035 957 1879 | 155.393 578 1802 | .006 435 2724 |
| 108 | 2.049 530 2358 | 157.429 535 3681 | .006 352 0482 |
| 109 | 2.063 193 7707 | 159.479 065 6039 | .006 270 4155 |
| 110 | 2.076 948 3958 | 161.542 259 3746 | .006 190 3307 |
| 111 | 2.090 794 7185 | 163.619 207 7704 | .006 111 7519 |
| 112 | 2.104 733 3499 | 165.710 002 4889 | .006 034 6387 |
| 113 | 2.118 764 9056 | 167.814 735 8388 | .005 958 9523 |
| 114 | 2.132 890 0050 | 169.933 500 7444 | .005 884 6549 |
| 115 | 2.147 109 2717 | 172.066 390 7494 | .005 811 7102 |
| 116 | 2.161 423 3335 | 174.213 500 0210 | .005 740 0833 |
| 117 | 2.175 832 8224 | 176.374 923 3545 | .005 669 7402 |
| 118 | 2.190 338 3745 | 178.550 756 1769 | .005 600 6484 |
| 119 | 2.204 940 6303 | 180.741 094 5514 | .005 532 7761 |
| 120 | 2.219 640 2345 | 182.946 035 1817 | .005 466 0928 |
| **n** | $s=(1+i)^n$ | $s_{\overline{n}\rceil}=\dfrac{(1+i)^n-1}{i}$ | $\dfrac{1}{s_{\overline{n}\rceil}}=\dfrac{i}{(1+i)^n-1}$ |

| PRESENT WORTH OF 1 _What $1 due in the future is worth today._ | PRESENT WORTH OF 1 PER PERIOD _What $1 payable periodically is worth today._ | PARTIAL PAYMENT _Annuity worth $1 today._ _Periodic payment necessary to pay off a loan of $1._ | P E R I O D S | RATE 2/3% |
|---|---|---|---|---|
| .666 765 3421 | 49.985 198 6778 | .020 005 9223 | 61 | |
| .662 349 6776 | 50.647 548 3554 | .019 744 2923 | 62 | |
| .657 963 2559 | 51.305 511 6113 | .019 491 0833 | 63 | .00666666 |
| .653 605 8834 | 51.959 117 4947 | .019 245 9004 | 64 | _per period_ |
| .649 277 3676 | 52.608 394 8623 | .019 008 3731 | 65 | |
| .644 977 5175 | 53.253 372 3798 | .018 778 1535 | 66 | |
| .640 706 1432 | 53.894 078 5229 | .018 554 9141 | 67 | |
| .636 463 0561 | 54.530 541 5791 | .018 338 3471 | 68 | |
| .632 248 0690 | 55.162 789 6481 | .018 128 1622 | 69 | |
| .628 060 9957 | 55.790 850 6438 | .017 924 0859 | 70 | |
| .623 901 6514 | 56.414 752 2952 | .017 725 8600 | 71 | |
| .619 769 8523 | 57.034 522 1475 | .017 533 2406 | 72 | |
| .615 665 4162 | 57.650 187 5637 | .017 345 9973 | 73 | |
| .611 588 1618 | 58.261 775 7256 | .017 163 9121 | 74 | |
| .607 537 9091 | 58.869 313 6347 | .016 986 7787 | 75 | |
| .603 514 4792 | 59.472 828 1139 | .016 814 4013 | 76 | |
| .599 517 6946 | 60.072 345 8085 | .016 646 5948 | 77 | |
| .595 547 3788 | 60.667 893 1873 | .016 483 1832 | 78 | |
| .591 603 3564 | 61.259 496 5437 | .016 323 9996 | 79 | |
| .587 685 4534 | 61.847 181 9970 | .016 168 8854 | 80 | |
| .583 793 4967 | 62.430 975 4937 | .016 017 6898 | 81 | ANNUALLY _If compounded annually nominal annual rate is_ 2/3% |
| .579 927 3146 | 63.010 902 8083 | .015 870 2694 | 82 | |
| .576 086 7364 | 63.586 989 5447 | .015 726 4876 | 83 | |
| .572 271 5924 | 64.159 261 1371 | .015 586 2144 | 84 | |
| .568 481 7143 | 64.727 742 8514 | .015 449 3260 | 85 | |
| .564 716 9348 | 65.292 459 7862 | .015 315 7042 | 86 | |
| .560 977 0875 | 65.853 436 8737 | .015 185 2363 | 87 | |
| .557 262 0075 | 66.410 698 8812 | .015 057 8147 | 88 | |
| .553 571 5306 | 66.964 270 4118 | .014 933 3367 | 89 | |
| .549 905 4940 | 67.514 175 9057 | .014 811 7042 | 90 | |
| .546 263 7357 | 68.060 439 6414 | .014 692 8231 | 91 | SEMIANNUALLY _If compounded semiannually nominal annual rate is_ 1 1/3% |
| .542 646 0951 | 68.603 085 7365 | .014 576 6008 | 92 | |
| .539 052 4123 | 69.142 138 1489 | .014 462 9603 | 93 | |
| .535 482 5288 | 69.677 620 6777 | .014 351 8104 | 94 | |
| .531 936 2869 | 70.209 556 9646 | .014 243 0752 | 95 | |
| .528 413 5300 | 70.737 970 4946 | .014 136 6793 | 96 | |
| .524 914 1027 | 71.262 884 5973 | .014 032 5501 | 97 | |
| .521 437 8503 | 71.784 322 4477 | .013 930 6184 | 98 | |
| .517 984 6196 | 72.302 307 0672 | .013 830 8173 | 99 | |
| .514 554 2578 | 72.816 861 3250 | .013 733 0830 | 100 | |
| .511 146 6137 | 73.328 007 9388 | .013 637 3540 | 101 | QUARTERLY _If compounded quarterly nominal annual rate is_ 2 2/3% |
| .507 761 5368 | 73.835 769 4756 | .013 543 5712 | 102 | |
| .504 398 8776 | 74.340 168 3533 | .013 451 6779 | 103 | |
| .501 058 4877 | 74.841 226 8410 | .013 361 6196 | 104 | |
| .497 740 2196 | 75.338 967 0606 | .013 273 3436 | 105 | |
| .494 443 9268 | 75.833 410 9873 | .013 186 7997 | 106 | |
| .491 169 4637 | 76.324 580 4510 | .013 101 9390 | 107 | |
| .487 916 6858 | 76.812 497 1368 | .013 018 7149 | 108 | |
| .484 685 4494 | 77.297 182 5862 | .012 937 0821 | 109 | |
| .481 475 6120 | 77.778 658 1982 | .012 856 9973 | 110 | |
| .478 287 0318 | 78.256 945 2300 | .012 778 4185 | 111 | MONTHLY _If compounded monthly nominal annual rate is_ 8% |
| .475 119 5680 | 78.732 064 7980 | .012 701 3054 | 112 | |
| .471 973 0808 | 79.204 037 8788 | .012 625 6189 | 113 | |
| .468 847 4313 | 79.672 885 3101 | .012 551 3215 | 114 | |
| .465 742 4814 | 80.138 627 7915 | .012 478 3769 | 115 | |
| .462 658 0941 | 80.601 285 8856 | .012 406 7500 | 116 | |
| .459 594 1332 | 81.060 880 0188 | .012 336 4069 | 117 | |
| .456 550 4635 | 81.517 430 4822 | .012 267 3150 | 118 | $i = .00666666$ |
| .453 526 9504 | 81.970 957 4327 | .012 199 4427 | 119 | $j_{(2)} = .01333333$ |
| .450 523 4607 | 82.421 480 8934 | .012 132 7594 | 120 | $j_{(4)} = .02666666$ $j_{(12)} = .08$ |
| $$v^n = \frac{1}{(1+i)^n}$$ | $$a_{\overline{n}|} = \frac{1-v^n}{i}$$ | $$\frac{1}{a_{\overline{n}|}} = \frac{i}{1-v^n}$$ | n | |

41

| P E R I O D S | AMOUNT OF 1 *How $1 left at compound interest will grow.* | AMOUNT OF 1 PER PERIOD *How $1 deposited periodically will grow.* | SINKING FUND *Periodic deposit that will grow to $1 at future date.* |
|---|---|---|---|
| 121 | 2.234 437 8361 | 185.165 675 4163 | .005 400 5690 |
| 122 | 2.249 334 0883 | 187.400 113 2524 | .005 336 1761 |
| 123 | 2.264 329 6489 | 189.649 447 3407 | .005 272 8864 |
| 124 | 2.279 425 1799 | 191.913 776 9896 | .005 210 6733 |
| 125 | 2.294 621 3478 | 194.193 202 1696 | .005 149 5108 |
| 126 | 2.309 918 8234 | 196.487 823 5174 | .005 089 3739 |
| 127 | 2.325 318 2823 | 198.797 742 3408 | .005 030 2382 |
| 128 | 2.340 820 4042 | 201.123 060 6231 | .004 972 0803 |
| 129 | 2.356 425 8735 | 203.463 881 0273 | .004 914 8772 |
| 130 | 2.372 135 3793 | 205.820 306 9008 | .004 858 6071 |
| 131 | 2.387 949 6152 | 208.192 442 2801 | .004 803 2483 |
| 132 | 2.403 869 2793 | 210.580 391 8953 | .004 748 7802 |
| 133 | 2.419 895 0745 | 212.984 261 1746 | .004 695 1826 |
| 134 | 2.436 027 7083 | 215.404 156 2491 | .004 642 4360 |
| 135 | 2.452 267 8930 | 217.840 183 9574 | .004 590 5213 |
| 136 | 2.468 616 3457 | 220.292 451 8505 | .004 539 4202 |
| 137 | 2.485 073 7880 | 222.761 068 1962 | .004 489 1148 |
| 138 | 2.501 640 9466 | 225.246 141 9841 | .004 439 5877 |
| 139 | 2.518 318 5529 | 227.747 782 9307 | .004 390 8221 |
| 140 | 2.535 107 3432 | 230.266 101 4836 | .004 342 8016 |
| 141 | 2.552 008 0588 | 232.801 208 8268 | .004 295 5103 |
| 142 | 2.569 021 4459 | 235.353 216 8856 | .004 248 9328 |
| 143 | 2.586 148 2555 | 237.922 238 3315 | .004 203 0539 |
| 144 | 2.603 389 2439 | 240.508 386 5871 | .004 157 8592 |
| 145 | 2.620 745 1722 | 243.111 775 8310 | .004 113 3343 |
| 146 | 2.638 216 8067 | 245.732 521 0032 | .004 069 4654 |
| 147 | 2.655 804 9187 | 248.370 737 8099 | .004 026 2392 |
| 148 | 2.673 510 2849 | 251.026 542 7286 | .003 983 6425 |
| 149 | 2.691 333 6868 | 253.700 053 0135 | .003 941 6626 |
| 150 | 2.709 275 9113 | 256.391 386 7002 | .003 900 2870 |
| 151 | 2.727 337 7507 | 259.100 662 6116 | .003 859 5038 |
| 152 | 2.745 520 0024 | 261.828 000 3623 | .003 819 3012 |
| 153 | 2.763 823 4691 | 264.573 520 3647 | .003 779 6677 |
| 154 | 2.782 248 9589 | 267.337 343 8338 | .003 740 5923 |
| 155 | 2.800 797 2853 | 270.119 592 7927 | .003 702 0639 |
| 156 | 2.819 469 2672 | 272.920 390 0780 | .003 664 0721 |
| 157 | 2.838 265 7290 | 275.739 859 3452 | .003 626 6066 |
| 158 | 2.857 187 5005 | 278.578 125 0742 | .003 589 6573 |
| 159 | 2.876 235 4172 | 281.435 312 5746 | .003 553 2144 |
| 160 | 2.895 410 3199 | 284.311 547 9918 | .003 517 2683 |
| 161 | 2.914 713 0554 | 287.206 958 3118 | .003 481 8098 |
| 162 | 2.934 144 4758 | 290.121 671 3672 | .003 446 8297 |
| 163 | 2.953 705 4390 | 293.055 815 8430 | .003 412 3192 |
| 164 | 2.973 396 8085 | 296.009 521 2819 | .003 378 2697 |
| 165 | 2.993 219 4539 | 298.982 918 0905 | .003 344 6727 |
| 166 | 3.013 174 2503 | 301.976 137 5444 | .003 311 5199 |
| 167 | 3.033 262 0786 | 304.989 311 7947 | .003 278 8034 |
| 168 | 3.053 483 8258 | 308.022 573 8733 | .003 246 5153 |
| 169 | 3.073 840 3847 | 311.076 057 6991 | .003 214 6479 |
| 170 | 3.094 332 6539 | 314.149 898 0838 | .003 183 1938 |
| 171 | 3.114 961 5383 | 317.244 230 7377 | .003 152 1456 |
| 172 | 3.135 727 9485 | 320.359 192 2759 | .003 121 4962 |
| 173 | 3.156 632 8015 | 323.494 920 2244 | .003 091 2386 |
| 174 | 3.177 677 0202 | 326.651 553 0259 | .003 061 3661 |
| 175 | 3.198 861 5336 | 329.829 230 0461 | .003 031 8720 |
| 176 | 3.220 187 2772 | 333.028 091 5798 | .003 002 7497 |
| 177 | 3.241 655 1924 | 336.248 278 8570 | .002 973 9929 |
| 178 | 3.263 266 2270 | 339.489 934 0493 | .002 945 5954 |
| 179 | 3.285 021 3352 | 342.753 200 2763 | .002 917 5512 |
| 180 | 3.306 921 4774 | 346.038 221 6115 | .002 889 8542 |
| n | $s=(1+i)^n$ | $s_{\overline{n}\rceil}=\dfrac{(1+i)^n-1}{i}$ | $\dfrac{1}{s_{\overline{n}\rceil}}=\dfrac{i}{(1+i)^n-1}$ |

.00666666

*per period*

ANNUALLY
If compounded
*annually*
nominal annual rate is

2/3%

SEMIANNUALLY
If compounded
*semiannually*
nominal annual rate is

1 1/3%

QUARTERLY
If compounded
*quarterly*
nominal annual rate is

2 2/3%

MONTHLY
If compounded
*monthly*
nominal annual rate is

8%

$i$ = .00666666
$j_{(2)}$ = .01333333
$j_{(4)}$ = .02666666
$j_{(12)}$ = .08

| PRESENT WORTH OF 1 | PRESENT WORTH OF 1 PER PERIOD | PARTIAL PAYMENT | P E R I O D S | RATE |
|---|---|---|---|---|
| *What $1 due in the future is worth today.* | *What $1 payable periodically is worth today.* | *Annuity worth $1 today.* *Periodic payment necessary to pay off a loan of $1.* | | **2/3%** |

| PRESENT WORTH OF 1 | PRESENT WORTH OF 1 PER PERIOD | PARTIAL PAYMENT | PERIODS |
|---|---|---|---|
| .447 539 8616 | 82.869 020 7550 | .012 067 2356 | 121 |
| .444 576 0215 | 83.313 596 7765 | .012 002 8427 | 122 |
| .441 631 8094 | 83.755 228 5859 | .011 939 5531 | 123 |
| .438 707 0955 | 84.193 935 6814 | .011 877 3400 | 124 |
| .435 801 7505 | 84.629 737 4318 | .011 816 1775 | 125 |
| .432 915 6461 | 85.062 653 0780 | .011 756 0406 | 126 |
| .430 048 6551 | 85.492 701 7331 | .011 696 9049 | 127 |
| .427 200 6508 | 85.919 902 3839 | .011 638 7469 | 128 |
| .424 371 5074 | 86.344 273 8913 | .011 581 5439 | 129 |
| .421 561 1001 | 86.765 834 9913 | .011 525 2737 | 130 |
| .418 769 3047 | 87.184 604 2960 | .011 469 9150 | 131 |
| .415 995 9980 | 87.600 600 2941 | .011 415 4469 | 132 |
| .413 241 0577 | 88.013 841 3517 | .011 361 8493 | 133 |
| .410 504 3619 | 88.424 345 7136 | .011 309 1026 | 134 |
| .407 785 7900 | 88.832 131 5036 | .011 257 1879 | 135 |
| .405 085 2218 | 89.237 216 7254 | .011 206 0868 | 136 |
| .402 402 5382 | 89.639 619 2637 | .011 155 7814 | 137 |
| .399 737 6208 | 90.039 356 8844 | .011 106 2544 | 138 |
| .397 090 3518 | 90.436 447 2362 | .011 057 4888 | 139 |
| .394 460 6143 | 90.830 907 8505 | .011 009 4683 | 140 |
| .391 848 2924 | 91.222 756 1429 | .010 962 1770 | 141 |
| .389 253 2706 | 91.612 009 4135 | .010 915 5995 | 142 |
| .386 675 4343 | 91.998 684 8478 | .010 869 7206 | 143 |
| .384 114 6699 | 92.382 799 5177 | .010 824 5258 | 144 |
| .381 570 8641 | 92.764 370 3818 | .010 780 0009 | 145 |
| .379 043 9048 | 93.143 414 2866 | .010 736 1321 | 146 |
| .376 533 6802 | 93.519 947 9668 | .010 692 9059 | 147 |
| .374 040 0797 | 93.893 988 0465 | .010 650 3091 | 148 |
| .371 562 9931 | 94.265 551 0396 | .010 608 3292 | 149 |
| .369 102 3110 | 94.634 653 3506 | .010 566 9537 | 150 |
| .366 657 9248 | 95.001 311 2754 | .010 526 1705 | 151 |
| .364 229 7267 | 95.365 541 0021 | .010 485 9679 | 152 |
| .361 817 6093 | 95.727 358 6113 | .010 446 3344 | 153 |
| .359 421 4662 | 96.086 780 0775 | .010 407 2589 | 154 |
| .357 041 1915 | 96.443 821 2690 | .010 368 7306 | 155 |
| .354 676 6803 | 96.798 497 9493 | .010 330 7388 | 156 |
| .352 327 8282 | 97.150 825 7775 | .010 293 2733 | 157 |
| .349 994 5313 | 97.500 820 3088 | .010 256 3240 | 158 |
| .347 676 6867 | 97.848 496 9955 | .010 219 8810 | 159 |
| .345 374 1921 | 98.193 871 1875 | .010 183 9350 | 160 |
| .343 086 9458 | 98.536 958 1333 | .010 148 4765 | 161 |
| .340 814 8468 | 98.877 772 9801 | .010 113 4964 | 162 |
| .338 557 7948 | 99.216 330 7750 | .010 078 9859 | 163 |
| .336 315 6902 | 99.552 646 4652 | .010 044 9364 | 164 |
| .334 088 4340 | 99.886 734 8992 | .010 011 3394 | 165 |
| .331 875 9278 | 100.218 610 8270 | .009 978 1866 | 166 |
| .329 678 0740 | 100.548 288 9010 | .009 945 4701 | 167 |
| .327 494 7755 | 100.875 783 6765 | .009 913 1820 | 168 |
| .325 325 9359 | 101.201 109 6124 | .009 881 3146 | 169 |
| .323 171 4595 | 101.524 281 0719 | .009 849 8604 | 170 |
| .321 031 2512 | 101.845 312 3231 | .009 818 8122 | 171 |
| .318 905 2164 | 102.164 217 5395 | .009 788 1629 | 172 |
| .316 793 2613 | 102.481 010 8008 | .009 757 9053 | 173 |
| .314 695 2927 | 102.795 706 0936 | .009 728 0328 | 174 |
| .312 611 2179 | 103.108 317 3115 | .009 698 5386 | 175 |
| .310 540 9450 | 103.418 858 2564 | .009 669 4164 | 176 |
| .308 484 3824 | 103.727 342 6388 | .009 640 6596 | 177 |
| .306 441 4395 | 104.033 784 0783 | .009 612 2621 | 178 |
| .304 412 0260 | 104.338 196 1043 | .009 584 2178 | 179 |
| .302 396 0523 | 104.640 592 1566 | .009 556 5208 | 180 |

**.00666666** *per period*

**ANNUALLY**
If compounded *annually* nominal annual rate is
**2/3%**

**SEMIANNUALLY**
If compounded *semiannually* nominal annual rate is
**1 1/3%**

**QUARTERLY**
If compounded *quarterly* nominal annual rate is
**2 2/3%**

**MONTHLY**
If compounded *monthly* nominal annual rate is
**8%**

$i = .00666666$
$j_{(2)} = .01333333$
$j_{(4)} = .02666666$
$j_{(12)} = .08$

| $v^n = \dfrac{1}{(1+i)^n}$ | $a_{\overline{n}|} = \dfrac{1-v^n}{i}$ | $\dfrac{1}{a_{\overline{n}|}} = \dfrac{i}{1-v^n}$ | n |
|---|---|---|---|

43

| P E R I O D S | AMOUNT OF 1 *How $1 left at compound interest will grow.* | AMOUNT OF 1 PER PERIOD *How $1 deposited periodically will grow.* | SINKING FUND *Periodic deposit that will grow to $1 at future date.* |
|---|---|---|---|
| 1 | 1.007 500 0000 | 1.000 000 0000 | 1.000 000 0000 |
| 2 | 1.015 056 2500 | 2.007 500 0000 | .498 132 0050 |
| 3 | 1.022 669 1719 | 3.022 556 2500 | .330 845 7866 |
| 4 | 1.030 339 1907 | 4.045 225 4219 | .247 205 0123 |
| 5 | 1.038 066 7346 | 5.075 564 6125 | .197 022 4155 |
| 6 | 1.045 852 2351 | 6.113 631 3471 | .163 568 9074 |
| 7 | 1.053 696 1269 | 7.159 483 5822 | .139 674 8786 |
| 8 | 1.061 598 8478 | 8.213 179 7091 | .121 755 5241 |
| 9 | 1.069 560 8392 | 9.274 778 5569 | .107 819 2858 |
| 10 | 1.077 582 5455 | 10.344 339 3961 | .096 671 2287 |
| 11 | 1.085 664 4146 | 11.421 921 9416 | .087 550 9398 |
| 12 | 1.093 806 8977 | 12.507 586 3561 | .079 951 4768 |
| 13 | 1.102 010 4494 | 13.601 393 2538 | .073 521 8798 |
| 14 | 1.110 275 5278 | 14.703 403 7032 | .068 011 4632 |
| 15 | 1.118 602 5942 | 15.813 679 2310 | .063 236 3908 |
| 16 | 1.126 992 1137 | 16.932 281 8252 | .059 058 7855 |
| 17 | 1.135 444 5545 | 18.059 273 9389 | .055 373 2118 |
| 18 | 1.143 960 3887 | 19.194 718 4934 | .052 097 6643 |
| 19 | 1.152 540 0916 | 20.338 678 8821 | .049 167 4020 |
| 20 | 1.161 184 1423 | 21.491 218 9738 | .046 530 6319 |
| 21 | 1.169 893 0234 | 22.652 403 1161 | .044 145 4266 |
| 22 | 1.178 667 2210 | 23.822 296 1394 | .041 977 4817 |
| 23 | 1.187 507 2252 | 25.000 963 3605 | .039 998 4587 |
| 24 | 1.196 413 5294 | 26.188 470 5857 | .038 184 7423 |
| 25 | 1.205 386 6309 | 27.384 884 1151 | .036 516 4956 |
| 26 | 1.214 427 0306 | 28.590 270 7459 | .034 976 9335 |
| 27 | 1.223 535 2333 | 29.804 697 7765 | .033 551 7578 |
| 28 | 1.232 711 7476 | 31.028 233 0099 | .032 228 7125 |
| 29 | 1.241 957 0857 | 32.260 944 7574 | .030 997 2323 |
| 30 | 1.251 271 7638 | 33.502 901 8431 | .029 848 1608 |
| 31 | 1.260 656 3021 | 34.754 173 6069 | .028 773 5226 |
| 32 | 1.270 111 2243 | 36.014 829 9090 | .027 766 3397 |
| 33 | 1.279 637 0585 | 37.284 941 1333 | .026 820 4795 |
| 34 | 1.289 234 3364 | 38.564 578 1918 | .025 930 5313 |
| 35 | 1.298 903 5940 | 39.853 812 5282 | .025 091 7023 |
| 36 | 1.308 645 3709 | 41.152 716 1222 | .024 299 7327 |
| 37 | 1.318 460 2112 | 42.461 361 4931 | .023 550 8228 |
| 38 | 1.328 348 6628 | 43.779 821 7043 | .022 841 5732 |
| 39 | 1.338 311 2778 | 45.108 170 3671 | .022 168 9329 |
| 40 | 1.348 348 6123 | 46.446 481 6449 | .021 530 1561 |
| 41 | 1.358 461 2269 | 47.794 830 2572 | .020 922 7650 |
| 42 | 1.368 649 6861 | 49.153 291 4841 | .020 344 5175 |
| 43 | 1.378 914 5588 | 50.521 941 1703 | .019 793 3804 |
| 44 | 1.389 256 4180 | 51.900 855 7290 | .019 267 5051 |
| 45 | 1.399 675 8411 | 53.290 112 1470 | .018 765 2073 |
| 46 | 1.410 173 4099 | 54.689 787 9881 | .018 284 9493 |
| 47 | 1.420 749 7105 | 56.099 961 3980 | .017 825 3242 |
| 48 | 1.431 405 3333 | 57.520 711 1085 | .017 385 0424 |
| 49 | 1.442 140 8733 | 58.952 116 4418 | .016 962 9194 |
| 50 | 1.452 956 9299 | 60.394 257 3151 | .016 557 8657 |
| 51 | 1.463 854 1068 | 61.847 214 2450 | .016 168 8770 |
| 52 | 1.474 833 0126 | 63.311 068 3518 | .015 795 0265 |
| 53 | 1.485 894 2602 | 64.785 901 3645 | .015 435 4571 |
| 54 | 1.497 038 4672 | 66.271 795 6247 | .015 089 3754 |
| 55 | 1.508 266 2557 | 67.768 834 0919 | .014 756 0455 |
| 56 | 1.519 578 2526 | 69.277 100 3476 | .014 434 7843 |
| 57 | 1.530 975 0895 | 70.796 678 6002 | .014 124 9564 |
| 58 | 1.542 457 4027 | 72.327 653 6897 | .013 825 9704 |
| 59 | 1.554 025 8332 | 73.870 111 0923 | .013 537 2749 |
| 60 | 1.565 681 0269 | 75.424 136 9255 | .013 258 3552 |
| n | $s = (1+i)^n$ | $s_{\overline{n}} = \dfrac{(1+i)^n - 1}{i}$ | $\dfrac{1}{s_{\overline{n}}} = \dfrac{i}{(1+i)^n - 1}$ |

.0075

*per period*

ANNUALLY
If compounded
*annually*
nominal annual rate is

3/4%

SEMIANNUALLY
If compounded
*semiannually*
nominal annual rate is

1½%

QUARTERLY
If compounded
*quarterly*
nominal annual rate is

3%

MONTHLY
If compounded
*monthly*
nominal annual rate is

9%

$i$ = .0075
$j_{(2)}$ = .015
$j_{(4)}$ = .03
$j_{(12)}$ = .09

| PRESENT WORTH OF 1 *What $1 due in the future is worth today.* | PRESENT WORTH OF 1 PER PERIOD *What $1 payable periodically is worth today.* | PARTIAL PAYMENT *Annuity worth $1 today.* *Periodic payment necessary to pay off a loan of $1.* | PERIODS | RATE 3/4% |
|---|---|---|---|---|
| .992 555 8313 | .992 555 8313 | 1.007 500 0000 | 1 | |
| .985 167 0782 | 1.977 722 9094 | .505 632 0050 | 2 | |
| .977 833 3282 | 2.955 556 2377 | .338 345 7866 | 3 | .0075 |
| .970 554 1719 | 3.926 110 4096 | .254 705 0123 | 4 | |
| .963 329 2029 | 4.889 439 6125 | .204 522 4155 | 5 | *per period* |
| .956 158 0178 | 5.845 597 6303 | .171 068 9074 | 6 | |
| .949 040 2162 | 6.794 637 8464 | .147 174 8786 | 7 | |
| .941 975 4006 | 7.736 613 2471 | .129 255 5241 | 8 | |
| .934 963 1768 | 8.671 576 4239 | .115 319 2858 | 9 | |
| .928 003 1532 | 9.599 579 5771 | .104 171 2287 | 10 | |
| .921 094 9411 | 10.520 674 5182 | .095 050 9398 | 11 | |
| .914 238 1550 | 11.434 912 6731 | .087 451 4768 | 12 | |
| .907 432 4119 | 12.342 345 0850 | .081 021 8798 | 13 | |
| .900 677 3319 | 13.243 022 4169 | .075 511 4632 | 14 | |
| .893 972 5378 | 14.136 994 9547 | .070 736 3908 | 15 | |
| .887 317 6554 | 15.024 312 6101 | .066 558 7855 | 16 | |
| .880 712 3131 | 15.905 024 9232 | .062 873 2118 | 17 | |
| .874 156 1420 | 16.779 181 0652 | .059 597 6643 | 18 | |
| .867 648 7762 | 17.646 829 8414 | .056 667 4020 | 19 | |
| .861 189 8523 | 18.508 019 6937 | .054 030 6319 | 20 | ANNUALLY *If compounded annually nominal annual rate is* |
| .854 779 0097 | 19.362 798 7034 | .051 645 4266 | 21 | |
| .848 415 8905 | 20.211 214 5940 | .049 477 4817 | 22 | |
| .842 100 1395 | 21.053 314 7335 | .047 498 4587 | 23 | |
| .835 831 4040 | 21.889 146 1374 | .045 684 7423 | 24 | 3/4% |
| .829 609 3340 | 22.718 755 4714 | .044 016 4956 | 25 | |
| .823 433 5821 | 23.542 189 0535 | .042 476 9335 | 26 | |
| .817 303 8036 | 24.359 492 8571 | .041 051 7578 | 27 | |
| .811 219 6562 | 25.170 712 5132 | .039 728 7125 | 28 | |
| .805 180 8001 | 25.975 893 3134 | .038 497 2323 | 29 | |
| .799 186 8984 | 26.775 080 2118 | .037 348 1608 | 30 | SEMIANNUALLY *If compounded semiannually nominal annual rate is* |
| .793 237 6163 | 27.568 317 8281 | .036 273 5226 | 31 | |
| .787 332 6216 | 28.355 650 4497 | .035 266 3397 | 32 | |
| .781 471 5847 | 29.137 122 0344 | .034 320 4795 | 33 | |
| .775 654 1784 | 29.912 776 2128 | .033 430 5313 | 34 | |
| .769 880 0778 | 30.682 656 2907 | .032 591 7023 | 35 | 1½% |
| .764 148 9606 | 31.446 805 2513 | .031 799 7327 | 36 | |
| .758 460 5068 | 32.205 265 7581 | .031 050 8228 | 37 | |
| .752 814 3988 | 32.958 080 1569 | .030 341 5732 | 38 | |
| .747 210 3214 | 33.705 290 4783 | .029 668 9329 | 39 | |
| .741 647 9617 | 34.446 938 4400 | .029 030 1561 | 40 | QUARTERLY *If compounded quarterly nominal annual rate is* |
| .736 127 0091 | 35.183 065 4492 | .028 422 7650 | 41 | |
| .730 647 1555 | 35.913 712 6046 | .027 844 5175 | 42 | |
| .725 208 0948 | 36.638 920 6994 | .027 293 3804 | 43 | |
| .719 809 5233 | 37.358 730 2227 | .026 767 5051 | 44 | |
| .714 451 1398 | 38.073 181 3625 | .026 265 2073 | 45 | 3% |
| .709 132 6449 | 38.782 314 0074 | .025 784 9493 | 46 | |
| .703 853 7419 | 39.486 167 7493 | .025 325 3242 | 47 | |
| .698 614 1359 | 40.184 781 8852 | .024 885 0424 | 48 | |
| .693 413 5344 | 40.878 195 4195 | .024 462 9194 | 49 | |
| .688 251 6470 | 41.566 447 0665 | .024 057 8657 | 50 | MONTHLY *If compounded monthly nominal annual rate is* |
| .683 128 1856 | 42.249 575 2521 | .023 668 8770 | 51 | |
| .678 042 8641 | 42.927 618 1163 | .023 295 0265 | 52 | |
| .672 995 3986 | 43.600 613 5149 | .022 935 4571 | 53 | |
| .667 985 5073 | 44.268 599 0222 | .022 589 3754 | 54 | |
| .663 012 9105 | 44.931 611 9327 | .022 256 0455 | 55 | 9% |
| .658 077 3305 | 45.589 689 2633 | .021 934 7843 | 56 | |
| .653 178 4918 | 46.242 867 7551 | .021 624 9564 | 57 | |
| .648 316 1209 | 46.891 183 8760 | .021 325 9704 | 58 | $i = .0075$ |
| .643 489 9463 | 47.534 673 8224 | .021 037 2749 | 59 | $j_{(2)} = .015$ |
| .638 699 6986 | 48.173 373 5210 | .020 758 3552 | 60 | $j_{(4)} = .03$ |
| $v^n = \dfrac{1}{(1+i)^n}$ | $a_{\overline{n}\rceil} = \dfrac{1-v^n}{i}$ | $\dfrac{1}{a_{\overline{n}\rceil}} = \dfrac{i}{1-v^n}$ | n | $j_{(12)} = .09$ |

45

| P E R I O D S | AMOUNT OF 1 *How $1 left at compound interest will grow.* | AMOUNT OF 1 PER PERIOD *How $1 deposited periodically will grow.* | SINKING FUND *Periodic deposit that will grow to $1 at future date.* |
|---|---|---|---|
| 1 | 1.010 000 0000 | 1.000 000 0000 | 1.000 000 0000 |
| 2 | 1.020 100 0000 | 2.010 000 0000 | .497 512 4378 |
| 3 | 1.030 301 0000 | 3.030 100 0000 | .330 022 1115 |
| 4 | 1.040 604 0100 | 4.060 401 0000 | .246 281 0939 |
| 5 | 1.051 010 0501 | 5.101 005 0100 | .196 039 7996 |
| 6 | 1.061 520 1506 | 6.152 015 0601 | .162 548 3667 |
| 7 | 1.072 135 3521 | 7.213 535 2107 | .138 628 2829 |
| 8 | 1.082 856 7056 | 8.285 670 5628 | .120 690 2920 |
| 9 | 1.093 685 2727 | 9.368 527 2684 | .106 740 3628 |
| 10 | 1.104 622 1254 | 10.462 212 5411 | .095 582 0766 |
| 11 | 1.115 668 3467 | 11.566 834 6665 | .086 454 0757 |
| 12 | 1.126 825 0301 | 12.682 503 0132 | .078 848 7887 |
| 13 | 1.138 093 2804 | 13.809 328 0433 | .072 414 8197 |
| 14 | 1.149 474 2132 | 14.947 421 3238 | .066 901 1717 |
| 15 | 1.160 968 9554 | 16.096 895 5370 | .062 123 7802 |
| 16 | 1.172 578 6449 | 17.257 864 4924 | .057 944 5968 |
| 17 | 1.184 304 4314 | 18.430 443 1373 | .054 258 0551 |
| 18 | 1.196 147 4757 | 19.614 747 5687 | .050 982 0479 |
| 19 | 1.208 108 9504 | 20.810 895 0444 | .048 051 7536 |
| 20 | 1.220 190 0399 | 22.019 003 9948 | .045 415 3149 |
| 21 | 1.232 391 9403 | 23.239 194 0347 | .043 030 7522 |
| 22 | 1.244 715 8598 | 24.471 585 9751 | .040 863 7185 |
| 23 | 1.257 163 0183 | 25.716 301 8348 | .038 885 8401 |
| 24 | 1.269 734 6485 | 26.973 464 8532 | .037 073 4722 |
| 25 | 1.282 431 9950 | 28.243 199 5017 | .035 406 7534 |
| 26 | 1.295 256 3150 | 29.525 631 4967 | .033 868 8776 |
| 27 | 1.308 208 8781 | 30.820 887 8117 | .032 445 5287 |
| 28 | 1.321 290 9669 | 32.129 096 6898 | .031 124 4356 |
| 29 | 1.334 503 8766 | 33.450 387 6567 | .029 895 0198 |
| 30 | 1.347 848 9153 | 34.784 891 5333 | .028 748 1132 |
| 31 | 1.361 327 4045 | 36.132 740 4486 | .027 675 7309 |
| 32 | 1.374 940 6785 | 37.494 067 8531 | .026 670 8857 |
| 33 | 1.388 690 0853 | 38.869 008 5316 | .025 727 4378 |
| 34 | 1.402 576 9862 | 40.257 698 6170 | .024 839 9694 |
| 35 | 1.416 602 7560 | 41.660 275 6031 | .024 003 6818 |
| 36 | 1.430 768 7836 | 43.076 878 3592 | .023 214 3098 |
| 37 | 1.445 076 4714 | 44.507 647 1427 | .022 468 0491 |
| 38 | 1.459 527 2361 | 45.952 723 6142 | .021 761 4958 |
| 39 | 1.474 122 5085 | 47.412 250 8503 | .021 091 5951 |
| 40 | 1.488 863 7336 | 48.886 373 3588 | .020 455 5980 |
| 41 | 1.503 752 3709 | 50.375 237 0924 | .019 851 0232 |
| 42 | 1.518 789 8946 | 51.878 989 4633 | .019 275 6260 |
| 43 | 1.533 977 7936 | 53.397 779 3580 | .018 727 3705 |
| 44 | 1.549 317 5715 | 54.931 757 1515 | .018 204 4058 |
| 45 | 1.564 810 7472 | 56.481 074 7231 | .017 705 0455 |
| 46 | 1.580 458 8547 | 58.045 885 4703 | .017 227 7499 |
| 47 | 1.596 263 4432 | 59.626 344 3250 | .016 771 1103 |
| 48 | 1.612 226 0777 | 61.222 607 7682 | .016 333 8354 |
| 49 | 1.628 348 3385 | 62.834 833 8459 | .015 914 7393 |
| 50 | 1.644 631 8218 | 64.463 182 1844 | .015 512 7309 |
| 51 | 1.661 078 1401 | 66.107 814 0062 | .015 126 8048 |
| 52 | 1.677 688 9215 | 67.768 892 1463 | .014 756 0329 |
| 53 | 1.694 465 8107 | 69.446 581 0678 | .014 399 5570 |
| 54 | 1.711 410 4688 | 71.141 046 8784 | .014 056 5826 |
| 55 | 1.728 524 5735 | 72.852 457 3472 | .013 726 3730 |
| 56 | 1.745 809 8192 | 74.580 981 9207 | .013 408 2440 |
| 57 | 1.763 267 9174 | 76.326 791 7399 | .013 101 5595 |
| 58 | 1.780 900 5966 | 78.090 059 6573 | .012 805 7272 |
| 59 | 1.798 709 6025 | 79.870 960 2539 | .012 520 1950 |
| 60 | 1.816 696 6986 | 81.669 669 8564 | .012 244 4477 |
| n | $s=(1+i)^n$ | $s_{\overline{n}|}=\dfrac{(1+i)^n-1}{i}$ | $\dfrac{1}{s_{\overline{n}|}}=\dfrac{i}{(1+i)^n-1}$ |

**ANNUALLY**
If compounded *annually* nominal annual rate is

**1%**

**SEMIANNUALLY**
If compounded *semiannually* nominal annual rate is

**2%**

**QUARTERLY**
If compounded *quarterly* nominal annual rate is

**4%**

**MONTHLY**
If compounded *monthly* nominal annual rate is

**12%**

$i = .01$
$j_{(2)} = .02$
$j_{(4)} = .04$
$j_{(12)} = .12$

| PRESENT WORTH OF 1<br>*What $1 due in the future is worth today.* | PRESENT WORTH OF 1 PER PERIOD<br>*What $1 payable periodically is worth today.* | PARTIAL PAYMENT<br>*Annuity worth $1 today.*<br>*Periodic payment necessary to pay off a loan of $1.* | P E R I O D S | RATE<br>**1%** |
|---|---|---|---|---|
| .990 099 0099 | .990 099 0099 | 1.010 000 0000 | 1 | |
| .980 296 0494 | 1.970 395 0593 | .507 512 4378 | 2 | |
| .970 590 1479 | 2.940 985 2072 | .340 022 1115 | 3 | .01 |
| .960 980 3445 | 3.901 965 5517 | .256 281 0939 | 4 | |
| .951 465 6876 | 4.853 431 2393 | .206 039 7996 | 5 | *per period* |
| .942 045 2353 | 5.795 476 4746 | .172 548 3667 | 6 | |
| .932 718 0547 | 6.728 194 5293 | .148 628 2829 | 7 | |
| .923 483 2225 | 7.651 677 7518 | .130 690 2920 | 8 | |
| .914 339 8242 | 8.566 017 5760 | .116 740 3628 | 9 | |
| .905 286 9547 | 9.471 304 5307 | .105 582 0766 | 10 | |
| .896 323 7175 | 10.367 628 2482 | .096 454 0757 | 11 | |
| .887 449 2253 | 11.255 077 4735 | .088 848 7887 | 12 | |
| .878 662 5993 | 12.133 740 0728 | .082 414 8197 | 13 | |
| .869 962 9696 | 13.003 703 0423 | .076 901 1717 | 14 | |
| .861 349 4748 | 13.865 052 5172 | .072 123 7802 | 15 | |
| .852 821 2622 | 14.717 873 7794 | .067 944 5968 | 16 | |
| .844 377 4873 | 15.562 251 2667 | .064 258 0551 | 17 | |
| .836 017 3142 | 16.398 268 5809 | .060 982 0479 | 18 | |
| .827 739 9150 | 17.226 008 4959 | .058 051 7536 | 19 | |
| .819 544 4703 | 18.045 552 9663 | .055 415 3149 | 20 | ANNUALLY<br>If compounded *annually* nominal annual rate is |
| .811 430 1687 | 18.856 983 1349 | .053 030 7522 | 21 | |
| .803 396 2066 | 19.660 379 3415 | .050 863 7185 | 22 | |
| .795 441 7887 | 20.455 821 1302 | .048 885 8401 | 23 | |
| .787 566 1274 | 21.243 387 2576 | .047 073 4722 | 24 | |
| .779 768 4430 | 22.023 155 7006 | .045 406 7534 | 25 | **1%** |
| .772 047 9634 | 22.795 203 6640 | .043 868 8776 | 26 | |
| .764 403 9241 | 23.559 607 5881 | .042 445 5287 | 27 | |
| .756 835 5684 | 24.316 443 1565 | .041 124 4356 | 28 | |
| .749 342 1470 | 25.065 785 3035 | .039 895 0198 | 29 | |
| .741 922 9178 | 25.807 708 2213 | .038 748 1132 | 30 | SEMIANNUALLY<br>If compounded *semiannually* nominal annual rate is |
| .734 577 1463 | 26.542 285 3676 | .037 675 7309 | 31 | |
| .727 304 1053 | 27.269 589 4729 | .036 670 8857 | 32 | |
| .720 103 0745 | 27.989 692 5474 | .035 727 4378 | 33 | |
| .712 973 3411 | 28.702 665 8885 | .034 839 9694 | 34 | |
| .705 914 1991 | 29.408 580 0876 | .034 003 6818 | 35 | **2%** |
| .698 924 9496 | 30.107 505 0373 | .033 214 3098 | 36 | |
| .692 004 9006 | 30.799 509 9379 | .032 468 0491 | 37 | |
| .685 153 3670 | 31.484 663 3048 | .031 761 4958 | 38 | |
| .678 369 6702 | 32.163 032 9751 | .031 091 5951 | 39 | |
| .671 653 1389 | 32.834 686 1140 | .030 455 5980 | 40 | QUARTERLY<br>If compounded *quarterly* nominal annual rate is |
| .665 003 1078 | 33.499 689 2217 | .029 851 0232 | 41 | |
| .658 418 9186 | 34.158 108 1403 | .029 275 6260 | 42 | |
| .651 899 9194 | 34.810 008 0597 | .028 727 3705 | 43 | |
| .645 445 4648 | 35.455 453 5245 | .028 204 4058 | 44 | |
| .639 054 9156 | 36.094 508 4401 | .027 705 0455 | 45 | **4%** |
| .632 727 6392 | 36.727 236 0793 | .027 227 7499 | 46 | |
| .626 463 0091 | 37.353 699 0884 | .026 771 1103 | 47 | |
| .620 260 4051 | 37.973 959 4935 | .026 333 8354 | 48 | |
| .614 119 2129 | 38.588 078 7064 | .025 914 7393 | 49 | |
| .608 038 8247 | 39.196 117 5311 | .025 512 7309 | 50 | MONTHLY<br>If compounded *monthly* nominal annual rate is |
| .602 018 6383 | 39.798 136 1694 | .025 126 8048 | 51 | |
| .596 058 0577 | 40.394 194 2271 | .024 756 0329 | 52 | |
| .590 156 4928 | 40.984 350 7199 | .024 399 5570 | 53 | |
| .584 313 3592 | 41.568 664 0791 | .024 056 5826 | 54 | |
| .578 528 0784 | 42.147 192 1576 | .023 726 3730 | 55 | **12%** |
| .572 800 0776 | 42.719 992 2352 | .023 408 2440 | 56 | |
| .567 128 7898 | 43.287 121 0250 | .023 101 5595 | 57 | |
| .561 513 6532 | 43.848 634 6782 | .022 805 7272 | 58 | $i = .01$ |
| .555 954 1121 | 44.404 588 7903 | .022 520 1950 | 59 | $j_{(2)} = .02$<br>$j_{(4)} = .04$ |
| .550 449 6159 | 44.955 038 4062 | .022 244 4477 | 60 | $j_{(12)} = .12$ |
| $v^n = \dfrac{1}{(1+i)^n}$ | $a_{\overline{n}|} = \dfrac{1-v^n}{i}$ | $\dfrac{1}{a_{\overline{n}|}} = \dfrac{i}{1-v^n}$ | n | |

| | P E R I O D S | AMOUNT OF 1<br>*How $1 left at compound interest will grow.* | AMOUNT OF 1 PER PERIOD<br>*How $1 deposited periodically will grow.* | SINKING FUND<br>*Periodic deposit that will grow to $1 at future date.* |
|---|---|---|---|---|
| **.0125**<br>*per period* | 1<br>2<br>3<br>4<br>5 | 1.012 500 0000<br>1.025 156 2500<br>1.037 970 7031<br>1.050 945 3369<br>1.064 082 1536 | 1.000 000 0000<br>2.012 500 0000<br>3.037 656 2500<br>4.075 626 9531<br>5.126 572 2900 | 1.000 000 0000<br>.496 894 4099<br>.329 201 1728<br>.245 361 0233<br>.195 062 1084 |
| | 6<br>7<br>8<br>9<br>10 | 1.077 383 1805<br>1.090 850 4703<br>1.104 486 1012<br>1.118 292 1774<br>1.132 270 8297 | 6.190 654 4437<br>7.268 037 6242<br>8.358 888 0945<br>9.463 374 1957<br>10.581 666 3731 | .161 533 8102<br>.137 588 7209<br>.119 633 1365<br>.105 670 5546<br>.094 503 0740 |
| | 11<br>12<br>13<br>14<br>15 | 1.146 424 2150<br>1.160 754 5177<br>1.175 263 9492<br>1.189 954 7486<br>1.204 829 1829 | 11.713 937 2028<br>12.860 361 4178<br>14.021 115 9356<br>15.196 379 8848<br>16.386 334 6333 | .085 368 3935<br>.077 758 3123<br>.071 320 9993<br>.065 805 1462<br>.061 026 4603 |
| | 16<br>17<br>18<br>19<br>20 | 1.219 889 5477<br>1.235 138 1670<br>1.250 577 3941<br>1.266 209 6116<br>1.282 037 2317 | 17.591 163 8162<br>18.811 053 3639<br>20.046 191 5310<br>21.296 768 9251<br>22.562 978 5367 | .056 846 7221<br>.053 160 2341<br>.049 884 7873<br>.046 955 4797<br>.044 320 3896 |
| **ANNUALLY**<br>If compounded<br>*annually*<br>nominal annual rate is<br>**1¼%** | 21<br>22<br>23<br>24<br>25 | 1.298 062 6971<br>1.314 288 4808<br>1.330 717 0868<br>1.347 351 0504<br>1.364 192 9385 | 23.845 015 7684<br>25.143 078 4655<br>26.457 366 9463<br>27.788 084 0331<br>29.135 435 0836 | .041 937 4854<br>.039 772 3772<br>.037 796 6561<br>.035 986 6480<br>.034 322 4667 |
| | 26<br>27<br>28<br>29<br>30 | 1.381 245 3503<br>1.398 510 9172<br>1.415 992 3036<br>1.433 692 2074<br>1.451 613 3600 | 30.499 628 0221<br>31.880 873 3724<br>33.279 384 2895<br>34.695 376 5932<br>36.129 068 8006 | .032 787 2851<br>.031 366 7693<br>.030 048 6329<br>.028 822 2841<br>.027 678 5434 |
| **SEMIANNUALLY**<br>If compounded<br>*semiannually*<br>nominal annual rate is<br>**2½%** | 31<br>32<br>33<br>34<br>35 | 1.469 758 5270<br>1.488 130 5086<br>1.506 732 1400<br>1.525 566 2917<br>1.544 635 8703 | 37.580 682 1606<br>39.050 440 6876<br>40.538 571 1962<br>42.045 303 3361<br>43.570 869 6278 | .026 609 4159<br>.025 607 9056<br>.024 667 8650<br>.023 783 8693<br>.022 951 1141 |
| | 36<br>37<br>38<br>39<br>40 | 1.563 943 8187<br>1.583 493 1165<br>1.603 286 7804<br>1.623 327 8652<br>1.643 619 4635 | 45.115 505 4982<br>46.679 449 3169<br>48.262 942 4334<br>49.866 229 2138<br>51.489 557 0790 | .022 165 3285<br>.021 422 7035<br>.020 719 8308<br>.020 053 6519<br>.019 421 4139 |
| **QUARTERLY**<br>If compounded<br>*quarterly*<br>nominal annual rate is<br>**5%** | 41<br>42<br>43<br>44<br>45 | 1.664 164 7068<br>1.684 966 7656<br>1.706 028 8502<br>1.727 354 2108<br>1.748 946 1384 | 53.133 176 5424<br>54.797 341 2492<br>56.482 308 0148<br>58.188 336 8650<br>59.915 691 0758 | .018 820 6327<br>.018 249 0606<br>.017 704 6589<br>.017 185 5745<br>.016 690 1188 |
| | 46<br>47<br>48<br>49<br>50 | 1.770 807 9652<br>1.792 943 0647<br>1.815 354 8531<br>1.838 046 7887<br>1.861 022 3736 | 61.664 637 2143<br>63.435 445 1795<br>65.228 388 2442<br>67.043 743 0973<br>68.881 789 8860 | .016 216 7499<br>.015 764 0574<br>.015 330 7483<br>.014 915 6350<br>.014 517 6251 |
| **MONTHLY**<br>If compounded<br>*monthly*<br>nominal annual rate is<br>**15%** | 51<br>52<br>53<br>54<br>55 | 1.884 285 1532<br>1.907 838 7177<br>1.931 686 7016<br>1.955 832 7854<br>1.980 280 6952 | 70.742 812 2596<br>72.627 097 4128<br>74.534 936 1305<br>76.466 622 8321<br>78.422 455 6175 | .014 135 7117<br>.013 768 9655<br>.013 416 5272<br>.013 077 6012<br>.012 751 4497 |
| $i$ = .0125<br>$j_{(2)}$ = .025<br>$j_{(4)}$ = .05<br>$j_{(12)}$ = .15 | 56<br>57<br>58<br>59<br>60 | 2.005 034 2039<br>2.030 097 1315<br>2.055 473 3456<br>2.081 166 7624<br>2.107 181 3470 | 80.402 736 3127<br>82.407 770 5166<br>84.437 867 6481<br>86.493 340 9937<br>88.574 507 7561 | .012 437 3877<br>.012 134 7780<br>.011 843 0276<br>.011 561 5837<br>.011 289 9301 |
| | **n** | $s=(1+i)^n$ | $s_{\overline{n}\mid} = \dfrac{(1+i)^n-1}{i}$ | $\dfrac{1}{s_{\overline{n}\mid}} = \dfrac{i}{(1+i)^n-1}$ |

| PRESENT WORTH OF 1 *What $1 due in the future is worth today.* | PRESENT WORTH OF 1 PER PERIOD *What $1 payable periodically is worth today.* | PARTIAL PAYMENT *Annuity worth $1 today.* *Periodic payment necessary to pay off a loan of $1.* | P E R I O D S | RATE $1\frac{1}{4}\%$ |
|---|---|---|---|---|
| .987 654 3210 | .987 654 3210 | 1.012 500 0000 | 1 | |
| .975 461 0578 | 1.963 115 3788 | .509 394 4099 | 2 | |
| .963 418 3287 | 2.926 533 7074 | .341 701 1728 | 3 | .0125 |
| .951 524 2752 | 3.878 057 9826 | .257 861 0233 | 4 | |
| .939 777 0619 | 4.817 835 0446 | .207 562 1084 | 5 | *per period* |
| .928 174 8760 | 5.746 009 9206 | .174 033 8102 | 6 | |
| .916 715 9269 | 6.662 725 8475 | .150 088 7209 | 7 | |
| .905 398 4463 | 7.568 124 2938 | .132 133 1365 | 8 | |
| .894 220 6877 | 8.462 344 9815 | .118 170 5546 | 9 | |
| .883 180 9262 | 9.345 525 9077 | .107 003 0740 | 10 | |
| .872 277 4579 | 10.217 803 3656 | .097 868 3935 | 11 | |
| .861 508 6004 | 11.079 311 9660 | .090 258 3123 | 12 | |
| .850 872 6918 | 11.930 184 6578 | .083 820 9993 | 13 | |
| .840 368 0906 | 12.770 552 7485 | .078 305 1462 | 14 | |
| .829 993 1759 | 13.600 545 9244 | .073 526 4603 | 15 | |
| .819 746 3466 | 14.420 292 2710 | .069 346 7221 | 16 | |
| .809 626 0213 | 15.229 918 2924 | .065 660 2341 | 17 | |
| .799 630 6384 | 16.029 548 9307 | .062 384 7873 | 18 | |
| .789 758 6552 | 16.819 307 5859 | .059 455 4797 | 19 | |
| .780 008 5483 | 17.599 316 1342 | .056 820 3896 | 20 | ANNUALLY |
| .770 378 8132 | 18.369 694 9474 | .054 437 4854 | 21 | If compounded *annually* nominal annual rate is |
| .760 867 9636 | 19.130 562 9110 | .052 272 3772 | 22 | |
| .751 474 5320 | 19.882 037 4430 | .050 296 6561 | 23 | |
| .742 197 0686 | 20.624 234 5116 | .048 486 6480 | 24 | $1\frac{1}{4}\%$ |
| .733 034 1418 | 21.357 268 6534 | .046 822 4667 | 25 | |
| .723 984 3376 | 22.081 252 9910 | .045 287 2851 | 26 | |
| .715 046 2594 | 22.796 299 2504 | .043 866 7693 | 27 | |
| .706 218 5278 | 23.502 517 7782 | .042 548 6329 | 28 | |
| .697 499 7805 | 24.200 017 5587 | .041 322 2841 | 29 | |
| .688 888 6721 | 24.888 906 2308 | .040 178 5434 | 30 | |
| .680 383 8737 | 25.569 290 1045 | .039 109 4159 | 31 | SEMIANNUALLY |
| .671 984 0728 | 26.241 274 1773 | .038 107 9056 | 32 | If compounded *semiannually* nominal annual rate is |
| .663 687 9731 | 26.904 962 1504 | .037 167 8650 | 33 | |
| .655 494 2944 | 27.560 456 4448 | .036 283 8693 | 34 | |
| .647 401 7723 | 28.207 858 2171 | .035 451 1141 | 35 | $2\frac{1}{2}\%$ |
| .639 409 1578 | 28.847 267 3749 | .034 665 3285 | 36 | |
| .631 515 2176 | 29.478 782 5925 | .033 922 7035 | 37 | |
| .623 718 7334 | 30.102 501 3259 | .033 219 8308 | 38 | |
| .616 018 5021 | 30.718 519 8281 | .032 553 6519 | 39 | |
| .608 413 3355 | 31.326 933 1635 | .031 921 4139 | 40 | |
| .600 902 0597 | 31.927 835 2233 | .031 320 6327 | 41 | QUARTERLY |
| .593 483 5158 | 32.521 318 7390 | .030 749 0606 | 42 | If compounded *quarterly* nominal annual rate is |
| .586 156 5588 | 33.107 475 2978 | .030 204 6589 | 43 | |
| .578 920 0581 | 33.686 395 3558 | .029 685 5745 | 44 | |
| .571 772 8968 | 34.258 168 2527 | .029 190 1188 | 45 | $5\%$ |
| .564 713 9722 | 34.822 882 2249 | .028 716 7499 | 46 | |
| .557 742 1948 | 35.380 624 4196 | .028 264 0574 | 47 | |
| .550 856 4886 | 35.931 480 9083 | .027 830 7483 | 48 | |
| .544 055 7913 | 36.475 536 6995 | .027 415 6350 | 49 | |
| .537 339 0531 | 37.012 875 7526 | .027 017 6251 | 50 | MONTHLY |
| .530 705 2376 | 37.543 580 9902 | .026 635 7117 | 51 | If compounded *monthly* nominal annual rate is |
| .524 153 3211 | 38.067 734 3114 | .026 268 9655 | 52 | |
| .517 682 2925 | 38.585 416 6038 | .025 916 5272 | 53 | |
| .511 291 1530 | 39.096 707 7568 | .025 577 6012 | 54 | |
| .504 978 9166 | 39.601 686 6734 | .025 251 4497 | 55 | $15\%$ |
| .498 744 6090 | 40.100 431 2824 | .024 937 3877 | 56 | |
| .492 587 2681 | 40.593 018 5505 | .024 634 7780 | 57 | |
| .486 505 9438 | 41.079 524 4943 | .024 343 0276 | 58 | $i = .0125$ |
| .480 499 6976 | 41.560 024 1919 | .024 061 5837 | 59 | $j_{(2)} = .025$ |
| .474 567 6026 | 42.034 591 7945 | .023 789 9301 | 60 | $j_{(4)} = .05$ $j_{(12)} = .15$ |
| $v^n = \dfrac{1}{(1+i)^n}$ | $a_{\overline{n}\rvert} = \dfrac{1-v^n}{i}$ | $\dfrac{1}{a_{\overline{n}\rvert}} = \dfrac{i}{1-v^n}$ | **n** | |

| P E R I O D S | AMOUNT OF 1 *How $1 left at compound interest will grow.* | AMOUNT OF 1 PER PERIOD *How $1 deposited periodically will grow.* | SINKING FUND *Periodic deposit that will grow to $1 at future date.* |
|---|---|---|---|
| 1 | 1.015 000 0000 | 1.000 000 0000 | 1.000 000 0000 |
| 2 | 1.030 225 0000 | 2.015 000 0000 | .496 277 9156 |
| 3 | 1.045 678 3750 | 3.045 225 0000 | .328 382 9602 |
| 4 | 1.061 363 5506 | 4.090 903 3750 | .244 444 7860 |
| 5 | 1.077 284 0039 | 5.152 266 9256 | .194 089 3231 |
| 6 | 1.093 443 2639 | 6.229 550 9295 | .160 525 2146 |
| 7 | 1.109 844 9129 | 7.322 994 1935 | .136 556 1645 |
| 8 | 1.126 492 5866 | 8.432 839 1064 | .118 584 0246 |
| 9 | 1.143 389 9754 | 9.559 331 6929 | .104 609 8234 |
| 10 | 1.160 540 8250 | 10.702 721 6683 | .093 434 1779 |
| 11 | 1.177 948 9374 | 11.863 262 4934 | .084 293 8442 |
| 12 | 1.195 618 1715 | 13.041 211 4308 | .076 679 9929 |
| 13 | 1.213 552 4440 | 14.236 829 6022 | .070 240 3574 |
| 14 | 1.231 755 7307 | 15.450 382 0463 | .064 723 3186 |
| 15 | 1.250 232 0667 | 16.682 137 7770 | .059 944 3557 |
| 16 | 1.268 985 5477 | 17.932 369 8436 | .055 765 0778 |
| 17 | 1.288 020 3309 | 19.201 355 3913 | .052 079 6569 |
| 18 | 1.307 340 6358 | 20.489 375 7221 | .048 805 7818 |
| 19 | 1.326 950 7454 | 21.796 716 3580 | .045 878 4701 |
| 20 | 1.346 855 0066 | 23.123 667 1033 | .043 245 7359 |
| 21 | 1.367 057 8316 | 24.470 522 1099 | .040 865 4950 |
| 22 | 1.387 563 6991 | 25.837 579 9415 | .038 703 3152 |
| 23 | 1.408 377 1546 | 27.225 143 6407 | .036 730 7520 |
| 24 | 1.429 502 8119 | 28.633 520 7953 | .034 924 1020 |
| 25 | 1.450 945 3541 | 30.063 023 6072 | .033 263 4539 |
| 26 | 1.472 709 5344 | 31.513 968 9613 | .031 731 9599 |
| 27 | 1.494 800 1774 | 32.986 678 4957 | .030 315 2680 |
| 28 | 1.517 222 1801 | 34.481 478 6732 | .029 001 0765 |
| 29 | 1.539 980 5128 | 35.998 700 8533 | .027 778 7802 |
| 30 | 1.563 080 2205 | 37.538 681 3661 | .026 639 1883 |
| 31 | 1.586 526 4238 | 39.101 761 5865 | .025 574 2954 |
| 32 | 1.610 324 3202 | 40.688 288 0103 | .024 577 0970 |
| 33 | 1.634 479 1850 | 42.298 612 3305 | .023 641 4375 |
| 34 | 1.658 996 3727 | 43.933 091 5155 | .022 761 8855 |
| 35 | 1.683 881 3183 | 45.592 087 8882 | .021 933 6303 |
| 36 | 1.709 139 5381 | 47.275 969 2065 | .021 152 3955 |
| 37 | 1.734 776 6312 | 48.985 108 7446 | .020 414 3673 |
| 38 | 1.760 798 2806 | 50.719 885 3758 | .019 716 1329 |
| 39 | 1.787 210 2548 | 52.480 683 6564 | .019 054 6298 |
| 40 | 1.814 018 4087 | 54.267 893 9113 | .018 427 1017 |
| 41 | 1.841 228 6848 | 56.081 912 3199 | .017 831 0610 |
| 42 | 1.868 847 1151 | 57.923 141 0047 | .017 264 2571 |
| 43 | 1.896 879 8218 | 59.791 988 1198 | .016 724 6488 |
| 44 | 1.925 333 0191 | 61.688 867 9416 | .016 210 3801 |
| 45 | 1.954 213 0144 | 63.614 200 9607 | .015 719 7604 |
| 46 | 1.983 526 2096 | 65.568 413 9751 | .015 251 2458 |
| 47 | 2.013 279 1028 | 67.551 940 1848 | .014 803 4238 |
| 48 | 2.043 478 2893 | 69.565 219 2875 | .014 374 9996 |
| 49 | 2.074 130 4637 | 71.608 697 5768 | .013 964 7841 |
| 50 | 2.105 242 4206 | 73.682 828 0405 | .013 571 6832 |
| 51 | 2.136 821 0569 | 75.788 070 4611 | .013 194 6887 |
| 52 | 2.168 873 3728 | 77.924 891 5180 | .012 832 8700 |
| 53 | 2.201 406 4734 | 80.093 764 8908 | .012 485 3664 |
| 54 | 2.234 427 5705 | 82.295 171 3642 | .012 151 3812 |
| 55 | 2.267 943 9840 | 84.529 598 9346 | .011 830 1756 |
| 56 | 2.301 963 1438 | 86.797 542 9186 | .011 521 0635 |
| 57 | 2.336 492 5909 | 89.099 506 0624 | .011 223 4068 |
| 58 | 2.371 539 9798 | 91.435 998 6534 | .010 936 6116 |
| 59 | 2.407 113 0795 | 93.807 538 6332 | .010 660 1241 |
| 60 | 2.443 219 7757 | 96.214 651 7126 | .010 393 4274 |
| n | $s = (1+i)^n$ | $s_{\overline{n}|} = \dfrac{(1+i)^n - 1}{i}$ | $\dfrac{1}{s_{\overline{n}|}} = \dfrac{i}{(1+i)^n - 1}$ |

.015

*per period*

ANNUALLY
If compounded
*annually*
nominal annual rate is

### 1½%

SEMIANNUALLY
If compounded
*semiannually*
nominal annual rate is

### 3%

QUARTERLY
If compounded
*quarterly*
nominal annual rate is

### 6%

MONTHLY
If compounded
*monthly*
nominal annual rate is

### 18%

$i = .015$
$j_{(2)} = .03$
$j_{(4)} = .06$
$j_{(12)} = .18$

| PRESENT WORTH OF 1 | PRESENT WORTH OF 1 PER PERIOD | PARTIAL PAYMENT | PERIODS | RATE |
|---|---|---|---|---|
| What $1 due in the future is worth today. | What $1 payable periodically is worth today. | Annuity worth $1 today. Periodic payment necessary to pay off a loan of $1. | | 1½% |
| .985 221 6749 | .985 221 6749 | 1.015 000 0000 | 1 | |
| .970 661 7486 | 1.955 883 4235 | .511 277 9156 | 2 | |
| .956 316 9937 | 2.912 200 4173 | .343 382 9602 | 3 | .015 |
| .942 184 2303 | 3.854 384 6476 | .259 444 7860 | 4 | per period |
| .928 260 3254 | 4.782 644 9730 | .209 089 3231 | 5 | |
| .914 542 1925 | 5.697 187 1655 | .175 525 2146 | 6 | |
| .901 026 7907 | 6.598 213 9561 | .151 556 1645 | 7 | |
| .887 711 1238 | 7.485 925 0799 | .133 584 0246 | 8 | |
| .874 592 2402 | 8.360 517 3201 | .119 609 8234 | 9 | |
| .861 667 2317 | 9.222 184 5519 | .108 434 1779 | 10 | |
| .848 933 2332 | 10.071 117 7851 | .099 293 8442 | 11 | |
| .836 387 4219 | 10.907 505 2070 | .091 679 9929 | 12 | |
| .824 027 0166 | 11.731 532 2236 | .085 240 3574 | 13 | |
| .811 849 2775 | 12.543 381 5011 | .079 723 3186 | 14 | |
| .799 851 5049 | 13.343 233 0060 | .074 944 3557 | 15 | |
| .788 031 0393 | 14.131 264 0453 | .070 765 0778 | 16 | |
| .776 385 2604 | 14.907 649 3057 | .067 079 6569 | 17 | |
| .764 911 5866 | 15.672 560 8924 | .063 805 7818 | 18 | |
| .753 607 4745 | 16.426 168 3669 | .060 878 4701 | 19 | |
| .742 470 4182 | 17.168 638 7851 | .058 245 7359 | 20 | |
| .731 497 9490 | 17.900 136 7341 | .055 865 4950 | 21 | ANNUALLY |
| .720 687 6345 | 18.620 824 3685 | .053 703 3152 | 22 | If compounded *annually* nominal annual rate is |
| .710 037 0783 | 19.330 861 4468 | .051 730 7520 | 23 | |
| .699 543 9195 | 20.030 405 3663 | .049 924 1020 | 24 | |
| .689 205 8320 | 20.719 611 1984 | .048 263 4539 | 25 | 1½% |
| .679 020 5242 | 21.398 631 7225 | .046 731 9599 | 26 | |
| .668 985 7381 | 22.067 617 4606 | .045 315 2680 | 27 | |
| .659 099 2494 | 22.726 716 7100 | .044 001 0765 | 28 | |
| .649 358 8664 | 23.376 075 5763 | .042 778 7802 | 29 | |
| .639 762 4299 | 24.015 838 0062 | .041 639 1883 | 30 | |
| .630 307 8127 | 24.646 145 8189 | .040 574 2954 | 31 | SEMIANNUALLY |
| .620 992 9189 | 25.267 138 7379 | .039 577 0970 | 32 | If compounded *semiannually* nominal annual rate is |
| .611 815 6837 | 25.878 954 4216 | .038 641 4375 | 33 | |
| .602 774 0726 | 26.481 728 4941 | .037 761 8855 | 34 | |
| .593 866 0814 | 27.075 594 5755 | .036 933 6303 | 35 | 3% |
| .585 089 7353 | 27.660 684 3109 | .036 152 3955 | 36 | |
| .576 443 0890 | 28.237 127 3999 | .035 414 3673 | 37 | |
| .567 924 2256 | 28.805 051 6255 | .034 716 1329 | 38 | |
| .559 531 2568 | 29.364 582 8822 | .034 054 6289 | 39 | |
| .551 262 3219 | 29.915 845 2042 | .033 427 1017 | 40 | |
| .543 115 5881 | 30.458 960 7923 | .032 831 0610 | 41 | QUARTERLY |
| .535 089 2494 | 30.994 050 0417 | .032 264 2571 | 42 | If compounded *quarterly* nominal annual rate is |
| .527 181 5265 | 31.521 231 5681 | .031 724 6488 | 43 | |
| .519 390 6665 | 32.040 622 2346 | .031 210 3804 | 44 | |
| .511 714 9423 | 32.552 337 1770 | .030 719 7604 | 45 | 6% |
| .504 152 6526 | 33.056 489 8295 | .030 251 2458 | 46 | |
| .496 702 1207 | 33.553 191 9503 | .029 803 4238 | 47 | |
| .489 361 6953 | 34.042 553 6456 | .029 374 9996 | 48 | |
| .482 129 7491 | 34.524 683 3947 | .028 964 7841 | 49 | |
| .475 004 6789 | 34.999 688 0736 | .028 571 6832 | 50 | |
| .467 984 9053 | 35.467 672 9789 | .028 194 6887 | 51 | MONTHLY |
| .461 068 8722 | 35.928 741 8511 | .027 832 8700 | 52 | If compounded *monthly* nominal annual rate is |
| .454 255 0465 | 36.382 996 8977 | .027 485 3664 | 53 | |
| .447 541 9178 | 36.830 538 8154 | .027 151 3812 | 54 | |
| .440 927 9978 | 37.271 466 8132 | .026 830 1756 | 55 | 18% |
| .434 411 8205 | 37.705 878 6337 | .026 521 0635 | 56 | |
| .427 991 9414 | 38.133 870 5751 | .026 223 4068 | 57 | |
| .421 666 9373 | 38.555 537 5124 | .025 936 6116 | 58 | $i = .015$ |
| .415 435 4062 | 38.970 972 9186 | .025 660 1241 | 59 | $j_{(2)} = .03$ |
| .409 295 9667 | 39.380 268 8853 | .025 393 4274 | 60 | $j_{(4)} = .06$ / $j_{(12)} = .18$ |
| $v^n = \dfrac{1}{(1+i)^n}$ | $a_{\overline{n}} = \dfrac{1-v^n}{i}$ | $\dfrac{1}{a_{\overline{n}}} = \dfrac{i}{1-v^n}$ | n | |

51

| P E R I O D S | AMOUNT OF 1<br>*How $1 left at compound interest will grow.* | AMOUNT OF<br>1 PER PERIOD<br>*How $1 deposited periodically will grow.* | SINKING FUND<br>*Periodic deposit that will grow to $1 at future date.* |
|---|---|---|---|
| 1 | 1.017 500 0000 | 1.000 000 0000 | 1.000 000 0000 |
| 2 | 1.035 306 2500 | 2.017 500 0000 | .495 662 9492 |
| 3 | 1.053 424 1094 | 3.052 806 2500 | .327 567 4635 |
| 4 | 1.071 859 0313 | 4.106 230 3594 | .243 532 3673 |
| 5 | 1.090 616 5643 | 5.178 089 3907 | .193 121 4246 |
| 6 | 1.109 702 3542 | 6.268 705 9550 | .159 522 5565 |
| 7 | 1.129 122 1454 | 7.378 408 3092 | .135 530 5857 |
| 8 | 1.148 881 7830 | 8.507 530 4546 | .117 542 9233 |
| 9 | 1.168 987 2142 | 9.656 412 2376 | .103 558 1306 |
| 10 | 1.189 444 4904 | 10.825 399 4517 | .092 375 3442 |
| 11 | 1.210 259 7690 | 12.014 843 9421 | .083 230 3778 |
| 12 | 1.231 439 3149 | 13.225 103 7111 | .075 613 7738 |
| 13 | 1.252 989 5030 | 14.456 543 0261 | .069 172 8305 |
| 14 | 1.274 916 8193 | 15.709 532 5290 | .063 655 6179 |
| 15 | 1.297 227 8636 | 16.984 449 3483 | .058 877 3872 |
| 16 | 1.319 929 3512 | 18.281 677 2119 | .054 699 5764 |
| 17 | 1.343 028 1149 | 19.601 606 5631 | .051 016 2265 |
| 18 | 1.366 531 1069 | 20.944 634 6779 | .047 744 9244 |
| 19 | 1.390 445 4012 | 22.311 165 7848 | .044 820 6073 |
| 20 | 1.414 778 1958 | 23.701 611 1860 | .042 191 2246 |
| 21 | 1.439 536 8142 | 25.116 389 3818 | .039 814 6399 |
| 22 | 1.464 728 7084 | 26.555 926 1960 | .037 656 3782 |
| 23 | 1.490 361 4608 | 28.020 654 9044 | .035 687 9596 |
| 24 | 1.516 442 7864 | 29.511 016 3652 | .033 885 6510 |
| 25 | 1.542 980 5352 | 31.027 459 1516 | .032 229 5163 |
| 26 | 1.569 982 6945 | 32.570 439 6868 | .030 702 6865 |
| 27 | 1.597 457 3917 | 34.140 422 3813 | .029 290 7917 |
| 28 | 1.625 412 8960 | 35.737 879 7730 | .027 981 5145 |
| 29 | 1.653 857 6217 | 37.363 292 6690 | .026 764 2365 |
| 30 | 1.682 800 1301 | 39.017 150 2907 | .025 629 7549 |
| 31 | 1.712 249 1324 | 40.699 950 4208 | .024 570 0545 |
| 32 | 1.742 213 4922 | 42.412 199 5532 | .023 578 1216 |
| 33 | 1.772 702 2283 | 44.154 413 0453 | .022 647 7928 |
| 34 | 1.803 724 5173 | 45.927 115 2736 | .021 773 6297 |
| 35 | 1.835 289 6963 | 47.730 839 7909 | .020 950 8151 |
| 36 | 1.867 407 2660 | 49.566 129 4873 | .020 175 0673 |
| 37 | 1.900 086 8932 | 51.433 536 7533 | .019 442 5673 |
| 38 | 1.933 338 4138 | 53.333 623 6465 | .018 749 8979 |
| 39 | 1.967 171 8361 | 55.266 962 0603 | .018 093 9926 |
| 40 | 2.001 597 3432 | 57.234 133 8963 | .017 472 0911 |
| 41 | 2.036 625 2967 | 59.235 731 2395 | .016 881 7026 |
| 42 | 2.072 266 2394 | 61.272 356 5362 | .016 320 5735 |
| 43 | 2.108 530 8986 | 63.344 622 7756 | .015 786 6596 |
| 44 | 2.145 430 1893 | 65.453 153 6742 | .015 278 1026 |
| 45 | 2.182 975 2176 | 67.598 583 8635 | .014 793 2093 |
| 46 | 2.221 177 2839 | 69.781 559 0811 | .014 330 4336 |
| 47 | 2.260 047 8864 | 72.002 736 3650 | .013 888 3611 |
| 48 | 2.299 598 7244 | 74.262 784 2514 | .013 465 6950 |
| 49 | 2.339 841 7021 | 76.562 382 9758 | .013 061 2445 |
| 50 | 2.380 788 9319 | 78.902 224 6779 | .012 673 9139 |
| 51 | 2.422 452 7382 | 81.283 013 6097 | .012 302 6935 |
| 52 | 2.464 845 6611 | 83.705 466 3479 | .011 946 6511 |
| 53 | 2.507 980 4602 | 86.170 312 0090 | .011 604 9249 |
| 54 | 2.551 870 1182 | 88.678 292 4691 | .011 276 7169 |
| 55 | 2.596 527 8453 | 91.230 162 5874 | .010 961 2871 |
| 56 | 2.641 967 0826 | 93.826 690 4326 | .010 657 9481 |
| 57 | 2.688 201 5065 | 96.468 657 5152 | .010 366 0611 |
| 58 | 2.735 245 0329 | 99.156 859 0217 | .010 085 0310 |
| 59 | 2.783 111 8210 | 101.892 104 0546 | .009 814 3032 |
| 60 | 2.831 816 2778 | 104.675 215 8756 | .009 553 3598 |
| **n** | $s=(1+i)^n$ | $s_{\overline{n}} = \dfrac{(1+i)^n-1}{i}$ | $\dfrac{1}{s_{\overline{n}}} = \dfrac{i}{(1+i)^n-1}$ |

.0175

*per period*

ANNUALLY
If compounded
*annually*
nominal annual rate is

# 1¾%

SEMIANNUALLY
If compounded
*semiannually*
nominal annual rate is

# 3½%

QUARTERLY
If compounded
*quarterly*
nominal annual rate is

# 7%

MONTHLY
If compounded
*monthly*
nominal annual rate is

# 21%

$i = .0175$
$j_{(2)} = .035$
$j_{(4)} = .07$
$j_{(12)} = .21$

| PRESENT WORTH OF 1<br>*What $1 due in the future is worth today.* | PRESENT WORTH OF 1 PER PERIOD<br>*What $1 payable periodically is worth today.* | PARTIAL PAYMENT<br>*Annuity worth $1 today.*<br>*Periodic payment necessary to pay off a loan of $1.* | PERIODS | RATE<br>$1\tfrac{3}{4}\%$ |
|---|---|---|---|---|
| .982 800 9828 | .982 800 9828 | 1.017 500 0000 | 1 | |
| .965 897 7718 | 1.948 698 7546 | .513 162 9492 | 2 | |
| .949 285 2794 | 2.897 984 0340 | .345 067 4635 | 3 | .0175 |
| .932 958 5056 | 3.830 942 5396 | .261 032 3673 | 4 | *per period* |
| .916 912 5362 | 4.747 855 0757 | .210 621 4246 | 5 | |
| .901 142 5417 | 5.648 997 6174 | .177 022 5565 | 6 | |
| .885 643 7756 | 6.534 641 3930 | .153 030 5857 | 7 | |
| .870 411 5731 | 7.405 052 9661 | .135 042 9233 | 8 | |
| .855 441 3495 | 8.260 494 3156 | .121 058 1306 | 9 | |
| .840 728 5990 | 9.101 222 9146 | .109 875 3442 | 10 | |
| .826 268 8934 | 9.927 491 8080 | .100 730 3778 | 11 | |
| .812 057 8805 | 10.739 549 6884 | .093 113 7738 | 12 | |
| .798 091 2830 | 11.537 640 9714 | .086 672 8305 | 13 | |
| .784 364 8973 | 12.322 005 8687 | .081 155 6179 | 14 | |
| .770 874 5919 | 13.092 880 4607 | .076 377 3872 | 15 | |
| .757 616 3066 | 13.850 496 7672 | .072 199 5764 | 16 | |
| .744 586 0507 | 14.595 082 8179 | .068 516 2265 | 17 | |
| .731 779 9024 | 15.326 862 7203 | .065 244 9244 | 18 | |
| .719 194 0073 | 16.046 056 7276 | .062 320 6073 | 19 | |
| .706 824 5772 | 16.752 881 3048 | .059 691 2246 | 20 | ANNUALLY<br>If compounded *annually* nominal annual rate is |
| .694 667 8891 | 17.447 549 1939 | .057 314 6399 | 21 | |
| .682 720 2841 | 18.130 269 4780 | .055 156 3782 | 22 | |
| .670 978 1662 | 18.801 247 6442 | .053 187 9596 | 23 | |
| .659 438 0012 | 19.460 685 6454 | .051 385 6510 | 24 | |
| .648 096 3157 | 20.108 781 9611 | .049 729 5163 | 25 | $1\tfrac{3}{4}\%$ |
| .636 949 6960 | 20.745 731 6571 | .048 202 6865 | 26 | |
| .625 994 7872 | 21.371 726 4443 | .046 790 7917 | 27 | |
| .615 228 2921 | 21.986 954 7364 | .045 481 5145 | 28 | |
| .604 646 9701 | 22.591 601 7066 | .044 264 2365 | 29 | |
| .594 247 6365 | 23.185 849 3431 | .043 129 7549 | 30 | SEMIANNUALLY<br>If compounded *semiannually* nominal annual rate is |
| .584 027 1612 | 23.769 876 5042 | .042 070 0545 | 31 | |
| .573 982 4680 | 24.343 858 9722 | .041 078 1216 | 32 | |
| .564 110 5336 | 24.907 969 5059 | .040 147 7928 | 33 | |
| .554 408 3869 | 25.462 377 8928 | .039 273 6297 | 34 | |
| .544 873 1075 | 26.007 251 0003 | .038 450 8151 | 35 | $3\tfrac{1}{2}\%$ |
| .535 501 8255 | 26.542 752 8258 | .037 675 0673 | 36 | |
| .526 291 7204 | 27.069 044 5462 | .036 942 5673 | 37 | |
| .517 240 0201 | 27.586 284 5663 | .036 249 8979 | 38 | |
| .508 344 0001 | 28.094 628 5664 | .035 593 9926 | 39 | |
| .499 600 9829 | 28.594 229 5493 | .034 972 0911 | 40 | QUARTERLY<br>If compounded *quarterly* nominal annual rate is |
| .491 008 3370 | 29.085 237 8863 | .034 381 7026 | 41 | |
| .482 563 4762 | 29.567 801 3625 | .033 820 5735 | 42 | |
| .474 263 8586 | 30.042 065 2211 | .033 286 6596 | 43 | |
| .466 106 9864 | 30.508 172 2075 | .032 778 1026 | 44 | |
| .458 090 4043 | 30.966 262 6117 | .032 293 2093 | 45 | $7\%$ |
| .450 211 6996 | 31.416 474 3113 | .031 830 4336 | 46 | |
| .442 468 5008 | 31.858 942 8121 | .031 388 3611 | 47 | |
| .434 858 4774 | 32.293 801 2895 | .030 965 6950 | 48 | |
| .427 379 3390 | 32.721 180 6285 | .030 561 2445 | 49 | |
| .420 028 8344 | 33.141 209 4629 | .030 173 9139 | 50 | MONTHLY<br>If compounded *monthly* nominal annual rate is |
| .412 804 7513 | 33.554 014 2142 | .029 802 6935 | 51 | |
| .405 704 9152 | 33.959 719 1294 | .029 446 6511 | 52 | |
| .398 727 1894 | 34.358 446 3188 | .029 104 9249 | 53 | |
| .391 869 4736 | 34.750 315 7925 | .028 776 7169 | 54 | |
| .385 129 7038 | 35.135 445 4963 | .028 461 2871 | 55 | $21\%$ |
| .378 505 8514 | 35.513 951 3477 | .028 157 9481 | 56 | |
| .371 995 9228 | 35.885 947 2705 | .027 866 0611 | 57 | |
| .365 597 9585 | 36.251 545 2290 | .027 585 0310 | 58 | $i = .0175$ |
| .359 310 0329 | 36.610 855 2619 | .027 314 3032 | 59 | $j_{(2)} = .035$ |
| .353 130 2535 | 36.963 985 5154 | .027 053 3598 | 60 | $j_{(4)} = .07$<br>$j_{(12)} = .21$ |
| $v^n = \dfrac{1}{(1+i)^n}$ | $a_{\overline{n}\rvert} = \dfrac{1-v^n}{i}$ | $\dfrac{1}{a_{\overline{n}\rvert}} = \dfrac{i}{1-v^n}$ | n | |

53

| P E R I O D S | AMOUNT OF 1 *How $1 left at compound interest will grow.* | AMOUNT OF 1 PER PERIOD *How $1 deposited periodically will grow.* | SINKING FUND *Periodic deposit that will grow to $1 at future date.* |
|---|---|---|---|
| 1 | 1.020 000 0000 | 1.000 000 0000 | 1.000 000 0000 |
| 2 | 1.040 400 0000 | 2.020 000 0000 | .495 049 5050 |
| 3 | 1.061 208 0000 | 3.060 400 0000 | .326 754 6726 |
| 4 | 1.082 432 1600 | 4.121 608 0000 | .242 623 7527 |
| 5 | 1.104 080 8032 | 5.204 040 1600 | .192 158 3941 |
| 6 | 1.126 162 4193 | 6.308 120 9632 | .158 525 8123 |
| 7 | 1.148 685 6676 | 7.434 283 3825 | .134 511 9561 |
| 8 | 1.171 659 3810 | 8.582 969 0501 | .116 509 7991 |
| 9 | 1.195 092 5686 | 9.754 628 4311 | .102 515 4374 |
| 10 | 1.218 994 4200 | 10.949 720 9997 | .091 326 5279 |
| 11 | 1.243 374 3084 | 12.168 715 4197 | .082 177 9428 |
| 12 | 1.268 241 7946 | 13.412 089 7281 | .074 559 5966 |
| 13 | 1.293 606 6305 | 14.680 331 5227 | .068 118 3527 |
| 14 | 1.319 478 7631 | 15.973 938 1531 | .062 601 9702 |
| 15 | 1.345 868 3383 | 17.293 416 9162 | .057 825 4723 |
| 16 | 1.372 785 7051 | 18.639 285 2545 | .053 650 1259 |
| 17 | 1.400 241 4192 | 20.012 070 9596 | .049 969 8408 |
| 18 | 1.428 246 2476 | 21.412 312 3788 | .046 702 1022 |
| 19 | 1.456 811 1725 | 22.840 558 6264 | .043 781 7663 |
| 20 | 1.485 947 3960 | 24.297 369 7989 | .041 156 7181 |
| 21 | 1.515 666 3439 | 25.783 317 1949 | .038 784 7689 |
| 22 | 1.545 979 6708 | 27.298 983 5388 | .036 631 4005 |
| 23 | 1.576 899 2642 | 28.844 963 2096 | .034 668 0976 |
| 24 | 1.608 437 2495 | 30.421 862 4738 | .032 871 0973 |
| 25 | 1.640 605 9945 | 32.030 299 7232 | .031 220 4384 |
| 26 | 1.673 418 1144 | 33.670 905 7177 | .029 699 2308 |
| 27 | 1.706 886 4766 | 35.344 323 8321 | .028 293 0862 |
| 28 | 1.741 024 2062 | 37.051 210 3087 | .026 989 6716 |
| 29 | 1.775 844 6903 | 38.792 234 5149 | .025 778 3552 |
| 30 | 1.811 361 5841 | 40.568 079 2052 | .024 649 9223 |
| 31 | 1.847 588 8158 | 42.379 440 7893 | .023 596 3472 |
| 32 | 1.884 540 5921 | 44.227 029 6051 | .022 610 6073 |
| 33 | 1.922 231 4039 | 46.111 570 1972 | .021 686 5311 |
| 34 | 1.960 676 0320 | 48.033 801 6011 | .020 818 6728 |
| 35 | 1.999 889 5527 | 49.994 477 6331 | .020 002 2092 |
| 36 | 2.039 887 3437 | 51.994 367 1858 | .019 232 8526 |
| 37 | 2.080 685 0906 | 54.034 254 5295 | .018 506 7789 |
| 38 | 2.122 298 7924 | 56.114 939 6201 | .017 820 5663 |
| 39 | 2.164 744 7682 | 58.237 238 4125 | .017 171 1439 |
| 40 | 2.208 039 6636 | 60.401 983 1807 | .016 555 7478 |
| 41 | 2.252 200 4569 | 62.610 022 8444 | .015 971 8836 |
| 42 | 2.297 244 4660 | 64.862 223 3012 | .015 417 2945 |
| 43 | 2.343 189 3553 | 67.159 467 7673 | .014 889 9334 |
| 44 | 2.390 053 1425 | 69.502 657 1226 | .014 387 9391 |
| 45 | 2.437 854 2053 | 71.892 710 2651 | .013 909 6161 |
| 46 | 2.486 611 2894 | 74.330 564 4704 | .013 453 4159 |
| 47 | 2.536 343 5152 | 76.817 175 7598 | .013 017 9220 |
| 48 | 2.587 070 3855 | 79.353 519 2750 | .012 601 8355 |
| 49 | 2.638 811 7932 | 81.940 589 6605 | .012 203 9639 |
| 50 | 2.691 588 0291 | 84.579 401 4537 | .011 823 2097 |
| 51 | 2.745 419 7897 | 87.270 989 4828 | .011 458 5615 |
| 52 | 2.800 328 1854 | 90.016 409 2724 | .011 109 0856 |
| 53 | 2.856 334 7492 | 92.816 737 4579 | .010 773 9189 |
| 54 | 2.913 461 4441 | 95.673 072 2070 | .010 452 2618 |
| 55 | 2.971 730 6730 | 98.586 533 6512 | .010 143 3732 |
| 56 | 3.031 165 2865 | 101.558 264 3242 | .009 846 5645 |
| 57 | 3.091 788 5922 | 104.589 429 6107 | .009 561 1957 |
| 58 | 3.153 624 3641 | 107.681 218 2029 | .009 286 6706 |
| 59 | 3.216 696 8513 | 110.834 842 5669 | .009 022 4335 |
| 60 | 3.281 030 7884 | 114.051 539 4183 | .008 767 9658 |
| n | $s=(1+i)^n$ | $s_{\overline{n}} = \dfrac{(1+i)^n - 1}{i}$ | $\dfrac{1}{s_{\overline{n}}} = \dfrac{i}{(1+i)^n - 1}$ |

.02

*per period*

ANNUALLY
If compounded
*annually*
nominal annual rate is

2%

SEMIANNUALLY
If compounded
*semiannually*
nominal annual rate is

4%

QUARTERLY
If compounded
*quarterly*
nominal annual rate is

8%

MONTHLY
If compounded
*monthly*
nominal annual rate is

24%

$i$ = .02
$j_{(2)}$ = .04
$j_{(4)}$ = .08
$j_{(12)}$ = .24

| PRESENT WORTH OF 1 | PRESENT WORTH OF 1 PER PERIOD | PARTIAL PAYMENT | P E R I O D S | RATE |
|---|---|---|---|---|
| What $1 due in the future is worth today. | What $1 payable periodically is worth today. | Annuity worth $1 today. Periodic payment necessary to pay off a loan of $1. | | 2% |
| .980 392 1569 | .980 392 1569 | 1.020 000 0000 | 1 | |
| .961 168 7812 | 1.941 560 9381 | .515 049 5050 | 2 | |
| .942 322 3345 | 2.883 883 2726 | .346 754 6726 | 3 | .02 |
| .923 845 4260 | 3.807 728 6987 | .262 623 7527 | 4 | per period |
| .905 730 8098 | 4.713 459 5085 | .212 158 3941 | 5 | |
| .887 971 3822 | 5.601 430 8907 | .178 525 8123 | 6 | |
| .870 560 1786 | 6.471 991 0693 | .154 511 9561 | 7 | |
| .853 490 3712 | 7.325 481 4405 | .136 509 7991 | 8 | |
| .836 755 2659 | 8.162 236 7064 | .122 515 4374 | 9 | |
| .820 348 2999 | 8.982 585 0062 | .111 326 5279 | 10 | |
| .804 263 0391 | 9.786 848 0453 | .102 177 9428 | 11 | |
| .788 493 1756 | 10.575 341 2209 | .094 559 5966 | 12 | |
| .773 032 5251 | 11.348 373 7460 | .088 118 3527 | 13 | |
| .757 875 0246 | 12.106 248 7706 | .082 601 9702 | 14 | |
| .743 014 7300 | 12.849 263 5006 | .077 825 4723 | 15 | |
| .728 445 8137 | 13.577 709 3143 | .073 650 1259 | 16 | |
| .714 162 5625 | 14.291 871 8768 | .069 969 8408 | 17 | |
| .700 159 3750 | 14.992 031 2517 | .066 702 1022 | 18 | |
| .686 430 7598 | 15.678 462 0115 | .063 781 7663 | 19 | |
| .672 971 3331 | 16.351 433 3446 | .061 156 7181 | 20 | |
| .659 775 8168 | 17.011 209 1614 | .058 784 7689 | 21 | ANNUALLY |
| .646 839 0361 | 17.658 048 1974 | .056 631 4005 | 22 | If compounded *annually* nominal annual rate is |
| .634 155 9177 | 18.292 204 1151 | .054 668 0976 | 23 | |
| .621 721 4879 | 18.913 925 6031 | .052 871 0973 | 24 | |
| .609 530 8705 | 19.523 456 4736 | .051 220 4384 | 25 | 2% |
| .597 579 2848 | 20.121 035 7584 | .049 699 2308 | 26 | |
| .585 862 0440 | 20.706 897 8024 | .048 293 0862 | 27 | |
| .574 374 5529 | 21.281 272 3553 | .046 989 6716 | 28 | |
| .563 112 3068 | 21.844 384 6620 | .045 778 3552 | 29 | |
| .552 070 8890 | 22.396 455 5510 | .044 649 9223 | 30 | |
| .541 245 9696 | 22.937 701 5206 | .043 596 3472 | 31 | SEMIANNUALLY |
| .530 633 3035 | 23.468 334 8241 | .042 610 6073 | 32 | If compounded *semiannually* nominal annual rate is |
| .520 228 7289 | 23.988 563 5530 | .041 686 5311 | 33 | |
| .510 028 1656 | 24.498 591 7187 | .040 818 6728 | 34 | |
| .500 027 6134 | 24.998 619 3320 | .040 002 2092 | 35 | 4% |
| .490 223 1504 | 25.488 842 4824 | .039 232 8526 | 36 | |
| .480 610 9317 | 25.969 453 4141 | .038 506 7789 | 37 | |
| .471 187 1880 | 26.440 640 6021 | .037 820 5663 | 38 | |
| .461 948 2235 | 26.902 588 8256 | .037 171 1439 | 39 | |
| .452 890 4152 | 27.355 479 2407 | .036 555 7478 | 40 | QUARTERLY |
| .444 010 2110 | 27.799 489 4517 | .035 971 8836 | 41 | If compounded *quarterly* nominal annual rate is |
| .435 304 1284 | 28.234 793 5801 | .035 417 2945 | 42 | |
| .426 768 7533 | 28.661 562 3334 | .034 889 9334 | 43 | |
| .418 400 7386 | 29.079 963 0720 | .034 387 9391 | 44 | |
| .410 196 8025 | 29.490 159 8745 | .033 909 6161 | 45 | 8% |
| .402 153 7280 | 29.892 313 6025 | .033 453 4159 | 46 | |
| .394 268 3607 | 30.286 581 9632 | .033 017 9220 | 47 | |
| .386 537 6086 | 30.673 119 5718 | .032 601 8355 | 48 | |
| .378 958 4398 | 31.052 078 0115 | .032 203 9639 | 49 | |
| .371 527 8821 | 31.423 605 8937 | .031 823 2097 | 50 | MONTHLY |
| .364 243 0217 | 31.787 848 9153 | .031 458 5615 | 51 | If compounded *monthly* nominal annual rate is |
| .357 101 0017 | 32.144 949 9170 | .031 109 0856 | 52 | |
| .350 099 0212 | 32.495 048 9382 | .030 773 9189 | 53 | |
| .343 294 3345 | 32.838 283 2728 | .030 452 2618 | 54 | |
| .336 504 2496 | 33.174 787 5223 | .030 143 3732 | 55 | 24% |
| .329 906 1270 | 33.504 693 6494 | .029 846 5645 | 56 | |
| .323 437 3794 | 33.828 131 0288 | .029 561 1957 | 57 | |
| .317 095 4700 | 34.145 226 4988 | .029 286 6706 | 58 | $i \ = .02$ |
| .310 877 9118 | 34.456 104 4106 | .029 022 4335 | 59 | $j_{(2)} = .04$ |
| .304 782 2665 | 34.760 886 6770 | .028 767 9658 | 60 | $j_{(4)} = .08$ |
| $v^n = \dfrac{1}{(1+i)^n}$ | $a_{\overline{n}|} = \dfrac{1-v^n}{i}$ | $\dfrac{1}{a_{\overline{n}|}} = \dfrac{i}{1-v^n}$ | n | $j_{(12)} = .24$ |

| P E R I O D S | AMOUNT OF 1<br>*How $1 left at compound interest will grow.* | AMOUNT OF 1 PER PERIOD<br>*How $1 deposited periodically will grow.* | SINKING FUND<br>*Periodic deposit that will grow to $1 at future date.* |
|---|---|---|---|
| 1 | 1.022 500 0000 | 1.000 000 0000 | 1.000 000 0000 |
| 2 | 1.045 506 2500 | 2.022 500 0000 | .494 437 5773 |
| 3 | 1.069 030 1406 | 3.068 006 2500 | .325 944 5772 |
| 4 | 1.093 083 3188 | 4.137 036 3906 | .241 718 9277 |
| 5 | 1.117 677 6935 | 5.230 119 7094 | .191 200 2125 |
| 6 | 1.142 825 4416 | 6.347 797 4029 | .157 534 9584 |
| 7 | 1.168 539 0140 | 7.490 622 8444 | .133 500 2470 |
| 8 | 1.194 831 1418 | 8.659 161 8584 | .115 484 6181 |
| 9 | 1.221 714 8425 | 9.853 993 0003 | .101 481 7039 |
| 10 | 1.249 203 4265 | 11.075 707 8428 | .090 287 6831 |
| 11 | 1.277 310 5036 | 12.324 911 2692 | .081 136 4868 |
| 12 | 1.306 049 9899 | 13.602 221 7728 | .073 517 4015 |
| 13 | 1.335 436 1147 | 14.908 271 7627 | .067 076 8561 |
| 14 | 1.365 483 4272 | 16.243 707 8773 | .061 562 2989 |
| 15 | 1.396 206 8044 | 17.609 191 3046 | .056 788 5250 |
| 16 | 1.427 621 4575 | 19.005 398 1089 | .052 616 6300 |
| 17 | 1.459 742 9402 | 20.433 019 5664 | .048 940 3926 |
| 18 | 1.492 587 1564 | 21.892 762 5066 | .045 677 1958 |
| 19 | 1.526 170 3674 | 23.385 349 6630 | .042 761 8152 |
| 20 | 1.560 509 2007 | 24.911 520 0304 | .040 142 0708 |
| 21 | 1.595 620 6577 | 26.472 029 2311 | .037 775 7214 |
| 22 | 1.631 522 1225 | 28.067 649 8888 | .035 628 2056 |
| 23 | 1.668 231 3703 | 29.699 172 0113 | .033 670 9724 |
| 24 | 1.705 766 5761 | 31.367 403 3816 | .031 880 2289 |
| 25 | 1.744 146 3240 | 33.073 169 9577 | .030 235 9889 |
| 26 | 1.783 389 6163 | 34.817 316 2817 | .028 721 3406 |
| 27 | 1.823 515 8827 | 36.600 705 8980 | .027 321 8774 |
| 28 | 1.864 544 9901 | 38.424 221 7807 | .026 025 2506 |
| 29 | 1.906 497 2523 | 40.288 766 7708 | .024 820 8143 |
| 30 | 1.949 393 4405 | 42.195 264 0232 | .023 699 3422 |
| 31 | 1.993 254 7929 | 44.144 657 4637 | .022 652 7978 |
| 32 | 2.038 103 0258 | 46.137 912 2566 | .021 674 1493 |
| 33 | 2.083 960 3439 | 48.176 015 2824 | .020 757 2169 |
| 34 | 2.130 849 4516 | 50.259 975 6262 | .019 896 5477 |
| 35 | 2.178 793 5643 | 52.390 825 0778 | .019 087 3115 |
| 36 | 2.227 816 4194 | 54.569 618 6421 | .018 325 2151 |
| 37 | 2.277 942 2889 | 56.797 435 0615 | .017 606 4289 |
| 38 | 2.329 195 9904 | 59.075 377 3504 | .016 927 5262 |
| 39 | 2.381 602 9002 | 61.404 573 3408 | .016 285 4319 |
| 40 | 2.435 188 9654 | 63.786 176 2410 | .015 677 3781 |
| 41 | 2.489 980 7171 | 66.221 365 2064 | .015 100 8666 |
| 42 | 2.546 005 2833 | 68.711 345 9235 | .014 553 6372 |
| 43 | 2.603 290 4022 | 71.257 351 2068 | .014 033 6398 |
| 44 | 2.661 864 4362 | 73.860 641 6090 | .013 539 0105 |
| 45 | 2.721 756 3860 | 76.522 506 0452 | .013 068 0508 |
| 46 | 2.782 995 9047 | 79.244 262 4312 | .012 619 2101 |
| 47 | 2.845 613 3126 | 82.027 258 3359 | .012 191 0694 |
| 48 | 2.909 639 6121 | 84.872 871 6484 | .011 782 3279 |
| 49 | 2.975 106 5034 | 87.782 511 2605 | .011 391 7908 |
| 50 | 3.042 046 3997 | 90.757 617 7639 | .011 018 3588 |
| 51 | 3.110 492 4437 | 93.799 664 1636 | .010 661 0190 |
| 52 | 3.180 478 5237 | 96.910 156 6073 | .010 318 8359 |
| 53 | 3.252 039 2904 | 100.090 635 1309 | .009 990 9447 |
| 54 | 3.325 210 1745 | 103.342 674 4214 | .009 676 5446 |
| 55 | 3.400 027 4034 | 106.667 884 5958 | .009 374 8930 |
| 56 | 3.476 528 0200 | 110.067 911 9993 | .009 085 3000 |
| 57 | 3.554 749 9004 | 113.544 440 0192 | .008 807 1243 |
| 58 | 3.634 731 7732 | 117.099 189 9197 | .008 539 7687 |
| 59 | 3.716 513 2381 | 120.733 921 6929 | .008 282 6764 |
| 60 | 3.800 134 7859 | 124.450 434 9310 | .008 035 3275 |
| **n** | $s=(1+i)^n$ | $s_{\overline{n}\mid}=\dfrac{(1+i)^n-1}{i}$ | $\dfrac{1}{s_{\overline{n}\mid}}=\dfrac{i}{(1+i)^n-1}$ |

.0225

*per period*

ANNUALLY
If compounded *annually* nominal annual rate is

2¼%

SEMIANNUALLY
If compounded *semiannually* nominal annual rate is

4½%

QUARTERLY
If compounded *quarterly* nominal annual rate is

9%

MONTHLY
If compounded *monthly* nominal annual rate is

27%

$i\ =\ .0225$
$j_{(2)}\ =\ .045$
$j_{(4)}\ =\ .09$
$j_{(12)}\ =\ .27$

| PRESENT WORTH OF 1<br>*What $1 due in the future is worth today.* | PRESENT WORTH OF 1 PER PERIOD<br>*What $1 payable periodically is worth today.* | PARTIAL PAYMENT<br>*Annuity worth $1 today.*<br>*Periodic payment necessary to pay off a loan of $1.* | PERIODS | RATE<br>**2¼%** |
|---|---|---|---|---|
| .977 995 1100 | .977 995 1100 | 1.022 500 0000 | 1 | |
| .956 474 4352 | 1.934 469 5453 | .516 937 5773 | 2 | |
| .935 427 3205 | 2.869 896 8658 | .348 444 5772 | 3 | .0225 |
| .914 843 3453 | 3.784 740 2110 | .264 218 9277 | 4 | |
| .894 712 3181 | 4.679 452 5291 | .213 700 2125 | 5 | *per period* |
| .875 024 2720 | 5.554 476 8011 | .180 034 9584 | 6 | |
| .855 769 4591 | 6.410 246 2602 | .156 000 2470 | 7 | |
| .836 938 3464 | 7.247 184 6066 | .137 984 6181 | 8 | |
| .818 521 6101 | 8.065 706 2167 | .123 981 7039 | 9 | |
| .800 510 1322 | 8.866 216 3489 | .112 787 6831 | 10 | |
| .782 894 9948 | 9.649 111 3436 | .103 636 4868 | 11 | |
| .765 667 4765 | 10.414 778 8202 | .096 017 4015 | 12 | |
| .748 819 0480 | 11.163 597 8681 | .089 576 8561 | 13 | |
| .732 341 3672 | 11.895 939 2354 | .084 062 2989 | 14 | |
| .716 226 2760 | 12.612 165 5113 | .079 288 5250 | 15 | |
| .700 465 7956 | 13.312 631 3069 | .075 116 6300 | 16 | |
| .685 052 1228 | 13.997 683 4298 | .071 440 3926 | 17 | |
| .669 977 6262 | 14.667 661 0560 | .068 177 1958 | 18 | |
| .655 234 8423 | 15.322 895 8983 | .065 261 8152 | 19 | |
| .640 816 4717 | 15.963 712 3700 | .062 642 0708 | 20 | ANNUALLY<br>If compounded *annually* nominal annual rate is<br>**2¼%** |
| .626 715 3757 | 16.590 427 7457 | .060 275 7214 | 21 | |
| .612 924 5728 | 17.203 352 3185 | .058 128 2056 | 22 | |
| .599 437 2350 | 17.802 789 5536 | .056 170 9724 | 23 | |
| .586 246 6846 | 18.389 036 2382 | .054 380 2289 | 24 | |
| .573 346 3908 | 18.962 382 6291 | .052 735 9889 | 25 | |
| .560 729 9666 | 19.523 112 5957 | .051 221 3406 | 26 | |
| .548 391 1654 | 20.071 503 7610 | .049 821 8774 | 27 | |
| .536 323 8781 | 20.607 827 6392 | .048 525 2506 | 28 | |
| .524 522 1302 | 21.192 349 7693 | .047 320 8143 | 29 | |
| .512 980 0784 | 21.645 329 8478 | .046 199 3422 | 30 | SEMIANNUALLY<br>If compounded *semiannually* nominal annual rate is<br>**4½%** |
| .501 692 0082 | 22.147 021 8560 | .045 152 7978 | 31 | |
| .490 652 3308 | 22.637 674 1868 | .044 174 1493 | 32 | |
| .479 855 5802 | 23.117 529 7670 | .043 257 2169 | 33 | |
| .469 296 4110 | 23.586 826 1780 | .042 396 5477 | 34 | |
| .458 969 5951 | 24.045 795 7731 | .041 587 3115 | 35 | |
| .448 870 0197 | 24.494 665 7928 | .040 825 2151 | 36 | |
| .438 992 6843 | 24.933 658 4771 | .040 106 4289 | 37 | |
| .429 332 6985 | 25.362 991 1756 | .039 427 5262 | 38 | |
| .419 885 2798 | 25.782 876 4554 | .038 785 4319 | 39 | |
| .410 645 7504 | 26.193 522 2057 | .038 177 3781 | 40 | QUARTERLY<br>If compounded *quarterly* nominal annual rate is<br>**9%** |
| .401 609 5358 | 26.595 131 7416 | .037 600 8666 | 41 | |
| .392 772 1622 | 26.987 903 9037 | .037 053 6372 | 42 | |
| .384 129 2540 | 27.372 033 1577 | .036 533 6398 | 43 | |
| .375 676 5320 | 27.747 709 6897 | .036 039 0105 | 44 | |
| .367 409 8112 | 28.115 119 5009 | .035 568 0508 | 45 | |
| .359 324 9988 | 28.474 444 4997 | .035 119 2101 | 46 | |
| .351 418 0917 | 28.825 862 5913 | .034 691 0694 | 47 | |
| .343 685 1753 | 29.169 547 7666 | .034 282 3279 | 48 | |
| .336 122 4208 | 29.505 670 1874 | .033 891 7908 | 49 | |
| .328 726 0839 | 29.834 396 2713 | .033 518 3588 | 50 | MONTHLY<br>If compounded *monthly* nominal annual rate is<br>**27%** |
| .321 492 5026 | 30.155 888 7739 | .033 161 0190 | 51 | |
| .314 418 0954 | 30.470 306 8693 | .032 818 8359 | 52 | |
| .307 499 3598 | 30.777 806 2291 | .032 490 9447 | 53 | |
| .300 732 8703 | 31.078 539 0994 | .032 176 5446 | 54 | |
| .294 115 2765 | 31.372 654 3760 | .031 874 8930 | 55 | |
| .287 643 3022 | 31.660 297 6782 | .031 585 3000 | 56 | |
| .281 313 7430 | 31.941 611 4212 | .031 307 1243 | 57 | |
| .275 123 4651 | 32.216 734 8863 | .031 039 7687 | 58 | $i$ = .0225 |
| .269 069 4035 | 32.485 804 2898 | .030 782 6764 | 59 | $j_{(2)}$ = .045 |
| .263 148 5609 | 32.748 952 8506 | .030 535 3275 | 60 | $j_{(4)}$ = .09 |
| $v^n = \dfrac{1}{(1+i)^n}$ | $a_{\overline{n}|} = \dfrac{1-v^n}{i}$ | $\dfrac{1}{a_{\overline{n}|}} = \dfrac{i}{1-v^n}$ | n | $j_{(12)}$ = .27 |

| P E R I O D S | AMOUNT OF 1<br>*How $1 left at compound interest will grow.* | AMOUNT OF 1 PER PERIOD<br>*How $1 deposited periodically will grow.* | SINKING FUND<br>*Periodic deposit that will grow to $1 at future date.* |
|---|---|---|---|
| 1 | 1.025 000 0000 | 1.000 000 0000 | 1.000 000 0000 |
| 2 | 1.050 625 0000 | 2.025 000 0000 | .493 827 1605 |
| 3 | 1.076 890 6250 | 3.075 625 0000 | .325 137 1672 |
| 4 | 1.103 812 8906 | 4.152 515 6250 | .240 817 8777 |
| 5 | 1.131 408 2129 | 5.256 328 5156 | .190 246 8609 |
| 6 | 1.159 693 4182 | 6.387 736 7285 | .156 549 9711 |
| 7 | 1.188 685 7537 | 7.547 430 1467 | .132 495 4296 |
| 8 | 1.218 402 8975 | 8.736 115 9004 | .114 467 3458 |
| 9 | 1.248 862 9699 | 9.954 518 7979 | .100 456 8900 |
| 10 | 1.280 084 5442 | 11.203 381 7679 | .089 258 7632 |
| 11 | 1.312 086 6578 | 12.483 466 3121 | .080 105 9558 |
| 12 | 1.344 888 8242 | 13.795 552 9699 | .072 487 1270 |
| 13 | 1.378 511 0449 | 15.140 441 7941 | .066 048 2708 |
| 14 | 1.412 973 8210 | 16.518 952 8390 | .060 536 5249 |
| 15 | 1.448 298 1665 | 17.931 926 6599 | .055 766 4561 |
| 16 | 1.484 505 6207 | 19.380 224 8264 | .051 598 9886 |
| 17 | 1.521 618 2612 | 20.864 730 4471 | .047 927 7699 |
| 18 | 1.559 658 7177 | 22.386 348 7083 | .044 670 0805 |
| 19 | 1.598 650 1856 | 23.946 007 4260 | .041 760 6151 |
| 20 | 1.638 616 4403 | 25.544 657 6116 | .039 147 1287 |
| 21 | 1.679 581 8513 | 27.183 274 0519 | .036 787 3273 |
| 22 | 1.721 571 3976 | 28.862 855 9032 | .034 646 6061 |
| 23 | 1.764 610 6825 | 30.584 427 3008 | .032 696 3781 |
| 24 | 1.808 725 9496 | 32.349 037 9833 | .030 912 8204 |
| 25 | 1.853 944 0983 | 34.157 763 9329 | .029 275 9210 |
| 26 | 1.900 292 7008 | 36.011 708 0312 | .027 768 7467 |
| 27 | 1.947 800 0183 | 37.912 000 7320 | .026 376 8722 |
| 28 | 1.996 495 0188 | 39.859 800 7503 | .025 087 9327 |
| 29 | 2.046 407 3942 | 41.856 295 7690 | .023 891 2685 |
| 30 | 2.097 567 5791 | 43.902 703 1633 | .022 777 6407 |
| 31 | 2.150 006 7686 | 46.000 270 7424 | .021 739 0025 |
| 32 | 2.203 756 9378 | 48.150 277 5109 | .020 768 3123 |
| 33 | 2.258 850 8612 | 50.354 034 4487 | .019 859 3819 |
| 34 | 2.315 322 1327 | 52.612 885 3099 | .019 006 7508 |
| 35 | 2.373 205 1861 | 54.928 207 4426 | .018 205 5823 |
| 36 | 2.432 535 3157 | 57.301 412 6287 | .017 451 5767 |
| 37 | 2.493 348 6986 | 59.733 947 9444 | .016 740 8992 |
| 38 | 2.555 682 4161 | 62.227 296 6430 | .016 070 1180 |
| 39 | 2.619 574 4765 | 64.782 979 0591 | .015 436 1534 |
| 40 | 2.685 063 8384 | 67.402 553 5356 | .014 836 2332 |
| 41 | 2.752 190 4343 | 70.087 617 3740 | .014 267 8555 |
| 42 | 2.820 995 1952 | 72.839 807 8083 | .013 728 7567 |
| 43 | 2.891 520 0751 | 75.660 803 0035 | .013 216 8833 |
| 44 | 2.963 808 0770 | 78.552 323 0786 | .012 730 3683 |
| 45 | 3.037 903 2789 | 81.516 131 1556 | .012 267 5106 |
| 46 | 3.113 850 8609 | 84.554 034 4345 | .011 826 7568 |
| 47 | 3.191 697 1324 | 87.667 885 2954 | .011 406 6855 |
| 48 | 3.271 489 5607 | 90.859 582 4277 | .011 005 9938 |
| 49 | 3.353 276 7997 | 94.131 071 9884 | .010 623 4847 |
| 50 | 3.437 108 7197 | 97.484 348 7881 | .010 258 0569 |
| 51 | 3.523 036 4377 | 100.921 457 5078 | .009 908 6956 |
| 52 | 3.611 112 3486 | 104.444 493 9455 | .009 574 4635 |
| 53 | 3.701 390 1574 | 108.055 606 2942 | .009 254 4944 |
| 54 | 3.793 924 9113 | 111.756 996 4515 | .008 947 9856 |
| 55 | 3.888 773 0341 | 115.550 921 3628 | .008 654 1932 |
| 56 | 3.985 992 3599 | 119.439 694 3969 | .008 372 4260 |
| 57 | 4.085 642 1689 | 123.425 686 7568 | .008 102 0412 |
| 58 | 4.187 783 2231 | 127.511 328 9257 | .007 842 4404 |
| 59 | 4.292 477 8037 | 131.699 112 1489 | .007 593 0656 |
| 60 | 4.399 789 7488 | 135.991 589 9526 | .007 353 3959 |
| **n** | $s=(1+i)^n$ | $s_{\overline{n}|}=\dfrac{(1+i)^n-1}{i}$ | $\dfrac{1}{s_{\overline{n}|}}=\dfrac{i}{(1+i)^n-1}$ |

.025
*per period*

ANNUALLY
If compounded *annually* nominal annual rate is
$2\frac{1}{2}\%$

SEMIANNUALLY
If compounded *semiannually* nominal annual rate is
5%

QUARTERLY
If compounded *quarterly* nominal annual rate is
10%

MONTHLY
If compounded *monthly* nominal annual rate is
30%

$i = .025$
$j_{(2)} = .05$
$j_{(4)} = .1$
$j_{(12)} = .3$

| PRESENT WORTH OF 1 | PRESENT WORTH OF 1 PER PERIOD | PARTIAL PAYMENT | P E R I O D S | RATE |
|---|---|---|---|---|
| *What $1 due in the future is worth today.* | *What $1 payable periodically is worth today.* | *Annuity worth $1 today.* *Periodic payment necessary to pay off a loan of $1.* | | **2½%** |
| .975 609 7561 | .975 609 7561 | 1.025 000 0000 | 1 | |
| .951 814 3962 | 1.927 424 1523 | .518 827 1605 | 2 | |
| .928 599 4109 | 2.856 023 5632 | .350 137 1672 | 3 | .025 |
| .905 950 6448 | 3.761 974 2080 | .265 817 8777 | 4 | *per period* |
| .883 854 2876 | 4.645 828 4956 | .215 246 8609 | 5 | |
| .862 296 8660 | 5.508 125 3616 | .181 549 9711 | 6 | |
| .841 265 2351 | 6.349 390 5967 | .157 495 4296 | 7 | |
| .820 746 5708 | 7.170 137 1675 | .139 467 3458 | 8 | |
| .800 728 3618 | 7.970 865 5292 | .125 456 8900 | 9 | |
| .781 198 4017 | 8.752 063 9310 | .114 258 7632 | 10 | |
| .762 144 7822 | 9.514 208 7131 | .105 105 9558 | 11 | |
| .743 555 8850 | 10.257 764 5982 | .097 487 1270 | 12 | |
| .725 420 3757 | 10.983 184 9738 | .091 048 2708 | 13 | |
| .707 727 1958 | 11.690 912 1696 | .085 536 5249 | 14 | |
| .690 465 5568 | 12.381 377 7264 | .080 766 4561 | 15 | |
| .673 624 9335 | 13.055 002 6599 | .076 598 9886 | 16 | |
| .657 195 0571 | 13.712 197 7170 | .072 927 7699 | 17 | |
| .641 165 9093 | 14.353 363 6264 | .069 670 0805 | 18 | |
| .625 527 7164 | 14.978 891 3428 | .066 760 6151 | 19 | |
| .610 270 9429 | 15.589 162 2856 | .064 147 1287 | 20 | |
| .595 386 2857 | 16.184 548 5714 | .061 787 3273 | 21 | ANNUALLY |
| .580 864 6690 | 16.765 413 2404 | .059 646 6061 | 22 | If compounded *annually* |
| .566 697 2380 | 17.332 110 4784 | .057 696 3781 | 23 | nominal annual rate is |
| .552 875 3542 | 17.884 985 8326 | .055 912 8204 | 24 | |
| .539 390 5894 | 18.424 376 4220 | .054 275 9210 | 25 | **2½%** |
| .526 234 7214 | 18.950 611 1434 | .052 768 7467 | 26 | |
| .513 399 7282 | 19.464 010 8717 | .051 376 8722 | 27 | |
| .500 877 7836 | 19.964 888 6553 | .050 087 9327 | 28 | |
| .488 661 2523 | 20.453 549 9076 | .048 891 2685 | 29 | |
| .476 742 6852 | 20.930 292 5928 | .047 777 6407 | 30 | |
| .465 114 8148 | 21.395 407 4076 | .046 739 0025 | 31 | SEMIANNUALLY |
| .453 770 5510 | 21.849 177 9586 | .045 768 3123 | 32 | If compounded *semiannually* |
| .442 702 9766 | 22.291 880 9352 | .044 859 3819 | 33 | nominal annual rate is |
| .431 905 3430 | 22.723 786 2783 | .044 006 7508 | 34 | |
| .421 371 0664 | 23.145 157 3447 | .043 205 5823 | 35 | **5%** |
| .411 093 7233 | 23.556 251 0680 | .042 451 5767 | 36 | |
| .401 067 0471 | 23.957 318 1151 | .041 740 8992 | 37 | |
| .391 284 9240 | 24.348 603 0391 | .041 070 1180 | 38 | |
| .381 741 3893 | 24.730 344 4284 | .040 436 1534 | 39 | |
| .372 430 6237 | 25.102 775 0521 | .039 836 2332 | 40 | |
| .363 346 9499 | 25.466 122 0020 | .039 267 8555 | 41 | QUARTERLY |
| .354 484 8292 | 25.820 606 8313 | .038 728 7567 | 42 | If compounded *quarterly* |
| .345 838 8578 | 26.166 445 6890 | .038 216 8833 | 43 | nominal annual rate is |
| .337 403 7637 | 26.503 849 4527 | .037 730 3683 | 44 | |
| .329 174 4036 | 26.833 023 8563 | .037 267 5106 | 45 | **10%** |
| .321 145 7596 | 27.154 169 6159 | .036 826 7568 | 46 | |
| .313 312 9362 | 27.467 482 5521 | .036 406 6855 | 47 | |
| .305 671 1573 | 27.773 153 7094 | .036 005 9938 | 48 | |
| .298 215 7632 | 28.071 369 4726 | .035 623 4847 | 49 | |
| .290 942 2080 | 28.362 311 6805 | .035 258 0569 | 50 | |
| .283 846 0566 | 28.646 157 7371 | .034 908 6956 | 51 | MONTHLY |
| .276 922 9820 | 28.923 080 7191 | .034 574 4635 | 52 | If compounded *monthly* |
| .270 168 7629 | 29.193 249 4821 | .034 254 4944 | 53 | nominal annual rate is |
| .263 579 2809 | 29.456 828 7630 | .033 947 9856 | 54 | |
| .257 150 5180 | 29.713 979 2810 | .033 654 1932 | 55 | **30%** |
| .250 878 5541 | 29.964 857 8351 | .033 372 4260 | 56 | |
| .244 759 5650 | 30.209 617 4001 | .033 102 0412 | 57 | |
| .238 789 8195 | 30.448 407 2196 | .032 842 4404 | 58 | $i = .025$ |
| .232 965 6776 | 30.681 372 8972 | .032 593 0656 | 59 | $j_{(2)} = .05$ |
| .227 283 5879 | 30.908 656 4851 | .032 353 3959 | 60 | $j_{(4)} = .1$ |
| $v^n = \dfrac{1}{(1+i)^n}$ | $a_{\overline{n}|} = \dfrac{1-v^n}{i}$ | $\dfrac{1}{a_{\overline{n}|}} = \dfrac{i}{1-v^n}$ | n | $j_{(12)} = .3$ |

| P E R I O D S | AMOUNT OF 1 *How $1 left at compound interest will grow.* | AMOUNT OF 1 PER PERIOD *How $1 deposited periodically will grow.* | SINKING FUND *Periodic deposit that will grow to $1 at future date.* |
|---|---|---|---|
| 1 | 1.030 000 0000 | 1.000 000 0000 | 1.000 000 0000 |
| 2 | 1.060 900 0000 | 2.030 000 0000 | .492 610 8374 |
| 3 | 1.092 727 0000 | 3.090 900 0000 | .323 530 3633 |
| 4 | 1.125 508 8100 | 4.183 627 0000 | .239 027 0452 |
| 5 | 1.159 274 0743 | 5.309 135 8100 | .188 354 5714 |
| 6 | 1.194 052 2965 | 6.468 409 8843 | .154 597 5005 |
| 7 | 1.229 873 8654 | 7.662 462 1808 | .130 506 3538 |
| 8 | 1.266 770 0814 | 8.892 336 0463 | .112 456 3888 |
| 9 | 1.304 773 1838 | 10.159 106 1276 | .098 433 8570 |
| 10 | 1.343 916 3793 | 11.463 879 3115 | .087 230 5066 |
| 11 | 1.384 233 8707 | 12.807 795 6908 | .078 077 4478 |
| 12 | 1.425 760 8868 | 14.192 029 5615 | .070 462 0855 |
| 13 | 1.468 533 7135 | 15.617 790 4484 | .064 029 5440 |
| 14 | 1.512 589 7249 | 17.086 324 1618 | .058 526 3390 |
| 15 | 1.557 967 4166 | 18.598 913 8867 | .053 766 5805 |
| 16 | 1.604 706 4391 | 20.156 881 3033 | .049 610 8493 |
| 17 | 1.652 847 6323 | 21.761 587 7424 | .045 952 5294 |
| 18 | 1.702 433 0612 | 23.414 435 3747 | .042 708 6959 |
| 19 | 1.753 506 0531 | 25.116 868 4359 | .039 813 8806 |
| 20 | 1.806 111 2347 | 26.870 374 4890 | .037 215 7076 |
| 21 | 1.860 294 5717 | 28.676 485 7236 | .034 871 7765 |
| 22 | 1.916 103 4089 | 30.536 780 2954 | .032 747 3948 |
| 23 | 1.973 586 5111 | 32.452 883 7042 | .030 813 9027 |
| 24 | 2.032 794 1065 | 34.426 470 2153 | .029 047 4159 |
| 25 | 2.093 777 9297 | 36.459 264 3218 | .027 427 8710 |
| 26 | 2.156 591 2675 | 38.553 042 2515 | .025 938 2903 |
| 27 | 2.221 289 0056 | 40.709 633 5190 | .024 564 2103 |
| 28 | 2.287 927 6757 | 42.930 922 5246 | .023 293 2334 |
| 29 | 2.356 565 5060 | 45.218 850 2003 | .022 114 6711 |
| 30 | 2.427 262 4712 | 47.575 415 7063 | .021 019 2593 |
| 31 | 2.500 080 3453 | 50.002 678 1775 | .019 998 9288 |
| 32 | 2.575 082 7557 | 52.502 758 5228 | .019 046 6183 |
| 33 | 2.652 335 2384 | 55.077 841 2785 | .018 156 1219 |
| 34 | 2.731 905 2955 | 57.730 176 5169 | .017 321 9633 |
| 35 | 2.813 862 4544 | 60.462 081 8124 | .016 539 2916 |
| 36 | 2.898 278 3280 | 63.275 944 2668 | .015 803 7942 |
| 37 | 2.985 226 6778 | 66.174 222 5948 | .015 111 6244 |
| 38 | 3.074 783 4782 | 69.159 449 2726 | .014 459 3401 |
| 39 | 3.167 026 9825 | 72.234 232 7508 | .013 843 8516 |
| 40 | 3.262 037 7920 | 75.401 259 7333 | .013 262 3779 |
| 41 | 3.359 898 9258 | 78.663 297 5253 | .012 712 4089 |
| 42 | 3.460 695 8935 | 82.023 196 4511 | .012 191 6731 |
| 43 | 3.564 516 7703 | 85.483 892 3446 | .011 698 1103 |
| 44 | 3.671 452 2734 | 89.048 409 1149 | .011 229 8469 |
| 45 | 3.781 595 8417 | 92.719 861 3884 | .010 785 1757 |
| 46 | 3.895 043 7169 | 96.501 457 2300 | .010 362 5378 |
| 47 | 4.011 895 0284 | 100.396 500 9469 | .009 960 5065 |
| 48 | 4.132 251 8793 | 104.408 395 9753 | .009 577 7738 |
| 49 | 4.256 219 4356 | 108.540 647 8546 | .009 213 1383 |
| 50 | 4.383 906 0187 | 112.796 867 2902 | .008 865 4944 |
| 51 | 4.515 423 1993 | 117.180 773 3089 | .008 533 8232 |
| 52 | 4.650 885 8952 | 121.696 196 5082 | .008 217 1837 |
| 53 | 4.790 412 4721 | 126.347 082 4035 | .007 914 7059 |
| 54 | 4.934 124 8463 | 131.137 494 8756 | .007 625 5841 |
| 55 | 5.082 148 5917 | 136.071 619 7218 | .007 349 0710 |
| 56 | 5.234 613 0494 | 141.153 768 3135 | .007 084 4726 |
| 57 | 5.391 651 4409 | 146.388 381 3629 | .006 831 1432 |
| 58 | 5.553 400 9841 | 151.780 032 8038 | .006 588 4819 |
| 59 | 5.720 003 0136 | 157.333 433 7879 | .006 355 9281 |
| 60 | 5.891 603 1040 | 163.053 436 8015 | .006 132 9587 |
| **n** | $s=(1+i)^n$ | $s_{\overline{n}} = \dfrac{(1+i)^n - 1}{i}$ | $\dfrac{1}{s_{\overline{n}}} = \dfrac{i}{(1+i)^n - 1}$ |

.03
*per period*

ANNUALLY
If compounded
*annually*
nominal annual rate is
**3%**

SEMIANNUALLY
If compounded
*semiannually*
nominal annual rate is
**6%**

QUARTERLY
If compounded
*quarterly*
nominal annual rate is
**12%**

MONTHLY
If compounded
*monthly*
nominal annual rate is
**36%**

$i = .03$
$j_{(2)} = .06$
$j_{(4)} = .12$
$j_{(12)} = .36$

60

| PRESENT WORTH OF 1<br>*What $1 due in the future is worth today.* | PRESENT WORTH OF 1 PER PERIOD<br>*What $1 payable periodically is worth today.* | PARTIAL PAYMENT<br>*Annuity worth $1 today.*<br>*Periodic payment necessary to pay off a loan of $1.* | PERIODS | RATE<br>**3%** |
|---|---|---|---|---|
| .970 873 7864 | .970 873 7864 | 1.030 000 0000 | 1 | |
| .942 595 9091 | 1.913 469 6955 | .522 610 8374 | 2 | |
| .915 141 6594 | 2.828 611 3549 | .353 530 3633 | 3 | .03 |
| .888 487 0479 | 3.717 098 4028 | .269 027 0452 | 4 | |
| .862 608 7844 | 4.579 707 1872 | .218 354 5714 | 5 | *per period* |
| .837 484 2567 | 5.417 191 4439 | .184 597 5005 | 6 | |
| .813 091 5113 | 6.230 282 9552 | .160 506 3538 | 7 | |
| .789 409 2343 | 7.019 692 1895 | .142 456 3888 | 8 | |
| .766 416 7323 | 7.786 108 9219 | .128 433 8570 | 9 | |
| .744 093 9149 | 8.530 202 8368 | .117 230 5066 | 10 | |
| .722 421 2766 | 9.252 624 1134 | .108 077 4478 | 11 | |
| .701 379 8802 | 9.954 003 9936 | .100 462 0855 | 12 | |
| .680 951 3400 | 10.634 955 3336 | .094 029 5440 | 13 | |
| .661 117 8058 | 11.296 073 1394 | .088 526 3390 | 14 | |
| .641 861 9474 | 11.937 935 0868 | .083 766 5805 | 15 | |
| .623 166 9392 | 12.561 102 0260 | .079 610 8493 | 16 | |
| .605 016 4458 | 13.166 118 4718 | .075 952 5294 | 17 | |
| .587 394 6076 | 13.753 513 0795 | .072 708 6959 | 18 | |
| .570 286 0268 | 14.323 799 1063 | .069 813 8806 | 19 | |
| .553 675 7542 | 14.877 474 8605 | .067 215 7076 | 20 | |
| .537 549 2759 | 15.415 024 1364 | .064 871 7765 | 21 | ANNUALLY |
| .521 892 5009 | 15.936 916 6372 | .062 747 3948 | 22 | If compounded *annually* |
| .506 691 7484 | 16.443 608 3857 | .060 813 9027 | 23 | nominal annual rate is |
| .491 933 7363 | 16.935 542 1220 | .059 047 4159 | 24 | |
| .477 605 5693 | 17.413 147 6913 | .057 427 8710 | 25 | **3%** |
| .463 694 7274 | 17.876 842 4187 | .055 938 2903 | 26 | |
| .450 189 0558 | 18.327 031 4745 | .054 564 2103 | 27 | |
| .437 076 7532 | 18.764 108 2277 | .053 293 2334 | 28 | |
| .424 346 3623 | 19.188 454 5900 | .052 114 6711 | 29 | |
| .411 986 7595 | 19.600 441 3495 | .051 019 2593 | 30 | SEMIANNUALLY |
| .399 987 1452 | 20.000 428 4946 | .049 998 9288 | 31 | If compounded *semiannually* |
| .388 337 0341 | 20.388 765 5288 | .049 046 6183 | 32 | nominal annual rate is. |
| .377 026 2467 | 20.765 791 7755 | .048 156 1219 | 33 | |
| .366 044 8997 | 21.131 836 6752 | .047 321 9633 | 34 | |
| .355 383 3978 | 21.487 220 0731 | .046 539 2916 | 35 | **6%** |
| .345 032 4251 | 21.832 252 4981 | .045 803 7942 | 36 | |
| .334 982 9369 | 22.167 235 4351 | .045 111 6244 | 37 | |
| .325 226 1524 | 22.492 461 5874 | .044 459 3401 | 38 | |
| .315 753 5460 | 22.808 215 1334 | .043 843 8516 | 39 | |
| .306 556 8408 | 23.114 771 9742 | .043 262 3779 | 40 | QUARTERLY |
| .297 628 0008 | 23.412 399 9750 | .042 712 4089 | 41 | If compounded *quarterly* |
| .288 959 2240 | 23.701 359 1990 | .042 191 6731 | 42 | nominal annual rate is |
| .280 542 9360 | 23.981 902 1349 | .041 698 1103 | 43 | |
| .272 371 7825 | 24.254 273 9174 | .041 229 8469 | 44 | |
| .264 438 6238 | 24.518 712 5412 | .040 785 1757 | 45 | **12%** |
| .256 736 5279 | 24.775 449 0691 | .040 362 5378 | 46 | |
| .249 258 7650 | 25.024 707 8341 | .039 960 5065 | 47 | |
| .241 998 8009 | 25.266 706 6350 | .039 577 7738 | 48 | |
| .234 950 2922 | 25.501 656 9272 | .039 213 1383 | 49 | |
| .228 107 0798 | 25.729 764 0070 | .038 865 4944 | 50 | MONTHLY |
| .221 463 1843 | 25.951 227 1913 | .038 533 8232 | 51 | If compounded *monthly* |
| .215 012 8003 | 26.166 239 9915 | .038 217 1837 | 52 | nominal annual rate is |
| .208 750 2915 | 26.374 990 2830 | .037 914 7059 | 53 | |
| .202 670 1859 | 26.577 660 4690 | .037 625 5841 | 54 | |
| .196 767 1708 | 26.774 427 6398 | .037 349 0710 | 55 | **36%** |
| .191 036 0882 | 26.965 463 7279 | .037 084 4726 | 56 | |
| .185 471 9303 | 27.150 935 6582 | .036 831 1432 | 57 | |
| .180 069 8352 | 27.331 005 4934 | .036 588 4819 | 58 | $i = .03$ |
| .174 825 0827 | 27.505 830 5761 | .036 355 9281 | 59 | $j_{(2)} = .06$ |
| .169 733 0900 | 27.675 563 6661 | .036 132 9587 | 60 | $j_{(4)} = .12$<br>$j_{(12)} = .36$ |
| $v^n = \dfrac{1}{(1+i)^n}$ | $a_{\overline{n}\|} = \dfrac{1-v^n}{i}$ | $\dfrac{1}{a_{\overline{n}\|}} = \dfrac{i}{1-v^n}$ | n | |

| RATE<br>3½% | P E R I O D S | AMOUNT OF 1<br>How $1 left at compound interest will grow. | AMOUNT OF<br>1 PER PERIOD<br>How $1 deposited periodically will grow. | SINKING FUND<br>Periodic deposit that will grow to $1 at future date. |
|---|---|---|---|---|
| .035<br>per period | 1<br>2<br>·3<br>4<br>5 | 1.035 000 0000<br>1.071 225 0000<br>1.108 717 8750<br>1.147 523 0006<br>1.187 686 3056 | 1.000 000 0000<br>2.035 000 0000<br>3.106 225 0000<br>4.214 942 8750<br>5.362 465 8756 | 1.000 000 0000<br>.491 400 4914<br>.321 934 1806<br>.237 251 1395<br>.186 481 3732 |
| | 6<br>7<br>8<br>9<br>10 | 1.229 255 3263<br>1.272 279 2628<br>1.316 809 0370<br>1.362 897 3533<br>1.410 598 7606 | 6.550 152 1813<br>7.779 407 5076<br>9.051 686 7704<br>10.368 495 8073<br>11.731 393 1606 | .152 668 2087<br>.128 544 4938<br>.110 476 6465<br>.096 446 0051<br>.085 241 3679 |
| | 11<br>12<br>13<br>14<br>15 | 1.459 969 7172<br>1.511 068 6573<br>1.563 956 0604<br>1.618 694 5225<br>1.675 348 8308 | 13.141 991 9212<br>14.601 961 6385<br>16.113 030 2958<br>17.676 986 3562<br>19.295 680 8786 | .076 091 9658<br>.068 483 9493<br>.062 061 5726<br>.056 570 7287<br>.051 825 0694 |
| ANNUALLY<br>If compounded<br>annually<br>nominal annual rate is<br>3½% | 16<br>17<br>18<br>19<br>20 | 1.733 986 0398<br>1.794 675 5512<br>1.857 489 1955<br>1.922 501 3174<br>1.989 788 8635 | 20.971 029 7094<br>22.705 015 7492<br>24.499 691 3004<br>26.357 180 4960<br>28.279 681 8133 | .047 684 8306<br>.044 043 1317<br>.040 816 8408<br>.037 940 3252<br>.035 361 0768 |
| | 21<br>22<br>23<br>24<br>25 | 2.059 431 4737<br>2.131 511 5753<br>2.206 114 4804<br>2.283 328 4872<br>2.363 244 9843 | 30.269 470 6768<br>32.328 902 1505<br>34.460 413 7257<br>36.666 528 2061<br>38.949 856 6933 | .033 036 5870<br>.030 932 0742<br>.029 018 8042<br>.027 272 8303<br>.025 674 0354 |
| SEMIANNUALLY<br>If compounded<br>semiannually<br>nominal annual rate is<br>7% | 26<br>27<br>28<br>29<br>30 | 2.445 958 5587<br>2.531 567 1083<br>2.620 171 9571<br>2.711 877 9756<br>2.806 793 7047 | 41.313 101 6776<br>43.759 060 2363<br>46.290 627 3446<br>48.910 799 3017<br>51.622 677 2772 | .024 205 3963<br>.022 852 4103<br>.021 602 6452<br>.020 445 3825<br>.019 371 3316 |
| | 31<br>32<br>33<br>34<br>35 | 2.905 031 4844<br>3.006 707 5863<br>3.111 942 3518<br>3.220 860 3342<br>3.333 590 4459 | 54.429 470 9819<br>57.334 502 4663<br>60.341 210 0526<br>63.453 152 4044<br>66.674 012 7386 | .018 372 3998<br>.017 441 5048<br>.016 572 4221<br>.015 759 6583<br>.014 998 3473 |
| QUARTERLY<br>If compounded<br>quarterly<br>nominal annual rate is<br>14% | 36<br>37<br>38<br>39<br>40 | 3.450 266 1115<br>3.571 025 4254<br>3.696 011 3152<br>3.825 371 7113<br>3.959 259 7212 | 70.007 603 1845<br>73.457 869 2959<br>77.028 894 7213<br>80.724 906 0365<br>84.550 277 7478 | .014 284 1628<br>.013 613 2454<br>.012 982 1414<br>.012 387 7506<br>.011 827 2823 |
| | 41<br>42<br>43<br>44<br>45 | 4.097 833 8114<br>4.241 257 9948<br>4.389 702 0246<br>4.543 341 5955<br>4.702 358 5513 | 88.509 537 4690<br>92.607 371 2804<br>96.848 629 2752<br>101.238 331 2998<br>105.781 672 8953 | .011 298 2174<br>.010 798 2765<br>.010 325 3914<br>.009 877 6816<br>.009 453 4334 |
| | 46<br>47<br>48<br>49<br>50 | 4.866 941 1006<br>5.037 284 0392<br>5.213 588 9805<br>5.396 064 5948<br>5.584 926 8557 | 110.484 031 4467<br>115.350 972 5473<br>120.388 256 5864<br>125.601 845 5670<br>130.997 910 1618 | .009 051 0817<br>.008 669 1944<br>.008 306 4580<br>.007 961 6665<br>.007 633 7096 |
| MONTHLY<br>If compounded<br>monthly<br>nominal annual rate is<br>42% | 51<br>52<br>53<br>54<br>55 | 5.780 399 2956<br>5.982 713 2710<br>6.192 108 2354<br>6.408 832 0237<br>6.633 141 1445 | 136.582 837 0175<br>142.363 236 3131<br>148.345 949 5840<br>154.538 057 8195<br>160.946 889 8432 | .007 321 5641<br>.007 024 2854<br>.006 740 9997<br>.006 470 8979<br>.006 213 2297 |
| i = .035<br>j(2) = .07<br>j(4) = .14<br>j(12) = .42 | 56<br>57<br>58<br>59<br>60 | 6.865 301 0846<br>7.105 586 6225<br>7.354 282 1543<br>7.611 682 0297<br>7.878 090 9008 | 167.580 030 9877<br>174.445 332 0722<br>181.550 918 6948<br>188.905 200 8491<br>196.516 882 8788 | .005 967 2981<br>.005 732 4549<br>.005 508 0966<br>.005 293 6605<br>.005 088 6213 |
| | n | $s=(1+i)^n$ | $s_{\overline{n}|}=\dfrac{(1+i)^n-1}{i}$ | $\dfrac{1}{s_{\overline{n}|}}=\dfrac{i}{(1+i)^n-1}$ |

| PRESENT WORTH OF 1<br>*What $1 due in the future is worth today.* | PRESENT WORTH OF 1 PER PERIOD<br>*What $1 payable periodically is worth today.* | PARTIAL PAYMENT<br>*Annuity worth $1 today.*<br>*Periodic payment necessary to pay off a loan of $1.* | PERIODS | RATE<br>**3½%** |
|---|---|---|---|---|
| .966 183 5749 | .966 183 5749 | 1.035 000 0000 | 1 | |
| .933 510 7004 | 1.899 694 2752 | .526 400 4914 | 2 | |
| .901 942 7057 | 2.801 636 9809 | .356 934 1806 | 3 | .035 |
| .871 442 2277 | 3.673 079 2086 | .272 251 1395 | 4 | |
| .841 973 1669 | 4.515 052 3755 | .221 481 3732 | 5 | *per period* |
| .813 500 6443 | 5.328 553 0198 | .187 668 2087 | 6 | |
| .785 990 9607 | 6.114 543 9805 | .163 544 4938 | 7 | |
| .759 411 5562 | 6.873 955 5367 | .145 476 6465 | 8 | |
| .733 730 9722 | 7.607 686 5089 | .131 446 0051 | 9 | |
| .708 918 8137 | 8.316 605 3226 | .120 241 3679 | 10 | |
| .684 945 7137 | 9.001 551 0363 | .111 091 9658 | 11 | |
| .661 783 2983 | 9.663 334 3346 | .103 483 9493 | 12 | |
| .639 404 1529 | 10.302 738 4875 | .097 061 5726 | 13 | |
| .617 781 7903 | 10.920 520 2778 | .091 570 7287 | 14 | |
| .596 890 6186 | 11.517 410 8964 | .086 825 0694 | 15 | |
| .576 705 9117 | 12.094 116 8081 | .082 684 8306 | 16 | |
| .557 203 7794 | 12.651 320 5876 | .079 043 1317 | 17 | |
| .538 361 1396 | 13.189 681 7271 | .075 816 8408 | 18 | |
| .520 155 6904 | 13.709 837 4175 | .072 940 3252 | 19 | |
| .502 565 8844 | 14.212 403 3020 | .070 361 0768 | 20 | ANNUALLY<br>If compounded<br>*annually*<br>nominal annual rate is |
| .485 570 9028 | 14.697 974 2048 | .068 036 5870 | 21 | |
| .469 150 6308 | 15.167 124 8355 | .065 932 0742 | 22 | |
| .453 285 6336 | 15.620 410 4691 | .064 018 8042 | 23 | |
| .437 957 1339 | 16.058 367 6030 | .062 272 8303 | 24 | |
| .423 146 9893 | 16.481 514 5923 | .060 674 0354 | 25 | **3½%** |
| .408 837 6708 | 16.890 352 2631 | .059 205 3963 | 26 | |
| .395 012 2423 | 17.285 364 5054 | .057 852 4103 | 27 | |
| .381 654 3404 | 17.667 018 8458 | .056 602 6452 | 28 | |
| .368 748 1550 | 18.035 767 0008 | .055 445 3825 | 29 | |
| .356 278 4106 | 18.392 045 4114 | .054 371 3316 | 30 | SEMIANNUALLY<br>If compounded<br>*semiannually*<br>nominal annual rate is |
| .344 230 3484 | 18.736 275 7598 | .053 372 3998 | 31 | |
| .332 589 7086 | 19.068 865 4684 | .052 441 5048 | 32 | |
| .321 342 7136 | 19.390 208 1820 | .051 572 4221 | 33 | |
| .310 476 0518 | 19.700 684 2338 | .050 759 6583 | 34 | |
| .299 976 8617 | 20.000 661 0955 | .049 998 3473 | 35 | **7%** |
| .289 832 7166 | 20.290 493 8121 | .049 284 1628 | 36 | |
| .280 031 6102 | 20.570 525 4223 | .048 613 2454 | 37 | |
| .270 561 9422 | 20.841 087 3645 | .047 982 1414 | 38 | |
| .261 412 5046 | 21.102 499 8691 | .047 387 7506 | 39 | |
| .252 572 4682 | 21.355 072 3373 | .046 827 2823 | 40 | QUARTERLY<br>If compounded<br>*quarterly*<br>nominal annual rate is |
| .244 031 3702 | 21.599 103 7075 | .046 298 2174 | 41 | |
| .235 779 1017 | 21.834 882 8092 | .045 798 2765 | 42 | |
| .227 805 8953 | 22.062 688 7046 | .045 325 3914 | 43 | |
| .220 102 3143 | 22.282 791 0189 | .044 877 6816 | 44 | |
| .212 659 2409 | 22.495 450 2598 | .044 453 4334 | 45 | **14%** |
| .205 467 8656 | 22.700 918 1254 | .044 051 0817 | 46 | |
| .198 519 6769 | 22.899 437 8023 | .043 669 1944 | 47 | |
| .191 806 4511 | 23.091 244 2535 | .043 306 4580 | 48 | |
| .185 320 2426 | 23.276 564 4961 | .042 961 6665 | 49 | |
| .179 053 3745 | 23.455 617 8706 | .042 633 7096 | 50 | MONTHLY<br>If compounded<br>*monthly*<br>nominal annual rate is |
| .172 998 4295 | 23.628 616 3001 | .042 321 5641 | 51 | |
| .167 148 2411 | 23.795 764 5412 | .042 024 2854 | 52 | |
| .161 495 8851 | 23.957 260 4263 | .041 740 9997 | 53 | |
| .156 034 6716 | 24.113 295 0978 | .041 470 8979 | 54 | |
| .150 758 1368 | 24.264 053 2346 | .041 213 2297 | 55 | **42%** |
| .145 660 0355 | 24.409 713 2702 | .040 967 2981 | 56 | |
| .140 734 3339 | 24.550 447 6040 | .040 732 4549 | 57 | |
| .135 975 2018 | 24.686 422 8058 | .040 508 0966 | 58 | $i \ \ = .035$ |
| .131 377 0066 | 24.817 799 8124 | .040 293 6605 | 59 | $j_{(2)} = .07$ |
| .126 934 3059 | 24.944 734 1182 | .040 088 6213 | 60 | $j_{(4)} = .14$<br>$j_{(12)} = .42$ |
| $v^n = \dfrac{1}{(1+i)^n}$ | $a_{\overline{n}|} = \dfrac{1-v^n}{i}$ | $\dfrac{1}{a_{\overline{n}|}} = \dfrac{i}{1-v^n}$ | n | |

63

| P E R I O D S | AMOUNT OF 1<br>*How $1 left at compound interest will grow.* | AMOUNT OF 1 PER PERIOD<br>*How $1 deposited periodically will grow.* | SINKING FUND<br>*Periodic deposit that will grow to $1 at future date.* |
|---|---|---|---|
| 1 | 1.040 000 0000 | 1.000 000 0000 | 1.000 000 0000 |
| 2 | 1.081 600 0000 | 2.040 000 0000 | .490 196 0784 |
| 3 | 1.124 864 0000 | 3.121 600 0000 | .320 348 5392 |
| 4 | 1.169 858 5600 | 4.246 464 0000 | .235 490 0454 |
| 5 | 1.216 652 9024 | 5.416 322 5600 | .184 627 1135 |
| 6 | 1.265 319 0185 | 6.632 975 4624 | .150 761 9025 |
| 7 | 1.315 931 7792 | 7.898 294 4809 | .126 609 6120 |
| 8 | 1.368 569 0504 | 9.214 226 2601 | .108 527 8320 |
| 9 | 1.423 311 8124 | 10.582 795 3105 | .094 492 9927 |
| 10 | 1.480 244 2849 | 12.006 107 1230 | .083 290 9443 |
| 11 | 1.539 454 0563 | 13.486 351 4079 | .074 149 0393 |
| 12 | 1.601 032 2186 | 15.025 805 4642 | .066 552 1727 |
| 13 | 1.665 073 5073 | 16.626 837 6828 | .060 143 7278 |
| 14 | 1.731 676 4476 | 18.291 911 1901 | .054 668 9731 |
| 15 | 1.800 943 5055 | 20.023 587 6377 | .049 941 1004 |
| 16 | 1.872 981 2457 | 21.824 531 1432 | .045 819 9992 |
| 17 | 1.947 900 4956 | 23.697 512 3889 | .042 198 5221 |
| 18 | 2.025 816 5154 | 25.645 412 8845 | .038 993 3281 |
| 19 | 2.106 849 1760 | 27.671 229 3998 | .036 138 6184 |
| 20 | 2.191 123 1430 | 29.778 078 5758 | .033 581 7503 |
| 21 | 2.278 768 0688 | 31.969 201 7189 | .031 280 1054 |
| 22 | 2.369 918 7915 | 34.247 969 7876 | .029 198 8111 |
| 23 | 2.464 715 5432 | 36.617 888 5791 | .027 309 0568 |
| 24 | 2.563 304 1649 | 39.082 604 1223 | .025 586 8313 |
| 25 | 2.665 836 3315 | 41.645 908 2872 | .024 011 9628 |
| 26 | 2.772 469 7847 | 44.311 744 6187 | .022 567 3805 |
| 27 | 2.883 368 5761 | 47.084 214 4034 | .021 238 5406 |
| 28 | 2.998 703 3192 | 49.967 582 9796 | .020 012 9752 |
| 29 | 3.118 651 4519 | 52.966 286 2987 | .018 879 9342 |
| 30 | 3.243 397 5100 | 56.084 937 7507 | .017 830 0991 |
| 31 | 3.373 133 4104 | 59.328 335 2607 | .016 855 3524 |
| 32 | 3.508 058 7468 | 62.701 468 6711 | .015 948 5897 |
| 33 | 3.648 381 0967 | 66.209 527 4180 | .015 103 5665 |
| 34 | 3.794 316 3406 | 69.857 908 5147 | .014 314 7715 |
| 35 | 3.946 088 9942 | 73.652 224 8553 | .013 577 3224 |
| 36 | 4.103 932 5540 | 77.598 313 8495 | .012 886 8780 |
| 37 | 4.268 089 8561 | 81.702 246 4035 | .012 239 5655 |
| 38 | 4.438 813 4504 | 85.970 336 2596 | .011 631 9191 |
| 39 | 4.616 365 9884 | 90.409 149 7100 | .011 060 8274 |
| 40 | 4.801 020 6279 | 95.025 515 6984 | .010 523 4893 |
| 41 | 4.993 061 4531 | 99.826 536 3264 | .010 017 3765 |
| 42 | 5.192 783 9112 | 104.819 597 7794 | .009 540 2007 |
| 43 | 5.400 495 2676 | 110.012 381 6906 | .009 089 8859 |
| 44 | 5.616 515 0783 | 115.412 876 9582 | .008 664 5444 |
| 45 | 5.841 175 6815 | 121.029 392 0365 | .008 262 4558 |
| 46 | 6.074 822 7087 | 126.870 567 7180 | .007 882 0488 |
| 47 | 6.317 815 6171 | 132.945 390 4267 | .007 521 8855 |
| 48 | 6.570 528 2418 | 139.263 206 0438 | .007 180 6476 |
| 49 | 6.833 349 3714 | 145.833 734 2855 | .006 857 1240 |
| 50 | 7.106 683 3463 | 152.667 083 6570 | .006 550 2004 |
| 51 | 7.390 950 6801 | 159.773 767 0032 | .006 258 8497 |
| 52 | 7.686 588 7073 | 167.164 717 6834 | .005 982 1236 |
| 53 | 7.994 052 2556 | 174.851 306 3907 | .005 719 1451 |
| 54 | 8.313 814 3459 | 182.845 358 6463 | .005 469 1025 |
| 55 | 8.646 366 9197 | 191.159 172 9922 | .005 231 2426 |
| 56 | 8.992 221 5965 | 199.805 539 9119 | .005 004 8662 |
| 57 | 9.351 910 4603 | 208.797 761 5083 | .004 789 3234 |
| 58 | 9.725 986 8787 | 218.149 671 9687 | .004 584 0087 |
| 59 | 10.115 026 3539 | 227.875 658 8474 | .004 388 3581 |
| 60 | 10.519 627 4081 | 237.990 685 2013 | .004 201 8451 |
| n | $s=(1+i)^n$ | $s_{\overline{n}|}=\dfrac{(1+i)^n-1}{i}$ | $\dfrac{1}{s_{\overline{n}|}}=\dfrac{i}{(1+i)^n-1}$ |

.04
*per period*

ANNUALLY
If compounded
*annually*
nominal annual rate is

4%

SEMIANNUALLY
If compounded
*semiannually*
nominal annual rate is

8%

QUARTERLY
If compounded
*quarterly*
nominal annual rate is

16%

MONTHLY
If compounded
*monthly*
nominal annual rate is

48%

$i = .04$
$j_{(2)} = .08$
$j_{(4)} = .16$
$j_{(12)} = .48$

| PRESENT WORTH OF 1  *What $1 due in the future is worth today.* | PRESENT WORTH OF 1 PER PERIOD  *What $1 payable periodically is worth today.* | PARTIAL PAYMENT  *Annuity worth $1 today.*  Periodic payment necessary to pay off a loan of $1. | P E R I O D S | RATE  **4%** |
|---|---|---|---|---|
| .961 538 4615 | .961 538 4615 | 1.040 000 0000 | 1 | |
| .924 556 2130 | 1.886 094 6746 | .530 196 0784 | 2 | |
| .888 996 3587 | 2.775 091 0332 | .360 348 5392 | 3 | .04 |
| .854 804 1910 | 3.629 895 2243 | .275 490 0454 | 4 | |
| .821 927 1068 | 4.451 822 3310 | .224 627 1135 | 5 | *per period* |
| .790 314 5257 | 5.242 136 8567 | .190 761 9025 | 6 | |
| .759 917 8132 | 6.002 054 6699 | .166 609 6120 | 7 | |
| .730 690 2050 | 6.732 744 8750 | .148 527 8320 | 8 | |
| .702 586 7356 | 7.435 331 6105 | .134 492 9927 | 9 | |
| .675 564 1688 | 8.110 895 7794 | .123 290 9443 | 10 | |
| .649 580 9316 | 8.760 476 7109 | .114 149 0393 | 11 | |
| .624 597 0496 | 9.385 073 7605 | .106 552 1727 | 12 | |
| .600 574 0861 | 9.985 647 8466 | .100 143 7278 | 13 | |
| .577 475 0828 | 10.563 122 9295 | .094 668 9731 | 14 | |
| .555 264 5027 | 11.118 387 4322 | .089 941 1004 | 15 | |
| .533 908 1757 | 11.652 295 6079 | .085 819 9992 | 16 | |
| .513 373 2459 | 12.165 668 8537 | .082 198 5221 | 17 | |
| .493 628 1210 | 12.659 296 9747 | .078 993 3281 | 18 | |
| .474 642 4240 | 13.133 939 3988 | .076 138 6184 | 19 | |
| .456 386 9462 | 13.590 326 3450 | .073 581 7503 | 20 | |
| .438 833 6021 | 14.029 159 9471 | .071 280 1054 | 21 | ANNUALLY  If compounded *annually* nominal annual rate is |
| .421 955 3867 | 14.451 115 3337 | .069 198 8111 | 22 | |
| .405 726 3333 | 14.856 841 6671 | .067 309 0568 | 23 | |
| .390 121 4743 | 15.246 963 1414 | .065 586 8313 | 24 | |
| .375 116 8023 | 15.622 079 9437 | .064 011 9628 | 25 | **4%** |
| .360 689 2329 | 15.982 769 1766 | .062 567 3805 | 26 | |
| .346 816 5701 | 16.329 585 7467 | .061 238 5406 | 27 | |
| .333 477 4713 | 16.663 063 2180 | .060 012 9752 | 28 | |
| .320 651 4147 | 16.983 714 6327 | .058 879 9342 | 29 | |
| .308 318 6680 | 17.292 033 3007 | .057 830 0991 | 30 | SEMIANNUALLY  If compounded *semiannually* nominal annual rate is |
| .296 460 2577 | 17.588 493 5583 | .056 855 3524 | 31 | |
| .285 057 9401 | 17.873 551 4984 | .055 948 5897 | 32 | |
| .274 094 1731 | 18.147 645 6715 | .055 103 5665 | 33 | |
| .263 552 0896 | 18.411 197 7611 | .054 314 7715 | 34 | |
| .253 415 4707 | 18.664 613 2318 | .053 577 3224 | 35 | **8%** |
| .243 668 7219 | 18.908 281 9537 | .052 886 8780 | 36 | |
| .234 296 8479 | 19.142 578 8016 | .052 239 5655 | 37 | |
| .225 285 4307 | 19.367 864 2323 | .051 631 9191 | 38 | |
| .216 620 6064 | 19.584 484 8388 | .051 060 8274 | 39 | |
| .208 289 0447 | 19.792 773 8834 | .050 523 4893 | 40 | QUARTERLY  If compounded *quarterly* nominal annual rate is |
| .200 277 9276 | 19.993 051 8110 | .050 017 3765 | 41 | |
| .192 574 9303 | 20.185 626 7413 | .049 540 2007 | 42 | |
| .185 168 2023 | 20.370 794 9436 | .049 089 8859 | 43 | |
| .178 046 3483 | 20.548 841 2919 | .048 664 5444 | 44 | |
| .171 198 4118 | 20.720 039 7038 | .048 262 4558 | 45 | **16%** |
| .164 613 8575 | 20.884 653 5613 | .047 882 0488 | 46 | |
| .158 282 5553 | 21.042 936 1166 | .047 521 8855 | 47 | |
| .152 194 7647 | 21.195 130 8814 | .047 180 6476 | 48 | |
| .146 341 1199 | 21.341 472 0013 | .046 857 1240 | 49 | |
| .140 712 6153 | 21.482 184 6167 | .046 550 2004 | 50 | MONTHLY  If compounded *monthly* nominal annual rate is |
| .135 300 5917 | 21.617 485 2083 | .046 258 8497 | 51 | |
| .130 096 7228 | 21.747 581 9311 | .045 982 1236 | 52 | |
| .125 093 0027 | 21.872 674 9337 | .045 719 1451 | 53 | |
| .120 281 7333 | 21.992 956 6671 | .045 469 1025 | 54 | |
| .115 655 5128 | 22.108 612 1799 | .045 231 2426 | 55 | **48%** |
| .111 207 2239 | 22.219 819 4037 | .045 004 8662 | 56 | |
| .106 930 0229 | 22.326 749 4267 | .044 789 3234 | 57 | $i \quad = .04$ |
| .102 817 3297 | 22.429 566 7564 | .044 584 0087 | 58 | $j_{(2)} = .08$ |
| .098 862 8171 | 22.528 429 5735 | .044 388 3581 | 59 | $j_{(4)} = .16$ |
| .095 060 4010 | 22.623 489 9745 | .044 201 8451 | 60 | $j_{(12)} = .48$ |
| $v^n = \dfrac{1}{(1+i)^n}$ | $a_{\overline{n}|} = \dfrac{1-v^n}{i}$ | $\dfrac{1}{a_{\overline{n}|}} = \dfrac{i}{1-v^n}$ | n | |

| P E R I O D S | AMOUNT OF 1<br>*How $1 left at compound interest will grow.* | AMOUNT OF 1 PER PERIOD<br>*How $1 deposited periodically will grow.* | SINKING FUND<br>*Periodic deposit that will grow to $1 at future date.* |
|---|---|---|---|
| 1 | 1.050 000 0000 | 1.000 000 0000 | 1.000 000 0000 |
| 2 | 1.102 500 0000 | 2.050 000 0000 | .487 804 8780 |
| 3 | 1.157 625 0000 | 3.152 500 0000 | .317 208 5646 |
| 4 | 1.215 506 2500 | 4.310 125 0000 | .232 011 8326 |
| 5 | 1.276 281 5625 | 5.525 631 2500 | .180 974 7981 |
| 6 | 1.340 095 6406 | 6.801 912 8125 | .147 017 4681 |
| 7 | 1.407 100 4227 | 8.142 008 4531 | .122 819 8184 |
| 8 | 1.477 455 4438 | 9.549 108 8758 | .104 721 8136 |
| 9 | 1.551 328 2160 | 11.026 564 3196 | .090 690 0800 |
| 10 | 1.628 894 6268 | 12.577 892 5355 | .079 504 5750 |
| 11 | 1.710 339 3581 | 14.206 787 1623 | .070 388 8915 |
| 12 | 1.795 856 3260 | 15.917 126 5204 | .062 825 4100 |
| 13 | 1.885 649 1423 | 17.712 982 8465 | .056 455 7652 |
| 14 | 1.979 931 5994 | 19.598 631 9888 | .051 023 9695 |
| 15 | 2.078 928 1794 | 21.578 563 5882 | .046 342 2876 |
| 16 | 2.182 874 5884 | 23.657 491 7676 | .042 269 9080 |
| 17 | 2.292 018 3178 | 25.840 366 3560 | .038 699 1417 |
| 18 | 2.406 619 2337 | 28.132 384 6738 | .035 546 2223 |
| 19 | 2.526 950 1954 | 30.539 003 9075 | .032 745 0104 |
| 20 | 2.653 297 7051 | 33.065 954 1029 | .030 242 5872 |
| 21 | 2.785 962 5904 | 35.719 251 8080 | .027 996 1071 |
| 22 | 2.925 260 7199 | 38.505 214 3984 | .025 970 5086 |
| 23 | 3.071 523 7559 | 41.430 475 1184 | .024 136 8219 |
| 24 | 3.225 099 9437 | 44.501 998 8743 | .022 470 9008 |
| 25 | 3.386 354 9409 | 47.727 098 8180 | .020 952 4573 |
| 26 | 3.555 672 6879 | 51.113 453 7589 | .019 564 3207 |
| 27 | 3.733 456 3223 | 54.669 126 4468 | .018 291 8599 |
| 28 | 3.920 129 1385 | 58.402 582 7692 | .017 122 5304 |
| 29 | 4.116 135 5954 | 62.322 711 9076 | .016 045 5149 |
| 30 | 4.321 942 3752 | 66.438 847 5030 | .015 051 4351 |
| 31 | 4.538 039 4939 | 70.760 789 8782 | .014 132 1204 |
| 32 | 4.764 941 4686 | 75.298 829 3721 | .013 280 4189 |
| 33 | 5.003 188 5420 | 80.063 770 8407 | .012 490 0437 |
| 34 | 5.253 347 9691 | 85.066 959 3827 | .011 755 4454 |
| 35 | 5.516 015 3676 | 90.320 307 3518 | .011 071 7072 |
| 36 | 5.791 816 1360 | 95.836 322 7194 | .010 434 4571 |
| 37 | 6.081 406 9428 | 101.628 138 8554 | .009 839 7945 |
| 38 | 6.385 477 2899 | 107.709 545 7982 | .009 284 2282 |
| 39 | 6.704 751 1544 | 114.095 023 0881 | .008 764 6242 |
| 40 | 7.039 988 7121 | 120.799 774 2425 | .008 278 1612 |
| 41 | 7.391 988 1477 | 127.839 762 9546 | .007 822 2924 |
| 42 | 7.761 587 5551 | 155.231 751 1023 | .007 394 7131 |
| 43 | 8.149 666 9329 | 142.993 338 6575 | .006 993 3328 |
| 44 | 8.557 150 2795 | 151.143 005 5903 | .006 616 2506 |
| 45 | 8.985 007 7935 | 159.700 155 8699 | .006 261 7347 |
| 46 | 9.434 258 1832 | 168.685 163 6633 | .005 928 2036 |
| 47 | 9.905 971 0923 | 178.119 421 8465 | .005 614 2109 |
| 48 | 10.401 269 6469 | 188.025 392 9388 | .005 318 4306 |
| 49 | 10.921 333 1293 | 198.426 662 5858 | .005 039 6453 |
| 50 | 11.467 399 7858 | 209.347 995 7151 | .004 776 7355 |
| 51 | 12.040 769 7750 | 220.815 395 5008 | .004 528 6697 |
| 52 | 12.642 808 2638 | 232.856 165 2759 | .004 294 4966 |
| 53 | 13.274 948 6770 | 245.498 973 5397 | .004 073 3368 |
| 54 | 13.938 696 1108 | 258.773 922 2166 | .003 864 3770 |
| 55 | 14.635 630 9164 | 272.712 618 3275 | .003 666 8637 |
| 56 | 15.367 412 4622 | 287.348 249 2439 | .003 480 0978 |
| 57 | 16.135 783 0853 | 302.715 661 7060 | .003 303 4300 |
| 58 | 16.942 572 2396 | 318.851 444 7913 | .003 136 2568 |
| 59 | 17.789 700 8515 | 335.794 017 0309 | .002 978 0161 |
| 60 | 18.679 185 8941 | 353.583 717 8825 | .002 828 1845 |
| **n** | $s=(1+i)^n$ | $s_{\overline{n}|}=\dfrac{(1+i)^n-1}{i}$ | $\dfrac{1}{s_{\overline{n}|}}=\dfrac{i}{(1+i)^n-1}$ |

.05

*per period*

ANNUALLY
If compounded
*annually*
nominal annual rate is

5%

SEMIANNUALLY
If compounded
*semiannually*
nominal annual rate is

10%

QUARTERLY
If compounded
*quarterly*
nominal annual rate is

20%

MONTHLY
If compounded
*monthly*
nominal annual rate is

60%

$i\ \ = .05$
$j_{(2)} = .1$
$j_{(4)} = .2$
$j_{(12)} = .6$

| PRESENT WORTH OF 1 | PRESENT WORTH OF 1 PER PERIOD | PARTIAL PAYMENT | PERIODS | RATE |
|---|---|---|---|---|
| *What $1 due in the future is worth today.* | *What $1 payable periodically is worth today.* | *Annuity worth $1 today.*<br>*Periodic payment necessary to pay off a loan of $1.* | | **5%** |
| .952 380 9524 | .952 380 9524 | 1.050 000 0000 | 1 | |
| .907 029 4785 | 1.859 410 4308 | .537 804 8780 | 2 | |
| .863 837 5985 | 2.723 248 0294 | .367 208 5646 | 3 | .05 |
| .822 702 4748 | 3.545 950 5042 | .282 011 8326 | 4 | *per period* |
| .783 526 1665 | 4.329 476 6706 | .230 974 7981 | 5 | |
| .746 215 3966 | 5.075 692 0673 | .197 017 4681 | 6 | |
| .710 681 3301 | 5.786 373 3974 | .172 819 8184 | 7 | |
| .676 839 3620 | 6.463 212 7594 | .154 721 8136 | 8 | |
| .644 608 9162 | 7.107 821 6756 | .140 690 0800 | 9 | |
| .613 913 2535 | 7.721 734 9292 | .129 504 5750 | 10 | |
| .584 679 2891 | 8.306 414 2183 | .120 388 8915 | 11 | |
| .556 837 4182 | 8.863 251 6364 | .112 825 4100 | 12 | |
| .530 321 3506 | 9.393 572 9871 | .106 455 7652 | 13 | |
| .505 067 9530 | 9.898 640 9401 | .101 023 9695 | 14 | |
| .481 017 0981 | 10.379 658 0382 | .096 342 2876 | 15 | |
| .458 111 5220 | 10.837 769 5602 | .092 269 9080 | 16 | |
| .436 296 6876 | 11.274 066 2478 | .088 699 1417 | 17 | |
| .415 520 6549 | 11.689 586 9027 | .085 546 2223 | 18 | |
| .395 733 9570 | 12.085 320 8597 | .082 745 0104 | 19 | |
| .376 889 4829 | 12.462 210 3425 | .080 242 5872 | 20 | ANNUALLY |
| .358 942 3646 | 12.821 152 7072 | .077 996 1071 | 21 | If compounded *annually* nominal annual rate is |
| .341 849 8711 | 13.163 002 5783 | .075 970 5086 | 22 | |
| .325 571 3058 | 13.488 573 8841 | .074 136 8219 | 23 | |
| .310 067 9103 | 13.798 641 7943 | .072 470 9008 | 24 | |
| .295 302 7717 | 14.093 944 5660 | .070 952 4573 | 25 | **5%** |
| .281 240 7350 | 14.375 185 3010 | .069 564 3207 | 26 | |
| .267 848 3190 | 14.643 033 6200 | .068 291 8599 | 27 | |
| .255 093 6371 | 14.898 127 2571 | .067 122 5304 | 28 | |
| .242 946 3211 | 15.141 073 5782 | .066 045 5149 | 29 | |
| .231 377 4487 | 15.372 451 0269 | .065 051 4351 | 30 | SEMIANNUALLY |
| .220 359 4749 | 15.592 810 5018 | .064 132 1204 | 31 | If compounded *semiannually* nominal annual rate is |
| .209 866 1666 | 15.802 676 6684 | .063 280 4189 | 32 | |
| .199 872 5396 | 16.002 549 2080 | .062 490 0437 | 33 | |
| .190 354 7996 | 16.192 904 0076 | .061 755 4454 | 34 | |
| .181 290 2854 | 16.374 194 2929 | .061 071 7072 | 35 | **10%** |
| .172 657 4146 | 16.546 851 7076 | .060 434 4571 | 36 | |
| .164 435 6330 | 16.711 287 3405 | .059 839 7945 | 37 | |
| .156 605 3647 | 16.867 892 7053 | .059 284 2282 | 38 | |
| .149 147 9664 | 17.017 040 6717 | .058 764 6242 | 39 | |
| .142 045 6823 | 17.159 086 3540 | .058 278 1612 | 40 | QUARTERLY |
| .135 281 6022 | 17.294 367 9562 | .057 822 2924 | 41 | If compounded *quarterly* nominal annual rate is |
| .128 839 6211 | 17.423 207 5773 | .057 394 7131 | 42 | |
| .122 704 4011 | 17.545 911 9784 | .056 993 3328 | 43 | |
| .116 861 3344 | 17.662 773 3128 | .056 616 2506 | 44 | |
| .111 296 5089 | 17.774 069 8217 | .056 261 7347 | 45 | **20%** |
| .105 996 6752 | 17.880 066 4968 | .055 928 2036 | 46 | |
| .100 949 2144 | 17.981 015 7113 | .055 614 2109 | 47 | |
| .096 142 1090 | 18.077 157 8203 | .055 318 4306 | 48 | |
| .091 563 9133 | 18.168 721 7336 | .055 039 6453 | 49 | |
| .087 203 7270 | 18.255 925 4606 | .054 776 7355 | 50 | MONTHLY |
| .083 051 1685 | 18.338 976 6291 | .054 528 6697 | 51 | If compounded *monthly* nominal annual rate is |
| .079 096 3510 | 18.418 072 9801 | .054 294 4966 | 52 | |
| .075 329 8581 | 18.493 402 8382 | .054 073 3368 | 53 | |
| .071 742 7220 | 18.565 145 5602 | .053 864 3770 | 54 | |
| .068 326 4019 | 18.633 471 9621 | .053 666 8637 | 55 | **60%** |
| .065 072 7637 | 18.698 544 7258 | .053 480 0978 | 56 | |
| .061 974 0607 | 18.760 518 7865 | .053 303 4300 | 57 | |
| .059 022 9149 | 18.819 541 7014 | .053 136 2568 | 58 | $i = .05$ |
| .056 212 2999 | 18.875 754 0013 | .052 978 0161 | 59 | $j_{(2)} = .1$ |
| .053 535 5237 | 18.929 289 5251 | .052 828 1845 | 60 | $j_{(4)} = .2$<br>$j_{(12)} = .6$ |
| $v^n = \dfrac{1}{(1+i)^n}$ | $a_{\overline{n}\|} = \dfrac{1-v^n}{i}$ | $\dfrac{1}{a_{\overline{n}\|}} = \dfrac{i}{1-v^n}$ | **n** | |

67

| P E R I O D S | AMOUNT OF 1<br>*How $1 left at compound interest will grow.* | AMOUNT OF 1 PER PERIOD<br>*How $1 deposited periodically will grow.* | SINKING FUND<br>*Periodic deposit that will grow to $1 at future date.* |
|---|---|---|---|
| 1 | 1.060 000 0000 | 1.000 000 0000 | 1.000 000 0000 |
| 2 | 1.123 600 0000 | 2.060 000 0000 | .485 436 8932 |
| 3 | 1.191 016 0000 | 3.183 600 0000 | .314 109 8128 |
| 4 | 1.262 476 9600 | 4.374 616 0000 | .228 591 4924 |
| 5 | 1.338 225 5776 | 5.637 092 9600 | .177 396 4004 |
| 6 | 1.418 519 1123 | 6.975 318 5376 | .143 362 6285 |
| 7 | 1.503 630 2590 | 8.393 837 6499 | .119 135 0181 |
| 8 | 1.593 848 0745 | 9.897 467 9088 | .101 035 9426 |
| 9 | 1.689 478 9590 | 11.491 315 9834 | .087 022 2350 |
| 10 | 1.790 847 6965 | 13.180 794 9424 | .075 867 9582 |
| 11 | 1.898 298 5583 | 14.971 642 6389 | .066 792 9381 |
| 12 | 2.012 196 4718 | 16.869 941 1973 | .059 277 0294 |
| 13 | 2.132 928 2601 | 18.882 137 6691 | .052 960 1053 |
| 14 | 2.260 903 9558 | 21.015 065 9292 | .047 584 9090 |
| 15 | 2.396 558 1931 | 23.275 969 8850 | .042 962 7640 |
| 16 | 2.540 351 6847 | 25.672 528 0781 | .038 952 1436 |
| 17 | 2.692 772 7858 | 28.212 879 7628 | .035 444 8042 |
| 18 | 2.854 339 1529 | 30.905 652 5485 | .032 356 5406 |
| 19 | 3.025 599 5021 | 33.759 991 7015 | .029 620 8604 |
| 20 | 3.207 135 4722 | 36.785 591 2035 | .027 184 5570 |
| 21 | 3.399 563 6005 | 39.992 726 6758 | .025 004 5467 |
| 22 | 3.603 537 4166 | 43.392 290 2763 | .023 045 5685 |
| 23 | 3.819 749 6616 | 46.995 827 6929 | .021 278 4847 |
| 24 | 4.048 934 6413 | 50.815 577 3545 | .019 679 0050 |
| 25 | 4.291 870 7197 | 54.864 511 9957 | .018 226 7182 |
| 26 | 4.549 382 9629 | 59.156 382 7155 | .016 904 3467 |
| 27 | 4.822 345 9407 | 63.705 765 6784 | .015 697 1663 |
| 28 | 5.111 686 6971 | 68.528 111 6191 | .014 592 5515 |
| 29 | 5.418 387 8990 | 73.639 798 3162 | .013 579 6135 |
| 30 | 5.743 491 1729 | 79.058 186 2152 | .012 648 9115 |
| 31 | 6.088 100 6433 | 84.801 677 3881 | .011 792 2196 |
| 32 | 6.453 386 6819 | 90.889 778 0314 | .011 002 3374 |
| 33 | 6.840 589 8828 | 97.343 164 7133 | .010 272 9350 |
| 34 | 7.251 025 2758 | 104.183 754 5961 | .009 598 4254 |
| 35 | 7.686 086 7923 | 111.434 779 8719 | .008 973 8590 |
| 36 | 8.147 251 9999 | 119.120 866 6642 | .008 394 8348 |
| 37 | 8.636 087 1198 | 127.268 118 6640 | .007 857 4274 |
| 38 | 9.154 252 3470 | 135.904 205 7839 | .007 358 1240 |
| 39 | 9.703 507 4879 | 145.058 458 1309 | .006 893 7724 |
| 40 | 10.285 717 9371 | 154.761 965 6188 | .006 461 5359 |
| 41 | 10.902 861 0134 | 165.047 683 5559 | .006 058 8551 |
| 42 | 11.557 032 6742 | 175.950 544 5692 | .005 683 4152 |
| 43 | 12.250 454 6346 | 187.507 577 2434 | .005 333 1178 |
| 44 | 12.985 481 9127 | 199.758 031 8780 | .005 006 0565 |
| 45 | 13.764 610 8274 | 212.743 513 7907 | .004 700 4958 |
| 46 | 14.590 487 4771 | 226.508 124 6181 | .004 414 8527 |
| 47 | 15.465 916 7257 | 241.098 612 0952 | .004 147 6805 |
| 48 | 16.393 871 7293 | 256.564 528 8209 | .003 897 6549 |
| 49 | 17.377 504 0330 | 272.958 400 5502 | .003 663 5619 |
| 50 | 18.420 154 2750 | 290.335 904 5832 | .003 444 2864 |
| 51 | 19.525 363 5315 | 308.756 058 8582 | .003 238 8028 |
| 52 | 20.696 885 3434 | 328.281 422 3897 | .003 046 1669 |
| 53 | 21.938 698 4640 | 348.978 307 7331 | .002 865 5076 |
| 54 | 23.255 020 3718 | 370.917 006 1970 | .002 696 0209 |
| 55 | 24.650 321 5941 | 394.172 026 5689 | .002 536 9634 |
| 56 | 26.129 340 8898 | 418.822 348 1630 | .002 387 6472 |
| 57 | 27.697 101 3432 | 444.951 689 0528 | .002 247 4350 |
| 58 | 29.358 927 4238 | 472.648 790 3959 | .002 115 7359 |
| 59 | 31.120 463 0692 | 502.007 717 8197 | .001 992 0012 |
| 60 | 32.987 690 8533 | 533.128 180 8889 | .001 875 7215 |
| **n** | $s=(1+i)^n$ | $s_{\overline{n}\rceil}=\dfrac{(1+i)^n-1}{i}$ | $\dfrac{1}{s_{\overline{n}\rceil}}=\dfrac{i}{(1+i)^n-1}$ |

ANNUALLY
If compounded *annually* nominal annual rate is

**6%**

SEMIANNUALLY
If compounded *semiannually* nominal annual rate is

**12%**

QUARTERLY
If compounded *quarterly* nominal annual rate is

**24%**

MONTHLY
If compounded *monthly* nominal annual rate is

**72%**

$i = .06$
$j_{(2)} = .12$
$j_{(4)} = .24$
$j_{(12)} = .72$

| PRESENT WORTH OF 1<br>*What $1 due in the future is worth today.* | PRESENT WORTH OF 1 PER PERIOD<br>*What $1 payable periodically is worth today.* | PARTIAL PAYMENT<br>*Annuity worth $1 today.*<br>*Periodic payment necessary to pay off a loan of $1.* | PERIODS | RATE<br>**6%** |
|---|---|---|---|---|
| .943 396 2264 | .943 396 2264 | 1.060 000 0000 | 1 | |
| .889 996 4400 | 1.833 392 6664 | .545 436 8932 | 2 | |
| .839 619 2830 | 2.673 011 9495 | .374 109 8128 | 3 | .06 |
| .792 093 6632 | 3.465 105 6127 | .288 591 4924 | 4 | |
| .747 258 1729 | 4.212 363 7856 | .237 396 4004 | 5 | *per period* |
| .704 960 5404 | 4.917 324 3260 | .203 362 6285 | 6 | |
| .665 057 1136 | 5.582 381 4396 | .179 135 0181 | 7 | |
| .627 412 3713 | 6.209 793 8110 | .161 035 9426 | 8 | |
| .591 898 4635 | 6.801 692 2745 | .147 022 2350 | 9 | |
| .558 394 7769 | 7.360 087 0514 | .135 867 9582 | 10 | |
| .526 787 5254 | 7.886 874 5768 | .126 792 9381 | 11 | |
| .496 969 3636 | 8.383 843 9404 | .119 277 0294 | 12 | |
| .468 839 0222 | 8.852 682 9626 | .112 960 1053 | 13 | |
| .442 300 9644 | 9.294 983 9270 | .107 584 9090 | 14 | |
| .417 265 0607 | 9.712 248 9877 | .102 962 7640 | 15 | |
| .393 646 2837 | 10.105 895 2715 | .098 952 1436 | 16 | |
| .371 364 4186 | 10.477 259 6901 | .095 444 8042 | 17 | |
| .350 343 7911 | 10.827 603 4812 | .092 356 5406 | 18 | |
| .330 513 0105 | 11.158 116 4917 | .089 620 8604 | 19 | |
| .311 804 7269 | 11.469 921 2186 | .087 184 5570 | 20 | |
| .294 155 4027 | 11.764 076 6213 | .085 004 5467 | 21 | ANNUALLY<br>If compounded *annually* nominal annual rate is |
| .277 505 0969 | 12.041 581 7182 | .083 045 5685 | 22 | |
| .261 797 2612 | 12.303 378 9794 | .081 278 4847 | 23 | |
| .246 978 5483 | 12.550 357 5278 | .079 679 0050 | 24 | |
| .232 998 6305 | 12.783 356 1583 | .078 226 7182 | 25 | **6%** |
| .219 810 0288 | 13.003 166 1870 | .076 904 3467 | 26 | |
| .207 367 9517 | 13.210 534 1387 | .075 697 1663 | 27 | |
| .195 630 1431 | 13.406 164 2818 | .074 592 5515 | 28 | |
| .184 556 7388 | 13.590 721 0206 | .073 579 6135 | 29 | |
| .174 110 1309 | 13.764 831 1515 | .072 648 9115 | 30 | |
| .164 254 8405 | 13.929 085 9920 | .071 792 2196 | 31 | SEMIANNUALLY<br>If compounded *semiannually* nominal annual rate is |
| .154 957 3967 | 14.084 043 3887 | .071 002 3374 | 32 | |
| .146 186 2233 | 14.230 229 6119 | .070 272 9350 | 33 | |
| .137 911 5314 | 14.368 141 1433 | .069 598 4254 | 34 | |
| .130 105 2183 | 14.498 246 3616 | .068 973 8590 | 35 | **12%** |
| .122 740 7720 | 14.620 987 1336 | .068 394 8348 | 36 | |
| .115 793 1811 | 14.736 780 3147 | .067 857 4274 | 37 | |
| .109 238 8501 | 14.846 019 1648 | .067 358 1240 | 38 | |
| .103 055 5190 | 14.949 074 6838 | .066 893 7724 | 39 | |
| .097 222 1877 | 15.046 296 8715 | .066 461 5359 | 40 | |
| .091 719 0450 | 15.138 015 9165 | .066 058 8551 | 41 | QUARTERLY<br>If compounded *quarterly* nominal annual rate is |
| .086 527 4010 | 15.224 543 3175 | .065 683 4152 | 42 | |
| .081 629 6235 | 15.306 172 9410 | .065 333 1178 | 43 | |
| .077 009 0788 | 15.383 182 0198 | .065 006 0565 | 44 | |
| .072 650 0743 | 15.455 832 0942 | .064 700 4958 | 45 | **24%** |
| .068 537 8060 | 15.524 369 9002 | .064 414 8527 | 46 | |
| .064 658 3075 | 15.589 028 2077 | .064 147 6805 | 47 | |
| .060 998 4033 | 15.650 026 6110 | .063 897 6549 | 48 | |
| .057 545 6635 | 15.707 572 2746 | .063 663 5619 | 49 | |
| .054 288 3618 | 15.761 860 6364 | .063 444 2864 | 50 | |
| .051 215 4357 | 15.813 076 0721 | .063 238 8028 | 51 | MONTHLY<br>If compounded *monthly* nominal annual rate is |
| .048 316 4488 | 15.861 392 5208 | .063 046 1669 | 52 | |
| .045 581 5554 | 15.906 974 0762 | .062 865 5076 | 53 | |
| .043 001 4674 | 15.949 975 5436 | .062 696 0209 | 54 | |
| .040 567 4221 | 15.990 542 9657 | .062 536 9634 | 55 | **72%** |
| .038 271 1529 | 16.028 814 1186 | .062 387 6472 | 56 | |
| .036 104 8612 | 16.064 918 9798 | .062 247 4350 | 57 | |
| .034 061 1898 | 16.098 980 1696 | .062 115 7359 | 58 | $i = .06$ |
| .032 133 1979 | 16.131 113 3676 | .061 992 0012 | 59 | $j_{(2)} = .12$ |
| .030 314 3377 | 16.161 427 7052 | .061 875 7215 | 60 | $j_{(4)} = .24$<br>$j_{(12)} = .72$ |
| $v^n = \dfrac{1}{(1+i)^n}$ | $a_{\overline{n}|} = \dfrac{1-v^n}{i}$ | $\dfrac{1}{a_{\overline{n}|}} = \dfrac{i}{1-v^n}$ | n | |

| RATE **7%** | P E R I O D S | AMOUNT OF 1<br>*How $1 left at compound interest will grow.* | AMOUNT OF 1 PER PERIOD<br>*How $1 deposited periodically will grow.* | SINKING FUND<br>*Periodic deposit that will grow to $1 at future date.* |
|---|---|---|---|---|
| .07<br>*per period* | 1 | 1.070 000 0000 | 1.000 000 0000 | 1.000 000 0000 |
| | 2 | 1.144 900 0000 | 2.070 000 0000 | .483 091 7874 |
| | 3 | 1.225 043 0000 | 3.214 900 0000 | .311 051 6657 |
| | 4 | 1.310 796 0100 | 4.439 943 0000 | .225 228 1167 |
| | 5 | 1.402 551 7307 | 5.750 739 0100 | .173 890 6944 |
| | 6 | 1.500 730 3518 | 7.153 290 7407 | .139 795 7998 |
| | 7 | 1.605 781 4765 | 8.654 021 0925 | .115 553 2196 |
| | 8 | 1.718 186 1798 | 10.259 802 5690 | .097 467 7625 |
| | 9 | 1.838 459 2124 | 11.977 988 7489 | .083 486 4701 |
| | 10 | 1.967 151 3573 | 13.816 447 9613 | .072 377 5027 |
| | 11 | 2.104 851 9523 | 15.783 599 3186 | .063 356 9048 |
| | 12 | 2.252 191 5890 | 17.888 451 2709 | .055 901 9887 |
| | 13 | 2.409 845 0002 | 20.140 642 8598 | .049 650 8481 |
| | 14 | 2.578 534 1502 | 22.550 487 8600 | .044 344 9386 |
| | 15 | 2.759 031 5407 | 25.129 022 0102 | .039 794 6247 |
| | 16 | 2.952 163 7486 | 27.888 053 5509 | .035 857 6477 |
| | 17 | 3.158 815 2110 | 30.840 217 2995 | .032 425 1931 |
| | 18 | 3.379 932 2757 | 33.999 032 5105 | .029 412 6017 |
| | 19 | 3.616 527 5350 | 37.378 964 7862 | .026 753 0148 |
| | 20 | 3.869 684 4625 | 40.995 492 3212 | .024 392 9257 |
| ANNUALLY<br>If compounded *annually* nominal annual rate is<br>**7%** | 21 | 4.140 562 3749 | 44.865 176 7837 | .022 289 0017 |
| | 22 | 4.430 401 7411 | 49.005 739 1586 | .020 405 7732 |
| | 23 | 4.740 529 8630 | 53.436 140 8997 | .018 713 9263 |
| | 24 | 5.072 366 9534 | 58.176 670 7627 | .017 189 0207 |
| | 25 | 5.427 432 6401 | 63.249 037 7160 | .015 810 5172 |
| | 26 | 5.807 352 9249 | 68.676 470 3562 | .014 561 0279 |
| | 27 | 6.213 867 6297 | 74.483 823 2811 | .013 425 7340 |
| | 28 | 6.648 838 3638 | 80.697 690 9108 | .012 391 9283 |
| | 29 | 7.114 257 0492 | 87.346 529 2745 | .011 448 6518 |
| | 30 | 7.612 255 0427 | 94.460 786 3237 | .010 586 4035 |
| SEMIANNUALLY<br>If compounded *semiannually* nominal annual rate is<br>**14%** | 31 | 8.145 112 8956 | 102.073 041 3664 | .009 796 9061 |
| | 32 | 8.715 270 7983 | 110.218 154 2621 | .009 072 9155 |
| | 33 | 9.325 339 7542 | 118.933 425 0604 | .008 408 0653 |
| | 34 | 9.978 113 5370 | 128.258 764 8146 | .007 796 7381 |
| | 35 | 10.676 581 4846 | 138.236 878 3516 | .007 233 9596 |
| | 36 | 11.423 942 1885 | 148.913 459 8363 | .006 715 3097 |
| | 37 | 12.223 618 1417 | 160.337 402 0248 | .006 236 8480 |
| | 38 | 13.079 271 4117 | 172.561 020 1665 | .005 795 0515 |
| | 39 | 13.994 820 4105 | 185.640 291 5782 | .005 386 7616 |
| | 40 | 14.974 457 8392 | 199.635 111 9887 | .005 009 1389 |
| QUARTERLY<br>If compounded *quarterly* nominal annual rate is<br>**28%** | 41 | 16.022 669 8880 | 214.609 569 8279 | .004 659 6245 |
| | 42 | 17.144 256 7801 | 230.632 239 7158 | .004 335 9072 |
| | 43 | 18.344 354 7547 | 247.776 496 4959 | .004 035 8953 |
| | 44 | 19.628 459 5875 | 266.120 851 2507 | .003 757 6913 |
| | 45 | 21.002 451 7587 | 285.749 310 8382 | .003 499 5710 |
| | 46 | 22.472 623 3818 | 306.751 762 5969 | .003 259 9650 |
| | 47 | 24.045 707 0185 | 329.224 385 9787 | .003 037 4421 |
| | 48 | 25.728 906 5098 | 353.270 092 9972 | .002 830 6953 |
| | 49 | 27.529 929 9655 | 378.998 999 5070 | .002 638 5294 |
| | 50 | 29.457 025 0631 | 406.528 929 4724 | .002 459 8495 |
| MONTHLY<br>If compounded *monthly* nominal annual rate is<br>**84%** | 51 | 31.519 016 8175 | 435.985 954 5355 | .002 293 6519 |
| | 52 | 33.725 347 9947 | 467.504 971 3530 | .002 139 0147 |
| | 53 | 36.086 122 3543 | 501.230 319 3477 | .001 995 0908 |
| | 54 | 38.612 150 9191 | 537.316 441 7021 | .001 861 1007 |
| | 55 | 41.315 001 4835 | 575.928 592 6212 | .001 736 3264 |
| $i$ = .07<br>$j_{(2)}$ = .14<br>$j_{(4)}$ = .28<br>$j_{(12)}$ = .84 | 56 | 44.207 051 5873 | 617.243 594 1047 | .001 620 1059 |
| | 57 | 47.301 545 1984 | 661.450 645 6920 | .001 511 8286 |
| | 58 | 50.612 653 3623 | 708.752 190 8905 | .001 410 9304 |
| | 59 | 54.155 539 0977 | 759.364 844 2528 | .001 316 8900 |
| | 60 | 57.946 426 8345 | 813.520 383 3505 | .001 229 2255 |
| | **n** | $s=(1+i)^n$ | $s_{\overline{n}\vert}=\dfrac{(1+i)^n-1}{i}$ | $\dfrac{1}{s_{\overline{n}\vert}}=\dfrac{i}{(1+i)^n-1}$ |

70

| PRESENT WORTH OF 1<br>*What $1 due in the future is worth today.* | PRESENT WORTH OF 1 PER PERIOD<br>*What $1 payable periodically is worth today.* | PARTIAL PAYMENT<br>*Annuity worth $1 today.*<br>*Periodic payment necessary to pay off a loan of $1.* | P E R I O D S | RATE<br>**7%** |
|---|---|---|---|---|
| .934 579 4393 | .934 579 4393 | 1.070 000 0000 | 1 | |
| .873 438 7283 | 1.808 018 1675 | .553 091 7874 | 2 | |
| .816 297 8769 | 2.624 316 0444 | .381 051 6657 | 3 | .07 |
| .762 895 2120 | 3.387 211 2565 | .295 228 1167 | 4 | *per period* |
| .712 986 1795 | 4.100 197 4359 | .243 890 6944 | 5 | |
| .666 342 2238 | 4.766 539 6598 | .209 795 7998 | 6 | |
| .622 749 7419 | 5.389 289 4016 | .185 553 2196 | 7 | |
| .582 009 1046 | 5.971 298 5062 | .167 467 7625 | 8 | |
| .543 933 7426 | 6.515 232 2488 | .153 486 4701 | 9 | |
| .508 349 2921 | 7.023 581 5409 | .142 377 5027 | 10 | |
| .475 092 7964 | 7.498 674 3373 | .133 356 9048 | 11 | |
| .444 011 9592 | 7.942 686 2966 | .125 901 9887 | 12 | |
| .414 964 4479 | 8.357 650 7444 | .119 650 8481 | 13 | |
| .387 817 2410 | 8.745 467 9855 | .114 344 9386 | 14 | |
| .362 446 0196 | 9.107 914 0051 | .109 794 6247 | 15 | |
| .338 734 5978 | 9.446 648 6029 | .105 857 6477 | 16 | |
| .316 574 3905 | 9.763 222 9934 | .102 425 1931 | 17 | |
| .295 863 9163 | 10.059 086 9097 | .099 412 6017 | 18 | |
| .276 508 3330 | 10.335 595 2427 | .096 753 0148 | 19 | |
| .258 419 0028 | 10.594 014 2455 | .094 392 9257 | 20 | |
| .241 513 0867 | 10.835 527 3323 | .092 289 0017 | 21 | **ANNUALLY**<br>If compounded *annually* nominal annual rate is |
| .225 713 1652 | 11.061 240 4974 | .090 405 7732 | 22 | |
| .210 946 8833 | 11.272 187 3808 | .088 713 9263 | 23 | |
| .197 146 6199 | 11.469 334 0007 | .087 189 0207 | 24 | |
| .184 249 1775 | 11.653 583 1783 | .085 810 5172 | 25 | **7%** |
| .172 195 4930 | 11.825 778 6713 | .084 561 0279 | 26 | |
| .160 930 3673 | 11.986 709 0386 | .083 425 7340 | 27 | |
| .150 402 2124 | 12.137 111 2510 | .082 391 9283 | 28 | |
| .140 562 8154 | 12.277 674 0664 | .081 448 6518 | 29 | |
| .131 367 1172 | 12.409 041 1835 | .080 586 4035 | 30 | |
| .122 773 0067 | 12.531 814 1902 | .079 796 9061 | 31 | **SEMIANNUALLY**<br>If compounded *semiannually* nominal annual rate is |
| .114 741 1277 | 12.646 555 3179 | .079 072 9155 | 32 | |
| .107 234 6988 | 12.753 790 0168 | .078 408 0653 | 33 | |
| .100 219 3447 | 12.854 009 3615 | .077 796 7381 | 34 | |
| .093 662 9390 | 12.947 672 3004 | .077 233 9596 | 35 | **14%** |
| .087 535 4570 | 13.035 207 7574 | .076 715 3097 | 36 | |
| .081 808 8383 | 13.117 016 5957 | .076 236 8480 | 37 | |
| .076 456 8582 | 13.193 473 4539 | .075 795 0515 | 38 | |
| .071 455 0077 | 13.264 928 4616 | .075 386 7616 | 39 | |
| .066 780 3810 | 13.331 708 8426 | .075 009 1389 | 40 | |
| .062 411 5710 | 13.394 120 4137 | .074 659 6245 | 41 | **QUARTERLY**<br>If compounded *quarterly* nominal annual rate is |
| .058 328 5711 | 13.452 448 9847 | .074 335 9072 | 42 | |
| .054 512 6832 | 13.506 961 6680 | .074 035 8953 | 43 | |
| .050 946 4329 | 13.557 908 1009 | .073 757 6913 | 44 | |
| .047 613 4887 | 13.605 521 5896 | .073 499 5710 | 45 | **28%** |
| .044 498 5876 | 13.650 020 1772 | .073 259 9650 | 46 | |
| .041 587 4650 | 13.691 607 6423 | .073 037 4421 | 47 | |
| .038 866 7898 | 13.730 474 4320 | .072 830 6953 | 48 | |
| .036 324 1026 | 13.766 798 5346 | .072 638 5294 | 49 | |
| .033 947 7594 | 13.800 746 2940 | .072 459 8495 | 50 | |
| .031 726 8780 | 13.832 473 1720 | .072 293 6519 | 51 | **MONTHLY**<br>If compounded *monthly* nominal annual rate is |
| .029 651 2878 | 13.862 124 4598 | .072 139 0147 | 52 | |
| .027 711 4839 | 13.889 835 9437 | .071 995 0908 | 53 | |
| .025 898 5831 | 13.915 734 5269 | .071 861 1007 | 54 | |
| .024 204 2833 | 13.939 938 8102 | .071 736 3264 | 55 | **84%** |
| .022 620 8255 | 13.962 559 6357 | .071 620 1059 | 56 | |
| .021 140 9584 | 13.983 700 5941 | .071 511 8286 | 57 | |
| .019 757 9051 | 14.003 458 4991 | .071 410 9304 | 58 | $i \cdot = .07$ |
| .018 465 3318 | 14.021 923 8310 | .071 316 8900 | 59 | $j_{(2)} = .14$ |
| .017 257 3195 | 14.039 181 1504 | .071 229 2255 | 60 | $j_{(4)} = .28$<br>$j_{(12)} = .84$ |
| $v^n = \dfrac{1}{(1+i)^n}$ | $a_{\overline{n}|} = \dfrac{1-v^n}{i}$ | $\dfrac{1}{a_{\overline{n}|}} = \dfrac{i}{1-v^n}$ | n | |

71

| P E R I O D S | AMOUNT OF 1<br>*How \$1 left at compound interest will grow.* | AMOUNT OF 1 PER PERIOD<br>*How \$1 deposited periodically will grow.* | SINKING FUND<br>*Periodic deposit that will grow to \$1 at future date.* |
|---|---|---|---|
| 1 | 1.080 000 0000 | 1.000 000 0000 | 1.000 000 0000 |
| 2 | 1.166 400 0000 | 2.080 000 0000 | .480 769 2308 |
| 3 | 1.259 712 0000 | 3.246 400 0000 | .308 033 5140 |
| 4 | 1.360 488 9600 | 4.506 112 0000 | .221 920 8045 |
| 5 | 1.469 328 0768 | 5.866 600 9600 | .170 456 4546 |
| 6 | 1.586 874 3229 | 7.335 929 0368 | .136 315 3862 |
| 7 | 1.713 824 2688 | 8.922 803 3597 | .112 072 4014 |
| 8 | 1.850 930 2103 | 10.636 627 6285 | .094 014 7606 |
| 9 | 1.999 004 6271 | 12.487 557 8388 | .080 079 7092 |
| 10 | 2.158 924 9973 | 14.486 562 4659 | .069 029 4887 |
| 11 | 2.331 638 9971 | 16.645 487 4632 | .060 076 3421 |
| 12 | 2.518 170 1168 | 18.977 126 4602 | .052 695 0169 |
| 13 | 2.719 623 7262 | 21.495 296 5771 | .046 521 8052 |
| 14 | 2.937 193 6243 | 24.214 920 3032 | .041 296 8528 |
| 15 | 3.172 169 1142 | 27.152 113 9275 | .036 829 5449 |
| 16 | 3.425 942 6433 | 30.324 283 0417 | .032 976 8720 |
| 17 | 3.700 018 0548 | 33.750 225 6850 | .029 629 4315 |
| 18 | 3.996 019 4992 | 37.450 243 7398 | .026 702 0959 |
| 19 | 4.315 701 0591 | 41.446 263 2390 | .024 127 6275 |
| 20 | 4.660 957 1438 | 45.761 964 2981 | .021 852 2088 |
| 21 | 5.033 833 7154 | 50.422 921 4420 | .019 832 2503 |
| 22 | 5.436 540 4126 | 55.456 755 1573 | .018 032 0684 |
| 23 | 5.871 463 6456 | 60.893 295 5699 | .016 422 1692 |
| 24 | 6.341 180 7372 | 66.764 759 2155 | .014 977 9616 |
| 25 | 6.848 475 1962 | 73.105 939 9527 | .013 678 7791 |
| 26 | 7.396 353 2119 | 79.954 415 1490 | .012 507 1267 |
| 27 | 7.988 061 4689 | 87.350 768 3609 | .011 448 0962 |
| 28 | 8.627 106 3864 | 95.338 829 8297 | .010 488 9057 |
| 29 | 9.317 274 8973 | 103.965 936 2161 | .009 618 5350 |
| 30 | 10.062 656 8891 | 113.283 211 1134 | .008 827 4334 |
| 31 | 10.867 669 4402 | 123.345 868 0025 | .008 107 2841 |
| 32 | 11.737 082 9954 | 134.213 537 4427 | .007 450 8132 |
| 33 | 12.676 049 6350 | 145.950 620 4381 | .006 851 6324 |
| 34 | 13.690 133 6059 | 158.626 670 0732 | .006 304 1101 |
| 35 | 14.785 344 2943 | 172.316 803 6790 | .005 803 2646 |
| 36 | 15.968 171 8379 | 187.102 147 9733 | .005 344 6741 |
| 37 | 17.245 625 5849 | 203.070 319 8112 | .004 924 4025 |
| 38 | 18.625 275 6317 | 220.315 945 3961 | .004 538 9361 |
| 39 | 20.115 297 6822 | 238.941 221 0278 | .004 185 1297 |
| 40 | 21.724 521 4968 | 259.056 518 7100 | .003 860 1615 |
| 41 | 23.462 483 2165 | 280.781 040 2068 | .003 561 4940 |
| 42 | 25.339 481 8739 | 304.243 523 4233 | .003 286 8407 |
| 43 | 27.366 640 4238 | 329.583 005 2972 | .003 034 1370 |
| 44 | 29.555 971 6577 | 356.949 645 7210 | .002 801 5156 |
| 45 | 31.920 449 3903 | 386.505 617 3787 | .002 587 2845 |
| 46 | 34.474 085 3415 | 418.426 066 7690 | .002 389 9085 |
| 47 | 37.232 012 1688 | 452.900 152 1105 | .002 207 9922 |
| 48 | 40.210 573 1423 | 490.132 164 2793 | .002 040 2660 |
| 49 | 43.427 418 9937 | 530.342 737 4217 | .001 885 5731 |
| 50 | 46.901 612 5132 | 573.770 156 4154 | .001 742 8582 |
| 51 | 50.653 741 5143 | 620.671 768 9286 | .001 611 1575 |
| 52 | 54.706 040 8354 | 671.325 510 4429 | .001 489 5903 |
| 53 | 59.082 524 1023 | 726.031 551 2783 | .001 377 3506 |
| 54 | 63.809 126 0304 | 785.114 075 3806 | .001 273 7003 |
| 55 | 68.913 856 1129 | 848.923 201 4111 | .001 177 9629 |
| 56 | 74.426 964 6019 | 917.837 057 5239 | .001 089 5180 |
| 57 | 80.381 121 7701 | 992.264 022 1259 | .001 007 7963 |
| 58 | 86.811 611 5117 | 1072.645 143 8959 | .000 932 2748 |
| 59 | 93.756 540 4326 | 1159.456 755 4076 | .000 862 4729 |
| 60 | 101.257 063 6672 | 1253.213 295 8402 | .000 797 9488 |
| **n** | $s=(1+i)^n$ | $s_{\overline{n}|}=\dfrac{(1+i)^n-1}{i}$ | $\dfrac{1}{s_{\overline{n}|}}=\dfrac{i}{(1+i)^n-1}$ |

.08

*per period*

ANNUALLY
If compounded
*annually*
nominal annual rate is

**8%**

SEMIANNUALLY
If compounded
*semiannually*
nominal annual rate is

**16%**

QUARTERLY
If compounded
*quarterly*
nominal annual rate is

**32%**

MONTHLY
If compounded
*monthly*
nominal annual rate is

**96%**

$i \quad = .08$
$j_{(2)} = .16$
$j_{(4)} = .32$
$j_{(12)} = .96$

| PRESENT WORTH OF 1 — What $1 due in the future is worth today. | PRESENT WORTH OF 1 PER PERIOD — What $1 payable periodically is worth today. | PARTIAL PAYMENT — *Annuity worth $1 today.* Periodic payment necessary to pay off a loan of $1. | PERIODS | RATE 8% |
|---|---|---|---|---|
| .925 925 9259 | .925 925 9259 | 1.080 000 0000 | 1 | |
| .857 338 8203 | 1.783 264 7462 | .560 769 2308 | 2 | |
| .793 832 2410 | 2.577 096 9872 | .388 033 5140 | 3 | .08 |
| .735 029 8528 | 3.312 126 8400 | .301 920 8045 | 4 | *per period* |
| .680 583 1970 | 3.992 710 0371 | .250 456 4546 | 5 | |
| .630 169 6269 | 4.622 879 6640 | .216 315 3862 | 6 | |
| .583 490 3953 | 5.206 370 0592 | .192 072 4014 | 7 | |
| .540 268 8845 | 5.746 638 9437 | .174 014 7606 | 8 | |
| .500 248 9671 | 6.246 887 9109 | .160 079 7092 | 9 | |
| .463 193 4881 | 6.710 081 3989 | .149 029 4887 | 10 | |
| .428 882 8593 | 7.138 964 2583 | .140 076 3421 | 11 | |
| .397 113 7586 | 7.536 078 0169 | .132 695 0169 | 12 | |
| .367 697 9247 | 7.903 775 9416 | .126 521 8052 | 13 | |
| .340 461 0414 | 8.244 236 9830 | .121 296 8528 | 14 | |
| .315 241 7050 | 8.559 478 6879 | .116 829 5449 | 15 | |
| .291 890 4676 | 8.851 369 1555 | .112 976 8720 | 16 | |
| .270 268 9514 | 9.121 638 1069 | .109 629 4315 | 17 | |
| .250 249 0291 | 9.371 887 1360 | .106 702 0959 | 18 | |
| .231 712 0640 | 9.603 599 2000 | .104 127 6275 | 19 | |
| .214 548 2074 | 9.818 147 4074 | .101 852 2088 | 20 | |
| .198 655 7476 | 10.016 803 1550 | .099 832 2503 | 21 | ANNUALLY — If compounded *annually* nominal annual rate is |
| .183 940 5070 | 10.200 743 6621 | .098 032 0684 | 22 | |
| .170 315 2843 | 10.371 058 9464 | .096 422 1692 | 23 | |
| .157 699 3373 | 10.528 758 2837 | .094 977 9616 | 24 | |
| .146 017 9049 | 10.674 776 1886 | .093 678 7791 | 25 | 8% |
| .135 201 7638 | 10.809 977 9524 | .092 507 1267 | 26 | |
| .125 186 8183 | 10.935 164 7707 | .091 448 0962 | 27 | |
| .115 913 7207 | 11.051 078 4914 | .090 488 9057 | 28 | |
| .107 327 5192 | 11.158 406 0106 | .089 618 5350 | 29 | |
| .099 377 3325 | 11.257 783 3431 | .088 827 4334 | 30 | |
| .092 016 0487 | 11.349 799 3918 | .088 107 2841 | 31 | SEMIANNUALLY — If compounded *semiannually* nominal annual rate is |
| .085 200 0451 | 11.434 999 4368 | .087 450 8132 | 32 | |
| .078 888 9306 | 11.513 888 3674 | .086 851 6324 | 33 | |
| .073 045 3061 | 11.586 933 6736 | .086 304 1101 | 34 | |
| .067 634 5427 | 11.654 568 2163 | .085 803 2646 | 35 | 16% |
| .062 624 5766 | 11.717 192 7928 | .085 344 6741 | 36 | |
| .057 985 7190 | 11.775 178 5119 | .084 924 4025 | 37 | |
| .053 690 4806 | 11.828 868 9925 | .084 538 9361 | 38 | |
| .049 713 4080 | 11.878 582 4004 | .084 185 1297 | 39 | |
| .046 030 9333 | 11.924 613 3337 | .083 860 1615 | 40 | |
| .042 621 2345 | 11.967 234 5683 | .083 561 4940 | 41 | QUARTERLY — If compounded *quarterly* nominal annual rate is |
| .039 464 1061 | 12.006 698 6743 | .083 286 8407 | 42 | |
| .036 540 8389 | 12.043 239 5133 | .083 034 1370 | 43 | |
| .033 834 1101 | 12.077 073 6234 | .082 801 5156 | 44 | |
| .031 327 8797 | 12.108 401 5032 | .082 587 2845 | 45 | 32% |
| .029 007 2961 | 12.137 408 7992 | .082 389 9085 | 46 | |
| .026 858 6075 | 12.164 267 4067 | .082 207 9922 | 47 | |
| .024 869 0810 | 12.189 136 4877 | .082 040 2660 | 48 | |
| .023 026 9268 | 12.212 163 4145 | .081 885 5731 | 49 | |
| .021 321 2286 | 12.233 484 6431 | .081 742 8582 | 50 | |
| .019 741 8783 | 12.253 226 5214 | .081 611 1575 | 51 | MONTHLY — If compounded *monthly* nominal annual rate is |
| .018 279 5169 | 12.271 506 0383 | .081 489 5903 | 52 | |
| .016 925 4786 | 12.288 431 5169 | .081 377 3506 | 53 | |
| .015 671 7395 | 12.304 103 2564 | .081 273 7003 | 54 | |
| .014 510 8699 | 12.318 614 1263 | .081 177 9629 | 55 | 96% |
| .013 435 9906 | 12.332 050 1170 | .081 089 5180 | 56 | |
| .012 440 7321 | 12.344 490 8490 | .081 007 7963 | 57 | |
| .011 519 1964 | 12.356 010 0454 | .080 932 2748 | 58 | $i = .08$ |
| .010 665 9226 | 12.366 675 9680 | .080 862 4729 | 59 | $j_{(2)} = .16$ |
| .009 875 8542 | 12.376 551 8222 | .080 797 9488 | 60 | $j_{(4)} = .32$ ; $j_{(12)} = .96$ |
| $v^n = \dfrac{1}{(1+i)^n}$ | $a_{\overline{n}} = \dfrac{1-v^n}{i}$ | $\dfrac{1}{a_{\overline{n}}} = \dfrac{i}{1-v^n}$ | n | |

## Table 3
### *Auxiliary Tables*

| Time Interval | Amount of 1 | Payment Equivalent to 1 per Period | Equivalent per Period to a Payment of 1 |
|---|---|---|---|
| *Fractional Parts of a Unit Period.* | *How 1 left at compound interest will grow for a time interval which is a fractional part of a unit period.* | *Payment at the end of each time interval equivalent to 1 at the end of each period.* | *Payment at the end of each period equivalent to 1 at the end of each time interval.* |

## 1/4% per Period          $i = .0025$

| | | | |
|---|---|---|---|
| 1-12 | 1.000 208 0950 | .083 237 9995 | 12.013 743 8011 |
| 1-6 | 1.000 416 2333 | .166 493 3203 | 6.006 246 9656 |
| 1-4 | 1.000 624 4149 | .249 765 9662 | 4.003 748 0493 |
| 1-3 | 1.000 832 6399 | .333 055 9407 | 3.002 498 6128 |
| 1-2 | 1.001 249 2197 | .499 687 8900 | 2.001 249 2197 |

## 1/3% per Period          $i = .00333333$

| | | | |
|---|---|---|---|
| 1-12 | 1.000 277 3543 | .083 206 2890 | 12.018 322 3177 |
| 1-6 | 1.000 554 7855 | .166 435 6556 | 6.008 327 9411 |
| 1-4 | 1.000 832 2937 | .249 688 1063 | 4.004 996 5336 |
| 1-3 | 1.001 109 8788 | .332 963 6473 | 3.003 330 8683 |
| 1-2 | 1.001 665 2801 | .499 584 0263 | 2.001 665 2801 |

## 5/12% per Period          $i = .00416666$

| | | | |
|---|---|---|---|
| 1-12 | 1.000 346 5609 | .083 174 6124 | 12.022 899 4619 |
| 1-6 | 1.000 693 2419 | .166 378 0499 | 6.010 408 2448 |
| 1-4 | 1.001 040 0430 | .249 610 3224 | 4.006 244 5859 |
| 1-3 | 1.001 386 9643 | .332 871 4400 | 3.004 162 8167 |
| 1-2 | 1.002 081 1677 | .499 480 2503 | 2.002 081 1677 |

## 1/2% per Period          $i = .005$

| | | | |
|---|---|---|---|
| 1-12 | 1.000 415 7148 | .083 142 9689 | 12.027 475 2355 |
| 1-6 | 1.000 831 6025 | .166 320 5017 | 6.012 487 8775 |
| 1-4 | 1.001 247 6631 | .249 532 6125 | 4.007 492 2070 |
| 1-3 | 1.001 663 8966 | .332 779 3159 | 3.004 994 4583 |
| 1-2 | 1.002 496 8828 | .499 376 5576 | 2.002 496 8828 |

## 3/4% per Period          $i = .0075$

| | | | |
|---|---|---|---|
| 1-12 | 1.000 622 8618 | .083 048 2402 | 12.041 194 3491 |
| 1-6 | 1.001 246 1116 | .166 148 2079 | 6.018 722 7583 |
| 1-4 | 1.001 869 7495 | .249 299 9354 | 4.011 232 4875 |
| 1-3 | 1.002 493 7759 | .332 503 4550 | 3.007 487 5467 |
| 1-2 | 1.003 742 9950 | .499 065 9992 | 2.003 742 9950 |

## 1% per Period          $i = .01$

| | | | |
|---|---|---|---|
| 1-12 | 1.000 829 5381 | .082 953 8114 | 12.054 901 1879 |
| 1-6 | 1.001 659 7644 | .165 976 4362 | 6.024 951 6304 |
| 1-4 | 1.002 490 6793 | .249 067 9314 | 4.014 968 9053 |
| 1-3 | 1.003 322 2835 | .332 228 3542 | 3.009 977 8882 |
| 1-2 | 1.004 987 5621 | .498 756 2112 | 2.004 987 5621 |

# Table 3 (Continued)
## *Auxiliary Tables*

| Time Interval | Amount of 1 | Payment Equivalent to 1 per Period | Equivalent per Period to a Payment of 1 |
|---|---|---|---|
| *Fractional Parts of a Unit Period.* | *How 1 left at compound interest will grow for a time interval which is a fractional part of a unit period.* | *Payment at the end of each time interval equivalent to 1 at the end of each period.* | *Payment at the end of each period equivalent to 1 at the end of each time interval.* |

## 1¼% per Period          $i = .0125$

| | | | |
|---|---|---|---|
| 1-12 | 1.001 035 7460 | .082 859 6812 | 12.068 595 7972 |
| 1-6 | 1.002 072 5648 | .165 805 1839 | 6.031 174 5161 |
| 1-4 | 1.003 110 4575 | .248 836 5972 | 4.018 701 4747 |
| 1-3 | 1.004 149 4251 | .331 954 0099 | 3.012 465 4931 |
| 1-2 | 1.006 230 5899 | .498 447 1900 | 2.006 230 5899 |

## 1½% per Period          $i = .015$

| | | | |
|---|---|---|---|
| 1-12 | 1.001 241 4877 | .082 765 8478 | 12.082 278 2225 |
| 1-6 | 1.002 484 5167 | .165 634 4483 | 6.037 391 4376 |
| 1-4 | 1.003 729 0889 | .248 605 9292 | 4.022 430 2099 |
| 1-3 | 1.004 975 2063 | .331 680 4182 | 3.014 950 3715 |
| 1-2 | 1.007 472 0840 | .498 138 9320 | 2.007 472 0840 |

## 1¾% per Period          $i = .0175$

| | | | |
|---|---|---|---|
| 1-12 | 1.001 446 7654 | .082 672 3096 | 12.095 948 5087 |
| 1-6 | 1.002 895 6240 | .165 464 2266 | 6.043 602 4169 |
| 1-4 | 1.004 346 5787 | .248 375 9242 | 4.026 155 1251 |
| 1-3 | 1.005 799 6326 | .331 407 5755 | 3.017 432 5334 |
| 1-2 | 1.008 712 0501 | .497 831 4338 | 2.008 712 0501 |

## 2% per Period          $i = .02$

| | | | |
|---|---|---|---|
| 1-12 | 1.001 651 5813 | .082 579 0651 | 12.109 606 7004 |
| 1-6 | 1.003 305 8903 | .165 294 5162 | 6.049 807 4758 |
| 1-4 | 1.004 962 9316 | .248 146 5787 | 4.029 876 2344 |
| 1-3 | 1.006 622 7096 | .331 135 4780 | 3.019 911 9890 |
| 1-2 | 1.009 950 4938 | .497 524 6918 | 2.009 950 4938 |

## 2¼% per Period          $i = .0225$

| | | | |
|---|---|---|---|
| 1-12 | 1.001 855 9375 | .082 486 1127 | 12.123 252 8421 |
| 1-6 | 1.003 715 3196 | .165 125 3144 | 6.056 006 6360 |
| 1-4 | 1.005 578 1525 | .247 917 8894 | 4.033 593 5518 |
| 1-3 | 1.007 444 4427 | .330 864 1222 | 3.022 388 7480 |
| 1-2 | 1.011 187 4208 | .497 218 7026 | 2.011 187 4208 |

## 2½% per Period          $i = .025$

| | | | |
|---|---|---|---|
| 1-12 | 1.002 059 8363 | .082 393 4508 | 12.136 886 9779 |
| 1-6 | 1.004 123 9155 | .164 956 6186 | 6.062 199 9193 |
| 1-4 | 1.006 192 2463 | .247 689 8530 | 4.037 307 0910 |
| 1-3 | 1.008 264 8376 | .330 593 5044 | 3.024 862 8204 |
| 1-2 | 1.012 422 8366 | .496 913 4626 | 2.012 422 8366 |

**Table 3 (Continued)**
*Auxiliary Tables*

| Time Interval | Amount of 1 | Payment Equivalent to 1 per Period | Equivalent per Period to a Payment of 1 |
|---|---|---|---|
| *Fractional Parts of a Unit Period.* | *How 1 left at compound interest will grow for a time interval which is a fractional part of a unit period.* | *Payment at the end of each time interval equivalent to 1 at the end of each period.* | *Payment at the end of each period equivalent to 1 at the end of each time interval.* |

## 3% per Period  $i = .03$

| | | | |
|---|---|---|---|
| 1-12 | 1.002 466 2698 | .082 208 9924 | 12.164 119 4069 |
| 1-6 | 1.004 938 6220 | .164 620 7344 | 6.074 568 9406 |
| 1-4 | 1.007 417 0718 | .247 235 7259 | 4.044 722 8905 |
| 1-3 | 1.009 901 6340 | .330 054 4683 | 3.029 802 9445 |
| 1-2 | 1.014 889 1565 | .496 305 2170 | 2.014 889 1565 |

## 3½% per Period  $i = .035$

| | | | |
|---|---|---|---|
| 1-12 | 1.002 870 8987 | .082 025 6777 | 12.191 304 3353 |
| 1-6 | 1.005 750 0395 | .164 286 8428 | 6.086 914 7098 |
| 1-4 | 1.008 637 4460 | .246 784 1714 | 4.052 123 7423 |
| 1-3 | 1.011 533 1419 | .329 518 3414 | 3.034 732 4392 |
| 1-2 | 1.017 349 4975 | .495 699 9277 | 2.017 349 4975 |

## 4% per Period  $i = .04$

| | | | |
|---|---|---|---|
| 1-12 | 1.003 273 7398 | .081 843 4946 | 12.218 442 1063 |
| 1-6 | 1.006 558 1969 | .163 954 9234 | 6.099 237 3951 |
| 1-4 | 1.009 853 4065 | .246 335 1637 | 4.059 509 7544 |
| 1-3 | 1.013 159 4038 | .328 985 0955 | 3.039 651 3814 |
| 1-2 | 1.019 803 9027 | .495 097 5680 | 2.019 803 9027 |

## 5% per Period  $i = .05$

| | | | |
|---|---|---|---|
| 1-12 | 1.004 074 1238 | .081 482 4757 | 12.272 577 5296 |
| 1-6 | 1.008 164 8461 | .163 296 9210 | 6.123 814 1763 |
| 1-4 | 1.012 272 2344 | .245 444 6886 | 4.074 237 6858 |
| 1-3 | 1.016 396 3568 | .327 927 1363 | 3.049 457 9110 |
| 1-2 | 1.024 695 0766 | .493 901 5319 | 2.024 695 0766 |

## 6% per Period  $i = .06$

| | | | |
|---|---|---|---|
| 1-12 | 1.004 867 5506 | .081 125 8428 | 12.326 528 3420 |
| 1-6 | 1.009 758 7942 | .162 646 5697 | 6.148 300 5890 |
| 1-4 | 1.014 673 8462 | .244 564 1028 | 4.088 907 5237 |
| 1-3 | 1.019 612 8224 | .326 880 3737 | 3.059 223 1301 |
| 1-2 | 1.029 563 0141 | .492 716 9016 | 2.029 563 0141 |

## 7% per Period  $i = .07$

| | | | |
|---|---|---|---|
| 1-12 | 1.005 654 1454 | .080 773 5055 | 12.380 297 1455 |
| 1-6 | 1.011 340 2601 | .162 003 7162 | 6.172 697 9071 |
| 1-4 | 1.017 058 5250 | .243 693 2143 | 4.103 520 0870 |
| 1-3 | 1.022 809 1218 | .325 844 5967 | 3.068 947 6213 |
| 1-2 | 1.034 408 0433 | .491 543 4754 | 2.034 408 0433 |

## 8% per Period  $i = .08$

| | | | |
|---|---|---|---|
| 1-12 | 1.006 434 0301 | .080 425 3764 | 12.433 886 4805 |
| 1-6 | 1.012 909 4570 | .161 368 2120 | 6.197 007 3742 |
| 1-4 | 1.019 426 5469 | .242 831 8364 | 4.118 076 1757 |
| 1-3 | 1.025 985 5680 | .324 819 6001 | 3.078 631 9538 |
| 1-2 | 1.039 230 4845 | .490 381 0568 | 2.039 230 4845 |

# Table 4
## Present Worth of 1

| n | 4% | 6% | 8% | 10% | 12% | 14% | 15% | 16% | 18% | 20% | 22% | 24% |
|---|----|----|----|-----|-----|-----|-----|-----|-----|-----|-----|-----|
| 1 | .962 | .943 | .926 | .909 | .893 | .877 | .870 | .862 | .847 | .833 | .820 | .806 |
| 2 | .925 | .890 | .857 | .826 | .797 | .769 | .756 | .743 | .718 | .694 | .672 | .650 |
| 3 | .889 | .840 | .794 | .751 | .712 | .675 | .658 | .641 | .609 | .579 | .551 | .524 |
| 4 | .855 | .792 | .735 | .683 | .636 | .592 | .572 | .552 | .516 | .482 | .451 | .423 |
| 5 | .822 | .747 | .681 | .621 | .567 | .519 | .498 | .476 | .437 | .402 | .370 | .341 |
| 6 | .790 | .705 | .630 | .564 | .507 | .456 | .433 | .410 | .370 | .335 | .303 | .275 |
| 7 | .760 | .665 | .583 | .513 | .452 | .400 | .377 | .354 | .314 | .279 | .249 | .222 |
| 8 | .731 | .627 | .540 | .467 | .404 | .351 | .328 | .305 | .266 | .233 | .204 | .179 |
| 9 | .703 | .592 | .500 | .424 | .361 | .308 | .286 | .263 | .225 | .194 | .167 | .144 |
| 10 | .676 | .558 | .463 | .386 | .322 | .270 | .249 | .227 | .191 | .162 | .137 | .116 |
| 11 | .650 | .527 | .429 | .350 | .287 | .237 | | .195 | .162 | .135 | .112 | .094 |
| 12 | .625 | .497 | .397 | .319 | .257 | .208 | | .168 | .137 | .112 | .092 | .076 |
| 13 | .601 | .469 | .368 | .290 | .229 | .182 | | .145 | .116 | .093 | .075 | .061 |
| 14 | .577 | .442 | .340 | .263 | .205 | .160 | | .125 | .099 | .078 | .062 | .049 |
| 15 | .555 | .417 | .315 | .239 | .183 | .140 | | .108 | .084 | .065 | .051 | .040 |
| 16 | .534 | .394 | .292 | .218 | .163 | .123 | | .093 | .071 | .054 | .042 | .032 |
| 17 | .513 | .371 | .270 | .198 | .146 | .108 | | .080 | .060 | .045 | .034 | .026 |
| 18 | .494 | .350 | .250 | .180 | .130 | .095 | | .069 | .051 | .038 | .028 | .021 |
| 19 | .475 | .331 | .232 | .164 | .116 | .083 | | .060 | .043 | .031 | .023 | .017 |
| 20 | .456 | .312 | .215 | .149 | .104 | .073 | | .051 | .037 | .026 | .019 | .014 |
| 21 | .439 | .294 | .199 | .135 | .093 | .064 | | .044 | .031 | .022 | .015 | .011 |
| 22 | .422 | .278 | .184 | .123 | .083 | .056 | | .038 | .026 | .018 | .013 | .009 |
| 23 | .406 | .262 | .170 | .112 | .074 | .049 | | .033 | .022 | .015 | .010 | .007 |
| 24 | .390 | .247 | .158 | .102 | .066 | .043 | | .028 | .019 | .013 | .008 | .006 |
| 25 | .375 | .233 | .146 | .092 | .059 | .038 | | .024 | .016 | .010 | .007 | .005 |
| 26 | .361 | .220 | .135 | .084 | .053 | .033 | | .021 | .014 | .009 | .006 | .004 |
| 27 | .347 | .207 | .125 | .076 | .047 | .029 | | .018 | .011 | .007 | .005 | .003 |
| 28 | .333 | .196 | .116 | .069 | .042 | .026 | | .016 | .010 | .006 | .004 | .002 |
| 29 | .321 | .185 | .107 | .063 | .037 | .022 | | .014 | .008 | .005 | .003 | .002 |
| 30 | .308 | .174 | .099 | .057 | .033 | .020 | | .012 | .007 | .004 | .003 | .002 |
| 31 | .296 | .164 | .092 | .052 | .030 | .017 | | .010 | .006 | .004 | .002 | .001 |
| 32 | .285 | .155 | .085 | .047 | .027 | .015 | | .009 | .005 | .003 | .002 | .001 |
| 33 | .274 | .146 | .079 | .043 | .024 | .013 | | .007 | .004 | .002 | .001 | .001 |
| 34 | .264 | .138 | .073 | .039 | .021 | .012 | | .006 | .004 | .002 | .001 | .001 |
| 35 | .253 | .130 | .068 | .036 | .019 | .010 | | .006 | .003 | .002 | .001 | .001 |
| 36 | .244 | .123 | .063 | .032 | .017 | .009 | | .005 | .003 | .001 | .001 | — |
| 37 | .234 | .116 | .058 | .029 | .015 | .008 | | .004 | .002 | .001 | .001 | — |
| 38 | .225 | .109 | .054 | .027 | .013 | .007 | | .004 | .002 | .001 | .001 | — |
| 39 | .217 | .103 | .050 | .024 | .012 | .006 | | .003 | .002 | .001 | — | — |
| 40 | .208 | .097 | .046 | .022 | .011 | .005 | | .003 | .001 | .001 | — | — |
| 41 | .200 | .092 | .043 | .020 | .010 | .005 | | .002 | .001 | .001 | — | — |
| 42 | .193 | .087 | .039 | .018 | .009 | .004 | | .002 | .001 | — | — | — |
| 43 | .185 | .082 | .037 | .017 | .008 | .004 | | .002 | .001 | — | — | — |
| 44 | .178 | .077 | .034 | .015 | .007 | .003 | | .001 | .001 | — | — | — |
| 45 | .171 | .073 | .031 | .014 | .006 | .003 | | .001 | .001 | — | — | — |
| 46 | .165 | .069 | .029 | .012 | .005 | .002 | | .001 | — | — | — | — |
| 47 | .158 | .065 | .027 | .011 | .005 | .002 | | .001 | — | — | — | — |
| 48 | .152 | .061 | .025 | .010 | .004 | .002 | | .001 | — | — | — | — |
| 49 | .146 | .058 | .023 | .009 | .004 | .002 | | .001 | — | — | — | — |
| 50 | .141 | .054 | .021 | .009 | .003 | .001 | | .001 | — | — | — | — |

| | 25% | 30% | 35% | 40% | 45% | 50% | 60% | 70% | 80% | 90% | 100% |
|---|-----|-----|-----|-----|-----|-----|-----|-----|-----|-----|------|
| 1 | .800 | .769 | .741 | .714 | .690 | .667 | .625 | .588 | .556 | .526 | .500 |
| 2 | .640 | .592 | .549 | .510 | .476 | .444 | .391 | .346 | .309 | .277 | .250 |
| 3 | .512 | .455 | .406 | .364 | .328 | .296 | .244 | .204 | .171 | .146 | .125 |
| 4 | .410 | .350 | .301 | .260 | .226 | .198 | .153 | .120 | .095 | .077 | .063 |
| 5 | .328 | .269 | .223 | .186 | .156 | .132 | .095 | .070 | .053 | .040 | .031 |
| 6 | .262 | .207 | .165 | .133 | .108 | .088 | .060 | .041 | .029 | .021 | .016 |
| 7 | .210 | .159 | .122 | .095 | .074 | .059 | .037 | .024 | .016 | .011 | .008 |
| 8 | .168 | .123 | .091 | .068 | .051 | .039 | .023 | .014 | .009 | .006 | .004 |
| 9 | .134 | .094 | .067 | .048 | .035 | .026 | .015 | .008 | .005 | .003 | .002 |
| 10 | .107 | .073 | .050 | .035 | .024 | .017 | .009 | .005 | .003 | .002 | .001 |
| 11 | .086 | .056 | .037 | .025 | .017 | .012 | .006 | .003 | .002 | .001 | — |
| 12 | .069 | .043 | .027 | .018 | .012 | .008 | .004 | .002 | .001 | — | — |
| 13 | .055 | .033 | .020 | .013 | .008 | .005 | .002 | .001 | — | — | — |
| 14 | .044 | .025 | .015 | .009 | .006 | .003 | .001 | .001 | — | — | — |
| 15 | .035 | .020 | .011 | .006 | .004 | .002 | .001 | — | — | — | — |
| 16 | .028 | .015 | .008 | .005 | .003 | .002 | .001 | — | — | — | — |
| 17 | .023 | .012 | .006 | .003 | .002 | .001 | — | — | — | — | — |
| 18 | .018 | .009 | .005 | .002 | .001 | .001 | — | — | — | — | — |
| 19 | .014 | .007 | .003 | .002 | .001 | — | — | — | — | — | — |
| 20 | .012 | .005 | .002 | .001 | .001 | — | — | — | — | — | — |

# Table 4 (Continued)
## Present Worth of 1 Per Period

| n | 4% | 6% | 8% | 10% | 12% | 14% | 16% | 18% | 20% | 22% | 24% |
|---|---|---|---|---|---|---|---|---|---|---|---|
| 1 | .962 | .943 | .926 | .909 | .893 | .877 | .862 | .847 | .833 | .820 | .806 |
| 2 | 1.886 | 1.833 | 1.783 | 1.736 | 1.690 | 1.647 | 1.605 | 1.566 | 1.528 | 1.492 | 1.457 |
| 3 | 2.775 | 2.673 | 2.577 | 2.487 | 2.402 | 2.322 | 2.246 | 2.174 | 2.106 | 2.042 | 1.981 |
| 4 | 3.630 | 3.465 | 3.312 | 3.170 | 3.037 | 2.914 | 2.798 | 2.690 | 2.589 | 2.494 | 2.404 |
| 5 | 4.452 | 4.212 | 3.993 | 3.791 | 3.605 | 3.433 | 3.274 | 3.127 | 2.991 | 2.864 | 2.745 |
| 6 | 5.242 | 4.917 | 4.623 | 4.355 | 4.111 | 3.889 | 3.685 | 3.498 | 3.326 | 3.167 | 3.020 |
| 7 | 6.002 | 5.582 | 5.206 | 4.868 | 4.564 | 4.288 | 4.039 | 3.812 | 3.605 | 3.416 | 3.242 |
| 8 | 6.733 | 6.210 | 5.747 | 5.335 | 4.968 | 4.639 | 4.344 | 4.078 | 3.837 | 3.619 | 3.421 |
| 9 | 7.435 | 6.802 | 6.247 | 5.759 | 5.328 | 4.946 | 4.607 | 4.303 | 4.031 | 3.786 | 3.566 |
| 10 | 8.111 | 7.360 | 6.710 | 6.145 | 5.650 | 5.216 | 4.833 | 4.494 | 4.192 | 3.923 | 3.682 |
| 11 | 8.760 | 7.887 | 7.139 | 6.495 | 5.938 | 5.453 | 5.029 | 4.656 | 4.327 | 4.035 | 3.776 |
| 12 | 9.385 | 8.384 | 7.536 | 6.814 | 6.194 | 5.660 | 5.197 | 4.793 | 4.439 | 4.127 | 3.851 |
| 13 | 9.986 | 8.853 | 7.904 | 7.103 | 6.424 | 5.842 | 5.342 | 4.910 | 4.533 | 4.203 | 3.912 |
| 14 | 10.563 | 9.295 | 8.244 | 7.367 | 6.628 | 6.002 | 5.468 | 5.008 | 4.611 | 4.265 | 3.962 |
| 15 | 11.118 | 9.712 | 8.559 | 7.606 | 6.811 | 6.142 | 5.575 | 5.092 | 4.675 | 4.315 | 4.001 |
| 16 | 11.652 | 10.106 | 8.851 | 7.824 | 6.974 | 6.265 | 5.668 | 5.162 | 4.730 | 4.357 | 4.033 |
| 17 | 12.166 | 10.477 | 9.122 | 8.022 | 7.120 | 6.373 | 5.749 | 5.222 | 4.775 | 4.391 | 4.059 |
| 18 | 12.659 | 10.828 | 9.372 | 8.201 | 7.250 | 6.467 | 5.818 | 5.273 | 4.812 | 4.419 | 4.080 |
| 19 | 13.134 | 11.158 | 9.604 | 8.365 | 7.366 | 6.550 | 5.877 | 5.316 | 4.843 | 4.442 | 4.097 |
| 20 | 13.590 | 11.470 | 9.818 | 8.514 | 7.469 | 6.623 | 5.929 | 5.353 | 4.870 | 4.460 | 4.110 |
| 21 | 14.029 | 11.764 | 10.017 | 8.649 | 7.562 | 6.687 | 5.973 | 5.384 | 4.891 | 4.476 | 4.121 |
| 22 | 14.451 | 12.042 | 10.201 | 8.772 | 7.645 | 6.743 | 6.011 | 5.410 | 4.909 | 4.488 | 4.130 |
| 23 | 14.857 | 12.303 | 10.371 | 8.883 | 7.718 | 6.792 | 6.044 | 5.432 | 4.925 | 4.499 | 4.137 |
| 24 | 15.247 | 12.550 | 10.529 | 8.985 | 7.784 | 6.835 | 6.073 | 5.451 | 4.937 | 4.507 | 4.143 |
| 25 | 15.622 | 12.783 | 10.675 | 9.077 | 7.843 | 6.873 | 6.097 | 5.467 | 4.948 | 4.514 | 4.147 |
| 26 | 15.983 | 13.003 | 10.810 | 9.161 | 7.896 | 6.906 | 6.118 | 5.480 | 4.956 | 4.520 | 4.151 |
| 27 | 16.330 | 13.211 | 10.935 | 9.237 | 7.943 | 6.935 | 6.136 | 5.492 | 4.964 | 4.524 | 4.154 |
| 28 | 16.663 | 13.406 | 11.051 | 9.307 | 7.984 | 6.961 | 6.152 | 5.502 | 4.970 | 4.528 | 4.157 |
| 29 | 16.984 | 13.591 | 11.158 | 9.370 | 8.022 | 6.983 | 6.166 | 5.510 | 4.975 | 4.531 | 4.159 |
| 30 | 17.292 | 13.765 | 11.258 | 9.427 | 8.055 | 7.003 | 6.177 | 5.517 | 4.979 | 4.534 | 4.160 |
| 31 | 17.588 | 13.929 | 11.350 | 9.479 | 8.085 | 7.020 | 6.187 | 5.523 | 4.982 | 4.536 | 4.161 |
| 32 | 17.874 | 14.084 | 11.435 | 9.526 | 8.112 | 7.035 | 6.196 | 5.528 | 4.985 | 4.538 | 4.162 |
| 33 | 18.148 | 14.230 | 11.514 | 9.569 | 8.135 | 7.048 | 6.203 | 5.532 | 4.988 | 4.539 | 4.163 |
| 34 | 18.411 | 14.368 | 11.587 | 9.609 | 8.157 | 7.060 | 6.210 | 5.536 | 4.990 | 4.540 | 4.164 |
| 35 | 18.665 | 14.498 | 11.655 | 9.644 | 8.176 | 7.070 | 6.215 | 5.539 | 4.992 | 4.541 | 4.164 |
| 36 | 18.908 | 14.621 | 11.717 | 9.677 | 8.192 | 7.079 | 6.220 | 5.541 | 4.993 | 4.542 | 4.165 |
| 37 | 19.143 | 14.737 | 11.775 | 9.706 | 8.208 | 7.087 | 6.224 | 5.543 | 4.994 | 4.543 | 4.165 |
| 38 | 19.368 | 14.846 | 11.829 | 9.733 | 8.221 | 7.094 | 6.228 | 5.545 | 4.995 | 4.543 | 4.165 |
| 39 | 19.584 | 14.949 | 11.879 | 9.757 | 8.233 | 7.100 | 6.231 | 5.547 | 4.996 | 4.544 | 4.166 |
| 40 | 19.793 | 15.046 | 11.925 | 9.779 | 8.244 | 7.105 | 6.233 | 5.548 | 4.997 | 4.544 | 4.166 |
| 41 | 19.993 | 15.138 | 11.967 | 9.799 | 8.253 | 7.110 | 6.236 | 5.549 | 4.997 | 4.544 | 4.166 |
| 42 | 20.186 | 15.225 | 12.007 | 9.817 | 8.262 | 7.114 | 6.238 | 5.550 | 4.998 | 4.544 | 4.166 |
| 43 | 20.371 | 15.306 | 12.043 | 9.834 | 8.270 | 7.117 | 6.239 | 5.551 | 4.998 | 4.545 | 4.166 |
| 44 | 20.549 | 15.383 | 12.077 | 9.849 | 8.276 | 7.120 | 6.241 | 5.552 | 4.998 | 4.545 | 4.166 |
| 45 | 20.720 | 15.456 | 12.108 | 9.863 | 8.283 | 7.123 | 6.242 | 5.552 | 4.999 | 4.545 | 4.166 |
| 46 | 20.885 | 15.524 | 12.137 | 9.875 | 8.288 | 7.126 | 6.243 | 5.553 | 4.999 | 4.545 | 4.166 |
| 47 | 21.043 | 15.589 | 12.164 | 9.887 | 8.293 | 7.128 | 6.244 | 5.553 | 4.999 | 4.545 | 4.166 |
| 48 | 21.195 | 15.650 | 12.189 | 9.897 | 8.297 | 7.130 | 6.245 | 5.554 | 4.999 | 4.545 | 4.167 |
| 49 | 21.341 | 15.708 | 12.212 | 9.906 | 8.301 | 7.131 | 6.246 | 5.554 | 4.999 | 4.545 | 4.167 |
| 50 | 21.482 | 15.762 | 12.233 | 9.915 | 8.304 | 7.133 | 6.246 | 5.554 | 4.999 | 4.545 | 4.167 |

| n | 25% | 30% | 35% | 40% | 45% | 50% | 60% | 70% | 80% | 90% | 100% |
|---|---|---|---|---|---|---|---|---|---|---|---|
| 1 | .800 | .769 | .741 | .714 | .690 | .667 | .625 | .588 | .556 | .526 | .500 |
| 2 | 1.440 | 1.361 | 1.289 | 1.224 | 1.165 | 1.111 | 1.016 | .934 | .864 | .803 | .750 |
| 3 | 1.952 | 1.816 | 1.696 | 1.589 | 1.493 | 1.407 | 1.260 | 1.138 | 1.036 | .949 | .875 |
| 4 | 2.362 | 2.166 | 1.997 | 1.849 | 1.720 | 1.605 | 1.412 | 1.258 | 1.131 | 1.026 | .938 |
| 5 | 2.689 | 2.436 | 2.220 | 2.035 | 1.876 | 1.737 | 1.508 | 1.328 | 1.184 | 1.066 | .969 |
| 6 | 2.951 | 2.643 | 2.385 | 2.168 | 1.983 | 1.824 | 1.567 | 1.369 | 1.213 | 1.087 | .984 |
| 7 | 3.161 | 2.802 | 2.508 | 2.263 | 2.057 | 1.883 | 1.605 | 1.394 | 1.230 | 1.099 | .992 |
| 8 | 3.329 | 2.925 | 2.598 | 2.331 | 2.109 | 1.922 | 1.628 | 1.408 | 1.239 | 1.105 | .996 |
| 9 | 3.463 | 3.019 | 2.665 | 2.379 | 2.144 | 1.948 | 1.642 | 1.417 | 1.244 | 1.108 | .998 |
| 10 | 3.571 | 3.092 | 2.715 | 2.414 | 2.168 | 1.965 | 1.652 | 1.421 | 1.246 | 1.109 | .999 |
| 11 | 3.656 | 3.147 | 2.752 | 2.438 | 2.185 | 1.977 | 1.657 | 1.424 | 1.248 | 1.110 | 1.000 |
| 12 | 3.725 | 3.190 | 2.779 | 2.456 | 2.196 | 1.985 | 1.661 | 1.426 | 1.249 | 1.111 | 1.000 |
| 13 | 3.780 | 3.223 | 2.799 | 2.469 | 2.204 | 1.990 | 1.663 | 1.427 | 1.249 | 1.111 | 1.000 |
| 14 | 3.824 | 3.249 | 2.814 | 2.478 | 2.210 | 1.993 | 1.664 | 1.428 | 1.250 | 1.111 | 1.000 |
| 15 | 3.859 | 3.268 | 2.825 | 2.484 | 2.214 | 1.995 | 1.665 | 1.428 | 1.250 | 1.111 | 1.000 |
| 16 | 3.887 | 3.283 | 2.834 | 2.489 | 2.216 | 1.997 | 1.666 | 1.428 | 1.250 | 1.111 | 1.000 |
| 17 | 3.910 | 3.295 | 2.840 | 2.492 | 2.218 | 1.998 | 1.666 | 1.428 | 1.250 | 1.111 | 1.000 |
| 18 | 3.928 | 3.304 | 2.844 | 2.494 | 2.219 | 1.999 | 1.666 | 1.428 | 1.250 | 1.111 | 1.000 |
| 19 | 3.942 | 3.311 | 2.848 | 2.496 | 2.220 | 1.999 | 1.666 | 1.429 | 1.250 | 1.111 | 1.000 |
| 20 | 3.954 | 3.316 | 2.850 | 2.497 | 2.221 | 1.999 | 1.667 | 1.429 | 1.250 | 1.111 | 1.000 |

78

## Table 5

### 1958 *Commissioners Standard Ordinary (CSO) Mortality Table*

Values for females age 0 to 14 are in the complete tables of the Society of Actuaries from which these data are reproduced with permission of the Society.

| Age x M | F | Number Living $l_x$ | Number Dying $d_x$ | Deaths per 1000 $1000q_x$ | Age x M | F | Number Living $l_x$ | Number Dying $d_x$ | Deaths per 1000 $1000q_x$ |
|---|---|---|---|---|---|---|---|---|---|
| 0 | | 10 000 000 | 70 800 | 7.08 | 50 | 53 | 8 762 306 | 72 902 | 8.32 |
| 1 | | 9 929 200 | 17 475 | 1.76 | 51 | 54 | 8 689 404 | 79 160 | 9.11 |
| 2 | | 9 911 725 | 15 066 | 1.52 | 52 | 55 | 8 610 244 | 85 758 | 9.96 |
| 3 | | 9 896 659 | 14 449 | 1.46 | 53 | 56 | 8 524 486 | 92 832 | 10.89 |
| 4 | | 9 882 210 | 13 835 | 1.40 | 54 | 57 | 8 431 654 | 100 337 | 11.90 |
| 5 | | 9 868 375 | 13 322 | 1.35 | 55 | 58 | 8 331 317 | 108 307 | 13.00 |
| 6 | | 9 855 053 | 12 812 | 1.30 | 56 | 59 | 8 223 010 | 116 849 | 14.21 |
| 7 | | 9 842 241 | 12 401 | 1.26 | 57 | 60 | 8 106 161 | 125 970 | 15.54 |
| 8 | | 9 829 840 | 12 091 | 1.23 | 58 | 61 | 7 980 191 | 135 663 | 17.00 |
| 9 | | 9 817 749 | 11 879 | 1.21 | 59 | 62 | 7 844 528 | 145 830 | 18.59 |
| 10 | | 9 805 870 | 11 865 | 1.21 | 60 | 63 | 7 698 698 | 156 592 | 20.34 |
| 11 | | 9 794 005 | 12 047 | 1.23 | 61 | 64 | 7 542 106 | 167 736 | 22.24 |
| 12 | 15 | 9 781 958 | 12 325 | 1.26 | 62 | 65 | 7 374 370 | 179 271 | 24.31 |
| 13 | 16 | 9 769 633 | 12 896 | 1.32 | 63 | 66 | 7 195 099 | 191 174 | 26.57 |
| 14 | 17 | 9 756 737 | 13 562 | 1.39 | 64 | 67 | 7 003 925 | 203 394 | 29.04 |
| 15 | 18 | 9 743 175 | 14 225 | 1.46 | 65 | 68 | 6 800 531 | 215 917 | 31.75 |
| 16 | 19 | 9 728 950 | 14 983 | 1.54 | 66 | 69 | 6 584 614 | 228 749 | 34.74 |
| 17 | 20 | 9 713 967 | 15 737 | 1.62 | 67 | 70 | 6 355 865 | 241 777 | 38.04 |
| 18 | 21 | 9 698 230 | 16 390 | 1.69 | 68 | 71 | 6 114 088 | 254 835 | 41.68 |
| 19 | 22 | 9 681 840 | 16 846 | 1.74 | 69 | 72 | 5 859 253 | 267 241 | 45.61 |
| 20 | 23 | 9 664 994 | 17 300 | 1.79 | 70 | 73 | 5 592 012 | 278 426 | 49.79 |
| 21 | 24 | 9 647 694 | 17 655 | 1.83 | 71 | 74 | 5 313 586 | 287 731 | 54.15 |
| 22 | 25 | 9 630 039 | 17 912 | 1.86 | 72 | 75 | 5 025 855 | 294 766 | 58.65 |
| 23 | 26 | 9 612 127 | 18 167 | 1.89 | 73 | 76 | 4 731 089 | 299 289 | 63.26 |
| 24 | 27 | 9 593 960 | 18 324 | 1.91 | 74 | 77 | 4 431 800 | 301 894 | 68.12 |
| 25 | 28 | 9 575 636 | 18 481 | 1.93 | 75 | 78 | 4 129 906 | 303 011 | 73.37 |
| 26 | 29 | 9 557 155 | 18 732 | 1.96 | 76 | 79 | 3 826 895 | 303 014 | 79.18 |
| 27 | 30 | 9 538 423 | 18 981 | 1.99 | 77 | 80 | 3 523 881 | 301 997 | 85.70 |
| 28 | 31 | 9 519 442 | 19 324 | 2.03 | 78 | 81 | 3 221 884 | 299 829 | 93.06 |
| 29 | 32 | 9 500 118 | 19 760 | 2.08 | 79 | 82 | 2 922 055 | 295 683 | 101.19 |
| 30 | 33 | 9 480 358 | 20 193 | 2.13 | 80 | 83 | 2 626 372 | 288 848 | 109.98 |
| 31 | 34 | 9 460 165 | 20 718 | 2.19 | 81 | 84 | 2 337 524 | 278 983 | 119.35 |
| 32 | 35 | 9 439 447 | 21 239 | 2.25 | 82 | 85 | 2 058 541 | 265 902 | 129.17 |
| 33 | 36 | 9 418 208 | 21 850 | 2.32 | 83 | 86 | 1 792 639 | 249 858 | 139.38 |
| 34 | 37 | 9 396 358 | 22 551 | 2.40 | 84 | 87 | 1 542 781 | 231 433 | 150.01 |
| 35 | 38 | 9 373 807 | 23 528 | 2.51 | 85 | 88 | 1 311 348 | 211 311 | 161.14 |
| 36 | 39 | 9 350 279 | 24 685 | 2.64 | 86 | 89 | 1 100 037 | 190 108 | 172.82 |
| 37 | 40 | 9 325 594 | 26 112 | 2.80 | 87 | 90 | 909 929 | 168 455 | 185.13 |
| 38 | 41 | 9 299 482 | 27 991 | 3.01 | 88 | 91 | 741 474 | 146 997 | 198.25 |
| 39 | 42 | 9 271 491 | 30 132 | 3.25 | 89 | 92 | 594 477 | 126 303 | 212.46 |
| 40 | 43 | 9 241 359 | 32 622 | 3.53 | 90 | 93 | 468 174 | 106 809 | 228.14 |
| 41 | 44 | 9 208 737 | 35 362 | 3.84 | 91 | 94 | 361 365 | 88 813 | 245.77 |
| 42 | 45 | 9 173 375 | 38 253 | 4.17 | 92 | 95 | 272 552 | 72 480 | 265.93 |
| 43 | 46 | 9 135 122 | 41 382 | 4.53 | 93 | 96 | 200 072 | 57 881 | 289.30 |
| 44 | 47 | 9 093 740 | 44 741 | 4.92 | 94 | 97 | 142 191 | 45 026 | 316.66 |
| 45 | 48 | 9 048 999 | 48 412 | 5.35 | 95 | 98 | 97 165 | 34 128 | 351.24 |
| 46 | 49 | 9 000 587 | 52 473 | 5.83 | 96 | 99 | 63 037 | 25 250 | 400.56 |
| 47 | 50 | 8 948 114 | 56 910 | 6.36 | 97 | 100 | 37 787 | 18 456 | 488.42 |
| 48 | 51 | 8 891 204 | 61 794 | 6.95 | 98 | 101 | 19 331 | 12 916 | 668.15 |
| 49 | 52 | 8 829 410 | 67 104 | 7.60 | 99 | 102 | 6 415 | 6 415 | 1000.00 |

## Table 6

*Commutation Columns, Interest at 2½%*

Values for females age 0 to 14 are in the complete tables of the Society of Actuaries from which these data are reproduced with permission of the Society.

| Age | | | | | | Annuity Due | Life Insurance |
|---|---|---|---|---|---|---|---|
| M | F | $D_x$ | $N_x$ | $C_x$ | $M_x$ | $\ddot{a}_x$ | $1000A_x$ |
| 0 |  | 10 000 000.0 | 324 850 105.9 | 69 073.171 | 2 076 826.724 | 32.48 5011 | 207.68 267 |
| 1 |  | 9 687 024.4 | 314 850 105.9 | 16 632.957 | 2 007 753.553 | 32.50 2252 | 207.26 216 |
| 2 |  | 9 434 122.6 | 305 163 081.5 | 13 990.279 | 1 991 120.596 | 32.34 6737 | 211.05 520 |
| 3 |  | 9 190 031.7 | 295 728 958.9 | 13 090.081 | 1 977 130.317 | 32.17 9319 | 215.13 857 |
| 4 |  | 8 952 794.5 | 286 538 927.2 | 12 228.124 | 1 964 040.236 | 32.00 5529 | 219.37 734 |
| 5 |  | 8 722 205.6 | 277 586 132.7 | 11 487.519 | 1 951 812.112 | 31.82 5222 | 223.77 506 |
| 6 |  | 8 497 981.4 | 268 863 927.1 | 10 778.290 | 1 940 324.593 | 31.63 8564 | 228.32 771 |
| 7 |  | 8 279 935.2 | 260 365 945.7 | 10 178.078 | 1 929 546.303 | 31.44 5409 | 233.03 882 |
| 8 |  | 8 067 807.5 | 252 086 010.5 | 9 681.607 | 1 919 368.225 | 31.24 5913 | 237.90 456 |
| 9 |  | 7 861 350.1 | 244 018 203.0 | 9 279.856 | 1 909 686.618 | 31.04 0241 | 242.92 095 |
| 10 |  | 7 660 330.0 | 236 156 852.9 | 9 042.848 | 1 900 406.762 | 30.82 8548 | 248.08 419 |
| 11 |  | 7 464 449.8 | 228 496 522.9 | 8 957.618 | 1 891 363.914 | 30.61 1301 | 253.38 290 |
| 12 | 15 | 7 273 432.5 | 221 032 073.1 | 8 940.806 | 1 882 406.296 | 30.38 8963 | 258.80 577 |
| 13 | 16 | 7 087 090.9 | 213 758 640.6 | 9 126.850 | 1 873 465.490 | 30.16 1690 | 264.34 901 |
| 14 | 17 | 6 905 108.2 | 206 671 549.7 | 9 364.094 | 1 864 338.640 | 29.93 0241 | 269.99 412 |
| 15 | 18 | 6 727 326.8 | 199 766 441.5 | 9 582.315 | 1 854 974.546 | 29.69 4773 | 275.73 724 |
| 16 | 19 | 6 553 663.3 | 193 039 114.7 | 9 846.754 | 1 845 392.231 | 29.45 5147 | 281.58 179 |
| 17 | 20 | 6 383 971.1 | 186 485 451.4 | 10 090.028 | 1 835 545.477 | 29.21 1512 | 287.52 409 |
| 18 | 21 | 6 218 174.5 | 180 101 480.3 | 10 252.399 | 1 825 455.449 | 28.96 3722 | 293.56 774 |
| 19 | 22 | 6 056 259.3 | 173 883 305.8 | 10 280.624 | 1 815 203.050 | 28.71 1338 | 299.72 347 |
| 20 | 23 | 5 898 265.0 | 167 827 046.5 | 10 300.183 | 1 804 922.426 | 28.45 3629 | 306.00 904 |
| 21 | 24 | 5 744 104.7 | 161 928 781.5 | 10 255.166 | 1 794 622.243 | 28.19 0430 | 312.42 854 |
| 22 | 25 | 5 593 749.4 | 156 184 676.8 | 10 150.681 | 1 784 367.077 | 27.92 1286 | 318.99 303 |
| 23 | 26 | 5 447 165.8 | 150 590 927.4 | 10 044.086 | 1 774 216.396 | 27.64 5740 | 325.71 368 |
| 24 | 27 | 5 304 264.0 | 145 143 761.6 | 9 883.793 | 1 764 172.310 | 27.36 3601 | 332.59 512 |
| 25 | 28 | 5 165 008.0 | 139 839 497.6 | 9 725.344 | 1 754 288.517 | 27.07 4401 | 339.64 875 |
| 26 | 29 | 5 029 306.8 | 134 674 489.6 | 9 617.004 | 1 744 563.173 | 26.77 7943 | 346.87 945 |
| 27 | 30 | 4 897 023.8 | 129 645 182.8 | 9 507.161 | 1 734 946.169 | 26.47 4281 | 354.28 584 |
| 28 | 31 | 4 768 077.0 | 124 748 159.0 | 9 442.890 | 1 725 439.008 | 26.16 3201 | 361.87 314 |
| 29 | 32 | 4 642 339.5 | 119 980 082.0 | 9 420.436 | 1 715 996.118 | 25.84 4745 | 369.64 038 |
| 30 | 33 | 4 519 691.4 | 115 337 742.5 | 9 392.064 | 1 706 575.682 | 25.51 8942 | 377.58 677 |
| 31 | 34 | 4 400 062.9 | 110 818 051.1 | 9 401.218 | 1 697 183.618 | 25.18 5561 | 385.71 804 |
| 32 | 35 | 4 283 343.1 | 106 417 988.2 | 9 402.569 | 1 687 782.400 | 24.84 4610 | 394.03 390 |
| 33 | 36 | 4 169 468.7 | 102 134 645.1 | 9 437.132 | 1 678 379.831 | 24.49 5842 | 402.54 046 |
| 34 | 37 | 4 058 337.2 | 97 965 176.4 | 9 502.339 | 1 668 942.699 | 24.13 9240 | 411.23 806 |
| 35 | 38 | 3 949 851.1 | 93 906 839.2 | 9 672.213 | 1 659 440.360 | 23.77 4780 | 420.12 732 |
| 36 | 39 | 3 843 841.0 | 89 956 988.1 | 9 900.340 | 1 649 768.147 | 23.40 2890 | 429.19 781 |
| 37 | 40 | 3 740 188.5 | 86 113 147.1 | 10 217.232 | 1 639 867.807 | 23.02 3745 | 438.44 523 |
| 38 | 41 | 3 638 747.1 | 82 372 958.6 | 10 685.323 | 1 629 650.575 | 22.63 7726 | 447.86 036 |
| 39 | 42 | 3 539 311.9 | 78 734 211.5 | 11 222.079 | 1 618 965.252 | 22.24 5627 | 457.42 373 |
| 40 | 43 | 3 441 765.1 | 75 194 899.6 | 11 853.104 | 1 607 743.173 | 21.84 7772 | 467.12 751 |
| 41 | 44 | 3 345 966.5 | 71 753 134.5 | 12 535.293 | 1 595 890.069 | 21.44 4666 | 476.95 937 |
| 42 | 45 | 3 251 822.3 | 68 407 168.0 | 13 229.374 | 1 583 354.776 | 21.03 6564 | 486.91 307 |
| 43 | 46 | 3 159 280.2 | 65 155 345.7 | 13 962.442 | 1 570 125.402 | 20.62 3478 | 496.98 833 |
| 44 | 47 | 3 068 262.1 | 61 996 065.5 | 14 727.592 | 1 556 162.960 | 20.20 5596 | 507.18 058 |
| 45 | 48 | 2 978 698.8 | 58 927 803.4 | 15 547.309 | 1 541 435.368 | 19.78 3069 | 517.48 615 |
| 46 | 49 | 2 890 500.4 | 55 949 104.6 | 16 440.470 | 1 525 888.059 | 19.35 6200 | 527.89 754 |
| 47 | 50 | 2 803 559.9 | 53 058 604.2 | 17 395.746 | 1 509 447.589 | 18.92 5440 | 538.40 390 |
| 48 | 51 | 2 717 784.6 | 50 255 044.3 | 18 427.945 | 1 492 051.843 | 18.49 1180 | 548.99 562 |
| 49 | 52 | 2 633 069.2 | 47 537 259.7 | 19 523.386 | 1 473 623.898 | 18.05 3935 | 559.66 015 |

## Table 6 (Continued)
*Commutation Columns, Interest at 2½%*

| Age $x$ M | F | $D_x$ | $N_x$ | $C_x$ | $M_x$ | Annuity Due $\ddot{a}_x$ | Life Insurance $1000A_x$ |
|---|---|---|---|---|---|---|---|
| 50 | 53 | 2 549 324.7 | 44 904 190.5 | 20 692.945 | 1 454 100.512 | 17.61 4151 | 570.38 655 |
| 51 | 54 | 2 466 453.1 | 42 354 865.8 | 21 921.223 | 1 433 407.567 | 17.17 2378 | 581.16 149 |
| 52 | 55 | 2 384 374.4 | 39 888 412.7 | 23 169.133 | 1 411 486.344 | 16.72 9089 | 591.97 345 |
| 53 | 56 | 2 303 049.8 | 37 504 038.3 | 24 468.592 | 1 388 317.211 | 16.28 4510 | 602.81 684 |
| 54 | 57 | 2 222 409.3 | 35 200 988.5 | 25 801.712 | 1 363 848.619 | 15.83 9111 | 613.68 022 |
| 55 | 58 | 2 142 402.5 | 32 978 579.2 | 27 171.903 | 1 338 046.907 | 15.39 3270 | 624.55 440 |
| 56 | 59 | 2 062 976.8 | 30 836 176.7 | 28 599.910 | 1 310 875.004 | 14.94 7418 | 635.42 886 |
| 57 | 60 | 1 984 060.4 | 28 773 199.9 | 30 080.354 | 1 282 275.094 | 14.50 2179 | 646.28 834 |
| 58 | 61 | 1 905 588.4 | 26 789 139.5 | 31 604.823 | 1 252 194.740 | 14.05 8198 | 657.11 711 |
| 59 | 62 | 1 827 505.8 | 24 883 551.1 | 33 144.766 | 1 220 589.917 | 13.61 6127 | 667.89 934 |
| 60 | 63 | 1 749 787.7 | 23 056 045.3 | 34 722.724 | 1 187 445.151 | 13.17 6482 | 678.62 241 |
| 61 | 64 | 1 672 387.3 | 21 306 257.6 | 36 286.629 | 1 152 722.427 | 12.74 0026 | 689.26 763 |
| 62 | 65 | 1 595 310.7 | 19 633 870.3 | 37 836.114 | 1 116 435.798 | 12.30 7239 | 699.82 342 |
| 63 | 66 | 1 518 564.6 | 18 038 559.6 | 39 364.201 | 1 078 599.684 | 11.87 8691 | 710.27 580 |
| 64 | 67 | 1 442 162.2 | 16 519 995.0 | 40 858.920 | 1 039 235.483 | 11.45 5019 | 720.60 929 |
| 65 | 68 | 1 366 128.5 | 15 077 832.8 | 42 316.694 | 998 376.563 | 11.03 6907 | 730.80 721 |
| 66 | 69 | 1 290 491.7 | 13 711 704.3 | 43 738.131 | 956 059.869 | 10.62 5178 | 740.84 930 |
| 67 | 70 | 1 215 278.1 | 12 421 212.6 | 45 101.621 | 912 321.738 | 10.22 0881 | 750.71 026 |
| 68 | 71 | 1 140 535.6 | 11 205 934.5 | 46 378.038 | 867 220.117 | 9.82 5151 | 760.36 216 |
| 69 | 72 | 1 066 339.6 | 10 065 398.9 | 47 449.596 | 820 842.079 | 9.43 9206 | 769.77 548 |
| 70 | 73 | 992 881.8 | 8 999 059.3 | 48 229.787 | 773 392.483 | 9.06 3576 | 778.93 711 |
| 71 | 74 | 920 435.3 | 8 006 177.5 | 48 625.978 | 725 162.696 | 8.69 8251 | 787.84 755 |
| 72 | 75 | 849 359.7 | 7 085 742.2 | 48 599.883 | 676 536.718 | 8.34 2452 | 796.52 557 |
| 73 | 76 | 780 043.7 | 6 236 382.5 | 48 142.066 | 627 936.835 | 7.99 4914 | 805.00 212 |
| 74 | 77 | 712 876.2 | 5 456 338.8 | 47 376.675 | 579 794.769 | 7.65 3978 | 813.31 761 |
| 75 | 78 | 648 112.3 | 4 743 462.6 | 46 392.163 | 532 418.094 | 7.31 8890 | 821.49 049 |
| 76 | 79 | 585 912.5 | 4 095 350.3 | 45 261.095 | 486 025.931 | 6.98 9696 | 829.51 965 |
| 77 | 80 | 526 360.9 | 3 509 437.8 | 44 008.963 | 440 764.836 | 6.66 7360 | 837.38 142 |
| 78 | 81 | 469 513.8 | 2 983 076.9 | 42 627.343 | 396 755.873 | 6.35 3545 | 845.03 559 |
| 79 | 82 | 415 434.9 | 2 513 563.1 | 41 012.583 | 354 128.530 | 6.05 0438 | 852.42 846 |
| 80 | 83 | 364 289.8 | 2 098 128.2 | 39 087.353 | 313 115.947 | 5.75 9503 | 859.52 433 |
| 81 | 84 | 316 317.3 | 1 733 838.4 | 36 831.617 | 274 028.594 | 5.48 1327 | 866.30 922 |
| 82 | 85 | 271 770.7 | 1 417 521.1 | 34 248.438 | 237 196.977 | 5.21 5872 | 872.78 348 |
| 83 | 86 | 230 893.7 | 1 145 750.4 | 31 397.029 | 202 948.539 | 4.96 2242 | 878.96 958 |
| 84 | 87 | 193 865.1 | 914 856.7 | 28 372.443 | 171 551.510 | 4.71 9038 | 884.90 146 |
| 85 | 88 | 160 764.2 | 720 991.6 | 25 273.751 | 143 179.067 | 4.48 4777 | 890.61 537 |
| 86 | 89 | 131 569.4 | 560 227.4 | 22 183.195 | 117 905.316 | 4.25 8037 | 896.14 543 |
| 87 | 90 | 106 177.2 | 428 658.0 | 19 177.136 | 95 722.121 | 4.03 7194 | 901.53 179 |
| 88 | 91 | 84 410.4 | 322 480.8 | 16 326.175 | 76 544.985 | 3.82 0392 | 906.81 936 |
| 89 | 92 | 66 025.4 | 238 070.4 | 13 685.661 | 60 218.810 | 3.60 5740 | 912.05 521 |
| 90 | 93 | 50 729.4 | 172 045.0 | 11 291.096 | 46 533.149 | 3.39 1426 | 917.28 167 |
| 91 | 94 | 38 201.0 | 121 315.6 | 9 159.693 | 35 242.053 | 3.17 5718 | 922.54 268 |
| 92 | 95 | 28 109.5 | 83 114.6 | 7 292.874 | 26 082.360 | 2.95 6815 | 927.88 417 |
| 93 | 96 | 20 131.1 | 55 005.1 | 5 681.888 | 18 789.486 | 2.73 2344 | 933.35 615 |
| 94 | 97 | 13 958.2 | 34 874.0 | 4 312.173 | 13 107.598 | 2.49 8460 | 939.06 077 |
| 95 | 98 | 9 305.6 | 20 915.8 | 3 188.745 | 8 795.425 | 2.24 7657 | 945.17 549 |
| 96 | 99 | 5 889.9 | 11 610.2 | 2 301.688 | 5 606.680 | 1.97 1205 | 951.91 429 |
| 97 | 100 | 3 444.5 | 5 720.3 | 1 641.341 | 3 304.992 | 1.66 0705 | 959.49 833 |
| 98 | 101 | 1 719.2 | 2 275.8 | 1 120.638 | 1 663.651 | 1.32 3755 | 967.68 904 |
| 99 | 102 | 556.6 | 556.6 | 543.013 | 543.013 | 1.00 0000 | 975.58 929 |

Table 7   Six-Place Logarithms of Numbers 100-150

| N | 0 | 1 | 2 | 3 | 4 | 5 | 6 | 7 | 8 | 9 | D |
|---|---|---|---|---|---|---|---|---|---|---|---|
| 100 | 00 0000 | 00 0434 | 00 0868 | 00 1301 | 00 1734 | 00 2166 | 00 2598 | 00 3029 | 00 3461 | 00 3891 | 432 |
| 101 | 4321 | 4751 | 5181 | 5609 | 6038 | 6466 | 6894 | 7321 | 7748 | 8174 | 428 |
| 102 | 8600 | 9026 | 9451 | 9876 | 01 0300 | 01 0724 | 01 1147 | 01 1570 | 01 1993 | 01 2415 | 424 |
| 103 | 01 2837 | 01 3259 | 01 3680 | 01 4100 | 4521 | 4940 | 5360 | 5779 | 6197 | 6616 | 420 |
| 104 | 7033 | 7451 | 7868 | 8284 | 8700 | 9116 | 9532 | 9947 | 02 0361 | 02 0775 | 416 |
| 105 | 02 1189 | 02 1603 | 02 2016 | 02 2428 | 02 2841 | 02 3252 | 02 3664 | 02 4075 | 4486 | 4896 | 412 |
| 106 | 5306 | 5715 | 6125 | 6533 | 6942 | 7350 | 7757 | 8164 | 8571 | 8978 | 408 |
| 107 | 9384 | 9789 | 03 0195 | 03 0600 | 03 1004 | 03 1408 | 03 1812 | 03 2216 | 03 2619 | 03 3021 | 404 |
| 108 | 03 3424 | 03 3826 | 4227 | 4628 | 5029 | 5430 | 5830 | 6230 | 6629 | 7028 | 400 |
| 109 | 7426 | 7825 | 8223 | 8620 | 9017 | 9414 | 9811 | 04 0207 | 04 0602 | 04 0998 | 397 |
| 110 | 04 1393 | 04 1787 | 04 2182 | 04 2576 | 04 2969 | 04 3362 | 04 3755 | 4148 | 4540 | 4932 | 393 |
| 111 | 5323 | 5714 | 6105 | 6495 | 6885 | 7275 | 7664 | 8053 | 8442 | 8830 | 390 |
| 112 | 9218 | 9606 | 9993 | 05 0380 | 05 0766 | 05 1153 | 05 1538 | 05 1924 | 05 2309 | 05 2694 | 386 |
| 113 | 05 3078 | 05 3463 | 05 3846 | 4230 | 4613 | 4996 | 5378 | 5760 | 6142 | 6524 | 383 |
| 114 | 6905 | 7286 | 7666 | 8046 | 8426 | 8805 | 9185 | 9563 | 9942 | 06 0320 | 379 |
| 115 | 06 0698 | 06 1075 | 06 1452 | 06 1829 | 06 2206 | 06 2582 | 06 2958 | 06 3333 | 06 3709 | 4083 | 376 |
| 116 | 4458 | 4832 | 5206 | 5580 | 5953 | 6326 | 6699 | 7071 | 7443 | 7815 | 373 |
| 117 | 8186 | 8557 | 8928 | 9298 | 9668 | 07 0038 | 07 0407 | 07 0776 | 07 1145 | 07 1514 | 370 |
| 118 | 07 1882 | 07 2250 | 07 2617 | 07 2985 | 07 3352 | 3718 | 4085 | 4451 | 4816 | 5182 | 366 |
| 119 | 5547 | 5912 | 6276 | 6640 | 7004 | 7368 | 7731 | 8094 | 8457 | 8819 | 363 |
| 120 | 9182 | 9543 | 9904 | 08 0266 | 08 0626 | 08 0987 | 08 1347 | 08 1707 | 08 2067 | 08 2426 | 360 |
| 121 | 08 2785 | 08 3144 | 08 3503 | 3861 | 4219 | 4576 | 4934 | 5291 | 5647 | 6004 | 357 |
| 122 | 6360 | 6716 | 7071 | 7426 | 7781 | 8136 | 8490 | 8845 | 9198 | 9552 | 355 |
| 123 | 9905 | 09 0258 | 09 0611 | 09 0963 | 09 1315 | 09 1667 | 09 2018 | 09 2370 | 09 2721 | 09 3071 | 352 |
| 124 | 09 3422 | 3772 | 4122 | 4471 | 4820 | 5169 | 5518 | 5866 | 6215 | 6562 | 349 |
| 125 | 6910 | 7257 | 7604 | 7951 | 8298 | 8644 | 8990 | 9335 | 9681 | 10 0026 | 346 |
| 126 | 10 0371 | 10 0715 | 10 1059 | 10 1403 | 10 1747 | 10 2091 | 10 2434 | 10 2777 | 10 3119 | 3462 | 343 |
| 127 | 3804 | 4146 | 4487 | 4828 | 5169 | 5510 | 5851 | 6191 | 6531 | 6871 | 341 |
| 128 | 7210 | 7549 | 7888 | 8227 | 8565 | 8903 | 9241 | 9579 | 9916 | 11 0253 | 338 |
| 129 | 11 0590 | 11 0926 | 11 1263 | 11 1599 | 11 1934 | 11 2270 | 11 2605 | 11 2940 | 11 3275 | 3609 | 335 |
| 130 | 3943 | 4277 | 4611 | 4944 | 5278 | 5611 | 5943 | 6276 | 6608 | 6940 | 333 |
| 131 | 7271 | 7603 | 7934 | 8265 | 8595 | 8926 | 9256 | 9586 | 9915 | 12 0245 | 330 |
| 132 | 12 0574 | 12 0903 | 12 1231 | 12 1560 | 12 1888 | 12 2216 | 12 2544 | 12 2871 | 12 3198 | 3525 | 328 |
| 133 | 3852 | 4178 | 4504 | 4830 | 5156 | 5481 | 5806 | 6131 | 6456 | 6781 | 325 |
| 134 | 7105 | 7429 | 7753 | 8076 | 8399 | 8722 | 9045 | 9368 | 9690 | 13 0012 | 323 |
| 135 | 13 0334 | 13 0655 | 13 0977 | 13 1298 | 13 1619 | 13 1939 | 13 2260 | 13 2580 | 13 2900 | 3219 | 321 |
| 136 | 3539 | 3858 | 4177 | 4496 | 4814 | 5133 | 5451 | 5769 | 6086 | 6403 | 318 |
| 137 | 6721 | 7037 | 7354 | 7671 | 7987 | 8303 | 8618 | 8934 | 9249 | 9564 | 316 |
| 138 | 9879 | 14 0194 | 14 0508 | 14 0822 | 14 1136 | 14 1450 | 14 1763 | 14 2076 | 14 2389 | 14 2702 | 314 |
| 139 | 14 3015 | 3327 | 3639 | 3951 | 4263 | 4574 | 4885 | 5196 | 5507 | 5818 | 311 |
| 140 | 6128 | 6438 | 6748 | 7058 | 7367 | 7676 | 7985 | 8294 | 8603 | 8911 | 309 |
| 141 | 9219 | 9527 | 9835 | 15 0142 | 15 0449 | 15 0756 | 15 1063 | 15 1370 | 15 1676 | 15 1982 | 307 |
| 142 | 15 2288 | 15 2594 | 15 2900 | 3205 | 3510 | 3815 | 4120 | 4424 | 4728 | 5032 | 305 |
| 143 | 5336 | 5640 | 5943 | 6246 | 6549 | 6852 | 7154 | 7457 | 7759 | 8061 | 303 |
| 144 | 8362 | 8664 | 8965 | 9266 | 9567 | 9868 | 16 0168 | 16 0469 | 16 0769 | 16 1068 | 301 |
| 145 | 16 1368 | 16 1667 | 16 1967 | 16 2266 | 16 2564 | 16 2863 | 3161 | 3460 | 3758 | 4055 | 299 |
| 146 | 4353 | 4650 | 4947 | 5244 | 5541 | 5838 | 6134 | 6430 | 6726 | 7022 | 297 |
| 147 | 7317 | 7613 | 7908 | 8203 | 8497 | 8792 | 9086 | 9380 | 9674 | 9968 | 295 |
| 148 | 17 0262 | 17 0555 | 17 0848 | 17 1141 | 17 1434 | 17 1726 | 17 2019 | 17 2311 | 17 2603 | 17 2895 | 293 |
| 149 | 3186 | 3478 | 3769 | 4060 | 4351 | 4641 | 4932 | 5222 | 5512 | 5802 | 291 |
| 150 | 6091 | 6381 | 6670 | 6959 | 7248 | 7536 | 7825 | 8113 | 8401 | 8689 | 289 |

## Proportional Parts

| n\d | 435 | 430 | 425 | 420 |
|---|---|---|---|---|
| 1 | 44 | 43 | 43 | 42 |
| 2 | 87 | 86 | 85 | 84 |
| 3 | 131 | 129 | 128 | 126 |
| 4 | 174 | 172 | 170 | 168 |
| 5 | 218 | 215 | 213 | 210 |
| 6 | 261 | 258 | 255 | 252 |
| 7 | 305 | 301 | 298 | 294 |
| 8 | 348 | 344 | 340 | 336 |
| 9 | 392 | 387 | 383 | 378 |

| n\d | 415 | 410 | 405 | 400 |
|---|---|---|---|---|
| 1 | 42 | 41 | 41 | 40 |
| 2 | 83 | 82 | 81 | 80 |
| 3 | 125 | 123 | 122 | 120 |
| 4 | 166 | 164 | 162 | 160 |
| 5 | 208 | 205 | 203 | 200 |
| 6 | 249 | 246 | 243 | 240 |
| 7 | 291 | 287 | 284 | 280 |
| 8 | 332 | 328 | 324 | 320 |
| 9 | 374 | 369 | 365 | 360 |

| n\d | 395 | 390 | 385 | 380 |
|---|---|---|---|---|
| 1 | 40 | 39 | 39 | 38 |
| 2 | 79 | 78 | 77 | 76 |
| 3 | 119 | 117 | 116 | 114 |
| 4 | 158 | 156 | 154 | 152 |
| 5 | 198 | 195 | 193 | 190 |
| 6 | 237 | 234 | 231 | 228 |
| 7 | 277 | 273 | 270 | 266 |
| 8 | 316 | 312 | 308 | 304 |
| 9 | 356 | 351 | 347 | 342 |

| n\d | 375 | 370 | 365 | 360 |
|---|---|---|---|---|
| 1 | 38 | 37 | 37 | 36 |
| 2 | 75 | 74 | 73 | 72 |
| 3 | 113 | 111 | 110 | 108 |
| 4 | 150 | 148 | 146 | 144 |
| 5 | 188 | 185 | 183 | 180 |
| 6 | 225 | 222 | 219 | 216 |
| 7 | 263 | 259 | 256 | 252 |
| 8 | 300 | 296 | 292 | 288 |
| 9 | 338 | 333 | 329 | 324 |

| n\d | 355 | 350 | 345 | 340 |
|---|---|---|---|---|
| 1 | 36 | 35 | 35 | 34 |
| 2 | 71 | 70 | 69 | 68 |
| 3 | 107 | 105 | 104 | 102 |
| 4 | 142 | 140 | 138 | 136 |
| 5 | 178 | 175 | 173 | 170 |
| 6 | 213 | 210 | 207 | 204 |
| 7 | 249 | 245 | 242 | 238 |
| 8 | 284 | 280 | 276 | 272 |
| 9 | 320 | 315 | 311 | 306 |

| n\d | 335 | 330 | 325 | 320 |
|---|---|---|---|---|
| 1 | 34 | 33 | 33 | 32 |
| 2 | 67 | 66 | 65 | 64 |
| 3 | 101 | 99 | 98 | 96 |
| 4 | 134 | 132 | 130 | 128 |
| 5 | 168 | 165 | 163 | 160 |
| 6 | 201 | 198 | 195 | 192 |
| 7 | 235 | 231 | 228 | 224 |
| 8 | 268 | 264 | 260 | 256 |
| 9 | 302 | 297 | 293 | 288 |

| n\d | 315 | 310 | 305 | 300 |
|---|---|---|---|---|
| 1 | 32 | 31 | 31 | 30 |
| 2 | 63 | 62 | 61 | 60 |
| 3 | 95 | 93 | 92 | 90 |
| 4 | 126 | 124 | 122 | 120 |
| 5 | 158 | 155 | 153 | 150 |
| 6 | 189 | 186 | 183 | 180 |
| 7 | 221 | 217 | 214 | 210 |
| 8 | 252 | 248 | 244 | 240 |
| 9 | 284 | 279 | 275 | 270 |

## Six-Place Logarithms of Numbers 150-200

| N | 0 | 1 | 2 | 3 | 4 | 5 | 6 | 7 | 8 | 9 | D |
|---|---|---|---|---|---|---|---|---|---|---|---|
| 150 | 17 6091 | 17 6381 | 17 6670 | 17 6959 | 17 7248 | 17 7536 | 17 7825 | 17 8113 | 17 8401 | 17 8689 | 289 |
| 151 | 8977 | 9264 | 9552 | 9839 | 18 0126 | 18 0413 | 18 0699 | 18 0986 | 18 1272 | 18 1558 | 287 |
| 152 | 18 1844 | 18 2129 | 18 2415 | 18 2700 | 2985 | 3270 | 3555 | 3839 | 4123 | 4407 | 285 |
| 153 | 4691 | 4975 | 5259 | 5542 | 5825 | 6108 | 6391 | 6674 | 6956 | 7239 | 283 |
| 154 | 7521 | 7803 | 8084 | 8366 | 8647 | 8928 | 9209 | 9490 | 9771 | 19 0051 | 281 |
| 155 | 19 0332 | 19 0612 | 19 0892 | 19 1171 | 19 1451 | 19 1730 | 19 2010 | 19 2289 | 19 2567 | 2846 | 279 |
| 156 | 3125 | 3403 | 3681 | 3959 | 4237 | 4514 | 4792 | 5069 | 5346 | 5623 | 278 |
| 157 | 5900 | 6176 | 6453 | 6729 | 7005 | 7281 | 7556 | 7832 | 8107 | 8382 | 276 |
| 158 | 8657 | 8932 | 9206 | 9481 | 9755 | 20 0029 | 20 0303 | 20 0577 | 20 0850 | 20 1124 | 274 |
| 159 | 20 1397 | 20 1670 | 20 1943 | 20 2216 | 20 2488 | 2761 | 3033 | 3305 | 3577 | 3848 | 272 |
| 160 | 4120 | 4391 | 4663 | 4934 | 5204 | 5475 | 5746 | 6016 | 6286 | 6556 | 271 |
| 161 | 6826 | 7096 | 7365 | 7634 | 7904 | 8173 | 8441 | 8710 | 8979 | 9247 | 269 |
| 162 | 9515 | 9783 | 21 0051 | 21 0319 | 21 0586 | 21 0853 | 21 1121 | 21 1388 | 21 1654 | 21 1921 | 267 |
| 163 | 21 2188 | 21 2454 | 2720 | 2986 | 3252 | 3518 | 3783 | 4049 | 4314 | 4579 | 266 |
| 164 | 4844 | 5109 | 5373 | 5638 | 5902 | 6166 | 6430 | 6694 | 6957 | 7221 | 264 |
| 165 | 7484 | 7747 | 8010 | 8273 | 8536 | 8798 | 9060 | 9323 | 9585 | 9846 | 262 |
| 166 | 22 0108 | 22 0370 | 22 0631 | 22 0892 | 22 1153 | 22 1414 | 22 1675 | 22 1936 | 22 2196 | 22 2456 | 261 |
| 167 | 2716 | 2976 | 3236 | 3496 | 3755 | 4015 | 4274 | 4533 | 4792 | 5051 | 259 |
| 168 | 5309 | 5568 | 5826 | 6084 | 6342 | 6600 | 6858 | 7115 | 7372 | 7630 | 258 |
| 169 | 7887 | 8144 | 8400 | 8657 | 8913 | 9170 | 9426 | 9682 | 9938 | 23 0193 | 256 |
| 170 | 23 0449 | 23 0704 | 23 0960 | 23 1215 | 23 1470 | 23 1724 | 23 1979 | 23 2234 | 23 2488 | 2742 | 255 |
| 171 | 2996 | 3250 | 3504 | 3757 | 4011 | 4264 | 4517 | 4770 | 5023 | 5276 | 253 |
| 172 | 5528 | 5781 | 6033 | 6285 | 6537 | 6789 | 7041 | 7292 | 7544 | 7795 | 252 |
| 173 | 8046 | 8297 | 8548 | 8799 | 9049 | 9299 | 9550 | 9800 | 24 0050 | 24 0300 | 250 |
| 174 | 24 0549 | 24 0799 | 24 1048 | 24 1297 | 24 1546 | 24 1795 | 24 2044 | 24 2293 | 2541 | 2790 | 249 |
| 175 | 3038 | 3286 | 3534 | 3782 | 4030 | 4277 | 4525 | 4772 | 5019 | 5266 | 248 |
| 176 | 5513 | 5759 | 6006 | 6252 | 6499 | 6745 | 6991 | 7237 | 7482 | 7728 | 246 |
| 177 | 7973 | 8219 | 8464 | 8709 | 8954 | 9198 | 9443 | 9687 | 9932 | 25 0176 | 245 |
| 178 | 25 0420 | 25 0664 | 25 0908 | 25 1151 | 25 1395 | 25 1638 | 25 1881 | 25 2125 | 25 2368 | 2610 | 243 |
| 179 | 2853 | 3096 | 3338 | 3580 | 3822 | 4064 | 4306 | 4548 | 4790 | 5031 | 242 |
| 180 | 5273 | 5514 | 5755 | 5996 | 6237 | 6477 | 6718 | 6958 | 7198 | 7439 | 241 |
| 181 | 7679 | 7918 | 8158 | 8398 | 8637 | 8877 | 9116 | 9355 | 9594 | 9833 | 239 |
| 182 | 26 0071 | 26 0310 | 26 0548 | 26 0787 | 26 1025 | 26 1263 | 26 1501 | 26 1739 | 26 1976 | 26 2214 | 238 |
| 183 | 2451 | 2688 | 2925 | 3162 | 3399 | 3636 | 3873 | 4109 | 4346 | 4582 | 237 |
| 184 | 4818 | 5054 | 5290 | 5525 | 5761 | 5996 | 6232 | 6467 | 6702 | 6937 | 235 |
| 185 | 7172 | 7406 | 7641 | 7875 | 8110 | 8344 | 8578 | 8812 | 9046 | 9279 | 234 |
| 186 | 9513 | 9746 | 9980 | 27 0213 | 27 0446 | 27 0679 | 27 0912 | 27 1144 | 27 1377 | 27 1609 | 233 |
| 187 | 27 1842 | 27 2074 | 27 2306 | 2538 | 2770 | 3001 | 3233 | 3464 | 3696 | 3927 | 232 |
| 188 | 4158 | 4389 | 4620 | 4850 | 5081 | 5311 | 5542 | 5772 | 6002 | 6232 | 230 |
| 189 | 6462 | 6692 | 6921 | 7151 | 7380 | 7609 | 7838 | 8067 | 8296 | 8525 | 229 |
| 190 | 8754 | 8982 | 9211 | 9439 | 9667 | 9895 | 28 0123 | 28 0351 | 28 0578 | 28 0806 | 228 |
| 191 | 28 1033 | 28 1261 | 28 1488 | 28 1715 | 28 1942 | 28 2169 | 2396 | 2622 | 2849 | 3075 | 227 |
| 192 | 3301 | 3527 | 3753 | 3979 | 4205 | 4431 | 4656 | 4882 | 5107 | 5332 | 226 |
| 193 | 5557 | 5782 | 6007 | 6232 | 6456 | 6681 | 6905 | 7130 | 7354 | 7578 | 225 |
| 194 | 7802 | 8026 | 8249 | 8473 | 8696 | 8920 | 9143 | 9366 | 9589 | 9812 | 223 |
| 195 | 29 0035 | 29 0257 | 29 0480 | 29 0702 | 29 0925 | 29 1147 | 29 1369 | 29 1591 | 29 1813 | 29 2034 | 222 |
| 196 | 2256 | 2478 | 2699 | 2920 | 3141 | 3363 | 3584 | 3804 | 4025 | 4246 | 221 |
| 197 | 4466 | 4687 | 4907 | 5127 | 5347 | 5567 | 5787 | 6007 | 6226 | 6446 | 220 |
| 198 | 6665 | 6884 | 7104 | 7323 | 7542 | 7761 | 7979 | 8198 | 8416 | 8635 | 219 |
| 199 | 8853 | 9071 | 9289 | 9507 | 9725 | 9943 | 30 0161 | 30 0378 | 30 0595 | 30 0813 | 218 |
| 200 | 30 1030 | 30 1247 | 30 1464 | 30 1681 | 30 1898 | 30 2114 | 2331 | 2547 | 2764 | 2980 | 217 |

## Proportional Parts

| n\d | 295 | 290 | 285 | 280 |
|---|---|---|---|---|
| 1 | 30 | 29 | 29 | 28 |
| 2 | 59 | 58 | 57 | 56 |
| 3 | 89 | 87 | 86 | 84 |
| 4 | 118 | 116 | 114 | 112 |
| 5 | 148 | 145 | 143 | 140 |
| 6 | 177 | 174 | 171 | 168 |
| 7 | 207 | 203 | 200 | 196 |
| 8 | 236 | 232 | 228 | 224 |
| 9 | 266 | 261 | 257 | 252 |

| n\d | 275 | 270 | 265 | 260 |
|---|---|---|---|---|
| 1 | 28 | 27 | 27 | 26 |
| 2 | 55 | 54 | 53 | 52 |
| 3 | 83 | 81 | 80 | 78 |
| 4 | 110 | 108 | 106 | 104 |
| 5 | 138 | 135 | 133 | 130 |
| 6 | 165 | 162 | 159 | 156 |
| 7 | 193 | 189 | 186 | 182 |
| 8 | 220 | 216 | 212 | 208 |
| 9 | 248 | 243 | 239 | 234 |

| n\d | 255 | 250 | 248 | 246 |
|---|---|---|---|---|
| 1 | 26 | 25 | 25 | 25 |
| 2 | 51 | 50 | 50 | 49 |
| 3 | 77 | 75 | 74 | 74 |
| 4 | 102 | 100 | 99 | 98 |
| 5 | 128 | 125 | 124 | 123 |
| 6 | 153 | 150 | 149 | 148 |
| 7 | 179 | 175 | 174 | 172 |
| 8 | 204 | 200 | 198 | 197 |
| 9 | 230 | 225 | 223 | 221 |

| n\d | 244 | 242 | 240 | 238 |
|---|---|---|---|---|
| 1 | 24 | 24 | 24 | 24 |
| 2 | 49 | 48 | 48 | 48 |
| 3 | 73 | 73 | 72 | 71 |
| 4 | 98 | 97 | 96 | 95 |
| 5 | 122 | 121 | 120 | 119 |
| 6 | 146 | 145 | 144 | 143 |
| 7 | 171 | 169 | 168 | 167 |
| 8 | 195 | 194 | 192 | 190 |
| 9 | 220 | 218 | 216 | 214 |

| n\d | 236 | 234 | 232 | 230 |
|---|---|---|---|---|
| 1 | 24 | 23 | 23 | 23 |
| 2 | 47 | 47 | 46 | 46 |
| 3 | 71 | 70 | 70 | 69 |
| 4 | 94 | 94 | 93 | 92 |
| 5 | 118 | 117 | 116 | 115 |
| 6 | 142 | 140 | 139 | 138 |
| 7 | 165 | 164 | 162 | 161 |
| 8 | 189 | 187 | 186 | 184 |
| 9 | 212 | 211 | 209 | 207 |

| n\d | 228 | 226 | 224 | 222 |
|---|---|---|---|---|
| 1 | 23 | 23 | 22 | 22 |
| 2 | 46 | 45 | 45 | 44 |
| 3 | 68 | 68 | 67 | 67 |
| 4 | 91 | 90 | 90 | 89 |
| 5 | 114 | 113 | 112 | 111 |
| 6 | 137 | 136 | 134 | 133 |
| 7 | 160 | 158 | 157 | 155 |
| 8 | 182 | 181 | 179 | 178 |
| 9 | 205 | 203 | 202 | 200 |

| n\d | 220 | 218 | 216 | 214 |
|---|---|---|---|---|
| 1 | 22 | 22 | 22 | 21 |
| 2 | 44 | 44 | 43 | 43 |
| 3 | 66 | 65 | 65 | 64 |
| 4 | 88 | 87 | 86 | 86 |
| 5 | 110 | 109 | 108 | 107 |
| 6 | 132 | 131 | 130 | 128 |
| 7 | 154 | 153 | 151 | 150 |
| 8 | 176 | 174 | 173 | 171 |
| 9 | 198 | 196 | 194 | 193 |

Six-Place Logarithms of Numbers 200-250

| N | 0 | 1 | 2 | 3 | 4 | 5 | 6 | 7 | 8 | 9 | D |
|---|---|---|---|---|---|---|---|---|---|---|---|
| 200 | 30 1030 | 30 1247 | 30 1464 | 30 1681 | 30 1898 | 30 2114 | 30 2331 | 30 2547 | 30 2764 | 30 2980 | 217 |
| 201 | 3196 | 3412 | 3628 | 3844 | 4059 | 4275 | 4491 | 4706 | 4921 | 5136 | 216 |
| 202 | 5351 | 5566 | 5781 | 5996 | 6211 | 6425 | 6639 | 6854 | 7068 | 7282 | 215 |
| 203 | 7496 | 7710 | 7924 | 8137 | 8351 | 8564 | 8778 | 8991 | 9204 | 9417 | 213 |
| 204 | 9630 | 9843 | 31 0056 | 31 0268 | 31 0481 | 31 0693 | 31 0906 | 31 1118 | 31 1330 | 31 1542 | 212 |
| 205 | 3i 1754 | 31 1966 | 2177 | 2389 | 2600 | 2812 | 3023 | 3234 | 3445 | 3656 | 211 |
| 206 | 3867 | 4078 | 4289 | 4499 | 4710 | 4920 | 5130 | 5340 | 5551 | 5760 | 210 |
| 207 | 5970 | 6180 | 6390 | 6599 | 6809 | 7018 | 7227 | 7436 | 7646 | 7854 | 209 |
| 208 | 8063 | 8272 | 8481 | 8689 | 8898 | 9106 | 9314 | 9522 | 9730 | 9938 | 208 |
| 209 | 32 0146 | 32 0354 | 32 0562 | 32 0769 | 32 0977 | 32 1184 | 32 1391 | 32 1598 | 32 1805 | 32 2012 | 207 |
| 210 | 2219 | 2426 | 2633 | 2839 | 3046 | 3252 | 3458 | 3665 | 3871 | 4077 | 206 |
| 211 | 4282 | 4488 | 4694 | 4899 | 5105 | 5310 | 5516 | 5721 | 5926 | 6131 | 205 |
| 212 | 6336 | 6541 | 6745 | 6950 | 7155 | 7359 | 7563 | 7767 | 7972 | 8176 | 204 |
| 213 | 8380 | 8583 | 8787 | 8991 | 9194 | 9398 | 9601 | 9805 | 33 0008 | 33 0211 | 203 |
| 214 | 33 0414 | 33 0617 | 33 0819 | 33 1022 | 33 1225 | 33 1427 | 33 1630 | 33 1832 | 2034 | 2236 | 202 |
| 215 | 2438 | 2640 | 2842 | 3044 | 3246 | 3447 | 3649 | 3850 | 4051 | 4253 | 202 |
| 216 | 4454 | 4655 | 4856 | 5057 | 5257 | 5458 | 5658 | 5859 | 6059 | 6260 | 201 |
| 217 | 6460 | 6660 | 6860 | 7060 | 7260 | 7459 | 7659 | 7858 | 8058 | 8257 | 200 |
| 218 | 8456 | 8656 | 8855 | 9054 | 9253 | 9451 | 9650 | 9849 | 34 0047 | 34 0246 | 199 |
| 219 | 34 0444 | 34 0642 | 34 0841 | 34 1039 | 34 1237 | 34 1435 | 34 1632 | 34 1830 | 2028 | 2225 | 198 |
| 220 | 2423 | 2620 | 2817 | 3014 | 3212 | 3409 | 3606 | 3802 | 3999 | 4196 | 197 |
| 221 | 4392 | 4589 | 4785 | 4981 | 5178 | 5374 | 5570 | 5766 | 5962 | 6157 | 196 |
| 222 | 6353 | 6549 | 6744 | 6939 | 7135 | 7330 | 7525 | 7720 | 7915 | 8110 | 195 |
| 223 | 8305 | 8500 | 8694 | 8889 | 9083 | 9278 | 9472 | 9666 | 9860 | 35 0054 | 194 |
| 224 | 35 0248 | 35 0442 | 35 0636 | 35 0829 | 35 1023 | 35 1216 | 35 1410 | 35 1603 | 35 1796 | 1989 | 193 |
| 225 | 2183 | 2375 | 2568 | 2761 | 2954 | 3147 | 3339 | 3532 | 3724 | 3916 | 193 |
| 226 | 4108 | 4301 | 4493 | 4685 | 4876 | 5068 | 5260 | 5452 | 5643 | 5834 | 192 |
| 227 | 6026 | 6217 | 6408 | 6599 | 6790 | 6981 | 7172 | 7363 | 7554 | 7744 | 191 |
| 228 | 7935 | 8125 | 8316 | 8506 | 8696 | 8886 | 9076 | 9266 | 9456 | 9646 | 190 |
| 229 | 9835 | 36 0025 | 36 0215 | 36 0404 | 36 0593 | 36 0783 | 36 0972 | 36 1161 | 36 1350 | 36 1539 | 189 |
| 230 | 36 1728 | 1917 | 2105 | 2294 | 2482 | 2671 | 2859 | 3048 | 3236 | 3424 | 188 |
| 231 | 3612 | 3800 | 3988 | 4176 | 4363 | 4551 | 4739 | 4926 | 5113 | 5301 | 188 |
| 232 | 5488 | 5675 | 5862 | 6049 | 6236 | 6423 | 6610 | 6796 | 6983 | 7169 | 187 |
| 233 | 7356 | 7542 | 7729 | 7915 | 8101 | 8287 | 8473 | 8659 | 8845 | 9030 | 186 |
| 234 | 9216 | 9401 | 9587 | 9772 | 9958 | 37 0143 | 37 0328 | 37 0513 | 37 0698 | 37 0883 | 185 |
| 235 | 37 1068 | 37 1253 | 37 1437 | 37 1622 | 37 1806 | 1991 | 2175 | 2360 | 2544 | 2728 | 184 |
| 236 | 2912 | 3096 | 3280 | 3464 | 3647 | 3831 | 4015 | 4198 | 4382 | 4565 | 184 |
| 237 | 4748 | 4932 | 5115 | 5298 | 5481 | 5664 | 5846 | 6029 | 6212 | 6394 | 183 |
| 238 | 6577 | 6759 | 6942 | 7124 | 7306 | 7488 | 7670 | 7852 | 8034 | 8216 | 182 |
| 239 | 8398 | 8580 | 8761 | 8943 | 9124 | 9306 | 9487 | 9668 | 9849 | 38 0030 | 181 |
| 240 | 38 0211 | 38 0392 | 38 0573 | 38 0754 | 38 0934 | 38 1115 | 38 1296 | 38 1476 | 38 1656 | 1837 | 181 |
| 241 | 2017 | 2197 | 2377 | 2557 | 2737 | 2917 | 3097 | 3277 | 3456 | 3636 | 180 |
| 242 | 3815 | 3995 | 4174 | 4353 | 4533 | 4712 | 4891 | 5070 | 5249 | 5428 | 179 |
| 243 | 5606 | 5785 | 5964 | 6142 | 6321 | 6499 | 6677 | 6856 | 7034 | 7212 | 178 |
| 244 | 7390 | 7568 | 7746 | 7923 | 8101 | 8279 | 8456 | 8634 | 8811 | 8989 | 178 |
| 245 | 9166 | 9343 | 9520 | 9698 | 9875 | 39 0051 | 39 0228 | 39 0405 | 39 0582 | 39 0759 | 177 |
| 246 | 39 0935 | 39 1112 | 39 1288 | 39 1464 | 39 1641 | 1817 | 1993 | 2169 | 2345 | 2521 | 176 |
| 247 | 2697 | 2873 | 3048 | 3224 | 3400 | 3575 | 3751 | 3926 | 4101 | 4277 | 176 |
| 248 | 4452 | 4627 | 4802 | 4977 | 5152 | 5326 | 5501 | 5676 | 5850 | 6025 | 175 |
| 249 | 6199 | 6374 | 6548 | 6722 | 6896 | 7071 | 7245 | 7419 | 7592 | 7766 | 174 |
| 250 | 7940 | 8114 | 8287 | 8461 | 8634 | 8808 | 8981 | 9154 | 9328 | 9501 | 173 |

Proportional Parts

| n\d | 220 | 218 | 216 | 214 |
|---|---|---|---|---|
| 1 | 22 | 22 | 22 | 21 |
| 2 | 44 | 44 | 43 | 43 |
| 3 | 66 | 65 | 65 | 64 |
| 4 | 88 | 87 | 86 | 86 |
| 5 | 110 | 109 | 108 | 107 |
| 6 | 132 | 131 | 130 | 128 |
| 7 | 154 | 153 | 151 | 150 |
| 8 | 176 | 174 | 173 | 171 |
| 9 | 198 | 196 | 194 | 193 |

| n\d | 212 | 210 | 208 | 206 |
|---|---|---|---|---|
| 1 | 21 | 21 | 21 | 21 |
| 2 | 42 | 42 | 42 | 41 |
| 3 | 64 | 63 | 62 | 62 |
| 4 | 85 | 84 | 83 | 82 |
| 5 | 106 | 105 | 104 | 103 |
| 6 | 127 | 126 | 125 | 124 |
| 7 | 148 | 147 | 146 | 144 |
| 8 | 170 | 168 | 166 | 165 |
| 9 | 191 | 189 | 187 | 185 |

| n\d | 204 | 202 | 200 | 198 |
|---|---|---|---|---|
| 1 | 20 | 20 | 20 | 20 |
| 2 | 41 | 40 | 40 | 40 |
| 3 | 61 | 61 | 60 | 59 |
| 4 | 82 | 81 | 80 | 79 |
| 5 | 102 | 101 | 100 | 99 |
| 6 | 122 | 121 | 120 | 119 |
| 7 | 143 | 141 | 140 | 139 |
| 8 | 163 | 162 | 160 | 158 |
| 9 | 184 | 182 | 180 | 178 |

| n\d | 196 | 194 | 192 | 190 |
|---|---|---|---|---|
| 1 | 20 | 19 | 19 | 19 |
| 2 | 39 | 39 | 38 | 38 |
| 3 | 59 | 58 | 58 | 57 |
| 4 | 78 | 78 | 77 | 76 |
| 5 | 98 | 97 | 96 | 95 |
| 6 | 118 | 116 | 115 | 114 |
| 7 | 137 | 136 | 134 | 133 |
| 8 | 157 | 155 | 154 | 152 |
| 9 | 176 | 175 | 173 | 171 |

| n\d | 188 | 186 | 184 | 182 |
|---|---|---|---|---|
| 1 | 19 | 19 | 18 | 18 |
| 2 | 38 | 37 | 37 | 36 |
| 3 | 56 | 56 | 55 | 55 |
| 4 | 75 | 74 | 74 | 73 |
| 5 | 94 | 93 | 92 | 91 |
| 6 | 113 | 112 | 110 | 109 |
| 7 | 132 | 130 | 129 | 127 |
| 8 | 150 | 149 | 147 | 146 |
| 9 | 169 | 167 | 166 | 164 |

| n\d | 180 | 178 | 176 | 175 |
|---|---|---|---|---|
| 1 | 18 | 18 | 18 | 18 |
| 2 | 36 | 36 | 35 | 35 |
| 3 | 54 | 53 | 53 | 53 |
| 4 | 72 | 71 | 70 | 70 |
| 5 | 90 | 89 | 88 | 88 |
| 6 | 108 | 107 | 106 | 105 |
| 7 | 126 | 125 | 123 | 123 |
| 8 | 144 | 142 | 141 | 140 |
| 9 | 162 | 160 | 158 | 158 |

| n\d | 174 | 173 | 172 | 171 |
|---|---|---|---|---|
| 1 | 17 | 17 | 17 | 17 |
| 2 | 35 | 35 | 34 | 34 |
| 3 | 52 | 52 | 52 | 51 |
| 4 | 70 | 69 | 69 | 68 |
| 5 | 87 | 87 | 86 | 86 |
| 6 | 104 | 104 | 103 | 103 |
| 7 | 122 | 121 | 120 | 120 |
| 8 | 139 | 138 | 138 | 137 |
| 9 | 157 | 156 | 155 | 154 |

Proportional Parts

| N | 0 | 1 | 2 | 3 | 4 | 5 | 6 | 7 | 8 | 9 | D |
|---|---|---|---|---|---|---|---|---|---|---|---|
| 250 | 39 7940 | 39 8114 | 39 8287 | 39 8461 | 39 8634 | 39 8808 | 39 8981 | 39 9154 | 39 9328 | 39 9501 | 173 |
| 251 | 9674 | 9847 | 40 0020 | 40 0192 | 40 0365 | 40 0538 | 40 0711 | 40 0883 | 40 1056 | 40 1228 | 173 |
| 252 | 40 1401 | 40 1573 | 1745 | 1917 | 2089 | 2261 | 2433 | 2605 | 2777 | 2949 | 172 |
| 253 | 3121 | 3292 | 3464 | 3635 | 3807 | 3978 | 4149 | 4320 | 4492 | 4663 | 171 |
| 254 | 4834 | 5005 | 5176 | 5346 | 5517 | 5688 | 5858 | 6029 | 6199 | 6370 | 171 |
| 255 | 6540 | 6710 | 6881 | 7051 | 7221 | 7391 | 7561 | 7731 | 7901 | 8070 | 170 |
| 256 | 8240 | 8410 | 8579 | 8749 | 8918 | 9087 | 9257 | 9426 | 9595 | 9764 | 169 |
| 257 | 9933 | 41 0102 | 41 0271 | 41 0440 | 41 0609 | 41 0777 | 41 0946 | 41 1114 | 41 1283 | 41 1451 | 169 |
| 258 | 41 1620 | 1788 | 1956 | 2124 | 2293 | 2461 | 2629 | 2796 | 2964 | 3132 | 168 |
| 259 | 3300 | 3467 | 3635 | 3803 | 3970 | 4137 | 4305 | 4472 | 4639 | 4806 | 167 |
| 260 | 4973 | 5140 | 5307 | 5474 | 5641 | 5808 | 5974 | 6141 | 6308 | 6474 | 167 |
| 261 | 6641 | 6807 | 6973 | 7139 | 7306 | 7472 | 7638 | 7804 | 7970 | 8135 | 166 |
| 262 | 8301 | 8467 | 8633 | 8798 | 8964 | 9129 | 9295 | 9460 | 9625 | 9791 | 165 |
| 263 | 9956 | 42 0121 | 42 0286 | 42 0451 | 42 0616 | 42 0781 | 42 0945 | 42 1110 | 42 1275 | 42 1439 | 165 |
| 264 | 42 1604 | 1768 | 1933 | 2097 | 2261 | 2426 | 2590 | 2754 | 2918 | 3082 | 164 |
| 265 | 3246 | 3410 | 3574 | 3737 | 3901 | 4065 | 4228 | 4392 | 4555 | 4718 | 164 |
| 266 | 4882 | 5045 | 5208 | 5371 | 5534 | 5697 | 5860 | 6023 | 6186 | 6349 | 163 |
| 267 | 6511 | 6674 | 6836 | 6999 | 7161 | 7324 | 7486 | 7648 | 7811 | 7973 | 162 |
| 268 | 8135 | 8297 | 8459 | 8621 | 8783 | 8944 | 9106 | 9268 | 9429 | 9591 | 162 |
| 269 | 9752 | 9914 | 43 0075 | 43 0236 | 43 0398 | 43 0559 | 43 0720 | 43 0881 | 43 1042 | 43 1203 | 161 |
| 270 | 43 1364 | 43 1525 | 1685 | 1846 | 2007 | 2167 | 2328 | 2488 | 2649 | 2809 | 161 |
| 271 | 2969 | 3130 | 3290 | 3450 | 3610 | 3770 | 3930 | 4090 | 4249 | 4409 | 160 |
| 272 | 4569 | 4729 | 4888 | 5048 | 5207 | 5367 | 5526 | 5685 | 5844 | 6004 | 159 |
| 273 | 6163 | 6322 | 6481 | 6640 | 6799 | 6957 | 7116 | 7275 | 7433 | 7592 | 159 |
| 274 | 7751 | 7909 | 8067 | 8226 | 8384 | 8542 | 8701 | 8859 | 9017 | 9175 | 158 |
| 275 | 9333 | 9491 | 9648 | 9806 | 9964 | 44 0122 | 44 0279 | 44 0437 | 44 0594 | 44 0752 | 158 |
| 276 | 44 0909 | 44 1066 | 44 1224 | 44 1381 | 44 1538 | 1695 | 1852 | 2009 | 2166 | 2323 | 157 |
| 277 | 2480 | 2637 | 2793 | 2950 | 3106 | 3263 | 3419 | 3576 | 3732 | 3889 | 157 |
| 278 | 4045 | 4201 | 4357 | 4513 | 4669 | 4825 | 4981 | 5137 | 5293 | 5449 | 156 |
| 279 | 5604 | 5760 | 5915 | 6071 | 6226 | 6382 | 6537 | 6692 | 6848 | 7003 | 155 |
| 280 | 7158 | 7313 | 7468 | 7623 | 7778 | 7933 | 8088 | 8242 | 8397 | 8552 | 155 |
| 281 | 8706 | 8861 | 9015 | 9170 | 9324 | 9478 | 9633 | 9787 | 9941 | 45 0095 | 154 |
| 282 | 45 0249 | 45 0403 | 45 0557 | 45 0711 | 45 0865 | 45 1018 | 45 1172 | 45 1326 | 45 1479 | 1633 | 154 |
| 283 | 1786 | 1940 | 2093 | 2247 | 2400 | 2553 | 2706 | 2859 | 3012 | 3165 | 153 |
| 284 | 3318 | 3471 | 3624 | 3777 | 3930 | 4082 | 4235 | 4387 | 4540 | 4692 | 153 |
| 285 | 4845 | 4997 | 5150 | 5302 | 5454 | 5606 | 5758 | 5910 | 6062 | 6214 | 152 |
| 286 | 6366 | 6518 | 6670 | 6821 | 6973 | 7125 | 7276 | 7428 | 7579 | 7731 | 152 |
| 287 | 7882 | 8033 | 8184 | 8336 | 8487 | 8638 | 8789 | 8940 | 9091 | 9242 | 151 |
| 288 | 9392 | 9543 | 9694 | 9845 | 9995 | 46 0146 | 46 0296 | 46 0447 | 46 0597 | 46 0748 | 151 |
| 289 | 46 0898 | 46 1048 | 46 1198 | 46 1348 | 46 1499 | 1649 | 1799 | 1948 | 2098 | 2248 | 150 |
| 290 | 2398 | 2548 | 2697 | 2847 | 2997 | 3146 | 3296 | 3445 | 3594 | 3744 | 150 |
| 291 | 3893 | 4042 | 4191 | 4340 | 4490 | 4639 | 4788 | 4936 | 5085 | 5234 | 149 |
| 292 | 5383 | 5532 | 5680 | 5829 | 5977 | 6126 | 6274 | 6423 | 6571 | 6719 | 149 |
| 293 | 6868 | 7016 | 7164 | 7312 | 7460 | 7608 | 7756 | 7904 | 8052 | 8200 | 148 |
| 294 | 8347 | 8495 | 8643 | 8790 | 8938 | 9085 | 9233 | 9380 | 9527 | 9675 | 148 |
| 295 | 9822 | 9969 | 47 0116 | 47 0263 | 47 0410 | 47 0557 | 47 0704 | 47 0851 | 47 0998 | 47 1145 | 147 |
| 296 | 47 1292 | 47 1438 | 1585 | 1732 | 1878 | 2025 | 2171 | 2318 | 2464 | 2610 | 146 |
| 297 | 2756 | 2903 | 3049 | 3195 | 3341 | 3487 | 3633 | 3779 | 3925 | 4071 | 146 |
| 298 | 4216 | 4362 | 4508 | 4653 | 4799 | 4944 | 5090 | 5235 | 5381 | 5526 | 146 |
| 299 | 5671 | 5816 | 5962 | 6107 | 6252 | 6397 | 6542 | 6687 | 6832 | 6976 | 145 |
| 300 | 7121 | 7266 | 7411 | 7555 | 7700 | 7844 | 7989 | 8133 | 8278 | 8422 | 145 |

| n\d | 170 | 169 | 168 | 167 |
|---|---|---|---|---|
| 1 | 17 | 17 | 17 | 17 |
| 2 | 34 | 34 | 34 | 33 |
| 3 | 51 | 51 | 50 | 50 |
| 4 | 68 | 68 | 67 | 67 |
| 5 | 85 | 85 | 84 | 84 |
| 6 | 102 | 101 | 101 | 100 |
| 7 | 119 | 118 | 118 | 117 |
| 8 | 136 | 135 | 134 | 134 |
| 9 | 153 | 152 | 151 | 150 |

| n\d | 166 | 165 | 164 | 163 |
|---|---|---|---|---|
| 1 | 17 | 17 | 16 | 16 |
| 2 | 33 | 33 | 33 | 33 |
| 3 | 50 | 50 | 49 | 49 |
| 4 | 66 | 66 | 66 | 65 |
| 5 | 83 | 83 | 82 | 82 |
| 6 | 100 | 99 | 98 | 98 |
| 7 | 116 | 116 | 115 | 114 |
| 8 | 133 | 132 | 131 | 130 |
| 9 | 149 | 149 | 148 | 147 |

| n\d | 162 | 161 | 160 | 159 |
|---|---|---|---|---|
| 1 | 16 | 16 | 16 | 16 |
| 2 | 32 | 32 | 32 | 32 |
| 3 | 49 | 48 | 48 | 48 |
| 4 | 65 | 64 | 64 | 64 |
| 5 | 81 | 81 | 80 | 80 |
| 6 | 97 | 97 | 96 | 95 |
| 7 | 113 | 113 | 112 | 111 |
| 8 | 130 | 129 | 128 | 127 |
| 9 | 146 | 145 | 144 | 143 |

| n\d | 158 | 157 | 156 | 155 |
|---|---|---|---|---|
| 1 | 16 | 16 | 16 | 16 |
| 2 | 32 | 31 | 31 | 31 |
| 3 | 47 | 47 | 47 | 47 |
| 4 | 63 | 63 | 62 | 62 |
| 5 | 79 | 79 | 78 | 78 |
| 6 | 95 | 94 | 94 | 93 |
| 7 | 111 | 110 | 109 | 109 |
| 8 | 126 | 126 | 125 | 124 |
| 9 | 142 | 141 | 140 | 140 |

| n\d | 154 | 153 | 152 | 151 |
|---|---|---|---|---|
| 1 | 15 | 15 | 15 | 15 |
| 2 | 31 | 31 | 30 | 30 |
| 3 | 46 | 46 | 46 | 45 |
| 4 | 62 | 61 | 61 | 60 |
| 5 | 77 | 77 | 76 | 76 |
| 6 | 92 | 92 | 91 | 91 |
| 7 | 108 | 107 | 106 | 106 |
| 8 | 123 | 122 | 122 | 121 |
| 9 | 139 | 138 | 137 | 136 |

| n\d | 150 | 149 | 148 | 147 |
|---|---|---|---|---|
| 1 | 15 | 15 | 15 | 15 |
| 2 | 30 | 30 | 30 | 29 |
| 3 | 45 | 45 | 44 | 44 |
| 4 | 60 | 60 | 59 | 59 |
| 5 | 75 | 75 | 74 | 74 |
| 6 | 90 | 89 | 89 | 88 |
| 7 | 105 | 104 | 104 | 103 |
| 8 | 120 | 119 | 118 | 118 |
| 9 | 135 | 134 | 133 | 132 |

| n\d | 146 | 145 | 144 |
|---|---|---|---|
| 1 | 15 | 15 | 14 |
| 2 | 29 | 29 | 29 |
| 3 | 44 | 44 | 43 |
| 4 | 58 | 58 | 58 |
| 5 | 73 | 73 | 72 |
| 6 | 88 | 87 | 86 |
| 7 | 102 | 102 | 101 |
| 8 | 117 | 116 | 115 |
| 9 | 131 | 131 | 130 |

Proportional Parts

| N | 0 | 1 | 2 | 3 | 4 | 5 | 6 | 7 | 8 | 9 | D |
|---|---|---|---|---|---|---|---|---|---|---|---|
| 300 | 47 7121 | 47 7266 | 47 7411 | 47 7555 | 47 7700 | 47 7844 | 47 7989 | 47 8133 | 47 8278 | 47 8422 | 145 |
| 301 | 8566 | 8711 | 8855 | 8999 | 9143 | 9287 | 9431 | 9575 | 9719 | 9863 | 144 |
| 302 | 48 0007 | 48 0151 | 48 0294 | 48 0438 | 48 0582 | 48 0725 | 48 0869 | 48 1012 | 48 1156 | 48 1299 | 144 |
| 303 | 1443 | 1586 | 1729 | 1872 | 2016 | 2159 | 2302 | 2445 | 2588 | 2731 | 143 |
| 304 | 2874 | 3016 | 3159 | 3302 | 3445 | 3587 | 3730 | 3872 | 4015 | 4157 | 143 |
| 305 | 4300 | 4442 | 4585 | 4727 | 4869 | 5011 | 5153 | 5295 | 5437 | 5579 | 142 |
| 306 | 5721 | 5863 | 6005 | 6147 | 6289 | 6430 | 6572 | 6714 | 6855 | 6997 | 142 |
| 307 | 7138 | 7280 | 7421 | 7563 | 7704 | 7845 | 7986 | 8127 | 8269 | 8410 | 141 |
| 308 | 8551 | 8692 | 8833 | 8974 | 9114 | 9255 | 9396 | 9537 | 9677 | 9818 | 141 |
| 309 | 9958 | 49 0099 | 49 0239 | 49 0380 | 49 0520 | 49 0661 | 49 0801 | 49 0941 | 49 1081 | 49 1222 | 140 |
| 310 | 49 1362 | 1502 | 1642 | 1782 | 1922 | 2062 | 2201 | 2341 | 2481 | 2621 | 140 |
| 311 | 2760 | 2900 | 3040 | 3179 | 3319 | 3458 | 3597 | 3737 | 3876 | 4015 | 139 |
| 312 | 4155 | 4294 | 4433 | 4572 | 4711 | 4850 | 4989 | 5128 | 5267 | 5406 | 139 |
| 313 | 5544 | 5683 | 5822 | 5960 | 6099 | 6238 | 6376 | 6515 | 6653 | 6791 | 139 |
| 314 | 6930 | 7068 | 7206 | 7344 | 7483 | 7621 | 7759 | 7897 | 8035 | 8173 | 138 |
| 315 | 8311 | 8448 | 8586 | 8724 | 8862 | 8999 | 9137 | 9275 | 9412 | 9550 | 138 |
| 316 | 9687 | 9824 | 9962 | 50 0099 | 50 0236 | 50 0374 | 50 0511 | 50 0648 | 50 0785 | 50 0922 | 137 |
| 317 | 50 1059 | 50 1196 | 50 1333 | 1470 | 1607 | 1744 | 1880 | 2017 | 2154 | 2291 | 137 |
| 318 | 2427 | 2564 | 2700 | 2837 | 2973 | 3109 | 3246 | 3382 | 3518 | 3655 | 136 |
| 319 | 3791 | 3927 | 4063 | 4199 | 4335 | 4471 | 4607 | 4743 | 4878 | 5014 | 136 |
| 320 | 5150 | 5286 | 5421 | 5557 | 5693 | 5828 | 5964 | 6099 | 6234 | 6370 | 136 |
| 321 | 6505 | 6640 | 6776 | 6911 | 7046 | 7181 | 7316 | 7451 | 7586 | 7721 | 135 |
| 322 | 7856 | 7991 | 8126 | 8260 | 8395 | 8530 | 8664 | 8799 | 8934 | 9068 | 135 |
| 323 | 9203 | 9337 | 9471 | 9606 | 9740 | 9874 | 51 0009 | 51 0143 | 51 0277 | 51 0411 | 134 |
| 324 | 51 0545 | 51 0679 | 51 0813 | 51 0947 | 51 1081 | 51 1215 | 1349 | 1482 | 1616 | 1750 | 134 |
| 325 | 1883 | 2017 | 2151 | 2284 | 2418 | 2551 | 2684 | 2818 | 2951 | 3084 | 133 |
| 326 | 3218 | 3351 | 3484 | 3617 | 3750 | 3883 | 4016 | 4149 | 4282 | 4415 | 133 |
| 327 | 4548 | 4681 | 4813 | 4946 | 5079 | 5211 | 5344 | 5476 | 5609 | 5741 | 133 |
| 328 | 5874 | 6006 | 6139 | 6271 | 6403 | 6535 | 6668 | 6800 | 6932 | 7064 | 132 |
| 329 | 7196 | 7328 | 7460 | 7592 | 7724 | 7855 | 7987 | 8119 | 8251 | 8382 | 132 |
| 330 | 8514 | 8646 | 8777 | 8909 | 9040 | 9171 | 9303 | 9434 | 9566 | 9697 | 131 |
| 331 | 9828 | 9959 | 52 0090 | 52 0221 | 52 0353 | 52 0484 | 52 0615 | 52 0745 | 52 0876 | 52 1007 | 131 |
| 332 | 52 1138 | 52 1269 | 1400 | 1530 | 1661 | 1792 | 1922 | 2053 | 2183 | 2314 | 131 |
| 333 | 2444 | 2575 | 2705 | 2835 | 2966 | 3096 | 3226 | 3356 | 3486 | 3616 | 130 |
| 334 | 3746 | 3876 | 4006 | 4136 | 4266 | 4396 | 4526 | 4656 | 4785 | 4915 | 130 |
| 335 | 5045 | 5174 | 5304 | 5434 | 5563 | 5693 | 5822 | 5951 | 6081 | 6210 | 129 |
| 336 | 6339 | 6469 | 6598 | 6727 | 6856 | 6985 | 7114 | 7243 | 7372 | 7501 | 129 |
| 337 | 7630 | 7759 | 7888 | 8016 | 8145 | 8274 | 8402 | 8531 | 8660 | 8788 | 129 |
| 338 | 8917 | 9045 | 9174 | 9302 | 9430 | 9559 | 9687 | 9815 | 9943 | 53 0072 | 128 |
| 339 | 53 0200 | 53 0328 | 53 0456 | 53 0584 | 53 0712 | 53 0840 | 53 0968 | 53 1096 | 53 1223 | 1351 | 128 |
| 340 | 1479 | 1607 | 1734 | 1862 | 1990 | 2117 | 2245 | 2372 | 2500 | 2627 | 128 |
| 341 | 2754 | 2882 | 3009 | 3136 | 3264 | 3391 | 3518 | 3645 | 3772 | 3899 | 127 |
| 342 | 4026 | 4153 | 4280 | 4407 | 4534 | 4661 | 4787 | 4914 | 5041 | 5167 | 127 |
| 343 | 5294 | 5421 | 5547 | 5674 | 5800 | 5927 | 6053 | 6180 | 6306 | 6432 | 126 |
| 344 | 6558 | 6685 | 6811 | 6937 | 7063 | 7189 | 7315 | 7441 | 7567 | 7693 | 126 |
| 345 | 7819 | 7945 | 8071 | 8197 | 8322 | 8448 | 8574 | 8699 | 8825 | 8951 | 126 |
| 346 | 9076 | 9202 | 9327 | 9452 | 9578 | 9703 | 9829 | 9954 | 54 0079 | 54 0204 | 125 |
| 347 | 54 0329 | 54 0455 | 54 0580 | 54 0705 | 54 0830 | 54 0955 | 54 1080 | 54 1205 | 1330 | 1454 | 125 |
| 348 | 1579 | 1704 | 1829 | 1953 | 2078 | 2203 | 2327 | 2452 | 2576 | 2701 | 125 |
| 349 | 2825 | 2950 | 3074 | 3199 | 3323 | 3447 | 3571 | 3696 | 3820 | 3944 | 124 |
| 350 | 4068 | 4192 | 4316 | 4440 | 4564 | 4688 | 4812 | 4936 | 5060 | 5183 | 124 |

| n\d | 145 | 144 | 143 | 142 |
|---|---|---|---|---|
| 1 | 15 | 14 | 14 | 14 |
| 2 | 29 | 29 | 29 | 28 |
| 3 | 44 | 43 | 43 | 43 |
| 4 | 58 | 58 | 57 | 57 |
| 5 | 73 | 72 | 72 | 71 |
| 6 | 87 | 86 | 86 | 85 |
| 7 | 102 | 101 | 100 | 99 |
| 8 | 116 | 115 | 114 | 114 |
| 9 | 131 | 130 | 129 | 128 |

| n\d | 141 | 140 | 139 | 138 |
|---|---|---|---|---|
| 1 | 14 | 14 | 14 | 14 |
| 2 | 28 | 28 | 28 | 28 |
| 3 | 42 | 42 | 42 | 41 |
| 4 | 56 | 56 | 56 | 55 |
| 5 | 71 | 70 | 70 | 69 |
| 6 | 85 | 84 | 83 | 83 |
| 7 | 99 | 98 | 97 | 97 |
| 8 | 113 | 112 | 111 | 110 |
| 9 | 127 | 126 | 125 | 124 |

| n\d | 137 | 136 | 135 | 134 |
|---|---|---|---|---|
| 1 | 14 | 14 | 14 | 13 |
| 2 | 27 | 27 | 27 | 27 |
| 3 | 41 | 41 | 41 | 40 |
| 4 | 55 | 54 | 54 | 54 |
| 5 | 69 | 68 | 68 | 67 |
| 6 | 82 | 82 | 81 | 80 |
| 7 | 96 | 95 | 95 | 94 |
| 8 | 110 | 109 | 108 | 107 |
| 9 | 123 | 122 | 122 | 121 |

| n\d | 133 | 132 | 131 | 130 |
|---|---|---|---|---|
| 1 | 13 | 13 | 13 | 13 |
| 2 | 27 | 26 | 26 | 26 |
| 3 | 40 | 40 | 39 | 39 |
| 4 | 53 | 53 | 52 | 52 |
| 5 | 67 | 66 | 66 | 65 |
| 6 | 80 | 79 | 79 | 78 |
| 7 | 93 | 92 | 92 | 91 |
| 8 | 106 | 106 | 105 | 104 |
| 9 | 120 | 119 | 118 | 117 |

| n\d | 129 | 128 | 127 |
|---|---|---|---|
| 1 | 13 | 13 | 13 |
| 2 | 26 | 26 | 25 |
| 3 | 39 | 38 | 38 |
| 4 | 52 | 51 | 51 |
| 5 | 65 | 64 | 64 |
| 6 | 77 | 77 | 76 |
| 7 | 90 | 90 | 89 |
| 8 | 103 | 102 | 102 |
| 9 | 116 | 115 | 114 |

| n\d | 126 | 125 | 124 |
|---|---|---|---|
| 1 | 13 | 13 | 12 |
| 2 | 25 | 25 | 25 |
| 3 | 38 | 38 | 37 |
| 4 | 50 | 50 | 50 |
| 5 | 63 | 63 | 62 |
| 6 | 76 | 75 | 74 |
| 7 | 88 | 88 | 87 |
| 8 | 101 | 100 | 99 |
| 9 | 113 | 113 | 112 |

Proportional Parts

| N | 0 | 1 | 2 | 3 | 4 | 5 | 6 | 7 | 8 | 9 | D |
|---|---|---|---|---|---|---|---|---|---|---|---|
| 350 | 54 4068 | 54 4192 | 54 4316 | 54 4440 | 54 4564 | 54 4688 | 54 4812 | 54 4936 | 54 5060 | 54 5183 | 124 |
| 351 | 5307 | 5431 | 5555 | 5678 | 5802 | 5925 | 6049 | 6172 | 6296 | 6419 | 124 |
| 352 | 6543 | 6666 | 6789 | 6913 | 7036 | 7159 | 7282 | 7405 | 7529 | 7652 | 123 |
| 353 | 7775 | 7898 | 8021 | 8144 | 8267 | 8389 | 8512 | 8635 | 8758 | 8881 | 123 |
| 354 | 9003 | 9126 | 9249 | 9371 | 9494 | 9616 | 9739 | 9861 | 9984 | 55 0106 | 123 |
| 355 | 55 0228 | 55 0351 | 55 0473 | 55 0595 | 55 0717 | 55 0840 | 55 0962 | 55 1084 | 55 1206 | 1328 | 122 |
| 356 | 1450 | 1572 | 1694 | 1816 | 1938 | 2060 | 2181 | 2303 | 2425 | 2547 | 122 |
| 357 | 2668 | 2790 | 2911 | 3033 | 3155 | 3276 | 3398 | 3519 | 3640 | 3762 | 121 |
| 358 | 3883 | 4004 | 4126 | 4247 | 4368 | 4489 | 4610 | 4731 | 4852 | 4973 | 121 |
| 359 | 5094 | 5215 | 5336 | 5457 | 5578 | 5699 | 5820 | 5940 | 6061 | 6182 | 121 |
| 360 | 6303 | 6423 | 6544 | 6664 | 6785 | 6905 | 7026 | 7146 | 7267 | 7387 | 120 |
| 361 | 7507 | 7627 | 7748 | 7868 | 7988 | 8108 | 8228 | 8349 | 8469 | 8589 | 120 |
| 362 | 8709 | 8829 | 8948 | 9068 | 9188 | 9308 | 9428 | 9548 | 9667 | 9787 | 120 |
| 363 | 9907 | 56 0026 | 56 0146 | 56 0265 | 56 0385 | 56 0504 | 56 0624 | 56 0743 | 56 0863 | 56 0982 | 119 |
| 364 | 56 1101 | 1221 | 1340 | 1459 | 1578 | 1698 | 1817 | 1936 | 2055 | 2174 | 119 |
| 365 | 2293 | 2412 | 2531 | 2650 | 2769 | 2887 | 3006 | 3125 | 3244 | 3362 | 119 |
| 366 | 3481 | 3600 | 3718 | 3837 | 3955 | 4074 | 4192 | 4311 | 4429 | 4548 | 119 |
| 367 | 4666 | 4784 | 4903 | 5021 | 5139 | 5257 | 5376 | 5494 | 5612 | 5730 | 118 |
| 368 | 5848 | 5966 | 6084 | 6202 | 6320 | 6437 | 6555 | 6673 | 6791 | 6909 | 118 |
| 369 | 7026 | 7144 | 7262 | 7379 | 7497 | 7614 | 7732 | 7849 | 7967 | 8084 | 118 |
| 370 | 8202 | 8319 | 8436 | 8554 | 8671 | 8788 | 8905 | 9023 | 9140 | 9257 | 117 |
| 371 | 9374 | 9491 | 9608 | 9725 | 9842 | 9959 | 57 0076 | 57 0193 | 57 0309 | 57 0426 | 117 |
| 372 | 57 0543 | 57 0660 | 57 0776 | 57 0893 | 57 1010 | 57 1126 | 1243 | 1359 | 1476 | 1592 | 117 |
| 373 | 1709 | 1825 | 1942 | 2058 | 2174 | 2291 | 2407 | 2523 | 2639 | 2755 | 116 |
| 374 | 2872 | 2988 | 3104 | 3220 | 3336 | 3452 | 3568 | 3684 | 3800 | 3915 | 116 |
| 375 | 4031 | 4147 | 4263 | 4379 | 4494 | 4610 | 4726 | 4841 | 4957 | 5072 | 116 |
| 376 | 5188 | 5303 | 5419 | 5534 | 5650 | 5765 | 5880 | 5996 | 6111 | 6226 | 115 |
| 377 | 6341 | 6457 | 6572 | 6687 | 6802 | 6917 | 7032 | 7147 | 7262 | 7377 | 115 |
| 378 | 7492 | 7607 | 7722 | 7836 | 7951 | 8066 | 8181 | 8295 | 8410 | 8525 | 115 |
| 379 | 8639 | 8754 | 8868 | 8983 | 9097 | 9212 | 9326 | 9441 | 9555 | 9669 | 114 |
| 380 | 9784 | 9898 | 58 0012 | 58 0126 | 58 0241 | 58 0355 | 58 0469 | 58 0583 | 58 0697 | 58 0811 | 114 |
| 381 | 58 0925 | 58 1039 | 1153 | 1267 | 1381 | 1495 | 1608 | 1722 | 1836 | 1950 | 114 |
| 382 | 2063 | 2177 | 2291 | 2404 | 2518 | 2631 | 2745 | 2858 | 2972 | 3085 | 114 |
| 383 | 3199 | 3312 | 3426 | 3539 | 3652 | 3765 | 3879 | 3992 | 4105 | 4218 | 113 |
| 384 | 4331 | 4444 | 4557 | 4670 | 4783 | 4896 | 5009 | 5122 | 5235 | 5348 | 113 |
| 385 | 5461 | 5574 | 5686 | 5799 | 5912 | 6024 | 6137 | 6250 | 6362 | 6475 | 113 |
| 386 | 6587 | 6700 | 6812 | 6925 | 7037 | 7149 | 7262 | 7374 | 7486 | 7599 | 112 |
| 387 | 7711 | 7823 | 7935 | 8047 | 8160 | 8272 | 8384 | 8496 | 8608 | 8720 | 112 |
| 388 | 8832 | 8944 | 9056 | 9167 | 9279 | 9391 | 9503 | 9615 | 9726 | 9838 | 112 |
| 389 | 9950 | 59 0061 | 59 0173 | 59 0284 | 59 0396 | 59 0507 | 59 0619 | 59 0730 | 59 0842 | 59 0953 | 112 |
| 390 | 59 1065 | 1176 | 1287 | 1399 | 1510 | 1621 | 1732 | 1843 | 1955 | 2066 | 111 |
| 391 | 2177 | 2288 | 2399 | 2510 | 2621 | 2732 | 2843 | 2954 | 3064 | 3175 | 111 |
| 392 | 3286 | 3397 | 3508 | 3618 | 3729 | 3840 | 3950 | 4061 | 4171 | 4282 | 111 |
| 393 | 4393 | 4503 | 4614 | 4724 | 4834 | 4945 | 5055 | 5165 | 5276 | 5386 | 110 |
| 394 | 5496 | 5606 | 5717 | 5827 | 5937 | 6047 | 6157 | 6267 | 6377 | 6487 | 110 |
| 395 | 6597 | 6707 | 6817 | 6927 | 7037 | 7146 | 7256 | 7366 | 7476 | 7586 | 110 |
| 396 | 7695 | 7805 | 7914 | 8024 | 8134 | 8243 | 8353 | 8462 | 8572 | 8681 | 110 |
| 397 | 8791 | 8900 | 9009 | 9119 | 9228 | 9337 | 9446 | 9556 | 9665 | 9774 | 109 |
| 398 | 9883 | 9992 | 60 0101 | 60 0210 | 60 0319 | 60 0428 | 60 0537 | 60 0646 | 60 0755 | 60 0864 | 109 |
| 399 | 60 0973 | 60 1082 | 1191 | 1299 | 1408 | 1517 | 1625 | 1734 | 1843 | 1951 | 109 |
| 400 | 2060 | 2169 | 2277 | 2386 | 2494 | 2603 | 2711 | 2819 | 2928 | 3036 | 108 |

| n\d | 124 | 123 | 122 |
|---|---|---|---|
| 1 | 12 | 12 | 12 |
| 2 | 25 | 25 | 24 |
| 3 | 37 | 37 | 37 |
| 4 | 50 | 49 | 49 |
| 5 | 62 | 62 | 61 |
| 6 | 74 | 74 | 73 |
| 7 | 87 | 86 | 85 |
| 8 | 99 | 98 | 98 |
| 9 | 112 | 111 | 110 |

| n\d | 121 | 120 | 119 |
|---|---|---|---|
| 1 | 12 | 12 | 12 |
| 2 | 24 | 24 | 24 |
| 3 | 36 | 36 | 36 |
| 4 | 48 | 48 | 48 |
| 5 | 61 | 60 | 60 |
| 6 | 73 | 72 | 71 |
| 7 | 85 | 84 | 83 |
| 8 | 97 | 96 | 95 |
| 9 | 109 | 108 | 107 |

| n\d | 118 | 117 | 116 |
|---|---|---|---|
| 1 | 12 | 12 | 12 |
| 2 | 24 | 23 | 23 |
| 3 | 35 | 35 | 35 |
| 4 | 47 | 47 | 46 |
| 5 | 59 | 58 | 58 |
| 6 | 71 | 70 | 70 |
| 7 | 83 | 82 | 81 |
| 8 | 94 | 94 | 93 |
| 9 | 106 | 105 | 104 |

| n\d | 115 | 114 | 113 |
|---|---|---|---|
| 1 | 12 | 11 | 11 |
| 2 | 23 | 23 | 23 |
| 3 | 35 | 34 | 34 |
| 4 | 46 | 46 | 45 |
| 5 | 58 | 57 | 57 |
| 6 | 69 | 68 | 68 |
| 7 | 81 | 80 | 79 |
| 8 | 92 | 91 | 90 |
| 9 | 104 | 103 | 102 |

| n\d | 112 | 111 | 110 |
|---|---|---|---|
| 1 | 11 | 11 | 11 |
| 2 | 22 | 22 | 22 |
| 3 | 34 | 33 | 33 |
| 4 | 45 | 44 | 44 |
| 5 | 56 | 56 | 55 |
| 6 | 67 | 67 | 66 |
| 7 | 78 | 78 | 77 |
| 8 | 90 | 89 | 88 |
| 9 | 101 | 100 | 99 |

| n\d | 109 | 108 |
|---|---|---|
| 1 | 11 | 11 |
| 2 | 22 | 22 |
| 3 | 33 | 32 |
| 4 | 44 | 43 |
| 5 | 55 | 54 |
| 6 | 65 | 65 |
| 7 | 76 | 76 |
| 8 | 87 | 86 |
| 9 | 98 | 97 |

## Six-Place Logarithms of Numbers 400-450

| N | 0 | 1 | 2 | 3 | 4 | 5 | 6 | 7 | 8 | 9 | D |
|---|---|---|---|---|---|---|---|---|---|---|---|
| 400 | 60 2060 | 60 2169 | 60 2277 | 60 2386 | 60 2494 | 60 2603 | 60 2711 | 60 2819 | 60 2928 | 60 3036 | 108 |
| 401 | 3144 | 3253 | 3361 | 3469 | 3577 | 3686 | 3794 | 3902 | 4010 | 4118 | 108 |
| 402 | 4226 | 4334 | 4442 | 4550 | 4658 | 4766 | 4874 | 4982 | 5089 | 5197 | 108 |
| 403 | 5305 | 5413 | 5521 | 5628 | 5736 | 5844 | 5951 | 6059 | 6166 | 6274 | 108 |
| 404 | 6381 | 6489 | 6596 | 6704 | 6811 | 6919 | 7026 | 7133 | 7241 | 7348 | 107 |
| 405 | 7455 | 7562 | 7669 | 7777 | 7884 | 7991 | 8098 | 8205 | 8312 | 8419 | 107 |
| 406 | 8526 | 8633 | 8740 | 8847 | 8954 | 9061 | 9167 | 9274 | 9381 | 9488 | 107 |
| 407 | 9594 | 9701 | 9808 | 9914 | 61 0021 | 61 0128 | 61 0234 | 61 0341 | 61 0447 | 61 0554 | 107 |
| 408 | 61 0660 | 61 0767 | 61 0873 | 61 0979 | 1086 | 1192 | 1298 | 1405 | 1511 | 1617 | 106 |
| 409 | 1723 | 1829 | 1936 | 2042 | 2148 | 2254 | 2360 | 2466 | 2572 | 2678 | 106 |
| 410 | 2784 | 2890 | 2996 | 3102 | 3207 | 3313 | 3419 | 3525 | 3630 | 3736 | 106 |
| 411 | 3842 | 3947 | 4053 | 4159 | 4264 | 4370 | 4475 | 4581 | 4686 | 4792 | 106 |
| 412 | 4897 | 5003 | 5108 | 5213 | 5319 | 5424 | 5529 | 5634 | 5740 | 5845 | 105 |
| 413 | 5950 | 6055 | 6160 | 6265 | 6370 | 6476 | 6581 | 6686 | 6790 | 6895 | 105 |
| 414 | 7000 | 7105 | 7210 | 7315 | 7420 | 7525 | 7629 | 7734 | 7839 | 7943 | 105 |
| 415 | 8048 | 8153 | 8257 | 8362 | 8466 | 8571 | 8676 | 8780 | 8884 | 8989 | 105 |
| 416 | 9093 | 9198 | 9302 | 9406 | 9511 | 9615 | 9719 | 9824 | 9928 | 62 0032 | 104 |
| 417 | 62 0136 | 62 0240 | 62 0344 | 62 0448 | 62 0552 | 62 0656 | 62 0760 | 62 0864 | 62 0968 | 1072 | 104 |
| 418 | 1176 | 1280 | 1384 | 1488 | 1592 | 1695 | 1799 | 1903 | 2007 | 2110 | 104 |
| 419 | 2214 | 2318 | 2421 | 2525 | 2628 | 2732 | 2835 | 2939 | 3042 | 3146 | 104 |
| 420 | 3249 | 3353 | 3456 | 3559 | 3663 | 3766 | 3869 | 3973 | 4076 | 4179 | 103 |
| 421 | 4282 | 4385 | 4488 | 4591 | 4695 | 4798 | 4901 | 5004 | 5107 | 5210 | 103 |
| 422 | 5312 | 5415 | 5518 | 5621 | 5724 | 5827 | 5929 | 6032 | 6135 | 6238 | 103 |
| 423 | 6340 | 6443 | 6546 | 6648 | 6751 | 6853 | 6956 | 7058 | 7161 | 7263 | 103 |
| 424 | 7366 | 7468 | 7571 | 7673 | 7775 | 7878 | 7980 | 8082 | 8185 | 8287 | 102 |
| 425 | 8389 | 8491 | 8593 | 8695 | 8797 | 8900 | 9002 | 9104 | 9206 | 9308 | 102 |
| 426 | 9410 | 9512 | 9613 | 9715 | 9817 | 9919 | 63 0021 | 63 0123 | 63 0224 | 63 0326 | 102 |
| 427 | 63 0428 | 63 0530 | 63 0631 | 63 0733 | 63 0835 | 63 0936 | 1038 | 1139 | 1241 | 1342 | 102 |
| 428 | 1444 | 1545 | 1647 | 1748 | 1849 | 1951 | 2052 | 2153 | 2255 | 2356 | 101 |
| 429 | 2457 | 2559 | 2660 | 2761 | 2862 | 2963 | 3064 | 3165 | 3266 | 3367 | 101 |
| 430 | 3468 | 3569 | 3670 | 3771 | 3872 | 3973 | 4074 | 4175 | 4276 | 4376 | 101 |
| 431 | 4477 | 4578 | 4679 | 4779 | 4880 | 4981 | 5081 | 5182 | 5283 | 5383 | 101 |
| 432 | 5484 | 5584 | 5685 | 5785 | 5886 | 5986 | 6087 | 6187 | 6287 | 6388 | 100 |
| 433 | 6488 | 6588 | 6688 | 6789 | 6889 | 6989 | 7089 | 7189 | 7290 | 7390 | 100 |
| 434 | 7490 | 7590 | 7690 | 7790 | 7890 | 7990 | 8090 | 8190 | 8290 | 8389 | 100 |
| 435 | 8489 | 8589 | 8689 | 8789 | 8888 | 8988 | 9088 | 9188 | 9287 | 9387 | 100 |
| 436 | 9486 | 9586 | 9686 | 9785 | 9885 | 9984 | 64 0084 | 64 0183 | 64 0283 | 64 0382 | 99 |
| 437 | 64 0481 | 64 0581 | 64 0680 | 64 0779 | 64 0879 | 64 0978 | 1077 | 1177 | 1276 | 1375 | 99 |
| 438 | 1474 | 1573 | 1672 | 1771 | 1871 | 1970 | 2069 | 2168 | 2267 | 2366 | 99 |
| 439 | 2465 | 2563 | 2662 | 2761 | 2860 | 2959 | 3058 | 3156 | 3255 | 3354 | 99 |
| 440 | 3453 | 3551 | 3650 | 3749 | 3847 | 3946 | 4044 | 4143 | 4242 | 4340 | 98 |
| 441 | 4439 | 4537 | 4636 | 4734 | 4832 | 4931 | 5029 | 5127 | 5226 | 5324 | 98 |
| 442 | 5422 | 5521 | 5619 | 5717 | 5815 | 5913 | 6011 | 6110 | 6208 | 6306 | 98 |
| 443 | 6404 | 6502 | 6600 | 6698 | 6796 | 6894 | 6992 | 7089 | 7187 | 7285 | 98 |
| 444 | 7383 | 7481 | 7579 | 7676 | 7774 | 7872 | 7969 | 8067 | 8165 | 8262 | 98 |
| 445 | 8360 | 8458 | 8555 | 8653 | 8750 | 8848 | 8945 | 9043 | 9140 | 9237 | 97 |
| 446 | 9335 | 9432 | 9530 | 9627 | 9724 | 9821 | 9919 | 65 0016 | 65 0113 | 65 0210 | 97 |
| 447 | 65 0308 | 65 0405 | 65 0502 | 65 0599 | 65 0696 | 65 0793 | 65 0890 | 0987 | 1084 | 1181 | 97 |
| 448 | 1278 | 1375 | 1472 | 1569 | 1666 | 1762 | 1859 | 1956 | 2053 | 2150 | 97 |
| 449 | 2246 | 2343 | 2440 | 2536 | 2633 | 2730 | 2826 | 2923 | 3019 | 3116 | 97 |
| 450 | 3213 | 3309 | 3405 | 3502 | 3598 | 3695 | 3791 | 3888 | 3984 | 4080 | 96 |

## Proportional Parts

| n\d | 109 | 108 | 107 |
|---|---|---|---|
| 1 | 11 | 11 | 11 |
| 2 | 22 | 22 | 21 |
| 3 | 33 | 32 | 32 |
| 4 | 44 | 43 | 43 |
| 5 | 55 | 54 | 54 |
| 6 | 65 | 65 | 64 |
| 7 | 76 | 76 | 75 |
| 8 | 87 | 86 | 86 |
| 9 | 98 | 97 | 96 |

| n\d | 106 | 105 | 104 |
|---|---|---|---|
| 1 | 11 | 11 | 10 |
| 2 | 21 | 21 | 21 |
| 3 | 32 | 32 | 31 |
| 4 | 42 | 42 | 42 |
| 5 | 53 | 53 | 52 |
| 6 | 64 | 63 | 62 |
| 7 | 74 | 74 | 73 |
| 8 | 85 | 84 | 83 |
| 9 | 95 | 95 | 94 |

| n\d | 103 | 102 |
|---|---|---|
| 1 | 10 | 10 |
| 2 | 21 | 20 |
| 3 | 31 | 31 |
| 4 | 41 | 41 |
| 5 | 52 | 51 |
| 6 | 62 | 61 |
| 7 | 72 | 71 |
| 8 | 82 | 82 |
| 9 | 93 | 92 |

| n\d | 101 | 100 |
|---|---|---|
| 1 | 10 | 10 |
| 2 | 20 | 20 |
| 3 | 30 | 30 |
| 4 | 40 | 40 |
| 5 | 51 | 50 |
| 6 | 61 | 60 |
| 7 | 71 | 70 |
| 8 | 81 | 80 |
| 9 | 91 | 90 |

| n\d | 99 | 98 |
|---|---|---|
| 1 | 9.9 | 9.8 |
| 2 | 19.8 | 19.6 |
| 3 | 29.7 | 29.4 |
| 4 | 39.6 | 39.2 |
| 5 | 49.5 | 49.0 |
| 6 | 59.4 | 58.8 |
| 7 | 69.3 | 68.6 |
| 8 | 79.2 | 78.4 |
| 9 | 89.1 | 88.2 |

| n\d | 97 | 96 |
|---|---|---|
| 1 | 9.7 | 9.6 |
| 2 | 19.4 | 19.2 |
| 3 | 29.1 | 28.8 |
| 4 | 38.8 | 38.4 |
| 5 | 48.5 | 48.0 |
| 6 | 58.2 | 57.6 |
| 7 | 67.9 | 67.2 |
| 8 | 77.6 | 76.8 |
| 9 | 87.3 | 86.4 |

Proportional Parts

| N | 0 | 1 | 2 | 3 | 4 | 5 | 6 | 7 | 8 | 9 | D |
|---|---|---|---|---|---|---|---|---|---|---|---|
| 450 | 65 3213 | 65 3309 | 65 3405 | 65 3502 | 65 3598 | 65 3695 | 65 3791 | 65 3888 | 65 3984 | 65 4080 | 96 |
| 451 | 4177 | 4273 | 4369 | 4465 | 4562 | 4658 | 4754 | 4850 | 4946 | 5042 | 96 |
| 452 | 5138 | 5235 | 5331 | 5427 | 5523 | 5619 | 5715 | 5810 | 5906 | 6002 | 96 |
| 453 | 6098 | 6194 | 6290 | 6386 | 6482 | 6577 | 6673 | 6769 | 6864 | 6960 | 96 |
| 454 | 7056 | 7152 | 7247 | 7343 | 7438 | 7534 | 7629 | 7725 | 7820 | 7916 | 96 |
| 455 | 8011 | 8107 | 8202 | 8298 | 8393 | 8488 | 8584 | 8679 | 8774 | 8870 | 95 |
| 456 | 8965 | 9060 | 9155 | 9250 | 9346 | 9441 | 9536 | 9631 | 9726 | 9821 | 95 |
| 457 | 9916 | 66 0011 | 66 0106 | 66 0201 | 66 0296 | 66 0391 | 66 0486 | 66 0581 | 66 0676 | 66 0771 | 95 |
| 458 | 66 0865 | 0960 | 1055 | 1150 | 1245 | 1339 | 1434 | 1529 | 1623 | 1718 | 95 |
| 459 | 1813 | 1907 | 2002 | 2096 | 2191 | 2286 | 2380 | 2475 | 2569 | 2663 | 95 |
| 460 | 2758 | 2852 | 2947 | 3041 | 3135 | 3230 | 3324 | 3418 | 3512 | 3607 | 94 |
| 461 | 3701 | 3795 | 3889 | 3983 | 4078 | 4172 | 4266 | 4360 | 4454 | 4548 | 94 |
| 462 | 4642 | 4736 | 4830 | 4924 | 5018 | 5112 | 5206 | 5299 | 5393 | 5487 | 94 |
| 463 | 5581 | 5675 | 5769 | 5862 | 5956 | 6050 | 6143 | 6237 | 6331 | 6424 | 94 |
| 464 | 6518 | 6612 | 6705 | 6799 | 6892 | 6986 | 7079 | 7173 | 7266 | 7360 | 94 |
| 465 | 7453 | 7546 | 7640 | 7733 | 7826 | 7920 | 8013 | 8106 | 8199 | 8293 | 93 |
| 466 | 8386 | 8479 | 8572 | 8665 | 8759 | 8852 | 8945 | 9038 | 9131 | 9224 | 93 |
| 467 | 9317 | 9410 | 9503 | 9596 | 9689 | 9782 | 9875 | 9967 | 67 0060 | 67 0153 | 93 |
| 468 | 67 0246 | 67 0339 | 67 0431 | 67 0524 | 67 0617 | 67 0710 | 67 0802 | 67 0895 | 0988 | 1080 | 93 |
| 469 | 1173 | 1265 | 1358 | 1451 | 1543 | 1636 | 1728 | 1821 | 1913 | 2005 | 93 |
| 470 | 2098 | 2190 | 2283 | 2375 | 2467 | 2560 | 2652 | 2744 | 2836 | 2929 | 92 |
| 471 | 3021 | 3113 | 3205 | 3297 | 3390 | 3482 | 3574 | 3666 | 3758 | 3850 | 92 |
| 472 | 3942 | 4034 | 4126 | 4218 | 4310 | 4402 | 4494 | 4586 | 4677 | 4769 | 92 |
| 473 | 4861 | 4953 | 5045 | 5137 | 5228 | 5320 | 5412 | 5503 | 5595 | 5687 | 92 |
| 474 | 5778 | 5870 | 5962 | 6053 | 6145 | 6236 | 6328 | 6419 | 6511 | 6602 | 92 |
| 475 | 6694 | 6785 | 6876 | 6968 | 7059 | 7151 | 7242 | 7333 | 7424 | 7516 | 91 |
| 476 | 7607 | 7698 | 7789 | 7881 | 7972 | 8063 | 8154 | 8245 | 8336 | 8427 | 91 |
| 477 | 8518 | 8609 | 8700 | 8791 | 8882 | 8973 | 9064 | 9155 | 9246 | 9337 | 91 |
| 478 | 9428 | 9519 | 9610 | 9700 | 9791 | 9882 | 9973 | 68 0063 | 68 0154 | 68 0245 | 91 |
| 479 | 68 0336 | 68 0426 | 68 0517 | 68 0607 | 68 0698 | 68 0789 | 68 0879 | 0970 | 1060 | 1151 | 91 |
| 480 | 1241 | 1332 | 1422 | 1513 | 1603 | 1693 | 1784 | 1874 | 1964 | 2055 | 90 |
| 481 | 2145 | 2235 | 2326 | 2416 | 2506 | 2596 | 2686 | 2777 | 2867 | 2957 | 90 |
| 482 | 3047 | 3137 | 3227 | 3317 | 3407 | 3497 | 3587 | 3677 | 3767 | 3857 | 90 |
| 483 | 3947 | 4037 | 4127 | 4217 | 4307 | 4396 | 4486 | 4576 | 4666 | 4756 | 90 |
| 484 | 4845 | 4935 | 5025 | 5114 | 5204 | 5294 | 5383 | 5473 | 5563 | 5652 | 90 |
| 485 | 5742 | 5831 | 5921 | 6010 | 6100 | 6189 | 6279 | 6368 | 6458 | 6547 | 89 |
| 486 | 6636 | 6726 | 6815 | 6904 | 6994 | 7083 | 7172 | 7261 | 7351 | 7440 | 89 |
| 487 | 7529 | 7618 | 7707 | 7796 | 7886 | 7975 | 8064 | 8153 | 8242 | 8331 | 89 |
| 488 | 8420 | 8509 | 8598 | 8687 | 8776 | 8865 | 8953 | 9042 | 9131 | 9220 | 89 |
| 489 | 9309 | 9398 | 9486 | 9575 | 9664 | 9753 | 9841 | 9930 | 69 0019 | 69 0107 | 89 |
| 490 | 69 0196 | 69 0285 | 69 0373 | 69 0462 | 69 0550 | 69 0639 | 69 0728 | 69 0816 | 0905 | 0993 | 89 |
| 491 | 1081 | 1170 | 1258 | 1347 | 1435 | 1524 | 1612 | 1700 | 1789 | 1877 | 88 |
| 492 | 1965 | 2053 | 2142 | 2230 | 2318 | 2406 | 2494 | 2583 | 2671 | 2759 | 88 |
| 493 | 2847 | 2935 | 3023 | 3111 | 3199 | 3287 | 3375 | 3463 | 3551 | 3639 | 88 |
| 494 | 3727 | 3815 | 3903 | 3991 | 4078 | 4166 | 4254 | 4342 | 4430 | 4517 | 88 |
| 495 | 4605 | 4693 | 4781 | 4868 | 4956 | 5044 | 5131 | 5219 | 5307 | 5394 | 88 |
| 496 | 5482 | 5569 | 5657 | 5744 | 5832 | 5919 | 6007 | 6094 | 6182 | 6269 | 87 |
| 497 | 6356 | 6444 | 6531 | 6618 | 6706 | 6793 | 6880 | 6968 | 7055 | 7142 | 87 |
| 498 | 7229 | 7317 | 7404 | 7491 | 7578 | 7665 | 7752 | 7839 | 7926 | 8014 | 87 |
| 499 | 8101 | 8188 | 8275 | 8362 | 8449 | 8535 | 8622 | 8709 | 8796 | 8883 | 87 |
| 500 | 8970 | 9057 | 9144 | 9231 | 9317 | 9404 | 9491 | 9578 | 9664 | 9751 | 87 |

| n\d | 97 | 96 |
|---|---|---|
| 1 | 9.7 | 9.6 |
| 2 | 19.4 | 19.2 |
| 3 | 29.1 | 28.8 |
| 4 | 38.8 | 38.4 |
| 5 | 48.5 | 48.0 |
| 6 | 58.2 | 57.6 |
| 7 | 67.9 | 67.2 |
| 8 | 77.6 | 76.8 |
| 9 | 87.3 | 86.4 |

| n\d | 95 | 94 |
|---|---|---|
| 1 | 9.5 | 9.4 |
| 2 | 19.0 | 18.8 |
| 3 | 28.5 | 28.2 |
| 4 | 38.0 | 37.6 |
| 5 | 47.5 | 47.0 |
| 6 | 57.0 | 56.4 |
| 7 | 66.5 | 65.8 |
| 8 | 76.0 | 75.2 |
| 9 | 85.5 | 84.6 |

| n\d | 93 | 92 |
|---|---|---|
| 1 | 9.3 | 9.2 |
| 2 | 18.6 | 18.4 |
| 3 | 27.9 | 27.6 |
| 4 | 37.2 | 36.8 |
| 5 | 46.5 | 46.0 |
| 6 | 55.8 | 55.2 |
| 7 | 65.1 | 64.4 |
| 8 | 74.4 | 73.6 |
| 9 | 83.7 | 82.8 |

| n\d | 91 | 90 |
|---|---|---|
| 1 | 9.1 | 9.0 |
| 2 | 18.2 | 18.0 |
| 3 | 27.3 | 27.0 |
| 4 | 36.4 | 36.0 |
| 5 | 45.5 | 45.0 |
| 6 | 54.6 | 54.0 |
| 7 | 63.7 | 63.0 |
| 8 | 72.8 | 72.0 |
| 9 | 81.9 | 81.0 |

| n\d | 89 | 88 |
|---|---|---|
| 1 | 8.9 | 8.8 |
| 2 | 17.8 | 17.6 |
| 3 | 26.7 | 26.4 |
| 4 | 35.6 | 35.2 |
| 5 | 44.5 | 44.0 |
| 6 | 53.4 | 52.8 |
| 7 | 62.3 | 61.6 |
| 8 | 71.2 | 70.4 |
| 9 | 80.1 | 79.2 |

| n\d | 87 | 86 |
|---|---|---|
| 1 | 8.7 | 8.6 |
| 2 | 17.4 | 17.2 |
| 3 | 26.1 | 25.8 |
| 4 | 34.8 | 34.4 |
| 5 | 43.5 | 43.0 |
| 6 | 52.2 | 51.6 |
| 7 | 60.9 | 60.2 |
| 8 | 69.6 | 68.8 |
| 9 | 78.3 | 77.4 |

| N | 0 | 1 | 2 | 3 | 4 | 5 | 6 | 7 | 8 | 9 | D |
|---|---|---|---|---|---|---|---|---|---|---|---|
| 500 | 69 8970 | 69 9057 | 69 9144 | 69 9231 | 69 9317 | 69 9404 | 69 9491 | 69 9578 | 69 9664 | 69 9751 | 87 |
| 501 | 9838 | 9924 | 70 0011 | 70 0098 | 70 0184 | 70 0271 | 70 0358 | 70 0444 | 70 0531 | 70 0617 | 87 |
| 502 | 70 0704 | 70 0790 | 0877 | 0963 | 1050 | 1136 | 1222 | 1309 | 1395 | 1482 | 86 |
| 503 | 1568 | 1654 | 1741 | 1827 | 1913 | 1999 | 2086 | 2172 | 2258 | 2344 | 86 |
| 504 | 2431 | 2517 | 2603 | 2689 | 2775 | 2861 | 2947 | 3033 | 3119 | 3205 | 86 |
| 505 | 3291 | 3377 | 3463 | 3549 | 3635 | 3721 | 3807 | 3893 | 3979 | 4065 | 86 |
| 506 | 4151 | 4236 | 4322 | 4408 | 4494 | 4579 | 4665 | 4751 | 4837 | 4922 | 86 |
| 507 | 5008 | 5094 | 5179 | 5265 | 5350 | 5436 | 5522 | 5607 | 5693 | 5778 | 86 |
| 508 | 5864 | 5949 | 6035 | 6120 | 6206 | 6291 | 6376 | 6462 | 6547 | 6632 | 85 |
| 509 | 6718 | 6803 | 6888 | 6974 | 7059 | 7144 | 7229 | 7315 | 7400 | 7485 | 85 |
| 510 | 7570 | 7655 | 7740 | 7826 | 7911 | 7996 | 8081 | 8166 | 8251 | 8336 | 85 |
| 511 | 8421 | 8506 | 8591 | 8676 | 8761 | 8846 | 8931 | 9015 | 9100 | 9185 | 85 |
| 512 | 9270 | 9355 | 9440 | 9524 | 9609 | 9694 | 9779 | 9863 | 9948 | 71 0033 | 85 |
| 513 | 71 0117 | 71 0202 | 71 0287 | 71 0371 | 71 0456 | 71 0540 | 71 0625 | 71 0710 | 71 0794 | 0879 | 85 |
| 514 | 0963 | 1048 | 1132 | 1217 | 1301 | 1385 | 1470 | 1554 | 1639 | 1723 | 84 |
| 515 | 1807 | 1892 | 1976 | 2060 | 2144 | 2229 | 2313 | 2397 | 2481 | 2566 | 84 |
| 516 | 2650 | 2734 | 2818 | 2902 | 2986 | 3070 | 3154 | 3238 | 3323 | 3407 | 84 |
| 517 | 3491 | 3575 | 3659 | 3742 | 3826 | 3910 | 3994 | 4078 | 4162 | 4246 | 84 |
| 518 | 4330 | 4414 | 4497 | 4581 | 4665 | 4749 | 4833 | 4916 | 5000 | 5084 | 84 |
| 519 | 5167 | 5251 | 5335 | 5418 | 5502 | 5586 | 5669 | 5753 | 5836 | 5920 | 84 |
| 520 | 6003 | 6087 | 6170 | 6254 | 6337 | 6421 | 6504 | 6588 | 6671 | 6754 | 83 |
| 521 | 6838 | 6921 | 7004 | 7088 | 7171 | 7254 | 7338 | 7421 | 7504 | 7587 | 83 |
| 522 | 7671 | 7754 | 7837 | 7920 | 8003 | 8086 | 8169 | 8253 | 8336 | 8419 | 83 |
| 523 | 8502 | 8585 | 8668 | 8751 | 8834 | 8917 | 9000 | 9083 | 9165 | 9248 | 83 |
| 524 | 9331 | 9414 | 9497 | 9580 | 9663 | 9745 | 9828 | 9911 | 9994 | 72 0077 | 83 |
| 525 | 72 0159 | 72 0242 | 72 0325 | 72 0407 | 72 0490 | 72 0573 | 72 0655 | 72 0738 | 72 0821 | 0903 | 83 |
| 526 | 0986 | 1068 | 1151 | 1233 | 1316 | 1398 | 1481 | 1563 | 1646 | 1728 | 82 |
| 527 | 1811 | 1893 | 1975 | 2058 | 2140 | 2222 | 2305 | 2387 | 2469 | 2552 | 82 |
| 528 | 2634 | 2716 | 2798 | 2881 | 2963 | 3045 | 3127 | 3209 | 3291 | 3374 | 82 |
| 529 | 3456 | 3538 | 3620 | 3702 | 3784 | 3866 | 3948 | 4030 | 4112 | 4194 | 82 |
| 530 | 4276 | 4358 | 4440 | 4522 | 4604 | 4685 | 4767 | 4849 | 4931 | 5013 | 82 |
| 531 | 5095 | 5176 | 5258 | 5340 | 5422 | 5503 | 5585 | 5667 | 5748 | 5830 | 82 |
| 532 | 5912 | 5993 | 6075 | 6156 | 6238 | 6320 | 6401 | 6483 | 6564 | 6646 | 82 |
| 533 | 6727 | 6809 | 6890 | 6972 | 7053 | 7134 | 7216 | 7297 | 7379 | 7460 | 81 |
| 534 | 7541 | 7623 | 7704 | 7785 | 7866 | 7948 | 8029 | 8110 | 8191 | 8273 | 81 |
| 535 | 8354 | 8435 | 8516 | 8597 | 8678 | 8759 | 8841 | 8922 | 9003 | 9084 | 81 |
| 536 | 9165 | 9246 | 9327 | 9408 | 9489 | 9570 | 9651 | 9732 | 9813 | 9893 | 81 |
| 537 | 9974 | 73 0055 | 73 0136 | 73 0217 | 73 0298 | 73 0378 | 73 0459 | 73 0540 | 73 0621 | 73 0702 | 81 |
| 538 | 73 0782 | 0863 | 0944 | 1024 | 1105 | 1186 | 1266 | 1347 | 1428 | 1508 | 81 |
| 539 | 1589 | 1669 | 1750 | 1830 | 1911 | 1991 | 2072 | 2152 | 2233 | 2313 | 81 |
| 540 | 2394 | 2474 | 2555 | 2635 | 2715 | 2796 | 2876 | 2956 | 3037 | 3117 | 80 |
| 541 | 3197 | 3278 | 3358 | 3438 | 3518 | 3598 | 3679 | 3759 | 3839 | 3919 | 80 |
| 542 | 3999 | 4079 | 4160 | 4240 | 4320 | 4400 | 4480 | 4560 | 4640 | 4720 | 80 |
| 543 | 4800 | 4880 | 4960 | 5040 | 5120 | 5200 | 5279 | 5359 | 5439 | 5519 | 80 |
| 544 | 5599 | 5679 | 5759 | 5838 | 5918 | 5998 | 6078 | 6157 | 6237 | 6317 | 80 |
| 545 | 6397 | 6476 | 6556 | 6635 | 6715 | 6795 | 6874 | 6954 | 7034 | 7113 | 80 |
| 546 | 7193 | 7272 | 7352 | 7431 | 7511 | 7590 | 7670 | 7749 | 7829 | 7908 | 79 |
| 547 | 7987 | 8067 | 8146 | 8225 | 8305 | 8384 | 8463 | 8543 | 8622 | 8701 | 79 |
| 548 | 8781 | 8860 | 8939 | 9018 | 9097 | 9177 | 9256 | 9335 | 9414 | 9493 | 79 |
| 549 | 9572 | 9651 | 9731 | 9810 | 9889 | 9968 | 74 0047 | 74 0126 | 74 0205 | 74 0284 | 79 |
| 550 | 74 0363 | 74 0442 | 74 0521 | 74 0600 | 74 0678 | 74 0757 | 0836 | 0915 | 0994 | 1073 | 79 |

| n\d | 87 | 86 |
|---|---|---|
| 1 | 8.7 | 8.6 |
| 2 | 17.4 | 17.2 |
| 3 | 26.1 | 25.8 |
| 4 | 34.8 | 34.4 |
| 5 | 43.5 | 43.0 |
| 6 | 52.2 | 51.6 |
| 7 | 60.9 | 60.2 |
| 8 | 69.6 | 68.8 |
| 9 | 78.3 | 77.4 |

| n\d | 85 | 84 |
|---|---|---|
| 1 | 8.5 | 8.4 |
| 2 | 17.0 | 16.8 |
| 3 | 25.5 | 25.2 |
| 4 | 34.0 | 33.6 |
| 5 | 42.5 | 42.0 |
| 6 | 51.0 | 50.4 |
| 7 | 59.5 | 58.8 |
| 8 | 68.0 | 67.2 |
| 9 | 76.5 | 75.6 |

| n\d | 83 | 82 |
|---|---|---|
| 1 | 8.3 | 8.2 |
| 2 | 16.6 | 16.4 |
| 3 | 24.9 | 24.6 |
| 4 | 33.2 | 32.8 |
| 5 | 41.5 | 41.0 |
| 6 | 49.8 | 49.2 |
| 7 | 58.1 | 57.4 |
| 8 | 66.4 | 65.6 |
| 9 | 74.7 | 73.8 |

| n\d | 81 | 80 |
|---|---|---|
| 1 | 8.1 | 8.0 |
| 2 | 16.2 | 16.0 |
| 3 | 24.3 | 24.0 |
| 4 | 32.4 | 32.0 |
| 5 | 40.5 | 40.0 |
| 6 | 48.6 | 48.0 |
| 7 | 56.7 | 56.0 |
| 8 | 64.8 | 64.0 |
| 9 | 72.9 | 72.0 |

| n\d | 79 |
|---|---|
| 1 | 7.9 |
| 2 | 15.8 |
| 3 | 23.7 |
| 4 | 31.6 |
| 5 | 39.5 |
| 6 | 47.4 |
| 7 | 55.3 |
| 8 | 63.2 |
| 9 | 71.1 |

# Six-Place Logarithms of Numbers 550-600

| N | 0 | 1 | 2 | 3 | 4 | 5 | 6 | 7 | 8 | 9 | D |
|---|---|---|---|---|---|---|---|---|---|---|---|
| 550 | 74 0363 | 74 0442 | 74 0521 | 74 0600 | 74 0678 | 74 0757 | 74 0836 | 74 0915 | 74 0994 | 74 1073 | 79 |
| 551 | 1152 | 1230 | 1309 | 1388 | 1467 | 1546 | 1624 | 1703 | 1782 | 1860 | 79 |
| 552 | 1939 | 2018 | 2096 | 2175 | 2254 | 2332 | 2411 | 2489 | 2568 | 2647 | 79 |
| 553 | 2725 | 2804 | 2882 | 2961 | 3039 | 3118 | 3196 | 3275 | 3353 | 3431 | 79 |
| 554 | 3510 | 3588 | 3667 | 3745 | 3823 | 3902 | 3980 | 4058 | 4136 | 4215 | 78 |
| 555 | 4293 | 4371 | 4449 | 4528 | 4606 | 4684 | 4762 | 4840 | 4919 | 4997 | 78 |
| 556 | 5075 | 5153 | 5231 | 5309 | 5387 | 5465 | 5543 | 5621 | 5699 | 5777 | 78 |
| 557 | 5855 | 5933 | 6011 | 6089 | 6167 | 6245 | 6323 | 6401 | 6479 | 6556 | 78 |
| 558 | 6634 | 6712 | 6790 | 6868 | 6945 | 7023 | 7101 | 7179 | 7256 | 7334 | 78 |
| 559 | 7412 | 7489 | 7567 | 7645 | 7722 | 7800 | 7878 | 7955 | 8033 | 8110 | 78 |
| 560 | 8188 | 8266 | 8343 | 8421 | 8498 | 8576 | 8653 | 8731 | 8808 | 8885 | 77 |
| 561 | 8963 | 9040 | 9118 | 9195 | 9272 | 9350 | 9427 | 9504 | 9582 | 9659 | 77 |
| 562 | 9736 | 9814 | 9891 | 9968 | 75 0045 | 75 0123 | 75 0200 | 75 0277 | 75 0354 | 75 0431 | 77 |
| 563 | 75 0508 | 75 0586 | 75 0663 | 75 0740 | 0817 | 0894 | 0971 | 1048 | 1125 | 1202 | 77 |
| 564 | 1279 | 1356 | 1433 | 1510 | 1587 | 1664 | 1741 | 1818 | 1895 | 1972 | 77 |
| 565 | 2048 | 2125 | 2202 | 2279 | 2356 | 2433 | 2509 | 2586 | 2663 | 2740 | 77 |
| 566 | 2816 | 2893 | 2970 | 3047 | 3123 | 3200 | 3277 | 3353 | 3430 | 3506 | 77 |
| 567 | 3583 | 3660 | 3736 | 3813 | 3889 | 3966 | 4042 | 4119 | 4195 | 4272 | 77 |
| 568 | 4348 | 4425 | 4501 | 4578 | 4654 | 4730 | 4807 | 4883 | 4960 | 5036 | 76 |
| 569 | 5112 | 5189 | 5265 | 5341 | 5417 | 5494 | 5570 | 5646 | 5722 | 5799 | 76 |
| 570 | 5875 | 5951 | 6027 | 6103 | 6180 | 6256 | 6332 | 6408 | 6484 | 6560 | 76 |
| 571 | 6636 | 6712 | 6788 | 6864 | 6940 | 7016 | 7092 | 7168 | 7244 | 7320 | 76 |
| 572 | 7396 | 7472 | 7548 | 7624 | 7700 | 7775 | 7851 | 7927 | 8003 | 8079 | 76 |
| 573 | 8155 | 8230 | 8306 | 8382 | 8458 | 8533 | 8609 | 8685 | 8761 | 8836 | 76 |
| 574 | 8912 | 8988 | 9063 | 9139 | 9214 | 9290 | 9366 | 9441 | 9517 | 9592 | 76 |
| 575 | 9668 | 9743 | 9819 | 9894 | 9970 | 76 0045 | 76 0121 | 76 0196 | 76 0272 | 76 0347 | 75 |
| 576 | 76 0422 | 76 0498 | 76 0573 | 76 0649 | 76 0724 | 0799 | 0875 | 0950 | 1025 | 1101 | 75 |
| 577 | 1176 | 1251 | 1326 | 1402 | 1477 | 1552 | 1627 | 1702 | 1778 | 1853 | 75 |
| 578 | 1928 | 2003 | 2078 | 2153 | 2228 | 2303 | 2378 | 2453 | 2529 | 2604 | 75 |
| 579 | 2679 | 2754 | 2829 | 2904 | 2978 | 3053 | 3128 | 3203 | 3278 | 3353 | 75 |
| 580 | 3428 | 3503 | 3578 | 3653 | 3727 | 3802 | 3877 | 3952 | 4027 | 4101 | 75 |
| 581 | 4176 | 4251 | 4326 | 4400 | 4475 | 4550 | 4624 | 4699 | 4774 | 4848 | 75 |
| 582 | 4923 | 4998 | 5072 | 5147 | 5221 | 5296 | 5370 | 5445 | 5520 | 5594 | 75 |
| 583 | 5669 | 5743 | 5818 | 5892 | 5966 | 6041 | 6115 | 6190 | 6264 | 6338 | 74 |
| 584 | 6413 | 6487 | 6562 | 6636 | 6710 | 6785 | 6859 | 6933 | 7007 | 7082 | 74 |
| 585 | 7156 | 7230 | 7304 | 7379 | 7453 | 7527 | 7601 | 7675 | 7749 | 7823 | 74 |
| 586 | 7898 | 7972 | 8046 | 8120 | 8194 | 8268 | 8342 | 8416 | 8490 | 8564 | 74 |
| 587 | 8638 | 8712 | 8786 | 8860 | 8934 | 9008 | 9082 | 9156 | 9230 | 9303 | 74 |
| 588 | 9377 | 9451 | 9525 | 9599 | 9673 | 9746 | 9820 | 9894 | 9968 | 77 0042 | 74 |
| 589 | 77 0115 | 77 0189 | 77 0263 | 77 0336 | 77 0410 | 77 0484 | 77 0557 | 77 0631 | 77 0705 | 0778 | 74 |
| 590 | 0852 | 0926 | 0999 | 1073 | 1146 | 1220 | 1293 | 1367 | 1440 | 1514 | 74 |
| 591 | 1587 | 1661 | 1734 | 1808 | 1881 | 1955 | 2028 | 2102 | 2175 | 2248 | 73 |
| 592 | 2322 | 2395 | 2468 | 2542 | 2615 | 2688 | 2762 | 2835 | 2908 | 2981 | 73 |
| 593 | 3055 | 3128 | 3201 | 3274 | 3348 | 3421 | 3494 | 3567 | 3640 | 3713 | 73 |
| 594 | 3786 | 3860 | 3933 | 4006 | 4079 | 4152 | 4225 | 4298 | 4371 | 4444 | 73 |
| 595 | 4517 | 4590 | 4663 | 4736 | 4809 | 4882 | 4955 | 5028 | 5100 | 5173 | 73 |
| 596 | 5246 | 5319 | 5392 | 5465 | 5538 | 5610 | 5683 | 5756 | 5829 | 5902 | 73 |
| 597 | 5974 | 6047 | 6120 | 6193 | 6265 | 6338 | 6411 | 6483 | 6556 | 6629 | 73 |
| 598 | 6701 | 6774 | 6846 | 6919 | 6992 | 7064 | 7137 | 7209 | 7282 | 7354 | 73 |
| 599 | 7427 | 7499 | 7572 | 7644 | 7717 | 7789 | 7862 | 7934 | 8006 | 8079 | 72 |
| 600 | 8151 | 8224 | 8296 | 8368 | 8441 | 8513 | 8585 | 8658 | 8730 | 8802 | 72 |

## Proportional Parts

| n\d | 79 | 78 |
|---|---|---|
| 1 | 7.9 | 7.8 |
| 2 | 15.8 | 15.6 |
| 3 | 23.7 | 23.4 |
| 4 | 31.6 | 31.2 |
| 5 | 39.5 | 39.0 |
| 6 | 47.4 | 46.8 |
| 7 | 55.3 | 54.6 |
| 8 | 63.2 | 62.4 |
| 9 | 71.1 | 70.2 |

| n\d | 77 | 76 |
|---|---|---|
| 1 | 7.7 | 7.6 |
| 2 | 15.4 | 15.2 |
| 3 | 23.1 | 22.8 |
| 4 | 30.8 | 30.4 |
| 5 | 38.5 | 38.0 |
| 6 | 46.2 | 45.6 |
| 7 | 53.9 | 53.2 |
| 8 | 61.6 | 60.8 |
| 9 | 69.3 | 68.4 |

| n\d | 75 | 74 |
|---|---|---|
| 1 | 7.5 | 7.4 |
| 2 | 15.0 | 14.8 |
| 3 | 22.5 | 22.2 |
| 4 | 30.0 | 29.6 |
| 5 | 37.5 | 37.0 |
| 6 | 45.0 | 44.4 |
| 7 | 52.5 | 51.8 |
| 8 | 60.0 | 59.2 |
| 9 | 67.5 | 66.6 |

| n\d | 73 |
|---|---|
| 1 | 7.3 |
| 2 | 14.6 |
| 3 | 21.9 |
| 4 | 29.2 |
| 5 | 36.5 |
| 6 | 43.8 |
| 7 | 51.1 |
| 8 | 58.4 |
| 9 | 65.7 |

| n\d | 72 |
|---|---|
| 1 | 7.2 |
| 2 | 14.4 |
| 3 | 21.6 |
| 4 | 28.8 |
| 5 | 36.0 |
| 6 | 43.2 |
| 7 | 50.4 |
| 8 | 57.6 |
| 9 | 64.8 |

Six-Place Logarithms of Numbers 600-650

| N | 0 | 1 | 2 | 3 | 4 | 5 | 6 | 7 | 8 | 9 | D |
|---|---|---|---|---|---|---|---|---|---|---|---|
| 600 | 77 8151 | 77 8224 | 77 8296 | 77 8368 | 77 8441 | 77 8513 | 77 8585 | 77 8658 | 77 8730 | 77 8802 | 72 |
| 601 | 8874 | 8947 | 9019 | 9091 | 9163 | 9236 | 9308 | 9380 | 9452 | 9524 | 72 |
| 602 | 9596 | 9669 | 9741 | 9813 | 9885 | 9957 | 78 0029 | 78 0101 | 78 0173 | 78 0245 | 72 |
| 603 | 78 0317 | 78 0389 | 78 0461 | 78 0533 | 78 0605 | 78 0677 | 0749 | 0821 | 0893 | 0965 | 72 |
| 604 | 1037 | 1109 | 1181 | 1253 | 1324 | 1396 | 1468 | 1540 | 1612 | 1684 | 72 |
| 605 | 1755 | 1827 | 1899 | 1971 | 2042 | 2114 | 2186 | 2258 | 2329 | 2401 | 72 |
| 606 | 2473 | 2544 | 2616 | 2688 | 2759 | 2831 | 2902 | 2974 | 3046 | 3117 | 72 |
| 607 | 3189 | 3260 | 3332 | 3403 | 3475 | 3546 | 3618 | 3689 | 3761 | 3832 | 71 |
| 608 | 3904 | 3975 | 4046 | 4118 | 4189 | 4261 | 4332 | 4403 | 4475 | 4546 | 71 |
| 609 | 4617 | 4689 | 4760 | 4831 | 4902 | 4974 | 5045 | 5116 | 5187 | 5259 | 71 |
| 610 | 5330 | 5401 | 5472 | 5543 | 5615 | 5686 | 5757 | 5828 | 5899 | 5970 | 71 |
| 611 | 6041 | 6112 | 6183 | 6254 | 6325 | 6396 | 6467 | 6538 | 6609 | 6680 | 71 |
| 612 | 6751 | 6822 | 6893 | 6964 | 7035 | 7106 | 7177 | 7248 | 7319 | 7390 | 71 |
| 613 | 7460 | 7531 | 7602 | 7673 | 7744 | 7815 | 7885 | 7956 | 8027 | 8098 | 71 |
| 614 | 8168 | 8239 | 8310 | 8381 | 8451 | 8522 | 8593 | 8663 | 8734 | 8804 | 71 |
| 615 | 8875 | 8946 | 9016 | 9087 | 9157 | 9228 | 9299 | 9369 | 9440 | 9510 | 71 |
| 616 | 9581 | 9651 | 9722 | 9792 | 9863 | 9933 | 79 0004 | 79 0074 | 79 0144 | 79 0215 | 70 |
| 617 | 79 0285 | 79 0356 | 79 0426 | 79 0496 | 79 0567 | 79 0637 | 0707 | 0778 | 0848 | 0918 | 70 |
| 618 | 0988 | 1059 | 1129 | 1199 | 1269 | 1340 | 1410 | 1480 | 1550 | 1620 | 70 |
| 619 | 1691 | 1761 | 1831 | 1901 | 1971 | 2041 | 2111 | 2181 | 2252 | 2322 | 70 |
| 620 | 2392 | 2462 | 2532 | 2602 | 2672 | 2742 | 2812 | 2882 | 2952 | 3022 | 70 |
| 621 | 3092 | 3162 | 3231 | 3301 | 3371 | 3441 | 3511 | 3581 | 3651 | 3721 | 70 |
| 622 | 3790 | 3860 | 3930 | 4000 | 4070 | 4139 | 4209 | 4279 | 4349 | 4418 | 70 |
| 623 | 4488 | 4558 | 4627 | 4697 | 4767 | 4836 | 4906 | 4976 | 5045 | 5115 | 70 |
| 624 | 5185 | 5254 | 5324 | 5393 | 5463 | 5532 | 5602 | 5672 | 5741 | 5811 | 70 |
| 625 | 5880 | 5949 | 6019 | 6088 | 6158 | 6227 | 6297 | 6366 | 6436 | 6505 | 69 |
| 626 | 6574 | 6644 | 6713 | 6782 | 6852 | 6921 | 6990 | 7060 | 7129 | 7198 | 69 |
| 627 | 7268 | 7337 | 7406 | 7475 | 7545 | 7614 | 7683 | 7752 | 7821 | 7890 | 69 |
| 628 | 7960 | 8029 | 8098 | 8167 | 8236 | 8305 | 8374 | 8443 | 8513 | 8582 | 69 |
| 629 | 8651 | 8720 | 8789 | 8858 | 8927 | 8996 | 9065 | 9134 | 9203 | 9272 | 69 |
| 630 | 9341 | 9409 | 9478 | 9547 | 9616 | 9685 | 9754 | 9823 | 9892 | 9961 | 69 |
| 631 | 80 0029 | 80 0098 | 80 0167 | 80 0236 | 80 0305 | 80 0373 | 80 0442 | 80 0511 | 80 0580 | 80 0648 | 69 |
| 632 | 0717 | 0786 | 0854 | 0923 | 0992 | 1061 | 1129 | 1198 | 1266 | 1335 | 69 |
| 633 | 1404 | 1472 | 1541 | 1609 | 1678 | 1747 | 1815 | 1884 | 1952 | 2021 | 69 |
| 634 | 2089 | 2158 | 2226 | 2295 | 2363 | 2432 | 2500 | 2568 | 2637 | 2705 | 68 |
| 635 | 2774 | 2842 | 2910 | 2979 | 3047 | 3116 | 3184 | 3252 | 3321 | 3389 | 68 |
| 636 | 3457 | 3525 | 3594 | 3662 | 3730 | 3798 | 3867 | 3935 | 4003 | 4071 | 68 |
| 637 | 4139 | 4208 | 4276 | 4344 | 4412 | 4480 | 4548 | 4616 | 4685 | 4753 | 68 |
| 638 | 4821 | 4889 | 4957 | 5025 | 5093 | 5161 | 5229 | 5297 | 5365 | 5433 | 68 |
| 639 | 5501 | 5569 | 5637 | 5705 | 5773 | 5841 | 5908 | 5976 | 6044 | 6112 | 68 |
| 640 | 6180 | 6248 | 6316 | 6384 | 6451 | 6519 | 6587 | 6655 | 6723 | 6790 | 68 |
| 641 | 6858 | 6926 | 6994 | 7061 | 7129 | 7197 | 7264 | 7332 | 7400 | 7467 | 68 |
| 642 | 7535 | 7603 | 7670 | 7738 | 7806 | 7873 | 7941 | 8008 | 8076 | 8143 | 68 |
| 643 | 8211 | 8279 | 8346 | 8414 | 8481 | 8549 | 8616 | 8684 | 8751 | 8818 | 67 |
| 644 | 8886 | 8953 | 9021 | 9088 | 9156 | 9223 | 9290 | 9358 | 9425 | 9492 | 67 |
| 645 | 9560 | 9627 | 9694 | 9762 | 9829 | 9896 | 9964 | 81 0031 | 81 0098 | 81 0165 | 67 |
| 646 | 81 0233 | 81 0300 | 81 0367 | 81 0434 | 81 0501 | 81 0569 | 81 0636 | 0703 | 0770 | 0837 | 67 |
| 647 | 0904 | 0971 | 1039 | 1106 | 1173 | 1240 | 1307 | 1374 | 1441 | 1508 | 67 |
| 648 | 1575 | 1642 | 1709 | 1776 | 1843 | 1910 | 1977 | 2044 | 2111 | 2178 | 67 |
| 649 | 2245 | 2312 | 2379 | 2445 | 2512 | 2579 | 2646 | 2713 | 2780 | 2847 | 67 |
| 650 | 2913 | 2980 | 3047 | 3114 | 3181 | 3247 | 3314 | 3381 | 3448 | 3514 | 67 |

Proportional Parts

| n\d | 73 | 72 |
|---|---|---|
| 1 | 7.3 | 7.2 |
| 2 | 14.6 | 14.4 |
| 3 | 21.9 | 21.6 |
| 4 | 29.2 | 28.8 |
| 5 | 36.5 | 36.0 |
| 6 | 43.8 | 43.2 |
| 7 | 51.1 | 50.4 |
| 8 | 58.4 | 57.6 |
| 9 | 65.7 | 64.8 |

| n\d | 71 | 70 |
|---|---|---|
| 1 | 7.1 | 7.0 |
| 2 | 14.2 | 14.0 |
| 3 | 21.3 | 21.0 |
| 4 | 28.4 | 28.0 |
| 5 | 35.5 | 35.0 |
| 6 | 42.6 | 42.0 |
| 7 | 49.7 | 49.0 |
| 8 | 56.8 | 56.0 |
| 9 | 63.9 | 63.0 |

| n\d | 69 | 68 |
|---|---|---|
| 1 | 6.9 | 6.8 |
| 2 | 13.8 | 13.6 |
| 3 | 20.7 | 20.4 |
| 4 | 27.6 | 27.2 |
| 5 | 34.5 | 34.0 |
| 6 | 41.4 | 40.8 |
| 7 | 48.3 | 47.6 |
| 8 | 55.2 | 54.4 |
| 9 | 62.1 | 61.2 |

| n\d | 67 |
|---|---|
| 1 | 6.7 |
| 2 | 13.4 |
| 3 | 20.1 |
| 4 | 26.8 |
| 5 | 33.5 |
| 6 | 40.2 |
| 7 | 46.9 |
| 8 | 53.6 |
| 9 | 60.3 |

| n\d | 66 |
|---|---|
| 1 | 6.6 |
| 2 | 13.2 |
| 3 | 19.8 |
| 4 | 26.4 |
| 5 | 33.0 |
| 6 | 39.6 |
| 7 | 46.2 |
| 8 | 52.8 |
| 9 | 59.4 |

Proportional Parts

| N | 0 | 1 | 2 | 3 | 4 | 5 | 6 | 7 | 8 | 9 | D |
|---|---|---|---|---|---|---|---|---|---|---|---|
| 650 | 81 2913 | 81 2980 | 81 3047 | 81 3114 | 81 3181 | 81 3247 | 81 3314 | 81 3381 | 81 3448 | 81 3514 | 67 |
| 651 | 3581 | 3648 | 3714 | 3781 | 3848 | 3914 | 3981 | 4048 | 4114 | 4181 | 67 |
| 652 | 4248 | 4314 | 4381 | 4447 | 4514 | 4581 | 4647 | 4714 | 4780 | 4847 | 67 |
| 653 | 4913 | 4980 | 5046 | 5113 | 5179 | 5246 | 5312 | 5378 | 5445 | 5511 | 66 |
| 654 | 5578 | 5644 | 5711 | 5777 | 5843 | 5910 | 5976 | 6042 | 6109 | 6175 | 66 |
| 655 | 6241 | 6308 | 6374 | 6440 | 6506 | 6573 | 6639 | 6705 | 6771 | 6838 | 66 |
| 656 | 6904 | 6970 | 7036 | 7102 | 7169 | 7235 | 7301 | 7367 | 7433 | 7499 | 66 |
| 657 | 7565 | 7631 | 7698 | 7764 | 7830 | 7896 | 7962 | 8028 | 8094 | 8160 | 66 |
| 658 | 8226 | 8292 | 8358 | 8424 | 8490 | 8556 | 8622 | 8688 | 8754 | 8820 | 66 |
| 659 | 8885 | 8951 | 9017 | 9083 | 9149 | 9215 | 9281 | 9346 | 9412 | 9478 | 66 |
| 660 | 9544 | 9610 | 9676 | 9741 | 9807 | 9873 | 9939 | 82 0004 | 82 0070 | 82 0136 | 66 |
| 661 | 82 0201 | 82 0267 | 82 0333 | 82 0399 | 82 0464 | 82 0530 | 82 0595 | 0661 | 0727 | 0792 | 66 |
| 662 | 0858 | 0924 | 0989 | 1055 | 1120 | 1186 | 1251 | 1317 | 1382 | 1448 | 66 |
| 663 | 1514 | 1579 | 1645 | 1710 | 1775 | 1841 | 1906 | 1972 | 2037 | 2103 | 65 |
| 664 | 2168 | 2233 | 2299 | 2364 | 2430 | 2495 | 2560 | 2626 | 2691 | 2756 | 65 |
| 665 | 2822 | 2887 | 2952 | 3018 | 3083 | 3148 | 3213 | 3279 | 3344 | 3409 | 65 |
| 666 | 3474 | 3539 | 3605 | 3670 | 3735 | 3800 | 3865 | 3930 | 3996 | 4061 | 65 |
| 667 | 4126 | 4191 | 4256 | 4321 | 4386 | 4451 | 4516 | 4581 | 4646 | 4711 | 65 |
| 668 | 4776 | 4841 | 4906 | 4971 | 5036 | 5101 | 5166 | 5231 | 5296 | 5361 | 65 |
| 669 | 5426 | 5491 | 5556 | 5621 | 5686 | 5751 | 5815 | 5880 | 5945 | 6010 | 65 |
| 670 | 6075 | 6140 | 6204 | 6269 | 6334 | 6399 | 6464 | 6528 | 6593 | 6658 | 65 |
| 671 | 6723 | 6787 | 6852 | 6917 | 6981 | 7046 | 7111 | 7175 | 7240 | 7305 | 65 |
| 672 | 7369 | 7434 | 7499 | 7563 | 7628 | 7692 | 7757 | 7821 | 7886 | 7951 | 65 |
| 673 | 8015 | 8080 | 8144 | 8209 | 8273 | 8338 | 8402 | 8467 | 8531 | 8595 | 64 |
| 674 | 8660 | 8724 | 8789 | 8853 | 8918 | 8982 | 9046 | 9111 | 9175 | 9239 | 64 |
| 675 | 9304 | 9368 | 9432 | 9497 | 9561 | 9625 | 9690 | 9754 | 9818 | 9882 | 64 |
| 676 | 9947 | 83 0011 | 83 0075 | 83 0139 | 83 0204 | 83 0268 | 83 0332 | 83 0396 | 83 0460 | 83 0525 | 64 |
| 677 | 83 0589 | 0653 | 0717 | 0781 | 0845 | 0909 | 0973 | 1037 | 1102 | 1166 | 64 |
| 678 | 1230 | 1294 | 1358 | 1422 | 1486 | 1550 | 1614 | 1678 | 1742 | 1806 | 64 |
| 679 | 1870 | 1934 | 1998 | 2062 | 2126 | 2189 | 2253 | 2317 | 2381 | 2445 | 64 |
| 680 | 2509 | 2573 | 2637 | 2700 | 2764 | 2828 | 2892 | 2956 | 3020 | 3083 | 64 |
| 681 | 3147 | 3211 | 3275 | 3338 | 3402 | 3466 | 3530 | 3593 | 3657 | 3721 | 64 |
| 682 | 3784 | 3848 | 3912 | 3975 | 4039 | 4103 | 4166 | 4230 | 4294 | 4357 | 64 |
| 683 | 4421 | 4484 | 4548 | 4611 | 4675 | 4739 | 4802 | 4866 | 4929 | 4993 | 64 |
| 684 | 5056 | 5120 | 5183 | 5247 | 5310 | 5373 | 5437 | 5500 | 5564 | 5627 | 63 |
| 685 | 5691 | 5754 | 5817 | 5881 | 5944 | 6007 | 6071 | 6134 | 6197 | 6261 | 63 |
| 686 | 6324 | 6387 | 6451 | 6514 | 6577 | 6641 | 6704 | 6767 | 6830 | 6894 | 63 |
| 687 | 6957 | 7020 | 7083 | 7146 | 7210 | 7273 | 7336 | 7399 | 7462 | 7525 | 63 |
| 688 | 7588 | 7652 | 7715 | 7778 | 7841 | 7904 | 7967 | 8030 | 8093 | 8156 | 63 |
| 689 | 8219 | 8282 | 8345 | 8408 | 8471 | 8534 | 8597 | 8660 | 8723 | 8786 | 63 |
| 690 | 8849 | 8912 | 8975 | 9038 | 9101 | 9164 | 9227 | 9289 | 9352 | 9415 | 63 |
| 691 | 9478 | 9541 | 9604 | 9667 | 9729 | 9792 | 9855 | 9918 | 9981 | 84 0043 | 63 |
| 692 | 84 0106 | 84 0169 | 84 0232 | 84 0294 | 84 0357 | 84 0420 | 84 0482 | 84 0545 | 84 0608 | 0671 | 63 |
| 693 | 0733 | 0796 | 0859 | 0921 | 0984 | 1046 | 1109 | 1172 | 1234 | 1297 | 63 |
| 694 | 1359 | 1422 | 1485 | 1547 | 1610 | 1672 | 1735 | 1797 | 1860 | 1922 | 63 |
| 695 | 1985 | 2047 | 2110 | 2172 | 2235 | 2297 | 2360 | 2422 | 2484 | 2547 | 62 |
| 696 | 2609 | 2672 | 2734 | 2796 | 2859 | 2921 | 2983 | 3046 | 3108 | 3170 | 62 |
| 697 | 3233 | 3295 | 3357 | 3420 | 3482 | 3544 | 3606 | 3669 | 3731 | 3793 | 62 |
| 698 | 3855 | 3918 | 3980 | 4042 | 4104 | 4166 | 4229 | 4291 | 4353 | 4415 | 62 |
| 699 | 4477 | 4539 | 4601 | 4664 | 4726 | 4788 | 4850 | 4912 | 4974 | 5036 | 62 |
| 700 | 5098 | 5160 | 5222 | 5284 | 5346 | 5408 | 5470 | 5532 | 5594 | 5656 | 62 |

| n\d | 67 |
|---|---|
| 1 | 6.7 |
| 2 | 13.4 |
| 3 | 20.1 |
| 4 | 26.8 |
| 5 | 33.5 |
| 6 | 40.2 |
| 7 | 46.9 |
| 8 | 53.6 |
| 9 | 60.3 |

| n\d | 66 |
|---|---|
| 1 | 6.6 |
| 2 | 13.2 |
| 3 | 19.8 |
| 4 | 26.4 |
| 5 | 33.0 |
| 6 | 39.6 |
| 7 | 46.2 |
| 8 | 52.8 |
| 9 | 59.4 |

| n\d | 65 |
|---|---|
| 1 | 6.5 |
| 2 | 13.0 |
| 3 | 19.5 |
| 4 | 26.0 |
| 5 | 32.5 |
| 6 | 39.0 |
| 7 | 45.5 |
| 8 | 52.0 |
| 9 | 58.5 |

| n\d | 64 |
|---|---|
| 1 | 6.4 |
| 2 | 12.8 |
| 3 | 19.2 |
| 4 | 25.6 |
| 5 | 32.0 |
| 6 | 38.4 |
| 7 | 44.8 |
| 8 | 51.2 |
| 9 | 57.6 |

| n\d | 63 |
|---|---|
| 1 | 6.3 |
| 2 | 12.6 |
| 3 | 18.9 |
| 4 | 25.2 |
| 5 | 31.5 |
| 6 | 37.8 |
| 7 | 44.1 |
| 8 | 50.4 |
| 9 | 56.7 |

| n\d | 62 |
|---|---|
| 1 | 6.2 |
| 2 | 12.4 |
| 3 | 18.6 |
| 4 | 24.8 |
| 5 | 31.0 |
| 6 | 37.2 |
| 7 | 43.4 |
| 8 | 49.6 |
| 9 | 55.8 |

## Six-Place Logarithms of Numbers 700-750

| N | 0 | 1 | 2 | 3 | 4 | 5 | 6 | 7 | 8 | 9 | D |
|---|---|---|---|---|---|---|---|---|---|---|---|
| 700 | 84 5098 | 84 5160 | 84 5222 | 84 5284 | 84 5346 | 84 5408 | 84 5470 | 84 5532 | 84 5594 | 84 5656 | 62 |
| 701 | 5718 | 5780 | 5842 | 5904 | 5966 | 6028 | 6090 | 6151 | 6213 | 6275 | 62 |
| 702 | 6337 | 6399 | 6461 | 6523 | 6585 | 6646 | 6708 | 6770 | 6832 | 6894 | 62 |
| 703 | 6955 | 7017 | 7079 | 7141 | 7202 | 7264 | 7326 | 7388 | 7449 | 7511 | 62 |
| 704 | 7573 | 7634 | 7696 | 7758 | 7819 | 7881 | 7943 | 8004 | 8066 | 8128 | 62 |
| 705 | 8189 | 8251 | 8312 | 8374 | 8435 | 8497 | 8559 | 8620 | 8682 | 8743 | 62 |
| 706 | 8805 | 8866 | 8928 | 8989 | 9051 | 9112 | 9174 | 9235 | 9297 | 9358 | 61 |
| 707 | 9419 | 9481 | 9542 | 9604 | 9665 | 9726 | 9788 | 9849 | 9911 | 9972 | 61 |
| 708 | 85 0033 | 85 0095 | 85 0156 | 85 0217 | 85 0279 | 85 0340 | 85 0401 | 85 0462 | 85 0524 | 85 0585 | 61 |
| 709 | 0646 | 0707 | 0769 | 0830 | 0891 | 0952 | 1014 | 1075 | 1136 | 1197 | 61 |
| 710 | 1258 | 1320 | 1381 | 1442 | 1503 | 1564 | 1625 | 1686 | 1747 | 1809 | 61 |
| 711 | 1870 | 1931 | 1992 | 2053 | 2114 | 2175 | 2236 | 2297 | 2358 | 2419 | 61 |
| 712 | 2480 | 2541 | 2602 | 2663 | 2724 | 2785 | 2846 | 2907 | 2968 | 3029 | 61 |
| 713 | 3090 | 3150 | 3211 | 3272 | 3333 | 3394 | 3455 | 3516 | 3577 | 3637 | 61 |
| 714 | 3698 | 3759 | 3820 | 3881 | 3941 | 4002 | 4063 | 4124 | 4185 | 4245 | 61 |
| 715 | 4306 | 4367 | 4428 | 4488 | 4549 | 4610 | 4670 | 4731 | 4792 | 4852 | 61 |
| 716 | 4913 | 4974 | 5034 | 5095 | 5156 | 5216 | 5277 | 5337 | 5398 | 5459 | 61 |
| 717 | 5519 | 5580 | 5640 | 5701 | 5761 | 5822 | 5882 | 5943 | 6003 | 6064 | 61 |
| 718 | 6124 | 6185 | 6245 | 6306 | 6366 | 6427 | 6487 | 6548 | 6608 | 6668 | 60 |
| 719 | 6729 | 6789 | 6850 | 6910 | 6970 | 7031 | 7091 | 7152 | 7212 | 7272 | 60 |
| 720 | 7332 | 7393 | 7453 | 7513 | 7574 | 7634 | 7694 | 7755 | 7815 | 7875 | 60 |
| 721 | 7935 | 7995 | 8056 | 8116 | 8176 | 8236 | 8297 | 8357 | 8417 | 8477 | 60 |
| 722 | 8537 | 8597 | 8657 | 8718 | 8778 | 8838 | 8898 | 8958 | 9018 | 9078 | 60 |
| 723 | 9138 | 9198 | 9258 | 9318 | 9379 | 9439 | 9499 | 9559 | 9619 | 9679 | 60 |
| 724 | 9739 | 9799 | 9859 | 9918 | 9978 | 86 0038 | 86 0098 | 86 0158 | 86 0218 | 86 0278 | 60 |
| 725 | 86 0338 | 86 0398 | 86 0458 | 86 0518 | 86 0578 | 0637 | 0697 | 0757 | 0817 | 0877 | 60 |
| 726 | 0937 | 0996 | 1056 | 1116 | 1176 | 1236 | 1295 | 1355 | 1415 | 1475 | 60 |
| 727 | 1534 | 1594 | 1654 | 1714 | 1773 | 1833 | 1893 | 1952 | 2012 | 2072 | 60 |
| 728 | 2131 | 2191 | 2251 | 2310 | 2370 | 2430 | 2489 | 2549 | 2608 | 2668 | 60 |
| 729 | 2728 | 2787 | 2847 | 2906 | 2966 | 3025 | 3085 | 3144 | 3204 | 3263 | 60 |
| 730 | 3323 | 3382 | 3442 | 3501 | 3561 | 3620 | 3680 | 3739 | 3799 | 3858 | 59 |
| 731 | 3917 | 3977 | 4036 | 4096 | 4155 | 4214 | 4274 | 4333 | 4392 | 4452 | 59 |
| 732 | 4511 | 4570 | 4630 | 4689 | 4748 | 4808 | 4867 | 4926 | 4985 | 5045 | 59 |
| 733 | 5104 | 5163 | 5222 | 5282 | 5341 | 5400 | 5459 | 5519 | 5578 | 5637 | 59 |
| 734 | 5696 | 5755 | 5814 | 5874 | 5933 | 5992 | 6051 | 6110 | 6169 | 6228 | 59 |
| 735 | 6287 | 6346 | 6405 | 6465 | 6524 | 6583 | 6642 | 6701 | 6760 | 6819 | 59 |
| 736 | 6878 | 6937 | 6996 | 7055 | 7114 | 7173 | 7232 | 7291 | 7350 | 7409 | 59 |
| 737 | 7467 | 7526 | 7585 | 7644 | 7703 | 7762 | 7821 | 7880 | 7939 | 7998 | 59 |
| 738 | 8056 | 8115 | 8174 | 8233 | 8292 | 8350 | 8409 | 8468 | 8527 | 8586 | 59 |
| 739 | 8644 | 8703 | 8762 | 8821 | 8879 | 8938 | 8997 | 9056 | 9114 | 9173 | 59 |
| 740 | 9232 | 9290 | 9349 | 9408 | 9466 | 9525 | 9584 | 9642 | 9701 | 9760 | 59 |
| 741 | 9818 | 9877 | 9935 | 9994 | 87 0053 | 87 0111 | 87 0170 | 87 0228 | 87 0287 | 87 0345 | 59 |
| 742 | 87 0404 | 87 0462 | 87 0521 | 87 0579 | 0638 | 0696 | 0755 | 0813 | 0872 | 0930 | 58 |
| 743 | 0989 | 1047 | 1106 | 1164 | 1223 | 1281 | 1339 | 1398 | 1456 | 1515 | 58 |
| 744 | 1573 | 1631 | 1690 | 1748 | 1806 | 1865 | 1923 | 1981 | 2040 | 2098 | 58 |
| 745 | 2156 | 2215 | 2273 | 2331 | 2389 | 2448 | 2506 | 2564 | 2622 | 2681 | 58 |
| 746 | 2739 | 2797 | 2855 | 2913 | 2972 | 3030 | 3088 | 3146 | 3204 | 3262 | 58 |
| 747 | 3321 | 3379 | 3437 | 3495 | 3553 | 3611 | 3669 | 3727 | 3785 | 3844 | 58 |
| 748 | 3902 | 3960 | 4018 | 4076 | 4134 | 4192 | 4250 | 4308 | 4366 | 4424 | 58 |
| 749 | 4482 | 4540 | 4598 | 4656 | 4714 | 4772 | 4830 | 4888 | 4945 | 5003 | 58 |
| 750 | 5061 | 5119 | 5177 | 5235 | 5293 | 5351 | 5409 | 5466 | 5524 | 5582 | 58 |

### Proportional Parts

| n\d | 62 | 61 |
|---|---|---|
| 1 | 6.2 | 6.1 |
| 2 | 12.4 | 12.2 |
| 3 | 18.6 | 18.3 |
| 4 | 24.8 | 24.4 |
| 5 | 31.0 | 30.5 |
| 6 | 37.2 | 36.6 |
| 7 | 43.4 | 42.7 |
| 8 | 49.6 | 48.8 |
| 9 | 55.8 | 54.9 |

| n\d | 60 |
|---|---|
| 1 | 6.0 |
| 2 | 12.0 |
| 3 | 18.0 |
| 4 | 24.0 |
| 5 | 30.0 |
| 6 | 36.0 |
| 7 | 42.0 |
| 8 | 48.0 |
| 9 | 54.0 |

| n\d | 59 |
|---|---|
| 1 | 5.9 |
| 2 | 11.8 |
| 3 | 17.7 |
| 4 | 23.6 |
| 5 | 29.5 |
| 6 | 35.4 |
| 7 | 41.3 |
| 8 | 47.2 |
| 9 | 53.1 |

| n\d | 58 |
|---|---|
| 1 | 5.8 |
| 2 | 11.6 |
| 3 | 17.4 |
| 4 | 23.2 |
| 5 | 29.0 |
| 6 | 34.8 |
| 7 | 40.6 |
| 8 | 46.4 |
| 9 | 52.2 |

| n\d | 57 |
|---|---|
| 1 | 5.7 |
| 2 | 11.4 |
| 3 | 17.1 |
| 4 | 22.8 |
| 5 | 28.5 |
| 6 | 34.2 |
| 7 | 39.9 |
| 8 | 45.6 |
| 9 | 51.3 |

Proportional Parts

| N | 0 | 1 | 2 | 3 | 4 | 5 | 6 | 7 | 8 | 9 | D |
|---|---|---|---|---|---|---|---|---|---|---|---|
| 750 | 87 5061 | 87 5119 | 87 5177 | 87 5235 | 87 5293 | 87 5351 | 87 5409 | 87 5466 | 87 5524 | 87 5582 | 58 |
| 751 | 5640 | 5698 | 5756 | 5813 | 5871 | 5929 | 5987 | 6045 | 6102 | 6160 | 58 |
| 752 | 6218 | 6276 | 6333 | 6391 | 6449 | 6507 | 6564 | 6622 | 6680 | 6737 | 58 |
| 753 | 6795 | 6853 | 6910 | 6968 | 7026 | 7083 | 7141 | 7199 | 7256 | 7314 | 58 |
| 754 | 7371 | 7429 | 7487 | 7544 | 7602 | 7659 | 7717 | 7774 | 7832 | 7889 | 58 |
| 755 | 7947 | 8004 | 8062 | 8119 | 8177 | 8234 | 8292 | 8349 | 8407 | 8464 | 57 |
| 756 | 8522 | 8579 | 8637 | 8694 | 8752 | 8809 | 8866 | 8924 | 8981 | 9039 | 57 |
| 757 | 9096 | 9153 | 9211 | 9268 | 9325 | 9383 | 9440 | 9497 | 9555 | 9612 | 57 |
| 758 | 9669 | 9726 | 9784 | 9841 | 9898 | 9956 | 88 0013 | 88 0070 | 88 0127 | 88 0185 | 57 |
| 759 | 88 0242 | 88 0299 | 88 0356 | 88 0413 | 88 0471 | 88 0528 | 0585 | 0642 | 0699 | 0756 | 57 |
| 760 | 0814 | 0871 | 0928 | 0985 | 1042 | 1099 | 1156 | 1213 | 1271 | 1328 | 57 |
| 761 | 1385 | 1442 | 1499 | 1556 | 1613 | 1670 | 1727 | 1784 | 1841 | 1898 | 57 |
| 762 | 1955 | 2012 | 2069 | 2126 | 2183 | 2240 | 2297 | 2354 | 2411 | 2468 | 57 |
| 763 | 2525 | 2581 | 2638 | 2695 | 2752 | 2809 | 2866 | 2923 | 2980 | 3037 | 57 |
| 764 | 3093 | 3150 | 3207 | 3264 | 3321 | 3377 | 3434 | 3491 | 3548 | 3605 | 57 |
| 765 | 3661 | 3718 | 3775 | 3832 | 3888 | 3945 | 4002 | 4059 | 4115 | 4172 | 57 |
| 766 | 4229 | 4285 | 4342 | 4399 | 4455 | 4512 | 4569 | 4625 | 4682 | 4739 | 57 |
| 767 | 4795 | 4852 | 4909 | 4965 | 5022 | 5078 | 5135 | 5192 | 5248 | 5305 | 57 |
| 768 | 5361 | 5418 | 5474 | 5531 | 5587 | 5644 | 5700 | 5757 | 5813 | 5870 | 57 |
| 769 | 5926 | 5983 | 6039 | 6096 | 6152 | 6209 | 6265 | 6321 | 6378 | 6434 | 56 |
| 770 | 6491 | 6547 | 6604 | 6660 | 6716 | 6773 | 6829 | 6885 | 6942 | 6998 | 56 |
| 771 | 7054 | 7111 | 7167 | 7223 | 7280 | 7336 | 7392 | 7449 | 7505 | 7561 | 56 |
| 772 | 7617 | 7674 | 7730 | 7786 | 7842 | 7898 | 7955 | 8011 | 8067 | 8123 | 56 |
| 773 | 8179 | 8236 | 8292 | 8348 | 8404 | 8460 | 8516 | 8573 | 8629 | 8685 | 56 |
| 774 | 8741 | 8797 | 8853 | 8909 | 8965 | 9021 | 9077 | 9134 | 9190 | 9246 | 56 |
| 775 | 9302 | 9358 | 9414 | 9470 | 9526 | 9582 | 9638 | 9694 | 9750 | 9806 | 56 |
| 776 | 9862 | 9918 | 9974 | 89 0030 | 89 0086 | 89 0141 | 89 0197 | 89 0253 | 89 0309 | 89 0365 | 56 |
| 777 | 89 0421 | 89 0477 | 89 0533 | 0589 | 0645 | 0700 | 0756 | 0812 | 0868 | 0924 | 56 |
| 778 | 0980 | 1035 | 1091 | 1147 | 1203 | 1259 | 1314 | 1370 | 1426 | 1482 | 56 |
| 779 | 1537 | 1593 | 1649 | 1705 | 1760 | 1816 | 1872 | 1928 | 1983 | 2039 | 56 |
| 780 | 2095 | 2150 | 2206 | 2262 | 2317 | 2373 | 2429 | 2484 | 2540 | 2595 | 56 |
| 781 | 2651 | 2707 | 2762 | 2818 | 2873 | 2929 | 2985 | 3040 | 3096 | 3151 | 56 |
| 782 | 3207 | 3262 | 3318 | 3373 | 3429 | 3484 | 3540 | 3595 | 3651 | 3706 | 56 |
| 783 | 3762 | 3817 | 3873 | 3928 | 3984 | 4039 | 4094 | 4150 | 4205 | 4261 | 55 |
| 784 | 4316 | 4371 | 4427 | 4482 | 4538 | 4593 | 4648 | 4704 | 4759 | 4814 | 55 |
| 785 | 4870 | 4925 | 4980 | 5036 | 5091 | 5146 | 5201 | 5257 | 5312 | 5367 | 55 |
| 786 | 5423 | 5478 | 5533 | 5588 | 5644 | 5699 | 5754 | 5809 | 5864 | 5920 | 55 |
| 787 | 5975 | 6030 | 6085 | 6140 | 6195 | 6251 | 6306 | 6361 | 6416 | 6471 | 55 |
| 788 | 6526 | 6581 | 6636 | 6692 | 6747 | 6802 | 6857 | 6912 | 6967 | 7022 | 55 |
| 789 | 7077 | 7132 | 7187 | 7242 | 7297 | 7352 | 7407 | 7462 | 7517 | 7572 | 55 |
| 790 | 7627 | 7682 | 7737 | 7792 | 7847 | 7902 | 7957 | 8012 | 8067 | 8122 | 55 |
| 791 | 8176 | 8231 | 8286 | 8341 | 8396 | 8451 | 8506 | 8561 | 8615 | 8670 | 55 |
| 792 | 8725 | 8780 | 8835 | 8890 | 8944 | 8999 | 9054 | 9109 | 9164 | 9218 | 55 |
| 793 | 9273 | 9328 | 9383 | 9437 | 9492 | 9547 | 9602 | 9656 | 9711 | 9766 | 55 |
| 794 | 9821 | 9875 | 9930 | 9985 | 90 0039 | 90 0094 | 90 0149 | 90 0203 | 90 0258 | 90 0312 | 55 |
| 795 | 90 0367 | 90 0422 | 90 0476 | 90 0531 | 0586 | 0640 | 0695 | 0749 | 0804 | 0859 | 55 |
| 796 | 0913 | 0968 | 1022 | 1077 | 1131 | 1186 | 1240 | 1295 | 1349 | 1404 | 55 |
| 797 | 1458 | 1513 | 1567 | 1622 | 1676 | 1731 | 1785 | 1840 | 1894 | 1948 | 54 |
| 798 | 2003 | 2057 | 2112 | 2166 | 2221 | 2275 | 2329 | 2384 | 2438 | 2492 | 54 |
| 799 | 2547 | 2601 | 2655 | 2710 | 2764 | 2818 | 2873 | 2927 | 2981 | 3036 | 54 |
| 800 | 3090 | 3144 | 3199 | 3253 | 3307 | 3361 | 3416 | 3470 | 3524 | 3578 | 54 |

n\d 58
1  5.8
2  11.6
3  17.4
4  23.2
5  29.0
6  34.8
7  40.6
8  46.4
9  52.2

n\d 57
1  5.7
2  11.4
3  17.1
4  22.8
5  28.5
6  34.2
7  39.9
8  45.6
9  51.3

n\d 56
1  5.6
2  11.2
3  16.8
4  22.4
5  28.0
6  33.6
7  39.2
8  44.8
9  50.4

n\d 55
1  5.5
2  11.0
3  16.5
4  22.0
5  27.5
6  33.0
7  38.5
8  44.0
9  49.5

n\d 54
1  5.4
2  10.8
3  16.2
4  21.6
5  27.0
6  32.4
7  37.8
8  43.2
9  48.6

| N | 0 | 1 | 2 | 3 | 4 | 5 | 6 | 7 | 8 | 9 | D |
|---|---|---|---|---|---|---|---|---|---|---|---|
| 800 | 90 3090 | 90 3144 | 90 3199 | 90 3253 | 90 3307 | 90 3361 | 90 3416 | 90 3470 | 90 3524 | 90 3578 | 54 |
| 801 | 3633 | 3687 | 3741 | 3795 | 3849 | 3904 | 3958 | 4012 | 4066 | 4120 | 54 |
| 802 | 4174 | 4229 | 4283 | 4337 | 4391 | 4445 | 4499 | 4553 | 4607 | 4661 | 54 |
| 803 | 4716 | 4770 | 4824 | 4878 | 4932 | 4986 | 5040 | 5094 | 5148 | 5202 | 54 |
| 804 | 5256 | 5310 | 5364 | 5418 | 5472 | 5526 | 5580 | 5634 | 5688 | 5742 | 54 |
| 805 | 5796 | 5850 | 5904 | 5958 | 6012 | 6066 | 6119 | 6173 | 6227 | 6281 | 54 |
| 806 | 6335 | 6389 | 6443 | 6497 | 6551 | 6604 | 6658 | 6712 | 6766 | 6820 | 54 |
| 807 | 6874 | 6927 | 6981 | 7035 | 7089 | 7143 | 7196 | 7250 | 7304 | 7358 | 54 |
| 808 | 7411 | 7465 | 7519 | 7573 | 7626 | 7680 | 7734 | 7787 | 7841 | 7895 | 54 |
| 809 | 7949 | 8002 | 8056 | 8110 | 8163 | 8217 | 8270 | 8324 | 8378 | 8431 | 54 |
| 810 | 8485 | 8539 | 8592 | 8646 | 8699 | 8753 | 8807 | 8860 | 8914 | 8967 | 54 |
| 811 | 9021 | 9074 | 9128 | 9181 | 9235 | 9289 | 9342 | 9396 | 9449 | 9503 | 54 |
| 812 | 9556 | 9610 | 9663 | 9716 | 9770 | 9823 | 9877 | 9930 | 9984 | 91 0037 | 53 |
| 813 | 91 0091 | 91 0144 | 91 0197 | 91 0251 | 91 0304 | 91 0358 | 91 0411 | 91 0464 | 91 0518 | 0571 | 53 |
| 814 | 0624 | 0678 | 0731 | 0784 | 0838 | 0891 | 0944 | 0998 | 1051 | 1104 | 53 |
| 815 | 1158 | 1211 | 1264 | 1317 | 1371 | 1424 | 1477 | 1530 | 1584 | 1637 | 53 |
| 816 | 1690 | 1743 | 1797 | 1850 | 1903 | 1956 | 2009 | 2063 | 2116 | 2169 | 53 |
| 817 | 2222 | 2275 | 2328 | 2381 | 2435 | 2488 | 2541 | 2594 | 2647 | 2700 | 53 |
| 818 | 2753 | 2806 | 2859 | 2913 | 2966 | 3019 | 3072 | 3125 | 3178 | 3231 | 53 |
| 819 | 3284 | 3337 | 3390 | 3443 | 3496 | 3549 | 3602 | 3655 | 3708 | 3761 | 53 |
| 820 | 3814 | 3867 | 3920 | 3973 | 4026 | 4079 | 4132 | 4184 | 4237 | 4290 | 53 |
| 821 | 4343 | 4396 | 4449 | 4502 | 4555 | 4608 | 4660 | 4713 | 4766 | 4819 | 53 |
| 822 | 4872 | 4925 | 4977 | 5030 | 5083 | 5136 | 5189 | 5241 | 5294 | 5347 | 53 |
| 823 | 5400 | 5453 | 5505 | 5558 | 5611 | 5664 | 5716 | 5769 | 5822 | 5875 | 53 |
| 824 | 5927 | 5980 | 6033 | 6085 | 6138 | 6191 | 6243 | 6296 | 6349 | 6401 | 53 |
| 825 | 6454 | 6507 | 6559 | 6612 | 6664 | 6717 | 6770 | 6822 | 6875 | 6927 | 53 |
| 826 | 6980 | 7033 | 7085 | 7138 | 7190 | 7243 | 7295 | 7348 | 7400 | 7453 | 53 |
| 827 | 7506 | 7558 | 7611 | 7663 | 7716 | 7768 | 7820 | 7873 | 7925 | 7978 | 52 |
| 828 | 8030 | 8083 | 8135 | 8188 | 8240 | 8293 | 8345 | 8397 | 8450 | 8502 | 52 |
| 829 | 8555 | 8607 | 8659 | 8712 | 8764 | 8816 | 8869 | 8921 | 8973 | 9026 | 52 |
| 830 | 9078 | 9130 | 9183 | 9235 | 9287 | 9340 | 9392 | 9444 | 9496 | 9549 | 52 |
| 831 | 9601 | 9653 | 9706 | 9758 | 9810 | 9862 | 9914 | 9967 | 92 0019 | 92 0071 | 52 |
| 832 | 92 0123 | 92 0176 | 92 0228 | 92 0280 | 92 0332 | 92 0384 | 92 0436 | 92 0489 | 0541 | 0593 | 52 |
| 833 | 0645 | 0697 | 0749 | 0801 | 0853 | 0906 | 0958 | 1010 | 1062 | 1114 | 52 |
| 834 | 1166 | 1218 | 1270 | 1322 | 1374 | 1426 | 1478 | 1530 | 1582 | 1634 | 52 |
| 835 | 1686 | 1738 | 1790 | 1842 | 1894 | 1946 | 1998 | 2050 | 2102 | 2154 | 52 |
| 836 | 2206 | 2258 | 2310 | 2362 | 2414 | 2466 | 2518 | 2570 | 2622 | 2674 | 52 |
| 837 | 2725 | 2777 | 2829 | 2881 | 2933 | 2985 | 3037 | 3089 | 3140 | 3192 | 52 |
| 838 | 3244 | 3296 | 3348 | 3399 | 3451 | 3503 | 3555 | 3607 | 3658 | 3710 | 52 |
| 839 | 3762 | 3814 | 3865 | 3917 | 3969 | 4021 | 4072 | 4124 | 4176 | 4228 | 52 |
| 840 | 4279 | 4331 | 4383 | 4434 | 4486 | 4538 | 4589 | 4641 | 4693 | 4744 | 52 |
| 841 | 4796 | 4848 | 4899 | 4951 | 5003 | 5054 | 5106 | 5157 | 5209 | 5261 | 52 |
| 842 | 5312 | 5364 | 5415 | 5467 | 5518 | 5570 | 5621 | 5673 | 5725 | 5776 | 52 |
| 843 | 5828 | 5879 | 5931 | 5982 | 6034 | 6085 | 6137 | 6188 | 6240 | 6291 | 51 |
| 844 | 6342 | 6394 | 6445 | 6497 | 6548 | 6600 | 6651 | 6702 | 6754 | 6805 | 51 |
| 845 | 6857 | 6908 | 6959 | 7011 | 7062 | 7114 | 7165 | 7216 | 7268 | 7319 | 51 |
| 846 | 7370 | 7422 | 7473 | 7524 | 7576 | 7627 | 7678 | 7730 | 7781 | 7832 | 51 |
| 847 | 7883 | 7935 | 7986 | 8037 | 8088 | 8140 | 8191 | 8242 | 8293 | 8345 | 51 |
| 848 | 8396 | 8447 | 8498 | 8549 | 8601 | 8652 | 8703 | 8754 | 8805 | 8857 | 51 |
| 849 | 8908 | 8959 | 9010 | 9061 | 9112 | 9163 | 9215 | 9266 | 9317 | 9368 | 51 |
| 850 | 9419 | 9470 | 9521 | 9572 | 9623 | 9674 | 9725 | 9776 | 9827 | 9879 | 51 |

n\d 55

| 1 | 5.5 |
|---|---|
| 2 | 11.0 |
| 3 | 16.5 |
| 4 | 22.0 |
| 5 | 27.5 |
| 6 | 33.0 |
| 7 | 38.5 |
| 8 | 44.0 |
| 9 | 49.5 |

n\d 54

| 1 | 5.4 |
|---|---|
| 2 | 10.8 |
| 3 | 16.2 |
| 4 | 21.6 |
| 5 | 27.0 |
| 6 | 32.4 |
| 7 | 37.8 |
| 8 | 43.2 |
| 9 | 48.6 |

n\d 53

| 1 | 5.3 |
|---|---|
| 2 | 10.6 |
| 3 | 15.9 |
| 4 | 21.2 |
| 5 | 26.5 |
| 6 | 31.8 |
| 7 | 37.1 |
| 8 | 42.4 |
| 9 | 47.7 |

n\d 52

| 1 | 5.2 |
|---|---|
| 2 | 10.4 |
| 3 | 15.6 |
| 4 | 20.8 |
| 5 | 26.0 |
| 6 | 31.2 |
| 7 | 36.4 |
| 8 | 41.6 |
| 9 | 46.8 |

n\d 51

| 1 | 5.1 |
|---|---|
| 2 | 10.2 |
| 3 | 15.3 |
| 4 | 20.4 |
| 5 | 25.5 |
| 6 | 30.6 |
| 7 | 35.7 |
| 8 | 40.8 |
| 9 | 45.9 |

Proportional Parts

| N | 0 | 1 | 2 | 3 | 4 | 5 | 6 | 7 | 8 | 9 | D |
|---|---|---|---|---|---|---|---|---|---|---|---|
| 850 | 92 9419 | 92 9470 | 92 9521 | 92 9572 | 92 9623 | 92 9674 | 92 9725 | 92 9776 | 92 9827 | 92 9879 | 51 |
| 851 | 9930 | 9981 | 93 0032 | 93 0083 | 93 0134 | 93 0185 | 93 0236 | 93 0287 | 93 0338 | 93 0389 | 51 |
| 852 | 93 0440 | 93 0491 | 0542 | 0592 | 0643 | 0694 | 0745 | 0796 | 0847 | 0898 | 51 |
| 853 | 0949 | 1000 | 1051 | 1102 | 1153 | 1204 | 1254 | 1305 | 1356 | 1407 | 51 |
| 854 | 1458 | 1509 | 1560 | 1610 | 1661 | 1712 | 1763 | 1814 | 1865 | 1915 | 51 |
| 855 | 1966 | 2017 | 2068 | 2118 | 2169 | 2220 | 2271 | 2322 | 2372 | 2423 | 51 |
| 856 | 2474 | 2524 | 2575 | 2626 | 2677 | 2727 | 2778 | 2829 | 2879 | 2930 | 51 |
| 857 | 2981 | 3031 | 3082 | 3133 | 3183 | 3234 | 3285 | 3335 | 3386 | 3437 | 51 |
| 858 | 3487 | 3538 | 3589 | 3639 | 3690 | 3740 | 3791 | 3841 | 3892 | 3943 | 51 |
| 859 | 3993 | 4044 | 4094 | 4145 | 4195 | 4246 | 4296 | 4347 | 4397 | 4448 | 51 |
| 860 | 4498 | 4549 | 4599 | 4650 | 4700 | 4751 | 4801 | 4852 | 4902 | 4953 | 50 |
| 861 | 5003 | 5054 | 5104 | 5154 | 5205 | 5255 | 5306 | 5356 | 5406 | 5457 | 50 |
| 862 | 5507 | 5558 | 5608 | 5658 | 5709 | 5759 | 5809 | 5860 | 5910 | 5960 | 50 |
| 863 | 6011 | 6061 | 6111 | 6162 | 6212 | 6262 | 6313 | 6363 | 6413 | 6463 | 50 |
| 864 | 6514 | 6564 | 6614 | 6665 | 6715 | 6765 | 6815 | 6865 | 6916 | 6966 | 50 |
| 865 | 7016 | 7066 | 7117 | 7167 | 7217 | 7267 | 7317 | 7367 | 7418 | 7468 | 50 |
| 866 | 7518 | 7568 | 7618 | 7668 | 7718 | 7769 | 7819 | 7869 | 7919 | 7969 | 50 |
| 867 | 8019 | 8069 | 8119 | 8169 | 8219 | 8269 | 8320 | 8370 | 8420 | 8470 | 50 |
| 868 | 8520 | 8570 | 8620 | 8670 | 8720 | 8770 | 8820 | 8870 | 8920 | 8970 | 50 |
| 869 | 9020 | 9070 | 9120 | 9170 | 9220 | 9270 | 9320 | 9369 | 9419 | 9469 | 50 |
| 870 | 9519 | 9569 | 9619 | 9669 | 9719 | 9769 | 9819 | 9869 | 9918 | 9968 | 50 |
| 871 | 94 0018 | 94 0068 | 94 0118 | 94 0168 | 94 0218 | 94 0267 | 94 0317 | 94 0367 | 94 0417 | 94 0467 | 50 |
| 872 | 0516 | 0566 | 0616 | 0666 | 0716 | 0765 | 0815 | 0865 | 0915 | 0964 | 50 |
| 873 | 1014 | 1064 | 1114 | 1163 | 1213 | 1263 | 1313 | 1362 | 1412 | 1462 | 50 |
| 874 | 1511 | 1561 | 1611 | 1660 | 1710 | 1760 | 1809 | 1859 | 1909 | 1958 | 50 |
| 875 | 2008 | 2058 | 2107 | 2157 | 2207 | 2256 | 2306 | 2355 | 2405 | 2455 | 50 |
| 876 | 2504 | 2554 | 2603 | 2653 | 2702 | 2752 | 2801 | 2851 | 2901 | 2950 | 50 |
| 877 | 3000 | 3049 | 3099 | 3148 | 3198 | 3247 | 3297 | 3346 | 3396 | 3445 | 49 |
| 878 | 3495 | 3544 | 3593 | 3643 | 3692 | 3742 | 3791 | 3841 | 3890 | 3939 | 49 |
| 879 | 3989 | 4038 | 4088 | 4137 | 4186 | 4236 | 4285 | 4335 | 4384 | 4433 | 49 |
| 880 | 4483 | 4532 | 4581 | 4631 | 4680 | 4729 | 4779 | 4828 | 4877 | 4927 | 49 |
| 881 | 4976 | 5025 | 5074 | 5124 | 5173 | 5222 | 5272 | 5321 | 5370 | 5419 | 49 |
| 882 | 5469 | 5518 | 5567 | 5616 | 5665 | 5715 | 5764 | 5813 | 5862 | 5912 | 49 |
| 883 | 5961 | 6010 | 6059 | 6108 | 6157 | 6207 | 6256 | 6305 | 6354 | 6403 | 49 |
| 884 | 6452 | 6501 | 6551 | 6600 | 6649 | 6698 | 6747 | 6796 | 6845 | 6894 | 49 |
| 885 | 6943 | 6992 | 7041 | 7090 | 7140 | 7189 | 7238 | 7287 | 7336 | 7385 | 49 |
| 886 | 7434 | 7483 | 7532 | 7581 | 7630 | 7679 | 7728 | 7777 | 7826 | 7875 | 49 |
| 887 | 7924 | 7973 | 8022 | 8070 | 8119 | 8168 | 8217 | 8266 | 8315 | 8364 | 49 |
| 888 | 8413 | 8462 | 8511 | 8560 | 8609 | 8657 | 8706 | 8755 | 8804 | 8853 | 49 |
| 889 | 8902 | 8951 | 8999 | 9048 | 9097 | 9146 | 9195 | 9244 | 9292 | 9341 | 49 |
| 890 | 9390 | 9439 | 9488 | 9536 | 9585 | 9634 | 9683 | 9731 | 9780 | 9829 | 49 |
| 891 | 9878 | 9926 | 9975 | 95 0024 | 95 0073 | 95 0121 | 95 0170 | 95 0219 | 95 0267 | 95 0316 | 49 |
| 892 | 95 0365 | 95 0414 | 95 0462 | 0511 | 0560 | 0608 | 0657 | 0706 | 0754 | 0803 | 49 |
| 893 | 0851 | 0900 | 0949 | 0997 | 1046 | 1095 | 1143 | 1192 | 1240 | 1289 | 49 |
| 894 | 1338 | 1386 | 1435 | 1483 | 1532 | 1580 | 1629 | 1677 | 1726 | 1775 | 49 |
| 895 | 1823 | 1872 | 1920 | 1969 | 2017 | 2066 | 2114 | 2163 | 2211 | 2260 | 48 |
| 896 | 2308 | 2356 | 2405 | 2453 | 2502 | 2550 | 2599 | 2647 | 2696 | 2744 | 48 |
| 897 | 2792 | 2841 | 2889 | 2938 | 2986 | 3034 | 3083 | 3131 | 3180 | 3228 | 48 |
| 898 | 3276 | 3325 | 3373 | 3421 | 3470 | 3518 | 3566 | 3615 | 3663 | 3711 | 48 |
| 899 | 3760 | 3808 | 3856 | 3905 | 3953 | 4001 | 4049 | 4098 | 4146 | 4194 | 48 |
| 900 | 4243 | 4291 | 4339 | 4387 | 4435 | 4484 | 4532 | 4580 | 4628 | 4677 | 48 |

| n\d | 52 |
|---|---|
| 1 | 5.2 |
| 2 | 10.4 |
| 3 | 15.6 |
| 4 | 20.8 |
| 5 | 26.0 |
| 6 | 31.2 |
| 7 | 36.4 |
| 8 | 41.6 |
| 9 | 46.8 |

| n\d | 51 |
|---|---|
| 1 | 5.1 |
| 2 | 10.2 |
| 3 | 15.3 |
| 4 | 20.4 |
| 5 | 25.5 |
| 6 | 30.6 |
| 7 | 35.7 |
| 8 | 40.8 |
| 9 | 45.9 |

| n\d | 50 |
|---|---|
| 1 | 5.0 |
| 2 | 10.0 |
| 3 | 15.0 |
| 4 | 20.0 |
| 5 | 25.0 |
| 6 | 30.0 |
| 7 | 35.0 |
| 8 | 40.0 |
| 9 | 45.0 |

| n\d | 49 |
|---|---|
| 1 | 4.9 |
| 2 | 9.8 |
| 3 | 14.7 |
| 4 | 19.6 |
| 5 | 24.5 |
| 6 | 29.4 |
| 7 | 34.3 |
| 8 | 39.2 |
| 9 | 44.1 |

| n\d | 48 |
|---|---|
| 1 | 4.8 |
| 2 | 9.6 |
| 3 | 14.4 |
| 4 | 19.2 |
| 5 | 24.0 |
| 6 | 28.8 |
| 7 | 33.6 |
| 8 | 38.4 |
| 9 | 43.2 |

Six-Place Logarithms of Numbers 900-950

Proportional Parts

| N | 0 | 1 | 2 | 3 | 4 | 5 | 6 | 7 | 8 | 9 | D |
|---|---|---|---|---|---|---|---|---|---|---|---|
| 900 | 95 4243 | 95 4291 | 95 4339 | 95 4387 | 95 4435 | 95 4484 | 95 4532 | 95 4580 | 95 4628 | 95 4677 | 48 |
| 901 | 4725 | 4773 | 4821 | 4869 | 4918 | 4966 | 5014 | 5062 | 5110 | 5158 | 48 |
| 902 | 5207 | 5255 | 5303 | 5351 | 5399 | 5447 | 5495 | 5543 | 5592 | 5640 | 48 |
| 903 | 5688 | 5736 | 5784 | 5832 | 5880 | 5928 | 5976 | 6024 | 6072 | 6120 | 48 |
| 904 | 6168 | 6216 | 6265 | 6313 | 6361 | 6409 | 6457 | 6505 | 6553 | 6601 | 48 |
| 905 | 6649 | 6697 | 6745 | 6793 | 6840 | 6888 | 6936 | 6984 | 7032 | 7080 | 48 |
| 906 | 7128 | 7176 | 7224 | 7272 | 7320 | 7368 | 7416 | 7464 | 7512 | 7559 | 48 |
| 907 | 7607 | 7655 | 7703 | 7751 | 7799 | 7847 | 7894 | 7942 | 7990 | 8038 | 48 |
| 908 | 8086 | 8134 | 8181 | 8229 | 8277 | 8325 | 8373 | 8421 | 8468 | 8516 | 48 |
| 909 | 8564 | 8612 | 8659 | 8707 | 8755 | 8803 | 8850 | 8898 | 8946 | 8994 | 48 |
| 910 | 9041 | 9089 | 9137 | 9185 | 9232 | 9280 | 9328 | 9375 | 9423 | 9471 | 48 |
| 911 | 9518 | 9566 | 9614 | 9661 | 9709 | 9757 | 9804 | 9852 | 9900 | 9947 | 48 |
| 912 | 9995 | 96 0042 | 96 0090 | 96 0138 | 96 0185 | 96 0233 | 96 0280 | 96 0328 | 96 0376 | 96 0423 | 48 |
| 913 | 96 0471 | 0518 | 0566 | 0613 | 0661 | 0709 | 0756 | 0804 | 0851 | 0899 | 48 |
| 914 | 0946 | 0994 | 1041 | 1089 | 1136 | 1184 | 1231 | 1279 | 1326 | 1374 | 48 |
| 915 | 1421 | 1469 | 1516 | 1563 | 1611 | 1658 | 1706 | 1753 | 1801 | 1848 | 47 |
| 916 | 1895 | 1943 | 1990 | 2038 | 2085 | 2132 | 2180 | 2227 | 2275 | 2322 | 47 |
| 917 | 2369 | 2417 | 2464 | 2511 | 2559 | 2606 | 2653 | 2701 | 2748 | 2795 | 47 |
| 918 | 2843 | 2890 | 2937 | 2985 | 3032 | 3079 | 3126 | 3174 | 3221 | 3268 | 47 |
| 919 | 3316 | 3363 | 3410 | 3457 | 3504 | 3552 | 3599 | 3646 | 3693 | 3741 | 47 |
| 920 | 3788 | 3835 | 3882 | 3929 | 3977 | 4024 | 4071 | 4118 | 4165 | 4212 | 47 |
| 921 | 4260 | 4307 | 4354 | 4401 | 4448 | 4495 | 4542 | 4590 | 4637 | 4684 | 47 |
| 922 | 4731 | 4778 | 4825 | 4872 | 4919 | 4966 | 5013 | 5061 | 5108 | 5155 | 47 |
| 923 | 5202 | 5249 | 5296 | 5343 | 5390 | 5437 | 5484 | 5531 | 5578 | 5625 | 47 |
| 924 | 5672 | 5719 | 5766 | 5813 | 5860 | 5907 | 5954 | 6001 | 6048 | 6095 | 47 |
| 925 | 6142 | 6189 | 6236 | 6283 | 6329 | 6376 | 6423 | 6470 | 6517 | 6564 | 47 |
| 926 | 6611 | 6658 | 6705 | 6752 | 6799 | 6845 | 6892 | 6939 | 6986 | 7033 | 47 |
| 927 | 7080 | 7127 | 7173 | 7220 | 7267 | 7314 | 7361 | 7408 | 7454 | 7501 | 47 |
| 928 | 7548 | 7595 | 7642 | 7688 | 7735 | 7782 | 7829 | 7875 | 7922 | 7969 | 47 |
| 929 | 8016 | 8062 | 8109 | 8156 | 8203 | 8249 | 8296 | 8343 | 8390 | 8436 | 47 |
| 930 | 8483 | 8530 | 8576 | 8623 | 8670 | 8716 | 8763 | 8810 | 8856 | 8903 | 47 |
| 931 | 8950 | 8996 | 9043 | 9090 | 9136 | 9183 | 9229 | 9276 | 9323 | 9369 | 47 |
| 932 | 9416 | 9463 | 9509 | 9556 | 9602 | 9649 | 9695 | 9742 | 9789 | 9835 | 47 |
| 933 | 9882 | 9928 | 9975 | 97 0021 | 97 0068 | 97 0114 | 97 0161 | 97 0207 | 97 0254 | 97 0300 | 47 |
| 934 | 97 0347 | 97 0393 | 97 0440 | 0486 | 0533 | 0579 | 0626 | 0672 | 0719 | 0765 | 46 |
| 935 | 0812 | 0858 | 0904 | 0951 | 0997 | 1044 | 1090 | 1137 | 1183 | 1229 | 46 |
| 936 | 1276 | 1322 | 1369 | 1415 | 1461 | 1508 | 1554 | 1601 | 1647 | 1693 | 46 |
| 937 | 1740 | 1786 | 1832 | 1879 | 1925 | 1971 | 2018 | 2064 | 2110 | 2157 | 46 |
| 938 | 2203 | 2249 | 2295 | 2342 | 2388 | 2434 | 2481 | 2527 | 2573 | 2619 | 46 |
| 939 | 2666 | 2712 | 2758 | 2804 | 2851 | 2897 | 2943 | 2989 | 3035 | 3082 | 46 |
| 940 | 3128 | 3174 | 3220 | 3266 | 3313 | 3359 | 3405 | 3451 | 3497 | 3543 | 46 |
| 941 | 3590 | 3636 | 3682 | 3728 | 3774 | 3820 | 3866 | 3913 | 3959 | 4005 | 46 |
| 942 | 4051 | 4097 | 4143 | 4189 | 4235 | 4281 | 4327 | 4374 | 4420 | 4466 | 46 |
| 943 | 4512 | 4558 | 4604 | 4650 | 4696 | 4742 | 4788 | 4834 | 4880 | 4926 | 46 |
| 944 | 4972 | 5018 | 5064 | 5110 | 5156 | 5202 | 5248 | 5294 | 5340 | 5386 | 46 |
| 945 | 5432 | 5478 | 5524 | 5570 | 5616 | 5662 | 5707 | 5753 | 5799 | 5845 | 46 |
| 946 | 5891 | 5937 | 5983 | 6029 | 6075 | 6121 | 6167 | 6212 | 6258 | 6304 | 46 |
| 947 | 6350 | 6396 | 6442 | 6488 | 6533 | 6579 | 6625 | 6671 | 6717 | 6763 | 46 |
| 948 | 6808 | 6854 | 6900 | 6946 | 6992 | 7037 | 7083 | 7129 | 7175 | 7220 | 46 |
| 949 | 7266 | 7312 | 7358 | 7403 | 7449 | 7495 | 7541 | 7586 | 7632 | 7678 | 46 |
| 950 | 7724 | 7769 | 7815 | 7861 | 7906 | 7952 | 7998 | 8043 | 8089 | 8135 | 46 |

n\d  49
1  4.9
2  9.8
3  14.7
4  19.6
5  24.5
6  29.4
7  34.3
8  39.2
9  44.1

n\d  48
1  4.8
2  9.6
3  14.4
4  19.2
5  24.0
6  28.8
7  33.6
8  38.4
9  43.2

n\d  47
1  4.7
2  9.4
3  14.1
4  18.8
5  23.5
6  28.2
7  32.9
8  37.6
9  42.3

n\d  46
1  4.6
2  9.2
3  13.8
4  18.4
5  23.0
6  27.6
7  32.2
8  36.8
9  41.4

n\d  45
1  4.5
2  9.0
3  13.5
4  18.0
5  22.5
6  27.0
7  31.5
8  36.0
9  40.5

## Six-Place Logarithms of Numbers 950-1000

| N | 0 | 1 | 2 | 3 | 4 | 5 | 6 | 7 | 8 | 9 | D |
|---|---|---|---|---|---|---|---|---|---|---|---|
| 950 | 97 7724 | 97 7769 | 97 7815 | 97 7861 | 97 7906 | 97 7952 | 97 7998 | 97 8043 | 97 8089 | 97 8135 | 46 |
| 951 | 8181 | 8226 | 8272 | 8317 | 8363 | 8409 | 8454 | 8500 | 8546 | 8591 | 46 |
| 952 | 8637 | 8683 | 8728 | 8774 | 8819 | 8865 | 8911 | 8956 | 9002 | 9047 | 46 |
| 953 | 9093 | 9138 | 9184 | 9230 | 9275 | 9321 | 9366 | 9412 | 9457 | 9503 | 46 |
| 954 | 9548 | 9594 | 9639 | 9685 | 9730 | 9776 | 9821 | 9867 | 9912 | 9958 | 46 |
| 955 | 98 0003 | 98 0049 | 98 0094 | 98 0140 | 98 0185 | 98 0231 | 98 0276 | 98 0322 | 98 0367 | 98 0412 | 45 |
| 956 | 0458 | 0503 | 0549 | 0594 | 0640 | 0685 | 0730 | 0776 | 0821 | 0867 | 45 |
| 957 | 0912 | 0957 | 1003 | 1048 | 1093 | 1139 | 1184 | 1229 | 1275 | 1320 | 45 |
| 958 | 1366 | 1411 | 1456 | 1501 | 1547 | 1592 | 1637 | 1683 | 1728 | 1773 | 45 |
| 959 | 1819 | 1864 | 1909 | 1954 | 2000 | 2045 | 2090 | 2135 | 2181 | 2226 | 45 |
| 960 | 2271 | 2316 | 2362 | 2407 | 2452 | 2497 | 2543 | 2588 | 2633 | 2678 | 45 |
| 961 | 2723 | 2769 | 2814 | 2859 | 2904 | 2949 | 2994 | 3040 | 3085 | 3130 | 45 |
| 962 | 3175 | 3220 | 3265 | 3310 | 3356 | 3401 | 3446 | 3491 | 3536 | 3581 | 45 |
| 963 | 3626 | 3671 | 3716 | 3762 | 3807 | 3852 | 3897 | 3942 | 3987 | 4032 | 45 |
| 964 | 4077 | 4122 | 4167 | 4212 | 4257 | 4302 | 4347 | 4392 | 4437 | 4482 | 45 |
| 965 | 4527 | 4572 | 4617 | 4662 | 4707 | 4752 | 4797 | 4842 | 4887 | 4932 | 45 |
| 966 | 4977 | 5022 | 5067 | 5112 | 5157 | 5202 | 5247 | 5292 | 5337 | 5382 | 45 |
| 967 | 5426 | 5471 | 5516 | 5561 | 5606 | 5651 | 5696 | 5741 | 5786 | 5830 | 45 |
| 968 | 5875 | 5920 | 5965 | 6010 | 6055 | 6100 | 6144 | 6189 | 6234 | 6279 | 45 |
| 969 | 6324 | 6369 | 6413 | 6458 | 6503 | 6548 | 6593 | 6637 | 6682 | 6727 | 45 |
| 970 | 6772 | 6817 | 6861 | 6906 | 6951 | 6996 | 7040 | 7085 | 7130 | 7175 | 45 |
| 971 | 7219 | 7264 | 7309 | 7353 | 7398 | 7443 | 7488 | 7532 | 7577 | 7622 | 45 |
| 972 | 7666 | 7711 | 7756 | 7800 | 7845 | 7890 | 7934 | 7979 | 8024 | 8068 | 45 |
| 973 | 8113 | 8157 | 8202 | 8247 | 8291 | 8336 | 8381 | 8425 | 8470 | 8514 | 45 |
| 974 | 8559 | 8604 | 8648 | 8693 | 8737 | 8782 | 8826 | 8871 | 8916 | 8960 | 45 |
| 975 | 9005 | 9049 | 9094 | 9138 | 9183 | 9227 | 9272 | 9316 | 9361 | 9405 | 45 |
| 976 | 9450 | 9494 | 9539 | 9583 | 9628 | 9672 | 9717 | 9761 | 9806 | 9850 | 44 |
| 977 | 9895 | 9939 | 9983 | 99 0028 | 99 0072 | 99 0117 | 99 0161 | 99 0206 | 99 0250 | 99 0294 | 44 |
| 978 | 99 0339 | 99 0383 | 99 0428 | 0472 | 0516 | 0561 | 0605 | 0650 | 0694 | 0738 | 44 |
| 979 | 0783 | 0827 | 0871 | 0916 | 0960 | 1004 | 1049 | 1093 | 1137 | 1182 | 44 |
| 980 | 1226 | 1270 | 1315 | 1359 | 1403 | 1448 | 1492 | 1536 | 1580 | 1625 | 44 |
| 981 | 1669 | 1713 | 1758 | 1802 | 1846 | 1890 | 1935 | 1979 | 2023 | 2067 | 44 |
| 982 | 2111 | 2156 | 2200 | 2244 | 2288 | 2333 | 2377 | 2421 | 2465 | 2509 | 44 |
| 983 | 2554 | 2598 | 2642 | 2686 | 2730 | 2774 | 2819 | 2863 | 2907 | 2951 | 44 |
| 984 | 2995 | 3039 | 3083 | 3127 | 3172 | 3216 | 3260 | 3304 | 3348 | 3392 | 44 |
| 985 | 3436 | 3480 | 3524 | 3568 | 3613 | 3657 | 3701 | 3745 | 3789 | 3833 | 44 |
| 986 | 3877 | 3921 | 3965 | 4009 | 4053 | 4097 | 4141 | 4185 | 4229 | 4273 | 44 |
| 987 | 4317 | 4361 | 4405 | 4449 | 4493 | 4537 | 4581 | 4625 | 4669 | 4713 | 44 |
| 988 | 4757 | 4801 | 4845 | 4889 | 4933 | 4977 | 5021 | 5065 | 5108 | 5152 | 44 |
| 989 | 5196 | 5240 | 5284 | 5328 | 5372 | 5416 | 5460 | 5504 | 5547 | 5591 | 44 |
| 990 | 5635 | 5679 | 5723 | 5767 | 5811 | 5854 | 5898 | 5942 | 5986 | 6030 | 44 |
| 991 | 6074 | 6117 | 6161 | 6205 | 6249 | 6293 | 6337 | 6380 | 6424 | 6468 | 44 |
| 992 | 6512 | 6555 | 6599 | 6643 | 6687 | 6731 | 6774 | 6818 | 6862 | 6906 | 44 |
| 993 | 6949 | 6993 | 7037 | 7080 | 7124 | 7168 | 7212 | 7255 | 7299 | 7343 | 44 |
| 994 | 7386 | 7430 | 7474 | 7517 | 7561 | 7605 | 7648 | 7692 | 7736 | 7779 | 44 |
| 995 | 7823 | 7867 | 7910 | 7954 | 7998 | 8041 | 8085 | 8129 | 8172 | 8216 | 44 |
| 996 | 8259 | 8303 | 8347 | 8390 | 8434 | 8477 | 8521 | 8564 | 8608 | 8652 | 44 |
| 997 | 8695 | 8739 | 8782 | 8826 | 8869 | 8913 | 8956 | 9000 | 9043 | 9087 | 44 |
| 998 | 9131 | 9174 | 9218 | 9261 | 9305 | 9348 | 9392 | 9435 | 9479 | 9522 | 44 |
| 999 | 9565 | 9609 | 9652 | 9696 | 9739 | 9783 | 9826 | 9870 | 9913 | 9957 | 43 |
| 1000 | 00 0000 | 00 0043 | 00 0087 | 00 0130 | 00 0174 | 00 0217 | 00 0260 | 00 0304 | 00 0347 | 00 0391 | 43 |

## Proportional Parts

| n\d | 46 |
|---|---|
| 1 | 4.6 |
| 2 | 9.2 |
| 3 | 13.8 |
| 4 | 18.4 |
| 5 | 23.0 |
| 6 | 27.6 |
| 7 | 32.2 |
| 8 | 36.8 |
| 9 | 41.4 |

| n\d | 45 |
|---|---|
| 1 | 4.5 |
| 2 | 9.0 |
| 3 | 13.5 |
| 4 | 18.0 |
| 5 | 22.5 |
| 6 | 27.0 |
| 7 | 31.5 |
| 8 | 36.0 |
| 9 | 40.5 |

| n\d | 44 |
|---|---|
| 1 | 4.4 |
| 2 | 8.8 |
| 3 | 13.2 |
| 4 | 17.6 |
| 5 | 22.0 |
| 6 | 26.4 |
| 7 | 30.8 |
| 8 | 35.2 |
| 9 | 39.6 |

| n\d | 43 |
|---|---|
| 1 | 4.3 |
| 2 | 8.6 |
| 3 | 12.9 |
| 4 | 17.2 |
| 5 | 21.5 |
| 6 | 25.8 |
| 7 | 30.1 |
| 8 | 34.4 |
| 9 | 38.7 |

# Table 8

*Reciprocals*

| $n$ | $1/n$ | $n$ | $1/n$ .0 | $n$ | $1/n$ .0 | $n$ | $1/n$ .00 | $n$ | $1/n$ .00 |
|---|---|---|---|---|---|---|---|---|---|
| 0 | ∞ | 50 | 2000000 | 100 | 10000000 | 150 | 6666667 | 200 | 5000000 |
| 1 | 1.0000000 | 51 | 1960784 | 101 | 09900990 | 151 | 6622517 | 201 | 4975124 |
| 2 | .5000000 | 52 | 1923077 | 102 | 09803922 | 152 | 6578947 | 202 | 4950495 |
| 3 | .3333333 | 53 | 1886792 | 103 | 09708738 | 153 | 6535948 | 203 | 4926108 |
| 4 | .2500000 | 54 | 1851852 | 104 | 09615385 | 154 | 6493506 | 204 | 4901961 |
| 5 | .2000000 | 55 | 1818182 | 105 | 09523810 | 155 | 6451613 | 205 | 4878049 |
| 6 | .1666667 | 56 | 1785714 | 106 | 09433962 | 156 | 6410256 | 206 | 4854369 |
| 7 | .1428571 | 57 | 1754386 | 107 | 09345794 | 157 | 6369427 | 207 | 4830918 |
| 8 | .1250000 | 58 | 1724138 | 108 | 09259259 | 158 | 6329114 | 208 | 4807692 |
| 9 | .1111111 | 59 | 1694915 | 109 | 09174312 | 159 | 6289308 | 209 | 4784689 |
| 10 | .1000000 | 60 | 1666667 | 110 | 09090909 | 160 | 6250000 | 210 | 4761905 |
| 11 | .09090909 | 61 | 1639344 | 111 | 09009009 | 161 | 6211180 | 211 | 4739336 |
| 12 | .08333333 | 62 | 1612903 | 112 | 08928571 | 162 | 6172840 | 212 | 4716981 |
| 13 | .07692308 | 63 | 1587302 | 113 | 08849558 | 163 | 6134969 | 213 | 4694836 |
| 14 | .07142857 | 64 | 1562500 | 114 | 08771930 | 164 | 6097561 | 214 | 4672897 |
| 15 | .06666667 | 65 | 1538462 | 115 | 08695652 | 165 | 6060606 | 215 | 4651163 |
| 16 | .06250000 | 66 | 1515152 | 116 | 08620690 | 166 | 6024096 | 216 | 4629630 |
| 17 | .05882353 | 67 | 1492537 | 117 | 08547009 | 167 | 5988024 | 217 | 4608295 |
| 18 | .05555556 | 68 | 1470588 | 118 | 08474576 | 168 | 5952381 | 218 | 4587156 |
| 19 | .05263158 | 69 | 1449275 | 119 | 08403361 | 169 | 5917160 | 219 | 4566210 |
| 20 | .05000000 | 70 | 1428571 | 120 | 08333333 | 170 | 5882353 | 220 | 4545455 |
| 21 | .04761905 | 71 | 1408451 | 121 | 08264463 | 171 | 5847953 | 221 | 4524887 |
| 22 | .04545455 | 72 | 1388889 | 122 | 08196721 | 172 | 5813953 | 222 | 4504505 |
| 23 | .04347826 | 73 | 1369863 | 123 | 08130081 | 173 | 5780347 | 223 | 4484305 |
| 24 | .04166667 | 74 | 1351351 | 124 | 08064516 | 174 | 5747126 | 224 | 4464286 |
| 25 | .04000000 | 75 | 1333333 | 125 | 08000000 | 175 | 5714286 | 225 | 4444444 |
| 26 | .03846154 | 76 | 1315789 | 126 | 07936508 | 176 | 5681818 | 226 | 4424779 |
| 27 | .03703704 | 77 | 1298701 | 127 | 07874016 | 177 | 5649718 | 227 | 4405286 |
| 28 | .03571429 | 78 | 1282051 | 128 | 07812500 | 178 | 5617978 | 228 | 4385965 |
| 29 | .03448276 | 79 | 1265823 | 129 | 07751938 | 179 | 5586592 | 229 | 4366812 |
| 30 | .03333333 | 80 | 1250000 | 130 | 07692308 | 180 | 5555556 | 230 | 4347826 |
| 31 | .03225806 | 81 | 1234568 | 131 | 07633588 | 181 | 5524862 | 231 | 4329004 |
| 32 | .03125000 | 82 | 1219512 | 132 | 07575758 | 182 | 5494505 | 232 | 4310345 |
| 33 | .03030303 | 83 | 1204819 | 133 | 07518797 | 183 | 5464481 | 233 | 4291845 |
| 34 | .02941176 | 84 | 1190476 | 134 | 07462687 | 184 | 5434783 | 234 | 4273504 |
| 35 | .02857143 | 85 | 1176471 | 135 | 07407407 | 185 | 5405405 | 235 | 4255319 |
| 36 | .02777778 | 86 | 1162791 | 136 | 07352941 | 186 | 5376344 | 236 | 4237288 |
| 37 | .02702703 | 87 | 1149425 | 137 | 07299270 | 187 | 5347594 | 237 | 4219409 |
| 38 | .02631579 | 88 | 1136364 | 138 | 07246377 | 188 | 5319149 | 238 | 4201681 |
| 39 | .02564103 | 89 | 1123596 | 139 | 07194245 | 189 | 5291005 | 239 | 4184100 |
| 40 | .02500000 | 90 | 1111111 | 140 | 07142857 | 190 | 5263158 | 240 | 4166667 |
| 41 | .02439024 | 91 | 1098901 | 141 | 07092199 | 191 | 5235602 | 241 | 4149378 |
| 42 | .02380952 | 92 | 1086957 | 142 | 07042254 | 192 | 5208333 | 242 | 4132231 |
| 43 | .02325581 | 92 | 1075269 | 143 | 06993007 | 193 | 5181347 | 243 | 4115226 |
| 44 | .02272727 | 94 | 1063830 | 144 | 06944444 | 194 | 5154639 | 244 | 4098361 |
| 45 | .02222222 | 95 | 1052632 | 145 | 06896552 | 195 | 5128205 | 245 | 4081633 |
| 46 | .02173913 | 96 | 1041667 | 146 | 06849315 | 196 | 5102041 | 246 | 4065041 |
| 47 | .02127660 | 97 | 1030928 | 147 | 06802721 | 197 | 5076142 | 247 | 4048583 |
| 48 | .02083333 | 98 | 1020408 | 148 | 06756757 | 198 | 5050505 | 248 | 4032258 |
| 49 | .02040816 | 99 | 1010101 | 149 | 06711409 | 199 | 5025126 | 249 | 4016064 |
| 50 | .02000000 | 100 | 1000000 | 150 | 06666667 | 200 | 5000000 | 250 | 4000000 |

Table 8 (Continued)

| $n$ | $1/n$ .00 | $n$ | $1/n$ .00 | $n$ | $1/n$ .00 | $n$ | $1/n$ .00 | $n$ | $1/n$ .00 |
|---|---|---|---|---|---|---|---|---|---|
| 250 | 4000000 | 300 | 3333333 | 350 | 2857143 | 400 | 2500000 | 450 | 2222222 |
| 251 | 3984064 | 301 | 3322259 | 351 | 2849003 | 401 | 2493766 | 451 | 2217295 |
| 252 | 3968254 | 302 | 3311258 | 352 | 2840909 | 402 | 2487562 | 452 | 2212389 |
| 253 | 3952569 | 303 | 3300330 | 353 | 2832861 | 403 | 2481390 | 453 | 2207506 |
| 254 | 3937008 | 304 | 3289474 | 354 | 2824859 | 404 | 2475248 | 454 | 2202643 |
| 255 | 3921569 | 305 | 3278689 | 355 | 2816901 | 405 | 2469136 | 455 | 2197802 |
| 256 | 3906250 | 306 | 3267974 | 356 | 2808989 | 406 | 2463054 | 456 | 2192982 |
| 257 | 3891051 | 307 | 3257329 | 357 | 2801120 | 407 | 2457002 | 457 | 2188184 |
| 258 | 3875969 | 308 | 3246753 | 358 | 2793296 | 408 | 2450980 | 458 | 2183406 |
| 259 | 3861004 | 309 | 3236246 | 359 | 2785515 | 409 | 2444988 | 459 | 2178649 |
| 260 | 3846154 | 310 | 3225806 | 360 | 2777778 | 410 | 2439024 | 460 | 2173913 |
| 261 | 3831418 | 311 | 3215434 | 361 | 2770083 | 411 | 2433090 | 461 | 2169197 |
| 262 | 3816794 | 312 | 3205128 | 362 | 2762431 | 412 | 2427184 | 462 | 2164502 |
| 263 | 3802281 | 313 | 3194888 | 363 | 2754821 | 413 | 2421308 | 463 | 2159827 |
| 264 | 3787879 | 314 | 3184713 | 364 | 2747253 | 414 | 2415459 | 464 | 2155172 |
| 265 | 3773585 | 315 | 3174603 | 365 | 2739726 | 415 | 2409639 | 465 | 2150538 |
| 266 | 3759398 | 316 | 3164557 | 376 | 2732240 | 416 | 2403846 | 466 | 2145923 |
| 267 | 3745318 | 317 | 3154574 | 367 | 2724796 | 417 | 2398082 | 467 | 2141328 |
| 268 | 3731343 | 318 | 3144654 | 368 | 2717391 | 418 | 2392344 | 468 | 2136752 |
| 269 | 3717472 | 319 | 3134796 | 369 | 2710027 | 419 | 2386635 | 469 | 2132196 |
| 270 | 3703704 | 320 | 3125000 | 370 | 2702703 | 420 | 2380952 | 470 | 2127660 |
| 271 | 3690037 | 321 | 3115265 | 371 | 2695418 | 421 | 2375297 | 471 | 2123142 |
| 272 | 3676471 | 322 | 3105590 | 372 | 2688172 | 422 | 2369668 | 472 | 2118644 |
| 273 | 3663004 | 323 | 3095975 | 373 | 2680965 | 423 | 2364066 | 473 | 2114165 |
| 274 | 3649635 | 324 | 3086420 | 374 | 2673797 | 424 | 2358491 | 474 | 2109705 |
| 275 | 3636364 | 325 | 3076923 | 375 | 2666667 | 425 | 2352941 | 475 | 2105263 |
| 276 | 3623188 | 326 | 3067485 | 376 | 2659574 | 426 | 2347418 | 476 | 2100840 |
| 277 | 3610108 | 327 | 3058104 | 377 | 2652520 | 427 | 2341920 | 477 | 2096436 |
| 278 | 3597122 | 328 | 3048780 | 378 | 2645503 | 428 | 2336449 | 478 | 2092050 |
| 279 | 3584229 | 329 | 3039514 | 379 | 2638522 | 429 | 2331002 | 479 | 2087683 |
| 280 | 3571429 | 330 | 3030303 | 380 | 2631579 | 430 | 2325581 | 480 | 2083333 |
| 281 | 3558719 | 331 | 3021148 | 381 | 2624672 | 431 | 2320186 | 481 | 2079002 |
| 282 | 3546099 | 332 | 3012048 | 382 | 2617801 | 432 | 2314815 | 482 | 2074689 |
| 283 | 3533569 | 333 | 3003003 | 383 | 2610966 | 433 | 2309469 | 483 | 2070393 |
| 284 | 3521127 | 334 | 2994012 | 384 | 2604167 | 434 | 2304147 | 484 | 2066116 |
| 285 | 3508772 | 335 | 2985075 | 385 | 2597403 | 435 | 2298851 | 485 | 2061856 |
| 286 | 3496503 | 336 | 2976190 | 386 | 2590674 | 436 | 2293578 | 486 | 2057613 |
| 287 | 3484321 | 337 | 2967359 | 387 | 2583979 | 437 | 2288330 | 487 | 2053388 |
| 288 | 3472222 | 338 | 2958580 | 388 | 2577320 | 438 | 2283105 | 488 | 2049180 |
| 289 | 3460208 | 339 | 2949853 | 389 | 2570694 | 439 | 2277904 | 489 | 2044990 |
| 290 | 3448276 | 340 | 2941176 | 390 | 2564103 | 440 | 2272727 | 490 | 2040816 |
| 291 | 3436426 | 341 | 2932551 | 391 | 2557545 | 441 | 2267574 | 491 | 2036660 |
| 292 | 3424658 | 342 | 2923977 | 392 | 2551020 | 442 | 2262443 | 492 | 2032520 |
| 293 | 3412969 | 343 | 2915452 | 393 | 2544529 | 443 | 2257336 | 493 | 2028398 |
| 294 | 3401361 | 344 | 2906977 | 394 | 2538071 | 444 | 2252252 | 494 | 2024291 |
| 295 | 3389831 | 345 | 2898551 | 395 | 2531646 | 445 | 2247191 | 495 | 2020202 |
| 296 | 3378378 | 346 | 2890173 | 396 | 2525253 | 446 | 2242152 | 496 | 2016129 |
| 297 | 3367003 | 347 | 2881844 | 397 | 2518892 | 447 | 2237136 | 497 | 2012072 |
| 298 | 3355705 | 348 | 2873563 | 398 | 2512563 | 448 | 2232143 | 498 | 2008032 |
| 299 | 3344482 | 349 | 2865330 | 399 | 2506266 | 449 | 2227171 | 499 | 2004008 |
| 300 | 3333333 | 350 | 2857143 | 400 | 2500000 | 450 | 2222222 | 500 | 2000000 |

# Table 8 (Continued)

| n | 1/n .00 | n | 1/n .00 | n | 1/n .00 | n | 1/n .00 | n | 1/n .00 |
|---|---|---|---|---|---|---|---|---|---|
| 500 | 2000000 | 550 | 1818182 | 600 | 1666667 | 650 | 1538462 | 700 | 1428571 |
| 501 | 1996008 | 551 | 1814882 | 601 | 1663894 | 651 | 1536098 | 701 | 1426534 |
| 502 | 1992032 | 552 | 1811594 | 602 | 1661130 | 652 | 1533742 | 702 | 1424501 |
| 503 | 1988072 | 553 | 1808318 | 603 | 1658375 | 653 | 1531394 | 703 | 1422475 |
| 504 | 1984127 | 554 | 1805054 | 604 | 1655629 | 654 | 1529052 | 704 | 1420455 |
| 505 | 1980198 | 555 | 1801802 | 605 | 1652893 | 655 | 1526718 | 705 | 1418440 |
| 506 | 1976285 | 556 | 1798561 | 606 | 1650165 | 656 | 1524390 | 706 | 1416431 |
| 507 | 1972387 | 557 | 1795332 | 607 | 1647446 | 657 | 1522070 | 707 | 1414427 |
| 508 | 1968504 | 558 | 1792115 | 608 | 1644737 | 658 | 1519757 | 708 | 1412429 |
| 509 | 1964637 | 559 | 1788909 | 609 | 1642036 | 659 | 1517451 | 709 | 1410437 |
| 510 | 1960784 | 560 | 1785714 | 610 | 1639344 | 660 | 1515152 | 710 | 1408451 |
| 511 | 1956947 | 561 | 1782531 | 611 | 1636661 | 661 | 1512859 | 711 | 1406470 |
| 512 | 1953125 | 562 | 1779359 | 612 | 1633987 | 662 | 1510574 | 712 | 1404494 |
| 513 | 1949318 | 563 | 1776199 | 613 | 1631321 | 663 | 1508296 | 713 | 1402525 |
| 514 | 1945525 | 564 | 1773050 | 614 | 1628664 | 664 | 1506024 | 714 | 1400560 |
| 515 | 1941748 | 565 | 1769912 | 615 | 1626016 | 665 | 1503759 | 715 | 1398601 |
| 516 | 1937984 | 566 | 1766784 | 616 | 1623377 | 666 | 1501502 | 716 | 1396648 |
| 517 | 1934236 | 567 | 1763668 | 617 | 1620746 | 667 | 1499250 | 717 | 1394700 |
| 518 | 1930502 | 568 | 1760563 | 618 | 1618123 | 668 | 1497006 | 718 | 1392758 |
| 519 | 1926782 | 569 | 1757469 | 619 | 1615509 | 669 | 1494768 | 719 | 1390821 |
| 520 | 1923077 | 570 | 1754386 | 620 | 1612903 | 670 | 1492537 | 720 | 1388889 |
| 521 | 1919386 | 571 | 1751313 | 621 | 1610306 | 671 | 1490313 | 721 | 1386963 |
| 522 | 1915709 | 572 | 1748252 | 622 | 1607717 | 672 | 1488095 | 722 | 1385042 |
| 523 | 1912046 | 573 | 1745201 | 623 | 1605136 | 673 | 1485884 | 723 | 1383126 |
| 524 | 1908397 | 574 | 1742160 | 624 | 1602564 | 674 | 1483680 | 724 | 1381215 |
| 525 | 1904762 | 575 | 1739130 | 625 | 1600000 | 675 | 1481481 | 725 | 1379310 |
| 526 | 1901141 | 576 | 1736111 | 626 | 1597444 | 676 | 1479290 | 726 | 1377410 |
| 527 | 1897533 | 577 | 1733102 | 627 | 1594896 | 677 | 1477105 | 727 | 1375516 |
| 528 | 1893939 | 578 | 1730104 | 628 | 1592357 | 678 | 1474926 | 728 | 1373626 |
| 529 | 1890359 | 579 | 1727116 | 629 | 1589825 | 679 | 1472754 | 729 | 1371742 |
| 530 | 1886792 | 580 | 1724138 | 630 | 1587302 | 680 | 1470588 | 730 | 1369863 |
| 531 | 1883239 | 581 | 1721170 | 631 | 1584786 | 681 | 1468429 | 731 | 1367989 |
| 532 | 1879699 | 582 | 1718213 | 632 | 1582278 | 682 | 1466276 | 732 | 1366120 |
| 533 | 1876173 | 583 | 1715266 | 633 | 1579779 | 673 | 1464129 | 733 | 1364256 |
| 534 | 1872659 | 584 | 1712329 | 634 | 1577287 | 684 | 1461988 | 734 | 1362398 |
| 535 | 1869159 | 585 | 1709402 | 635 | 1574803 | 685 | 1459854 | 735 | 1360544 |
| 536 | 1865672 | 586 | 1706485 | 636 | 1572327 | 686 | 1457726 | 736 | 1358696 |
| 537 | 1862197 | 587 | 1703578 | 637 | 1569859 | 687 | 1455604 | 737 | 1356852 |
| 538 | 1858736 | 588 | 1700680 | 638 | 1567398 | 688 | 1453488 | 738 | 1355014 |
| 539 | 1855288 | 589 | 1697793 | 639 | 1564945 | 689 | 1451379 | 739 | 1353180 |
| 540 | 1851852 | 590 | 1694915 | 640 | 1562500 | 690 | 1449275 | 740 | 1351351 |
| 541 | 1848429 | 591 | 1692047 | 641 | 1560062 | 691 | 1447178 | 741 | 1349528 |
| 542 | 1845018 | 592 | 1689189 | 642 | 1557632 | 692 | 1445087 | 742 | 1347709 |
| 543 | 1841621 | 593 | 1686341 | 643 | 1555210 | 693 | 1443001 | 743 | 1345895 |
| 544 | 1838235 | 594 | 1683502 | 644 | 1552795 | 694 | 1440922 | 744 | 1344086 |
| 545 | 1834862 | 595 | 1680672 | 645 | 1550388 | 695 | 1438849 | 745 | 1342282 |
| 546 | 1831502 | 596 | 1677852 | 646 | 1547988 | 696 | 1436782 | 746 | 1340483 |
| 547 | 1828154 | 597 | 1675042 | 647 | 1545595 | 697 | 1434720 | 747 | 1338688 |
| 548 | 1824818 | 598 | 1672241 | 648 | 1543210 | 698 | 1432665 | 748 | 1336898 |
| 549 | 1821494 | 599 | 1669449 | 649 | 1540832 | 699 | 1430615 | 749 | 1335113 |
| 550 | 1818182 | 600 | 1666667 | 650 | 1538462 | 700 | 1428571 | 750 | 1333333 |

**Table 8 (Continued)**

| n | 1/n .00 | n | 1/n .00 | n | 1/n .00 | n | 1/n .00 | n | 1/n .00 |
|---|---|---|---|---|---|---|---|---|---|
| 750 | 1333333 | 800 | 1250000 | 850 | 1176471 | 900 | 1111111 | 950 | 1052632 |
| 751 | 1331558 | 801 | 1248439 | 851 | 1175088 | 901 | 1109878 | 951 | 1051525 |
| 752 | 1329787 | 802 | 1246883 | 852 | 1173709 | 902 | 1108647 | 952 | 1050420 |
| 753 | 1328021 | 803 | 1245330 | 853 | 1172333 | 903 | 1107420 | 953 | 1049318 |
| 754 | 1326260 | 804 | 1243781 | 854 | 1170960 | 904 | 1106195 | 954 | 1048218 |
| 755 | 1324503 | 805 | 1242236 | 855 | 1169591 | 905 | 1104972 | 955 | 1047120 |
| 756 | 1322751 | 806 | 1240695 | 856 | 1168224 | 906 | 1103753 | 956 | 1046025 |
| 757 | 1321104 | 807 | 1239157 | 857 | 1166861 | 907 | 1102536 | 957 | 1044932 |
| 758 | 1319261 | 808 | 1237624 | 858 | 1165501 | 908 | 1101322 | 958 | 1043841 |
| 759 | 1317523 | 809 | 1236094 | 859 | 1164144 | 909 | 1100110 | 959 | 1042753 |
| 760 | 1315789 | 810 | 1234568 | 860 | 1162791 | 910 | 1098901 | 960 | 1041667 |
| 761 | 1314060 | 811 | 1233046 | 861 | 1161440 | 911 | 1097695 | 961 | 1040583 |
| 762 | 1312336 | 812 | 1231527 | 862 | 1160093 | 912 | 1096491 | 962 | 1039501 |
| 763 | 1310616 | 813 | 1230012 | 863 | 1158749 | 913 | 1095290 | 963 | 1038422 |
| 764 | 1308901 | 814 | 1228501 | 864 | 1157407 | 914 | 1094092 | 964 | 1037344 |
| 765 | 1307190 | 815 | 1226994 | 865 | 1156069 | 915 | 1092896 | 965 | 1036269 |
| 766 | 1035483 | 816 | 1225490 | 866 | 1154734 | 916 | 1091703 | 966 | 1035197 |
| 767 | 1303781 | 817 | 1223990 | 867 | 1153403 | 917 | 1090513 | 967 | 1034126 |
| 768 | 1302083 | 818 | 1222494 | 868 | 1152074 | 918 | 1089325 | 968 | 1033058 |
| 769 | 1300390 | 819 | 1221001 | 869 | 1150748 | 919 | 1088139 | 969 | 1031992 |
| 770 | 1298701 | 820 | 1219512 | 870 | 1149425 | 920 | 1086957 | 970 | 1030928 |
| 771 | 1297017 | 821 | 1218027 | 871 | 1148106 | 921 | 1085776 | 971 | 1029866 |
| 772 | 1295337 | 822 | 1216545 | 872 | 1146789 | 922 | 1084599 | 972 | 1028807 |
| 773 | 1293661 | 823 | 1215067 | 873 | 1145475 | 923 | 1083424 | 973 | 1027749 |
| 774 | 1291990 | 824 | 1213592 | 874 | 1144165 | 924 | 1082251 | 974 | 1026694 |
| 775 | 1290323 | 825 | 1212121 | 875 | 1142857 | 925 | 1081081 | 975 | 1025641 |
| 776 | 1288660 | 826 | 1210654 | 876 | 1141553 | 926 | 1079914 | 976 | 1024590 |
| 777 | 1287001 | 827 | 1209190 | 877 | 1140251 | 927 | 1078749 | 977 | 1023541 |
| 778 | 1285347 | 828 | 1207729 | 878 | 1138952 | 928 | 1077586 | 978 | 1022495 |
| 779 | 1283697 | 829 | 1206273 | 879 | 1137656 | 929 | 1076426 | 979 | 1021450 |
| 780 | 1282051 | 830 | 1204819 | 880 | 1136364 | 930 | 1075269 | 980 | 1020408 |
| 781 | 1280410 | 831 | 1203369 | 881 | 1135074 | 931 | 1074114 | 981 | 1019368 |
| 782 | 1278772 | 832 | 1201923 | 882 | 1133787 | 932 | 1072961 | 982 | 1018330 |
| 783 | 1277139 | 833 | 1200480 | 883 | 1132503 | 933 | 1071811 | 983 | 1017294 |
| 784 | 1275510 | 834 | 1199041 | 884 | 1131222 | 934 | 1070664 | 984 | 1016260 |
| 785 | 1273885 | 835 | 1197605 | 885 | 1129944 | 935 | 1069519 | 985 | 1015228 |
| 786 | 1272265 | 836 | 1196172 | 886 | 1128668 | 936 | 1068376 | 986 | 1014199 |
| 787 | 1270648 | 837 | 1194743 | 887 | 1127396 | 937 | 1067236 | 987 | 1013171 |
| 788 | 1269036 | 838 | 1193317 | 888 | 1126126 | 938 | 1066098 | 988 | 1012146 |
| 789 | 1267427 | 839 | 1191895 | 889 | 1124859 | 939 | 1064936 | 989 | 1011122 |
| 790 | 1265823 | 840 | 1190476 | 890 | 1123596 | 940 | 1063830 | 990 | 1010101 |
| 791 | 1264223 | 841 | 1189061 | 891 | 1122334 | 941 | 1062699 | 991 | 1009082 |
| 792 | 1262626 | 842 | 1187648 | 892 | 1121076 | 942 | 1061571 | 992 | 1008065 |
| 793 | 1261034 | 843 | 1186240 | 893 | 1119821 | 943 | 1060445 | 993 | 1007049 |
| 794 | 1259446 | 844 | 1184834 | 894 | 1118568 | 944 | 1059322 | 994 | 1006036 |
| 795 | 1257862 | 845 | 1183432 | 895 | 1117318 | 945 | 1058201 | 995 | 1005025 |
| 796 | 1256281 | 846 | 1182033 | 896 | 1116071 | 946 | 1057082 | 996 | 1004016 |
| 797 | 1254705 | 847 | 1180638 | 897 | 1114827 | 947 | 1055966 | 997 | 1003009 |
| 798 | 1253133 | 848 | 1179245 | 898 | 1113586 | 948 | 1054852 | 998 | 1002004 |
| 799 | 1251564 | 849 | 1177856 | 899 | 1112347 | 949 | 1053741 | 999 | 1001001 |
| 800 | 1250000 | 850 | 1176471 | 900 | 1111111 | 950 | 1052632 | 1000 | 1000000 |

# INDEX OF FORMULAS

## Simple Interest

1. $I = Prt$    Simple interest / 9
2. $S = P(1 + rt)$    Amount at simple interest / 14
3. $P = \dfrac{S}{1 + rt}$    Present value at simple interest / 27

## Bank Discount

4. $D = Sdt$    Bank discount / 47
5. $P = S(1 - dt)$    Proceeds at bank discount / 47
6. $S = \dfrac{P}{1 - dt}$    Maturity of loan for specified proceeds / 47
7. $r = \dfrac{d}{1 - dt}$    Interest rate equivalent to a bank discount rate / 49
8. $d = \dfrac{r}{1 + rt}$    Discount rate equivalent to an interest rate / 49

## Compound Interest

9. $S = P(1 + i)^n$    Amount at compound interest / 79
10. $r = (1 + i)^m - 1$    Effective interest rate / 92
11. $P = S(1 + i)^{-n}$    Present value at compound interest  97

## Ordinary Annuities

12. $S_n = Rs_{\overline{n}|} = R\dfrac{(1 + i)^n - 1}{i}$    Amount of an ordinary annuity / 138

13. $A_n = Ra_{\overline{n}|} = R\dfrac{1 - (1 + i)^{-n}}{i} = R\dfrac{1 - v^n}{i}$    Present value of an ordinary annuity / 144

14. $R = S_n \times \dfrac{1}{s_{\overline{n}|}}$    Periodic payment of an ordinary annuity when the amount is known / 153

15. $R = A_n \times \dfrac{1}{a_{\overline{n}|}}$    Periodic payment of an ordinary annuity when the present value is known / 153

## Annuities Due

16. $S_n = R(s_{\overline{n+1}|} - 1)$    Amount of an annuity due / 176
17. $A_n = R(a_{\overline{n-1}|} + 1)$    Present value of an annuity due / 177

## Deferred Annuities

18. $A_n = R(a_{\overline{m+n}|} - a_{\overline{m}|})$    Present value of a deferred annuity / 184

## Forborne Annuities

19. $S_n = R(s_{\overline{n+p}|} - s_{\overline{p}|})$    Amount of a forborne annuity / 188

## Perpetuities

20. $A_{\infty} = \dfrac{R}{i}$    Present value of a perpetuity, interest used as earned / 194

21. $A_{\infty} = \dfrac{R}{i} \cdot \dfrac{1}{s_{\overline{n}|}}$    Present value of a perpetuity, interest allowed to accumulate for n periods / 19